# VALUES
# AND
# THE FUTURE

# The impact of

# technological change

# on american values

The Free Press, New York / Collier-Macmillan, Limited, London

# VALUES
# AND
# THE FUTURE

*Edited by* Kurt Baier *and* Nicholas Rescher

# Preface

The seventeen essays in this collection present the bulk of the formalizable results of an investigation into the impact of current technological advances on American values. This investigation was made possible by a grant to the University of Pittsburgh from the Carnegie Corporation of New York and the International Business Machines Corporation also of New York. It was conducted by scholars from many institutions during 1965 and 1966, but its center was the Department of Philosophy of the University of Pittsburgh, and it was directed collaboratively by the undersigned.

The most ambitious ultimate aim of the investigation was to contribute toward the discovery of ways of guiding social change in directions which are at the least not incompatible with the realization of our deepest values, and perhaps even helpful to it. A more immediate and realistic aim was to identify and surmount some of the major conceptual and methodological obstacles which have prevented a systematic empirical investigation of this problem. The two most important obstacles of this kind confronted us with two large-scale preliminary tasks, not previously completed or even seriously tackled. One of these comprises the drawing up of an inventory of the values of an individual or a group; an inventory of the variety of changes which these values can, and in particular cases, do undergo during given periods of time; the identification of the various factors which make for such changes, with particular emphasis on those which promote or retard their realization. The other is the determination of the soundness or unsoundness of the values to which individuals or groups actually subscribe, which leads into the thorny problems that surround the nature and verification of value judgments.

Important and urgent though all these problems are generally acknowledged to be, attempts to cope with them are still in a very early and crude stage. It is no exaggeration to say that we do not have available even a suitable terminology in which to record an individual's or group's values, let alone precise instruments for ascertaining what they are or what changes they are undergoing. And we are in a still worse position with regard to determining the soundness of values. In view of this, it seemed appropriate to aim in the first place at clarification, to improve the conceptual apparatus for talking about values and value change, to remove the confusions hampering progress in the domain of evaluation, and to offer methodological suggestions for forecasting value change. Although many of these are properly philosophical tasks, philosophers cannot hope to do fruitful work of this sort or even to be understood by nonphilosophers, if they are not fully alive to the difficulties encountered by empirical investigators trying to cope with value problems. The investigation therefore took the form of a collaborative effort—extending over many months of common stimulation and criticism—involving philosophers and social scientists, primarily economists and sociologists, all working on problems relating to the interaction of technology and social values.

The time span under review was the period from the present to the year 2000. Four realms of primary concern were selected for consideration. The first was the detection of the most intimately value-relevant trends of technological development, such as that in the advance of computers, transportation, communication, and biomedicine. The second was the detection of trends of social change, such as those in sexual relations, the family, race relations, and the sphere of work and leisure. The third was the identification of economic trends, such as changes in productivity, organization of production, composition of product, and distribution of wealth. The fourth concerned forecasting changes in the values of important social groups, such as scientists, educators, corporation managers, and professional women.

Special studies in each of these four areas were carried out, within the framework of the project, by scholars of wide experience and competence in the field. Apart from their intrinsic interest and value, these inspired and well-informed analyses reveal clearly what *sort* of future these seasoned and sophisticated scientists and men of affairs anticipate, what sort of difference they envisage these changes to make for our lives, to what extent they envisage our present values to be realized or frustrated by these changes, and, lastly, which of these changes we should in their judgment resist and which promote, and why they think so. These prognostications of the future, in other words, lay bare the anatomy of our values and valuations, as these come to be subjected to the stresses and strains of the future.

The essays included in this volume cannot, of course, attempt to give a complete portrayal of our future way of life and our future values. They aim, rather, to draw attention to important areas of interaction between technology and values, to offer some ideas of where and how control of some social problems may be attempted in ways which are compatible with the dominant values of the persons affected, and to map out a framework of categories within which one can describe and analyze the values of a person or group, and the changes in these values over a period of time.

Some readers may wonder why such a selective examination of values should have concentrated so heavily on economics and should have omitted major areas such as religion, education, and politics (both national and international). These gaps must be excused rather than justified. The brief time and limited financial resources available to the project did not permit an effort on a larger scale. Since concentration was required, economics was the obvious field for selection. By common agreement, it is not only the theoretically most advanced field but also, from the point of view of future social developments, one of the most important. Moreover, religion and international relations were in part also excluded on the grounds that, although many important value changes might be expected in these areas, predictively reliable results are least likely to emerge in them. The project directors do, however, admit to some disappointment at having failed, despite considerable effort, to secure suitable contributions on value changes in the educational area.

No one can be more acutely aware of the limitations of this inquiry than those who have been intimately concerned in its conduct. The fact is that scientific research on values is a recent phenomenon, still very much in its youth, and their study in a future-oriented, predictive context, is certainly still in its infancy. Much remains to be done to extend and refine the ideas presented here, and to capitalize upon some of the promising prospects they open up for future research. We do, however, feel that it can justly be claimed for this inquiry that it represents at least the beginning of a serious, cooperative interdisciplinary attempt to provide some of the conceptual and methodological instruments through the use (and also criticism and improvement) of which the state of our knowledge in this very difficult but challenging domain can be advanced.

Some readers may look to this Preface for a summary of the results of this investigation. It was decided, however, to include such a survey in the Introduction by Alvin Toffler, which is also recommended to those who are interested only in limited aspects of this inquiry. They will find there the clearest indications of where to look for discussions relevant to their interests.

The editors gratefully acknowledge the generous assistance received from Professor Peter J. Caws, Consultant to the Carnegie Corporation of New York; Mr. Charles R. Bowen, Manager of Educational Projects, Department of Educational Affairs, International Business Machine Corporations; Professor Daniel Bell of Columbia University; Dr. Henry David, Executive Secretary of the National Research Council, Division of Behavioral Science, Washington, D.C.; Professor Leland Hazard of Carnegie-Mellon University; Professor Sterling McMurrin of the University of Utah; Dr. Emanuel Mesthene, Executive Director, Program on Technology and Society,

Harvard University; and Professor Herbert Simon, Associate Dean, Graduate School of Industrial Administration, Carnegie-Mellon University. The last six of these acted as Advisors to this Project, participated in many of our discussion sessions, and gave helpful advice and direction to our research efforts. Acknowledgment is due also to Dr. Olaf Helmer and his colleagues in the "Futures Group" at the RAND Corporation; Mr. Harvey S. Perloff of Resources for the Future, Inc.; Mr. John Dixon, Manager, Basic Systems Corporation, Washington, D.C.; Dr. David Goldberg of the U.S. Office of Education; Dr. Leon Greenberg, Assistant Commissioner for Productivity and Technological Development, Department of Labor; Dr. Donald Schon, Director, Institute of Applied Technology, National Bureau of Standards; Drs. Garth Mangum and Arnold Nemore, both of the then-active National Automation Commission, and Professor Michael Scriven of the University of California at Berkeley. The editors also wish to thank their colleagues in the Department of Philosophy: Professors Alan Anderson, Nuel Belnap, Adolf Grünbaum, John Robison, Jerome Schneewind, and Wilfrid Sellars. Their advice and criticisms have been of very great help to us. Lastly the editors wish to thank Miss Kathy Theakston for her assistance in typing the manuscript, Mrs. Sandy Kerr for reading the proofs, Miss Judy Bazy for typing part of the manuscript, reading the proofs, and preparing the name index, and Mr. Michael MacDonald for preparing the subject index.

PITTSBURGH                                        KURT BAIER
                                                 NICHOLAS RESCHER

# Notes on contributors

**KURT BAIER,** Professor of Philosophy at the University of Pittsburgh, studied law at the University of Vienna and earned a D.Phil. in philosophy at Oxford. He has taught at various universities in Australia and the United States, and has served as department chairman at the Australian National University and the University of Pittsburgh. His extensive writings on ethics, social philosophy, and the philosophy of mind include a book entitled *The Moral Point of View.*

**KENNETH BOULDING** is Professor of Economics at the University of Michigan, where he has also served as Director of the Center for Research on Conflict Resolution. In 1962 he was made an award by the American Council of Learned Societies for his distinguished scholarship in the Humanities, and he is currently President of the American Economic Association. Among his books are *Economic Analysis, The Economics of Peace,* and *Conflict and Defense.*

**DAVID BRAYBROOKE** is Professor of Philosophy and Politics at Dalhousie University. He has written extensively on problems in ethical theory, epistemology, and logical features of social policy making. He is the co-author with Charles E. Lindblom of *A Strategy of Decision: Policy Evaluation as a Social Process.*

**MARTIN BRONFENBRENNER** is Professor of Economics at the Carnegie-Mellon University. He has held professorial posts at several institutions and has served as an economist for the Department of Treasury and the Federal Reserve Bank of Chicago, as tax economist for the Supreme Commander of Allied Powers in Tokyo, Japan, and as economic consultant for the Economic Commission of Asia and the Far East, Bangkok. He is author of numerous articles in economic journals, primarily concerning monetary policy, income distribution, and the Japanese economy.

**JOHN KENNETH GALBRAITH** is Paul M. Warburg Professor of Economics at Harvard University and is well-known as a distinguished economist, author, and public servant. During World War II he was Deputy Administrator of the Office of Price Administration, and later served as Head of the Office of Economic Security Policy in the Department of State. He became Chairman of the Economic Advisory Committee of the Democratic Advisory Council, and from 1961–1963 served as United States Ambassador to India. He is recipient of many honorary degrees and author of such widely read and influential books as *American Capitalism,*

ix

*The Great Crash, 1929, Economic Development, The Affluent Society,* and *The New Industrial State.*

**BELA GOLD** is Timken Professor of Industrial Economics and Director of the Research Program in Industrial Economics at Case Western Reserve University. He has served as an economic advisor in the U.S. Department of Commerce and other Federal agencies, as Professor of Industry and Economic Research at the University of Pittsburgh, as Professorial Research Fellow at Nuffield College, Oxford and as a Visiting Professor at the Imperial College of Science and Technology. His publications include *Wartime Economic Planning in Agriculture* and *Foundations of Productivity Analysis,* as well as numerous papers concerned with industrial costs, technology, and growth.

**SONIA S. GOLD** is a Scholar of the Radcliffe Institute and Associate Professor of Economics at John Carroll University. She has served as an economist in several Federal agencies and on the Faculty of Carnegie Institute of Technology, and was Scholar-in-Residence at Radcliffe College in the fall of 1966.

**THEODORE J. GORDON** is presently Director of Space Stations and Planetary Systems at Douglas Aircraft Company and was formerly chief engineer for the upper stage of the U.S. Government's Saturn rocket. He served as test conductor for early Thor rocket launches and for the world's first Lunar probe, the latter of which he described in his first book, *First into Outer Space,* written in collaboration with Julian Scheer. His other books include *The Future* and *Ideas in Conflict.*

**LELAND HAZARD** is a lawyer who presently serves as a consultant to the Pittsburgh Plate Glass Company. He is Professor Emeritus of Industrial Administration and Law at the Carnegie-Mellon University and is the honorary Chairman of Metropolitan Pittsburgh's Educational TV station WQED. He has written articles which have appeared in the *Atlantic Monthly* and the *Harvard Business Review,* and is the author of *Empire Revisited.*

**OLAF HELMER** is Senior Mathematician at the RAND Corporation and has been Research Associate for the Institution of Government and Public Affairs. His primary interests are in operational gaming and scientific methodology. He is a member of the Organizing Committee of the Institute for the Future, and is the author of a book on *Social Technology.*

**BERTRAND DE JOUVENEL** is a distinguished economist who has served as a diplomatic correspondent and international reporter. He is a member of the French Commission of National Accounts and of the Commission for Planning 1985, Director of the monthly publication *Analyse & Prévision,* and President of the International Association FUTURIBLES. Professor of the Faculty of Law (Paris) and at the Fondation Nationale des Sciences Politiques, he has lectured on economics and on political philosophy at several foreign universities (Oxford, Cambridge, Berkeley, etc.). Books translated: *On Power, Sovereignty, The Ethics of Redistribution*, and *The Art of Conjecture*.

**DAVID LEWIS** is Professor of Architecture and Urban Design at the Carnegie-Mellon University. In 1963 he was co-recipient of the First National Award of House and Home. His many books include *End and Beginning*, *The Naked Eye*, and *The Pedestrian in the City*.

**JOHN P. POWELSON** is Professor of Economics at the University of Colorado and Consultant to the Inter-American Development Bank. He has also served as Economic Advisor to the Government of Bolivia and Director of the Programme on Integrated National Accounts at the Latin American Monetary Studies Center in Mexico. He is the author of *Latin America: Today's Economic and Social Revolution*, *National Income and Flow of Funds Analysis*, and *Economic Accounting*.

**NICHOLAS RESCHER** is Research Professor of Philosophy at the University of Pittsburgh, where he is also Associate Director of the Center for Philosophy of Science. He is editor of the *American Philosophical Quarterly*, a consultant to the RAND Corporation, and a member of the Advisory Council of the Institute for the Future. His many books in the areas of logic, the philosophy of science, and the history of philosophy include *Hypothetical Reasoning*, *Distributive Justice*, *The Philosophy of Leibniz*, and *The Development of Arabic Logic*.

**JEROME SCHNEEWIND** is Associate Professor of Philosophy at the University of Pittsburgh. His principal interests are ethics and 19th century British philosophy. Besides numerous articles, he has written *Backgrounds of English Victorian Literature*, and has edited works by John Stuart Mill. He is currently in England on a Guggenheim Fellowship, working on a book on moral philosophy at Cambridge from Whewell to Moore.

**ALVIN TOFFLER** is a writer who was formerly an Associate Editor of *Fortune*. He has served as advisor to the Rockefeller Brothers Fund study of the performing arts, and as a board member of the Salzburg Seminar in American Studies. He has contributed more than 100 articles to national magazines and scholarly journals and has written a much-discussed book, *The Culture Consumers*, on the social and economic structure of the arts in present-day America.

**JAMES A. WILSON** teaches sociopsychology in the Graduate School of Business at the University of Pittsburgh, where he also serves as Assistant to the Dean and Director of the Doctoral Program. Between 1962 and 1964, he was at The Queen's University of Belfast, United Kingdom, conducting research in psychological and sociological aspects of the contemporary migration of British Scientists to North America, and, he has since continued to work in this area.

# Contents

# VALUES
# AND
# THE FUTURE

# INTRODUCTION

# Value impact forecaster—
# A profession of the future

## *Alvin Toffler*

I

Early in 1967, a seventy-three year old psychology professor named James H. Bedford died of cancer in California. Minutes after his death, a team of experimenters packed his body in Dry Ice, later transferring it to a capsule containing liquid nitrogen at a temperature of $-196°$ centigrade. It was James Bedford's hope—shared by the members of this team—that his body could be stored indefinitely at extremely low temperatures, and thus preserved until medical science had learned to cure cancer, and restore life. At that time, according to their theory, his body might be defrosted, the disease cured, and Bedford restored to life. Bedford's friends believe that cryobiology, the science of life at low temperatures, will someday make possible a workable facsimile of immortality. They regard the California cancer victim as merely the first of an army of time-travellers who will soon be searching for new life through frozen death.

Whether or not they are right, the incident raises certain intriguing philosophical questions: Just how happy would Dr. Bedford be if he were given the gift of renewed life in some society of the future? Even assuming physical health, would he want to live as part of a society whose values he might loathe? And can we predict the values of the future?

Such questions seem academic, yet virtually all our actions are based on predictions about future values. Bedford's decision, for instance, implies a belief that, at some point in the future, someone's values will motivate a decision to commit resources to thawing the body and reviving it. This may or may not be an accurate prediction, but it is a prediction, nevertheless. Similarly, to choose a more routine example, when we travel we all make assumptions—in effect, predictions—about future values. Boarding a jet at LaGuardia, we assume that the pilot values life highly enough that he will do all in his power to prevent a crash. Moreover, we assume that he will still value life as highly two hours later when he circles in over O'Hare. We stake our lives, as it were, on a short term prediction about the state of the pilot's value system. Such predictions, whether they are accurate or not, lie behind not only small and routine social acts but also behind all our economic, social, and political programs.

The task of predicting future values, however, is growing more and more difficult. Throughout human history, the value system of society changed so slowly, so imperceptibly, that seen from the vantage point of a single lifetime, it appeared to be unchanged. This made prediction simple: Each generation could predict the values of the next with considerable accuracy merely by projecting its own forward. The members of each generation could (and usually did) assume that children, once grown, would in a large measure share the values of their fathers.

In the last 500 years, however, the rate of value change appears to have speeded up—to the point at which major shifts in the value system of a society become apparent *within* the span of a single lifetime and within even shorter periods.

This acceleration of value change is one of the most dramatic developments in the entire cultural history of the human race. It shatters the presumed identity between one generation and the next. It makes untenable the assumption that the values of future generations will resemble our own, and also makes it impossible to predict future values by simple straight-line projection.

Indeed, the increasing velocity of value change confronts us not merely with the question "What will future generations value?" but also with the more pressing question "What will we, ourselves, value a decade or two from now?" This question stares us in the face every day as we go about our business of making decisions in politics, in urban planning, in international affairs, education, science and technology—decisions that will reverberate powerfully at least through the end of this century. Which values should be served by these decisions, those we hold today or those we are likely to hold at some point in the future? Can the conflict between these be resolved? In whose favor and at what cost?

Man, as we know, can already obliterate the species through nuclear or bacteriological warfare. It appears likely that he will soon be able to alter genetic structure consciously and in the direction of specified goals. He will be able to build self-replicating machines and totally unfamiliar man-machine organisms. He can already alter personality through the use of drugs. He can stimulate the pleasure centers of the brain electronically. He can create a hedonistic hell on earth or a savage totalitarianism, or any of a variety of benign utopias, and virtually anything in between. But which future he chooses will depend, at least in part, on the values fed into the decision-making process. It will depend upon how clearly we come to understand and predict changes in that complex and shifting architecture of values that regulates human behavior.

Today our knowledge of this invisible architecture and how it changes is primitive. What is a "value" or a "value system?" How do values relate to one another? What configurations do they form? How do they change? What is the interplay of value systems within a society? Values are so inextricably woven into our language, thought and behavior patterns that they have fascinated philosophers for millennia. Yet they have proved so "quick-silvery" and complex that, despite their decisive role in human motivation, we remain desperately ignorant of the laws that govern them. Nearly seventy years ago Weber referred to the term "value" as "that unfortunate child of misery of our science." It is still a fair description of the place occupied by the concept of *value* in the social sciences.

The special relationship between value change and technology is the subject of the study with which we are here concerned. This relationship lies at the heart of many of the great controversies in philosophy, history, sociology, and economics. Did the values of Protestantism give rise to capitalism and modern technology, or did the development of what Marx termed "the means of production" determine the values of society? Which is the chicken and which the egg? If this formulation of the problem is incorrect—if the relationship between the two is reciprocal—what exactly are the points of linkage?

Egbert de Vries, the Dutch sociologist, once described an African community whose inhabitants thought it necessary to start a new fire in the fireplace after each act of sexual intercourse. This bothersome belief meant that following each sex act someone had to go to a neighboring hut to bring back a burning stick with which to spark a fresh fire. In turn, this made adultery embarrassingly difficult, since each act of intercourse was, in effect, publicized.

What changed all this was a simple bit of technological diffusion—the introduction of matches. Matches made it possible to light a new fire without first going to a neighbor's hut. The introduction of this technological artifact altered sexual behavior in the community. Did this bring with it a shift in values? Was adultery less or more frowned upon as a result? By facilitating the privacy of sex, did matches alter the valuation placed upon it? And what values led to the adoption of matches in the first place?

Before we chortle superciliously about this incident, perhaps it would be well to ask how the increasing use of birth-control pills is altering our own sexual values today? And what about other kinds of technological change?

What impact will widespread implantation of artificial organs have on our value system? Do the new communications technologies leave our values untouched?

It is doubtful that anyone in that primitive African village saw a connection between sexual values and little sulfur-tipped slivers of wood *before* matches came into widespread use. This is not surprising, however, since we are similarly myopic. Major technological innovations are pouring into our society at breakneck speed. Yet, there is no profession whose responsibility includes examining and reporting on the value implications of new technologies before their wholesale introduction into society. Moreover, even if there were such a profession, it would be limited at present to speculation and intuition, for the intellectual apparatus necessary to make such analyses and predictions does not yet exist.

The idea of a profession of "value impact forecasters" is nowhere referred to by the contributors to this volume. The study does not even address itself directly to many of the questions I have raised here. It does not, for example, deal anywhere with the rate of value change and its significance. It does not explore the question of the responsibility of one generation for the next. It does not take up as an issue the degree to which future values should be taken into account in making decisions now.

Nevertheless, the study here summarized lays some of the necessary groundwork for the birth of this profession of the future. Thus, the chief assumption running through most of the book is that we need scientific knowledge about the feedback relationships that make technology and values sensitive to one another.

The study takes as a premise not merely that a science of values is necessary, but that it is possible. It presupposes that we can study values and value change objectively, that it is possible to put forward hypotheses about the nature of value systems, to test these hypotheses, and ultimately to arrive at scientifically verified generalizations about the relationships of values to social behavior.

Given this, the study sets out to provide both a terminology and a theoretical framework for a science of values. It proposes a terminology that is comprehensible and exact, useful to social scientists and policy makers as well as philosophers, one that lends itself to objective and even quantitive statements. Finally, it provides a rich source of hypotheses for empirical testing. In short, without ever directly saying so, it sets about supplying the intellectual basis for the birth of value-impact forecasting.

The book consists of three parts. The first, and perhaps most important, is methodological. The second is rather loosely organized and exploratory, concerning itself with the interactions between technology and values. The third deals with the mechanisms of control through which values are translated into programs. Let us look at these parts before we return to discuss the implications of the study as a whole, its weaknesses and its unusual strengths.


## II

What is a value? Part One begins with the definitional. Professor Kurt Baier, Chairman of the Department of Philosophy at the University of Pittsburgh, defines a value, essentially, as an attitude for or against an event or phenomenon, based on a belief that it benefits or penalizes some individual, group or institution. By defining value in this way, Baier rejects the notion of value as something "intrinsic." It becomes a manifestation of behavior and, as such, observable and measurable.

Baier differentiates values from simpler, less intellectualized attitudes, from whims, norms, regulations and mores, but this is hardly enough, and he goes on to remind us that if we want to talk meaningfully we need to be quite specific about whose values we are discussing. We must determine which person, group or institution subscribes to the values in question. Then we must specify what state of affairs constitutes realization of the value— e.g., if some group holds "thrift" to be a value, we need to know how much thrift, thrift on whose part, etc.

Beyond this, we need to know what behavioral manifestations are admissible as evidence that a person, group or institution does, in fact, subscribe to the value in question. We must analyze the benefits or penalties involved and who the beneficiaries or penalized parties are.

By spelling all this out in careful detail, Baier forces the discussion down to a far more concrete level than that at which it is usually conducted, and moves the problem one step closer toward the measurability required if a science is to be built.

One might wish for a finer delineation of the meaning of "benefits" or "penalties," and for a far more thoroughgoing discussion of Baier's assertion that an objective basis exists for the valuation of values, that is, for judging the soundness of values themselves. But even with this ultimate issue not (at least for me) settled, the provision of a useful vocabulary must be regarded as an important contribution to the de-mystification of value discussion.

This is especially true if Baier's paper is read alongside that of Nicholas Rescher, his colleague in the University of Pittsburgh's Philosophy Department. For Rescher, in a contribution entitled "A Framework for Research," continues and extends the definitional task. He points out that just as "value" has a number of distinct and definable dimensions, so "value change" has more than one meaning. Rescher sets about enumerating the ways in which values change, distinguishing these ways from one another, and thus providing what I believe is the first systematic classification of types of value change. By implication, he reveals just how simplistic most of our discussions of "changing values" are.

Thus Rescher shows that value change occurs when a specific value is redistributed through society (when, in other words, it gains or loses adherents); when it elicits greater or less commitment from its holders; when its subscribers extend or restrict what they regard as its range of applicability (as when, for example, "equal opportunity" is extended to include Negroes); when the holders of a value alter the criteria by which they measure its attainment; when they revise the priorities of actions intended to implement the value or when they set different target dates for these actions; and so on. Certain types of changes may be characterized as "upgrading" a value; others are value "downgrading."

When Rescher's schema is combined with the Baier definitions, we get a complex, integrated conceptual tool that provides a "handle" for empirical research, a convenient, precise terminology that should prove useful to those engaged in applied research into consumer behavior, religion, sexual patterns or politics, as well as to philosophers and "pure" social scientists.

Rescher is less successful when he attempts to classify the causes of value change, but he is highly provocative when he discusses possible predictive methods. Linking the Baier-Rescher machinery to the concepts of cost-benefit theory, he suggests that if we can identify a few dominant values of a society—"the relatively stable centers around which the resolution of value conflicts will pivot"—we can predict change in subordinate values by studying the way that technological and other events increase or descrease the cost of their realization and the benefits to be derived from their fulfillment.

He illustrates this method by discussing likely changes with respect to nationalism, materialism, independence, social accountability, creative and intellectual achievement, organization, self-advancement and a number of other values.

If the conceptual framework erected by Baier and Rescher is to be anything more than an elegant toy, however, it needs to be tested. Ideally, it should be useful in probing the past as well as in describing the present and predicting the future. Thus the historian J. B. Schneewind undertakes to try it out retrospectively by applying it in an examination of the impact of technology in nineteenth century England.

"How," he asks, "are we to use this abstract scheme of concepts to interpret the enormous bulk of material made available to us by the work of historians, and to fit it in with the vast literature of self-interpretation produced by Victorian essayists, novelists, poets, philosophers, and social critics?" First, he suggests, we can investigate changes in the *beliefs* of value holders. Next, we can examine changes in *attitudes*. Finally, we can attempt to deduce from the materials changes in the *range* of individuals, groups or institutions toward which the value holders directed their attitudes.

Schneewind then proceeds to show how English attitudes toward work and toward centralized government were transformed during the nineteenth century as changing technology produced new problems and conditions of life. The picture he paints is detailed and persuasive—but only as persuasive as any history based on nonquantitative and essentially nonsystematic surveys of fiction, newspapers, and other written records of the period. These materials, despite their "enormous bulk," are still limited, selective, and uneven.

The attempt to apply the Baier-Rescher method is thus hampered by a lack of data in the form required. Schneewind contributes a number of suggestive theoretical insights. (In one, for example, he compares the ways in which value systems change with the ways in which the scientific community revises its conceptual schemes.) These comments support the notion that it is possible to discern the general laws regulating value change, but, apart from these, Schneewind's effort to apply the new analytic machinery to history is no more than partially successful. It is a vigorous and intelligent effort, but it merely dramatizes the immense difficulties that still stand in the way of truly scientific examination of the value systems of the past. For if we have problems with the Victorian era which is still close to us, and is comparatively well-documented, how much more fragmentary and biased are the records of earlier times?

If lack of adequate data hamstrings the historian, the same problem confronts the futurist—and will confront members of the new profession to which I have referred, value-impact forecasters, whose task it will be to spin out the value implications of proposed technologies.

The futurist must often—and especially when he is concerned with very long range prediction—rely on pure guesswork. Even guesswork, however, can, through a number of techniques, be treated in a systematic and rational fashion. One of these techniques is the "Delphi" method pioneered by Dr. Olaf Helmer and a number of his associates at the RAND Corporation. This method grows from the simple observation that when forced to make predictions about the far-out future, we frequently call in experts in the relevant field and ask them to do the best they can—i.e., to make informed guesses.

The Delphi method systematizes and rationalizes this procedure. First, a carefully selected panel of appropriate experts is assembled. Each is queried

independently. The responses of the others are then fed back to the participant so that he has an opportunity to revise his predictions on the basis of
his knowledge of their opinions. What emerges is a consensus or "con-
vergence" of expert opinion. This is presented in quantified form. The
sophistication of the procedure can be increased by weighting the responses
of individual experts according to the relevance of their expertise to the
specific question, according to their previous success at prediction, according
to their own sense of certainty, or some other principle.

Rescher's second paper, "A Statistical Study of American Values by the
Year 2000," illustrates the application of this method to the prediction of
values. A group of experts were asked what is likely to happen by the end of
the century to such values as love and affection, success, aesthetic beauty,
economic security, reference for life or devotion to family. Their predictions
make fascinating and, no doubt for some, hair-raising reading. The findings
are summarized in the paper and therefore need not be repeated here.

The exercise, however, suffers from a number of methodological weaknesses. The main one being the size and built-in bias of the panel of experts—
only fifty-eight in all, of whom twenty-nine were trained as natural
scientists and eight as social scientists. Ten were employed by IBM, fourteen
were drawn from the National Science Foundation staff, and ten more were
members of an informal interdisciplinary body at RAND—the RAND
"Futures Group."

Nevertheless, while one may criticize the panel selection or the way in
which certain questions were framed, one should not overlook the possibility
of applying the Delphi technique on a large scale, with one or more panels
drawn from government policy makers, scientists, educators, businessmen,
journalists and others in a position to sense the drift of values in society. Nor
should one overlook the possibility of combining this technique with other
predictive methods, such as simulation.

This, in fact, is exactly what was attempted experimentally at an unusual
all-day game played at the University of Pittsburgh on Saturday, September
17, 1966. With most of the authors in this book participating, an effort was
made to simulate the future interaction of technology and values. The day
began with Theodore J. Gordon, Director of Advance Space Stations and
Planetary Systems, Douglas Aircraft Company, delivering his paper on
"The Feedback between Values and Technology."

In this paper, Gordon deliberately sidesteps the question of whether
values precede technology (Weber), or technology comes first (Marx). Instead, he argues, both are part of a loop that includes research and planning.
It is possible to begin the study of value change at any point in this loop, he
says, but research is as good a place to start as any. The direction of research

is determined, according to Gordon, by four factors:    1) the interests of the researcher;    2) an acceptable challenge;    3) the solvability of the problem; and    4) the fundability of the project. All four, he observes, are deeply conditioned by the value system of society.

The research affected by these values results in technological changes in society. These, in turn, affect values. As he puts it, values change "to fit the world technology presents." For example, he points out, television and jet planes cannot but affect the distribution of values in various populations, and shifts in distribution fall within the meaning of value change as defined by Rescher.

Gordon then proceeds to examine a list of twenty potential technological developments for their political, economic and social implications. These developments range from ocean farming to weather control, from much-improved teaching machines to general immunization against disease. Gordon's imaginative comments about the potential ramifications of each of these are an important contribution to this book.

These twenty potential technological developments form the background against which the simulation game was played. The rules of this game are spelled out in Dr. Helmer's contribution to this volume, "Simulating Future Values." Here, in simplified form, is what happened.

The Pittsburgh participants were divided into groups. Two of these were termed "Social Planning Groups." The members of these two played the role of political and technological decision makers. Each group was given certain limited resources and told it could invest these selectively to help bring about some of the twenty technological developments previously discussed by Gordon. For example, a planning group might wish to allocate some of its limited resources to foster ocean farming, or nonlethal weaponry, or advanced teaching machines. It could not, however, provide support for all twenty potential developments; it had to choose among them.

But choose how? According to what criteria? To guide its decision making, one group was given the objective of maximizing gross national product between now and the year 2000. At the same time, the other was given quite a different objective; the enhancement of human freedom.

Each group thus faced the classic problem of real life decision makers. From among a variety of possible alternatives, it had to select those most likely to help it achieve its objective. Next it had to decide how much to invest in each of the technological innovations it chose to foster. These are hard decisions in life, and even in the game they proved difficult. As a participant, the writer can testify to the heated discussion among the players.

The game was also, like life, a chancy affair. Thus, neither group of planners could actually *guarantee* that any event would occur. The planners could only increase the probability of its occurrence. At the start, each of the twenty potential developments had a certain statistical probability of occurrence.[1] Ocean farming, for instance, began with a 30 percent probability. This meant that, as of the beginning of the game, there was only a 30 percent chance that by 2000 AD economically useful exploitation of the seas through farming would yield "at least 20 percent of the world's food supply."

It was this probability that the planners could raise. By allocating resources for the purpose, a group could, for example, increase the ocean farming probability to, say, 50 percent or 80 percent. In no case, however, could a probability be pushed above 95 percent. As in life, no planner could eliminate all chance.

Once the planning groups had met, decided how to invest their resources, and thereby altered the probabilities, fate, in the form of Dr. Helmer and a "probability die" took over. On the facets of this twenty-sided die certain numbers are printed. Some numbers appear more frequently than others, so that there are, for example, more eighties (representing 80 percent probability) than thirties (representing 30 percent probability). Thus the higher the probability conferred by the planners on some development such as ocean farming, the greater the likelihood that its number would turn up on a roll of the die.

The planners had been allowed to influence the future by raising the probability of certain events. Now chance was given the final word, as Dr. Helmer, with the planners watching intently, began to roll the die. Each development was called off and its probability announced. Then the die was tossed. If the number on the die did not correspond with the probability of the development, the event was declared not to have occurred. On the other hand, if an event had a probability of sixty, say, and a sixty turned up on the die, the event was declared to have happened. From each of the planning groups, therefore, there emerged a different list of technological advances presumed to have occurred between now and 2000 AD. The planners, aided, abetted or obstructed by chance, had brought forth certain technological developments.

Phase Two of the simulation now began. Technological developments carry all sorts of consequences in their wake, and the purpose of Phase Two was to examine these consequences systematically.

To this end, two groups of "Social Predictors" were called into being. Each group was handed one of the lists of technological developments produced by the planning groups with the aid of the probability die. These social prediction groups were then asked to explore the implications of each

1. These starting probabilities were derived from a Delphi exercise conducted by Helmer and Gordon independently of this study.

technological development on the list. To use ocean farming as an example once more, the predictors were told to assess the likelihood that this might bring with it an increase in life span, a reduction in the threat of war, or national territorial claims to the oceans, etc.

In this way, new lists were drawn up, this time showing the most likely consequences of the new technologies that the planners had influenced or brought into being through their allocational decisions. A cluster of consequences was associated with the technological developments generated by planning group one. A different set of consequences flowed from the decisions of planning group two. There thus emerged two different "worlds" of the year 2000, each reflecting the value input of its planning group.

The final stage of the simulation now began. Once more the participants were divided up—this time into six groups called "Evaluators." Each was told to simulate a different social group—teenagers, women, older people, the poor, the cultural elite, the middle class. Each evaluator group was asked to state its preference for one of the two worlds produced by the planners, using as criteria the values it thought its real world counterpart group might hold in the year 2000. Which world would the "teenagers of 2000" prefer? Which would the "cultural elite" choose? The poor? The elderly?

Now came the major surprise of the afternoon. For as the evaluators proceeded, it became clear that the two worlds were *not* radically different from one another. Despite the differing objectives of the planners, both worlds had many features in common. Both were more affluent and educated than our own at present. Both relied on many of the same technologies. The difference, except in one respect, was more of emphasis than of substance. They differed chiefly in that one of the two appeared to offer slightly more room for individual freedom than the other.

Why did the two worlds of the future resemble each other so strongly? First, as someone acutely pointed out, the players, despite varied expertise, represented in many respects a very homogeneous group. They were all intellectuals. Many were academics. Most undoubtedly share the values of the educated middle-class American. Thus, it was suggested, even though the planners were given different objectives, they interpreted these in terms of their own preexisting values. These shared values led to the selection of similar means to effectuate dissimilar ends.

Then, too, chance played a more powerful role in the game than it ordinarily does in real life—in the sense that planners in real life often have an opportunity to revise their plans in the light of new developments. Decision making is often a continuous multi-stage process, while in the game it was a "one-shot" proposition. The planners had no opportunity to alter their decisions after each roll of the die.

Given that both worlds were largely similar, with one seemingly more "open" than the other, it was not surprising that all the evaluation groups, without exception, preferred the freer of the two worlds. What was striking, however, were the margins of preference. For the groups simulating teen-agers, the poor and the aged all registered a far stronger preference for the freer world than did the others. There was a clear indication of difference between those groups that might be considered to be the least privileged and those—the middle class and cultural elite, for example—that might be regarded as most comfortable and complacent. The differences might also be attributed to an over-romantic view of the underprivileged held by the educated, middle-aged intellectuals who simulated them.

The exercise excited and exhausted its participants. For some, it under-lined the planner's problem of choice. For others, it suggested the relative importance of men to shape their future. For still others, it dramatized the primitive state of our efforts to predict value change.

Certainly, the inadequacies of the procedure were clearly demonstrated. In the real world, the problems of choice are not limited to twenty items, and conflicting groups rarely start with a single, clearly defined objective. Middle-aged intellectuals, no matter how they disport themselves, do not make good simulated teenagers. One could draw up a long list of such in-adequacies.

Still and all, most of these criticisms are directed at practice, not principle. It would be possible, for instance, to get actual teenagers to simulate the teenagers of the future. One might start with many more planning groups, each with many more objectives and many more choices— and with a good-sized computer to do the calculations. One might arrange for multi-stage decisions, so that each planning group might take the actions of the others into account. One might pit the groups against one another. One might start with a less ambitious thrust into the future—with a five or ten year horizon, rather than thirty some odd. In short, in criticizing the game, we must be extremely careful not to damn the baby along with the bathwater.

Furthermore, it should be possible to employ sophisticated simulation and Delphi techniques in combination with forecasting models based on empirically determined relationships between sub- and super-ordinate values. If we connect the analytical machinery constructed by Baier and Rescher with the predictive techniques suggested here, we may well take a long leap forward toward accuracy in the prediction of future states of the value system—a leap that must be taken if we are not to be overwhelmed by the technological future. This, in a sentence, is the central message of Part One of this book. It is a message of high significance for the social sciences.

III

Techniques alone, even if sophisticated, are not enough to form the basis for either a science or a profession. Technique must be wedded to theory. We need, in short, some over-arching, tentative conception of the ways in which technology and values interrelate. But if a scientific theory is defined as "a coordinated set of hypotheses which are found to be consistent with one another and with specially observed phenomena,"—which is the way Chambers'[2] defines it—then it is clear we are still a long way from arriving at one that even begins to explain the interaction of technology and values. We are, in fact, still at the stage in which we need hypotheses—many of them—to put to empirical test.

The authors of the papers in Part Two of this book do not set out specifically to provide such hypotheses. Yet the stimulating stream of ideas that flow from their papers are bound to provide imaginative researchers with the raw material from which to fashion them. The writers attack the problem from many different angles. They begin with different and often conflicting premises.

The name Bertrand de Jouvenel, for instance, is associated with the idea that the future is open, that at any given moment there are many "possible futures," and that it is our prerogative to choose among them. Jouvenel, a political economist, writer and philosopher, is also a leading figure in the "future studies" movement, and among those in this movement he has been, perhaps, the one most expressly interested in values as such. It is Jouvenel who opens Part Two with a forceful polemic.

While "it would be hard to find a phenomenon more dependent upon human decisions than the evolution of techniques," he charges, there is a new fatalism in Western society, "a feeling that our future is determined for us by the autonomous course of a super-human agency, whose god-like nature is acknowledged by the reverent use of a capital: Technology." If there has to be a capital letter, Jouvenel would rather it appear as in Values.

Thus he reminds us that decisions shaping the technology of tomorrow inevitably involve money. Only through investment can these decisions be effectuated. Those who control the flow of investment, therefore, control the direction of technology, and it is they who choose between the many possible futures. But, he implies, their conception of what is possible is treacherously narrow. They underestimate the staggering range of choice that confronts us.

Underdeveloped countries, for instance, in designing their technological destiny, can choose from an extremely wide repertoire of techniques already in use in the more developed countries. The particular techniques

2. *Chambers' Technical Dictionary* (New York, 1958; Third Edition).

they choose to transplant will alter the structure and texture of their society. But particularly because the range is so broad, it is the selection, and ultimately the values upon which the selection is based, that really counts.

Even the developed countries have a vast backlog of unexploited techniques upon which to draw. These unused techniques are to be found in research laboratories. They await application, and each year the backlog of innovation grows. Once again, it is the selection that is critical.

For this reason, those who choose—and among these the government is now preeminent—have it within their power to impose their values. "The guidance exercised upon R&D in general and more especially upon Research," writes Jouvenel, "is a determining influence of our social future. The process of allocation might be called the Ministry of the Future."

We encounter in another paper the rather startling idea that perhaps the power of the purse is on the wane. But for a moment it is worthwhile to examine further Jouvenel's assertion that we are freer than we think, with its implication that values are primary and technology secondary.

We find this same idea present, but unstated, in John P. Powelson's paper comparing the economic values of the U.S. with those of Latin America. Professor Powelson of the Department of Economics at the University of Colorado begins his argument by contrasting the so-called "market mystique," the heavy reliance placed on the market mechanism by North American economies, with the widespread existence of central planning, price control and state ownership in Latin American countries.

This contrast, he asserts, springs from a fundamental split in values. The dominant economic value in North America he describes as "productionist"—a positive attitude toward wealth based on the belief that it is a reward for invention, saving, sacrifice and all the Horatio Alger virtues. The dominant value in Latin America, on the other hand, he characterizes as "appropriationist"—a negative or mixed attitude toward wealth based on the belief that its present owners are "not those who themselves created it or inherited it," but rather those who "gained it by conquest or appropriation."

Cranked into the decision making apparatus, these sharply counterposed values result in sharply different economies, Powelson says. In this sense, he appears to support Jouvenel's insistence on the primacy of values. Yet it is equally possible that the values are effects, rather than causes, of the differing economic structures. To what degree, we need to know, does an existing economic system produce the value systems that sustain it?

Powelson's description of some of the wealth-redistribution mechanisms in Latin American economies and his proposals for revision of American diplomatic policies are interesting and insightful. But, unfortunately, he is handicapped by the same problem that crops up again and again in these discussions, a paucity of reliable data. In attributing values to Americans and Latin Americans, Professor Powelson makes what Baier terms "value imputations." The basis for these imputations, however, is slender. It consists chiefly of a number of opinion surveys which, as Powelson himself admirably notes, were conducted with something less than scientific rigor.

Better and more comprehensive data could shed light on the question of whether the economic system produces the values or the values produce the economic system. For example, it might well be possible to show that Latin American *campesinos* in remote communities, outside the centers where government economic controls operate, also hold the appropriationist view of wealth. If this were shown to be so, as hunch tells us it is, Powelson's thesis would be much strengthened, though still, by no means, conclusively demonstrated. We would also want to know how the level of technology (or the lack of technology) fits into the picture.

Technology, if it does nothing else, affects the attainability of values— but not always as we might expect. This point emerges from Sonia Gold's discussion of "The Professional Commitment of Educated Women." Assuming for the sake of argument that the goals enunciated by the Commission on National Goals convened during the Eisenhower administration are a more or less valid reflection of the American consensus, she observes that, as a society, we lack the resources to attain these goals at present. This gives us several options.

We might reduce the number of goals or lower the level of attainment of those we choose to pursue. In contrast, we might increase the workload of the present labor force. We might expand the work force by drawing educated women and others into it. Or, finally, we might introduce additional labor-saving technology to reduce manpower needs.

Starting with a gap between available resources and a fixed set of goals (each of which presumably represents a step toward the attainment of a value), our tendency is to think that technology will magically close the gap. Professor Gold argues, however, that while technology may reduce some manpower needs, it also has a way of generating new wants—thus requiring the setting of new goals.

If this is true, she says, then we ought not imagine that labor-saving technology alone will fill the resource gap. She regards it as equally un- likely that our affluent society will move toward an increase in workloads. She conjectures (but does nor make clear on what basis) that a reduction in the number of goals or attainment standards is also unlikely.

These assumptions lead her to the conclusion that we shall, in fact, opt to expand the work force by drawing educated women into it in much larger numbers than at present. This, in turn, leads her to concern herself with the factors that influence women to seek careers. To what degree do they respond to education and propaganda urging them to adopt a career? To what degree are their attitudes toward a profession fixed by value inculcation early in childhood? Does a conscious understanding and acceptance of national goals play any significant part in motivating them?

These are interesting questions, but one finds one's mind returning to a major premise of the discussion. This is the assumption that, faced with a gap between goals and available resources, Americans are more likely to try to increase the resources than decrease the goals. An intriguing point, it has to do not merely with the value placed upon achievement, but also with what might be termed a society's grasp of reality. In effect, it asks: To what degree does a society's comprehension of what is technologically possible mold its values?

This question, which no one else in the study has seen fit to raise, merits far more attention than it can be given here. Professor Gold's technical exposition of the ways in which the value system of society interacts with that of a large social group—in this case women—generates many such questions.

Whatever values women hold in the future, they are certain to be influenced by the urban revolution. In "The New Urban Structure," David Lewis, Professor of Architecture and Urban Design at the Carnegie Institute, paints a provocative picture of the city of the future. This city, he writes, will not only be larger and more complicated than the cities of today, but will be characterized by a highly fluid population pattern and by multiple centers. It will be, in his words, "infinitely additive and infinitely variable."

Lewis challenges the view that "tomorrow's cities will retain their present form—and gradually strangle themselves in a combined density of automobiles and people. This," he asserts, "is complete nonsense." The speed of travel and communications has so altered space-time relationships that it will necessarily destroy "the fixed, closed forms of our single-center cities."

If the city is to be "infinitely additive and infinitely variable," however, it will impose fewer restraints on those who add to or vary them. But according to what principles should they be changed? Planners plan and plans presuppose objectives based on a value hierarchy. But what values are to be served?

Lewis presents an exciting image of the city of tomorrow, but he is largely reticent on these points, thus leaving the implication that the new urban technology might be adapted to serve any master, that it is, itself, neutral.

This, however, is precisely what Leland Hazard disputes. For while Jouvenel and others stress the power of values to influence technology, Hazard, in "Challenges for Urban Policy," lays himself on the line in defense of the reverse proposition. A director of the Pittsburgh Plate Glass Corp., a lawyer and leader in the urban development program that has altered downtown Pittsburgh noticeably in recent years, Hazard states flatly: "I assume that technology has always been and will ever be a prime factor in the conceptualization of individuated or named values. I put technology first; it is a way of living, of being, perhaps of becoming."

Hazard selects four technological developments—high-speed mass transit, television, the computer, and the new contraceptives—and attempts to show how certain values will be either up or downgraded by them.

Hazard describes, for example, a possible mass transit system of the future based on light-weight, high-speed, low-noise trains, laced into the city in a close-knit network, and controlled by computer so that cars are automatically speeded or shunted to optimize traffic flow, with the entire system set so that no passenger need ever wait more than, say, two minutes, for a train. Such a system, by supplanting or restricting automobile use, would, according to Hazard, downgrade the value of "one's own undisciplined pleasure; self-reliance; prowess and ability; power; privacy; novelty. . . ." On the other hand, it would upgrade physical well-being, comfort, convenience in style of life, self-respect, love, affection, friendship, reasonableness and rationality, conscientiousness, service to others, equality and civil rights, democracy, social justice, peace and reverence for life. Hazard draws up similar lists for each of the other technological developments under consideration.

One may argue with these bold assertions, but Hazard is here doing in a rough and intuitive way what the future profession of value impact forecasting will (hopefully) be able to do scientifically. Hazard merely employs the general terms "upgrade" and "downgrade" as Rescher has used them. The value analysts of the future may go further and specify the particular types of changes that fall within these categories. Moreover, they will have to be far more specific in their description of each value in question, defining it along each of the dimensions spelled out by Baier, and they will, of course, have to make their "predictions" in terms of probabilities rather than certainties.

Hazard and Jouvenel have been juxtaposed here as if they represented opposite ends of the old chicken-egg dispute. In reality, neither is so extreme as to deny the reciprocality of value technology relationships. Yet one clearly emphasizes the primacy of values, while the other quite as strenuously insists on the primacy of technology. By contrast, Kenneth Boulding, an economist by trade and one of the most imaginative philosophers in the social sciences, bluntly refuses to deal with the problem in these terms.

"It is quite impossible," he states, "to say which precedes the other."

Thus, he notes, "it seems fairly certain . . . that there were changes in values . . . which were a necessary prerequisite for the rise of science, in the direction of introducing higher preferences for change, for the authority of nature rather than the authority of sacred books and ancient writers." These changes in values, however, were not unconnected with certain preceding changes in technologies, for instance the rise of the money economy, development of accounting, and the subsequent opportunities for more rational behavior in the light of better information. A strong case can be made out, indeed, that in the origins of science it was the machine that preceded the scientific or mechanical image of the world. The clock, for instance, preceded the Copernican-Newtonian image of the solar system as a great clock; the water pump preceded the discovery of the circulation of the blood, just as the steam engine preceded thermodynamics. . . ."

On the other hand, Boulding writes, there are also "changes which occur fairly spontaneously within the system of values and preferences." Referring to the Reformation, Boulding suggests that "once the authority of the Pope had been challenged and a high value had been placed in the Protestant countries on successful dissent, the legitimation of dissent in general is a fairly easy step." This value change, according to Boulding, then became a key element in the process of innovation, which lies at the core of technological change.

Boulding thus sweeps aside the search for "primacy" that forms the matrix of Part Two of this volume, preferring to accept that some complex interplay exists between technology and values, but refusing to commit himself, without more evidence than we now have, on the issue of which, if either, comes first. He thereby aligns himself with Gordon who, as noted earlier, sees technology and values as two parts of a closed loop. In short, as Part Two of the book ends, neither the chicken nor the egg triumphs.

If in Part One we examine some of the analytical tools necessary for the creation of a science of values, in Part Two we are asked to respond to a collection of highly varied statements about the interaction of values and technology. The worth of these statements lies not alone in the main theses they put forth, but in the interstices, the asides, the premises and second thoughts they compel us to consider. From this material a rich assortment of hypotheses may be derived. Part Two thus ends not with certainty, but with questions—the most basic input of any science.

## IV

With this as background, the book now moves forward to the central issue of control. If the world we build is to be decent and humane (in terms of present values), if we are to place limits on, for instance, invasions of privacy or tinkering with the gene, we must understand the mechanisms by which control over technological change can be exerted. We need to know who the controllers are—and what values they hold. Part Three devotes itself to these questions.

Jouvenel, in underscoring the wide array of choices available to the social policy maker, points to the decisive role played by capital. Those who control the flow of capital (and especially capital for research and development) control the future, he declares. Indeed, "Money talks!" is an old and largely unchallenged piece of folk wisdom.

Yet it is exactly this hallowed principle that is questioned by John Kenneth Galbraith, the Harvard economist and former ambassador to India. Money may still talk, he suggests, but perhaps not quite as loudly as before.

If we study the shifting relationships of what economists call the "factors of production"—land, labor, capital and entrepreneurial talent—we find that at one time land was the critical factor. With land went power. And land was only dethroned as the prime factor of production, Galbraith says, when the opening of vast new territories in the Americas and elsewhere made an abundant supply available to the developed countries of Europe.

Later came the rise of modern industry, and this was accompanied by a scarcity of capital. "Accordingly," writes Galbraith, "the man who owned or supplied the capital now had the strategically important factor of production," and he, in turn, became the recipient of power.

Today, Galbraith says, we are witnessing another radical shift in the relative importance of the factors of production. Land is no longer the critical factor; labor continues, on the whole, to be plentiful; even capital, Galbraith tells us, is now increasingly abundant. And so, he says, "power has passed to . . . a new factor of production. This is the structure of organization which combines and includes technical knowledge, talent and experience that modern industrial technology and planning require . . . It is on the effectiveness of this structure . . . that the success of the business enterprise now depends."

Galbraith, of course, is not the first to suggest that organization be regarded as a factor of production. More than half a century ago Alfred Marshall ranked it along with land, labor and capital. Nor is Galbraith the first to call attention to the growing importance of "technical knowledge, talent and experience" or its dispersal throughout the corporate structure. Both organization and knowledge are present even in the most primitive productive enterprise. One wonders, moreover, if clarity is served by lumping these two together and terming them a "new" factor.

If power has been dispersed through the corporate structure, it is because knowledge, too, has been dispersed and because in its specialized forms this knowledge is relatively scarce. The manager who sits at the top of the pinnacle today cannot possibly know what all his subordinates are supposed to do and the specialists he needs are not easy to come by. Even division and department managers are too far removed from the actual work to understand its intricacies. By delegating authority downward to project managers and team leaders who do have the expertise, the men at the top become increasingly dependent upon them, and as the skills required grow more refined and less interchangeable, the individual specialist is necessarily given greater rein. The distinction between line and staff begins to blur. Task forces and ad hoc organizational forms complicate the structure.

How then control this system? One of the implications of Galbraith's thesis is that capital, in losing its pivotal significance *vis à vis* other factors of production, might also be losing some of its efficacy as a control mechanism. Has the day arrived when one can exert more control over the end product by manipulating organizational structure than by controlling the flow of funds?

The idea seems strange to anyone brought up to associate money with power. Yet it is clear that at least under certain limited circumstances this is already so. Funds are obviously necessary, but any astute executive knows that he can effectively block the implementation of a policy, if he so wishes, simply by misorganizing it. Moreover, he knows that this kind of sabotage often goes undetected. The murder of a policy is made to resemble accidental death. How many federal policies have perished this way? It is also increasingly clear that the tightly organized enterprise can sometimes run rings around better capitalized but less rationally structured competitors.

If power in the corporation flows toward specialized knowledge, this process vests particular power in those whose specialized knowledge happens to be in the field of organization. The new breed of operations researchers, systems analysts, directors of organization, and even management consultants brought in from the outside represent a new node of concentrated power, and woe betide the chief executive of the future who fails to understand at least a little of their language.

Whether control is to be exerted through selective funding or, to a degree, through purposeful design of organization, whether power is concentrated at the top or diffused through the structure, it is still, however, possible to speak of manager and managed. Instruments of control may change and the managers' range of choice may be restricted by decisions made at lower levels, but the managerial group still deeply influences the rate and direction of technological and economic advance.

There is a tendency to identify managers with the corporate policies they espouse. Yet in making decisions they bring with them not merely the formal instructions of their superiors, but also their own personal ambitions and value systems. Corporate decisions are thus filtered through a screen of personal value systems. These may, in fact, prove powerful enough to deflect, twist, even reverse actions called for from above. Thus, in "The Private Production of Public Goods," David Braybrooke of Dalhousie University makes it plain that anyone who wants to control the forward movement of technology or to alter the structure of the economy would do well to take into account the personal values of managers.

Braybrooke begins with a discussion of the chief complaint made by Galbraith in *The Affluent Society*—that in the United States too much production is channelled into private consumption while the public sector starves. In private consumption, Braybrooke observes, if a consumer wants a product, he makes a decision and he buys. In contrast, no individual can buy air-pollution control or better traffic conditions or higher quality public education. The decision to purchase must be collective. Consumption, in other words, must be organized.

What might happen, Braybrooke asks, if federal, state and local governments organized consumption of public goods on a very large scale and contracted out their production to private corporations? As examples of the kinds of novel services or products these private corporations might offer, he lists the design and installation of small museums and zoos, the invention of novel sewage disposal systems, the creation of fire alarm networks linking private homes with fire departments, etc. The list might easily be extended to include the design and installation of cultural centers, schools, traffic controls and health facilities. Furthermore, in principle there is no reason why private corporations could not even take on the operation of such systems or institutions.

Such a solution to the problem of inadequate public consumption is quite feasible, he argues, because it is nicely compatible with the already existing values of the managerial group in business and industry. To substantiate this, he describes a cluster of values that he imputes to this managerial group. He cites evidence from various surveys to support the contention that managers actually hold such values. (This evidence, unfortunately, is of mixed reliability.)

He next proceeds to show how the expansion of private enterprise into a greatly enlarged market for public goods fits in with and seems to foster the attributed values.

Braybrooke's proposed solution to the problem neatly avoids the cliches of both the right and the left. But he has overlooked a major obstacle to any such program. For if we are to examine the values of corporate managers, in determining the feasibility of the proposal, we should also look at those held by public officials and by the voting and taxpaying public. It may be true that the private production of public goods accords with the values of managers. But unless there is some radical change in public values with respect to taxation and bond issues, government at all levels will continue to be hard put to raise the money it needs to carry out the program.

More important, however, from the viewpoint of the present study is Braybrooke's suggestion that we need to analyze the feasibility of a program in terms of the values, personal as well as corporate, of those who will be instrumental in carrying it out. He does not enlarge on this point, but it is clear that if we can accurately describe the values held by crucially placed participants, it becomes possible to take this factor into account in planning, and thereby improve control over output. This may well be another function of the social-value analysts or forecasters of the future.

The need to study the value systems of managers is underscored by Bela Gold, Professor of Industrial Economics at Case Institute of Technology, in a paper keenly critical of many widespread assumptions about the motivations behind major research and development efforts.

Gold begins by challenging the notion that major innovational programs in industry are set into motion by simple profit-and-loss considerations. Companies underwrite innovative research, he argues, to "build image," to maintain the morale of research staffs, and for a variety of other reasons that are only indirectly economic. Beyond this, he maintains, elaborate attempts to construct rational models for management decision making in this field have been disappointing, and it remains difficult to predict "the kinds of inventions or discoveries likely to occur; the kinds of applications likely to be made of new discoveries; how close to successful fruition given undertakings are; and even how alternative designs or carefully developed theoretical models will turn out."

Given so much uncertainty, managerial values come to play a dominant role in decision making. The value orientations of executives not only influence their choice of projects to support, but "are even likely to condition conceptions of how much and what kinds of information should be gathered before decisions can be made."

Researchers' values, too, enter into the choices made. But research specialists, Gold contends, "recommend proposals which are likely to gain managerial acceptance and which are also likely to enhance their own records of performance as appraised and rewarded by management. . . ." In effect, he says, the scientists and technicians tailor their proposals to meet the value specifications of the managers. Since the managers lack adequate data upon which to make rational decisions, the willingness of scientists to defer to them frequently results in disaster for both.

Gold's portrait of the scientist, however, appears at first glance to conflict with that painted in James Wilson's paper, "Motivations Underlying the Brain Drain." For if Gold suggests that scientists are easily bent, Wilson presents them in quite a different light.

In the last decade large numbers of English scientists and engineers have migrated to the United States. In 1962 the Royal Society estimated that this outflow was equal to about 12 percent of Britain's total annual crop of PhD's in science. The phenomenon, quickly dubbed "the brain-drain," occasioned widespread speculation about its sources. In his paper, Wilson reports on a survey he conducted in this country to find out not only who the migrants are, but also where they have settled, what they are now doing, and *why* they chose to leave their homeland.

His findings are based on responses from 517 individuals, mainly physicists and chemists, with a sprinkling of astronomers, mathematicians and engineers. All respondents were living in the United States when surveyed.

When we look at those who chose to uproot themselves, we find, according to Wilson, men who "appear to be more ambitious, more motivated, more interested in action and hard work, than the nonmigrants." Translated into value terms, this means that the migrants place a high value on achieving, that "they seem most to want an opportunity to use their rather extensive talents." Against this, the attractions of higher salaries, more research funds and better facilities are secondary. It is the desire to find work that is meaningful or fulfilling, work that permits them to make maximum use of their capabilities, that apparently drives them.

Such men, however, do not appear to fit Professor Gold's pattern. Will men who leave their homeland in pursuit of self-fulfillment tailor research proposals to meet the demands of not-too-well-informed managers? Is there not a conflict between the independence implied in one action and the conformity implied in the other?

It is true that Gold refers to researchers in general, while Wilson is describing a rather special subgroup. But even if this were not so, the conflict is more apparent than real. For it may well be that the migrants and other researchers who share their drive for fulfillment are more interested in the nature of their work than in the success of the project or the ultimate end to which their contributions are put.

It is possible to do very fulfilling work on a fascinating piece of a project that, as a whole, turns out to be a failure, or which, if a success, fosters some end purpose of which the researcher does not approve. It is possible, in other words, for the scientist to attain some of his own high priority values within a framework imposed by someone else. Yet what Wilson's work suggests is that the scientist's values cannot simply be taken for granted. Indeed, this applies not merely to the way in which the scientist's value system conforms or deviates from that of corporate management. The same is true of his values as they relate to the larger social system.

Thus, Wilson concludes, "the era of noncritical acceptance of an economic system, a society, a scientific establishment has ended for many. Now allegiance must be *earned* and especially is this true of those gifted and well-educated persons of scientific talent who are now potentially the most mobile of men, and paradoxically, those also who can make the largest contribution to their country and society of origin."

This suggests that in the future, as affluence rises and the elemental problems of food, clothing and shelter recede in importance, larger masses of educated people will, like these scientists, come to regard nationalism, regionalism or patriotism as secondary to individual fulfillment. It is no longer an empty belly alone that impels men to tear up their roots; other, more subtle and psychological needs are taking on a new importance. This, in turn, suggests that societies wishing to advance technologically must take these new needs—and the values associated with them—into account in their planning. Planning must concern itself with a whole range of issues related to psychic, as well as economic, welfare.

If planning is to take such factors into account, however, it must be far more sophisticated and comprehensive than at present. It must be based on far more, far better, and far more intelligently treated data. It must ramify through the entire society. Yet here we strike a complication important enough to give all enthusiastic technocrats pause. This is the apparent conflict between planning and individual liberty. It is this problem to which economist Martin Bronfenbrenner calls our attention in the final paper of the present study.

Until the turn of the century, he writes, most professional economists regarded socialism or centralized planning as utterly unworkable. Three important developments have changed this view, however. First, we have much better data than before on national income, production, consumption, employment, international trade, labor force, and a wide range of other economic topics.

Second, we have advanced techniques and theories that permit us to manipulate this and other information in new and more effective ways. The computer, if it does nothing else, allows us to process vast masses of data in no time at all. At the same time, Bronfenbrenner reminds us, we have developed sophisticated survey techniques, input-output theory, linear programming, stability analysis, and the ability to simulate complex economic processes with the help of the computer. Such techniques are already in wide use, he writes, "both in private planning by individual business firms and in public planning by cities like Pittsburgh, regions like the Upper Midwest, and countries like Egypt, Holland, and Poland."

In addition to better data and techniques for handling it, he says, we also have much better means to enforce "whatever controls planning may involve." As examples, he cites broad-based income taxes and social insurance schemes which, he says, have only become feasible fairly recently and which are now being automated. It is now possible to apply highly efficient direct controls such as rationing and allocation of producer goods over a long period. In addition, he notes, "auditory, visual, and radio controls have been devised to supervise production, provide continuous reporting of operations, and to put the right man in the right place at the right time. Some of the results, like the radio-directed taxi driver, have become familiar in the private economy. Others resemble the telescreen ("Big Brother Is Watching You") which Orwell forecast only for 1984." In short, the means for assuring adherence to a plan are far more numerous and effective nowadays than at the turn of the century.

All this, Bronfenbrenner contends, gives special point to Hayek's familiar thesis that planning must inevitably lead to totalitarianism. This is an argument that has never been satisfactorily answered, according to Bronfenbrenner. Moreover, to suggest that the market system does not by *itself* guarantee civil liberties does not make Hayek wrong. Thus Bronfenbrenner cautions against the headlong extension of planning.

This attack on planning runs counter to the spirit, if not the fine print, of most of the other contributions to this volume. None of the authors argues for an unthinking maximization of planning. But behind all the papers stands the assumption that potential advances in science and technology open such wide and dangerous choices that man must achieve far more sophisticated control over their development. This control necessarily implies planning, although it does not, as Braybrooke points out, necessarily mean an end to private enterprise.

While Bronfenbrenner may argue that Hayek's gloomy thesis has not been adequately disproved, it can also hardly be said to have been established beyond doubt. Bronfenbrenner does a service to those of us interested in civil liberties by sensitizing us to the real dangers that may lie ahead. There may, indeed, be a conflict between civil liberties and *ineffective* planning or between civil liberties and *effective* planning for purposes inimical to their preservation. But unless one adopts the position that individual freedom is absolute and that all rational activities, all step-by-step attempts to achieve pre-set goals, in some way constrain freedom, there is no necessary incompatibility between planning and liberty.

All plans represent a set of specifications drawn up for some aspect of the future. All plans imply an attempt to impose the values of the past (as expressed in the plan) on the future. In this sense, one might argue that planning restricts the freedom of the future. Yet the same is true of non-planning. Allowing events to take their "natural" or "unplanned" course also sets restraints on future behavior.

The danger is not so much that we will over plan. The danger is that our planning will be too simpleminded, that it will pursue too *few* objectives. A plan with a single purpose may prove highly effective—but at the cost of values not reflected on the plan. If we choose to maximize GNP and ignore all other considerations, we might well wind up with an Orwellian future. But if planning assigns weights to a wide variety of values and sees these values as ranked and interrelated, if part of the input are values favoring individual liberty, it is possible not merely to avoid tyranny, but to enhance freedom of the individual.

The real problem is to sort out the values that motivate our social and individual behavior, to analyze them clearly and profoundly, to uncover the conflicts between them, and then to choose, as consciously as we know how, which ones to give precedence. If a heightened understanding of the role of values in decision making contributes to our ability to do this, Part Three of this book, by exploring some of the mechanisms of control, is more than amply justified.


## V

What can one conclude from this study? Analysis and prediction are discussed. The relationship between technology and values is held up to scrutiny from a variety of angles. The crucial points of control and some of the values that enter into them are examined. What emerges?

First, the immensity of the problem. Men have sailed and drowned in the oceans since the beginning of human history. Yet it is only recently that the science of oceanography has developed. Today our scientific explorations of the seas tell us how little we really know about them. The value universe can be compared to a great, uncharted and invisible ocean, a part of Chardin's "noosphere." The study summarized here can be seen as an adventurous probe into the deeps. One surfaces with fresh awe for the complexity of the subject. The edges of the problem are scarcely penetrated. The methodologies and hypotheses suggested in this book all need to be sharpened. But they are *worth* improving upon. And that, given the scope of the problem, is high tribute.

Second, we learn from the successes and weaknesses of the project how wide a variety of intellectual disciplines must be drawn into the work. The organizers of this probe have gone out of their way to make it interdisciplinary. They have assembled economists, political scientists, philosophers, mathematicians, a businessman, a space engineer and others. Yet it soon becomes clear that, even so, they have not reached out far enough. Conspicuously absent from these pages, for example, are anthropologists, linguists, and behavioral psychologists, many of whom are intensely interested in these problems. Psychiatrists, advertising men, market research and opinion research experts—all have something to contribute to this work. The specialized knowledge of even so varied and impressive a group as are brought together here is still far too narrow and incomplete.

Third, this volume may also be faulted justifiably for failing to provide, at the start, a comprehensive state-of-the-art report on methodology. The work is presented as though it existed in a vacuum. What is lacking is not some drearily academic "review of the literature," but a brief descriptive summary of relevant work now going on elsewhere, some of which is exciting in its implications. In France, for example, CEPREL (Centre d'Études de la Prospection Economique à Moyen et Long Terme) is comparing investment decisions taken in implementation of the Fourth Plan with the value assumptions of the Plan. Operating on the assumption that the values consciously fed into the Plan are only the visible part of the value input, CEPREL researchers are working backward from what happened to what was supposed to happen to see if they can relate outcomes to unconsciously introduced value inputs. They are, so to speak, psychoanalyzing the Fourth Plan. They are value forecasting in reverse. Work like this is directly relevant to the problems discussed in this volume.

These inadequacies are minor, however, compared with the chief defect of the project—its failure, so far, to come to grips with the data problem. Writer after writer is hobbled by the shortage of concrete empirical data. It was originally an intention of the organizers of this project to "analyze and describe the existing value structure of our society," to draw, in other words, a profile of the present state of the American value system and its components. Nothing like this has been attempted.

To draw such a profile is, of course, an enormous undertaking. Yet this, or something like it, must be done before many of the hypotheses put forward by the writers in this volume can ever be tested. We need systematic surveys of the value systems held by important American subcultures, by different professions, age groups and socioeconomic groupings. Only from such extensive—and expensive—empirical research can we come up with concretely useful generalizations about the laws that govern value change. The task is formidable; but is it not impossible, and the Baier-Rescher terminology provides a valuable tool. If this project continues, as one hopes it will, then perhaps researchers armed with sufficient funds can undertake intensive and compatible surveys of the values of Negroes, college students, business executives, scientists and other groups, and begin to draw these pieces together into a tentative profile of the whole.

At the same time, it would be useful to single out one technological development of the recent past—jet aircraft, for example, or transistor radios—and attempt to study its impact on the values of a relevant social group such as executives or teenagers. Conversely, it would be helpful to single out a definable value—industriousness or craftsmanship, for example— attempt to determine how this particular value fits into the value system held by a social group, and then to examine how its position and definition alters over time, trying, while doing this, to correlate the changes with technological influences in the lives of the value holders.

Still another step in the project might be an effort to examine the relationship of technology to other value-altering forces. The development of large scale organization, for instance, while closely connected with tech- nology, is not the same as technology. Yet it, too, can be studied in terms of its impact on value systems. How does an increase of scale in terms of population size influence the value structure? The focus of this project is, quite justifiably, on technology. But technology is not the only force that triggers value change.

The kind of exacting and unspectacular empirical work described here must be done before we earn the right to speak at all realistically about the existence of a science of values.

If the work described in this volume is imperfect, however, if it is marred by gaps and crevices, a certain degree of fumbling and amateurish- ness, it is well to recall that these are the marks of most frontier efforts. An enormous problem has been attacked with energy, enthusiasm and intelli- gence. Only a fool would expect inner consistency, elegant articulation, and smooth perfection at the beginning of so ambitious an endeavor.

Moreover, despite the shortcomings alluded to, the study described here may well prove to be a major milestone on the way toward the develop- ment of a new and urgently needed kind of cost-benefit accounting: One that concerns itself not merely with the "practical" consequences of tech- nological policies, but with their potential value consequences as well. In the past, major technologies have been developed without serious attention to their likely impact on our way of life. Perhaps the most notorious examples are the automobile and television, both of which were injected into society in what, from our vantage point today, sometimes appears to have been a witless and irresponsible fashion. Just as the African villagers did not anticipate all the consequences of the introduction of matches, no one at the time the auto was introduced sought scientifically to determine what impact this technological novelty might have on urban organization or environmental pollution. These are examples of what is meant here by "practical" consequences. But if little advance attention was paid to these, how much scientific effort went into predicting the more subtle impact of the automobile on values—in the field of sexual behavior, family relationships, education, aesthetics, etc.?

Today there is a growing awareness of the interrelatedness of technologies and increasing, though still limited, attempts are being made to study "practical" consequences. Almost nothing, however—with the exception of the work reported here—is as yet being done to analyze proposed technological developments in terms of their value impact.

There is, thus, a striking need for the new profession referred to earlier —a group of men armed with scientific tools to review in advance all important technological decisions, examining them for their value implications, and drawing up their reports in forms that can be taken into account in cost-benefit appraisals.

Such "value-impact forecasters" should be a part of every corporation, research laboratory, government agency and foundation whose output includes technological innovations. Should the federal government sponsor the supersonic transport? Should foundations support satellite-based educational television networks? Should computer manufacturers move in the direction of producing classroom size-units or toward large time sharing educational utilities, instead? Decisions on all such questions will affect the existing value system. It is vitally urgent that we make an effort to know how. Only if potential value impacts are laid bare and opened to public discussion early in the game can we achieve anything like democratic control over the technological future.

The presence of such forecasters in the centers of technological research and development would also make scientists and technicians more aware of the social repercussions of their work. If, as seems probable, the research community will achieve a high degree of power within the society in the years ahead, it is important that its members acquire a sense of social responsibility commensurate with their power. Moral neutrality may or may not be a defensible position for a researcher to adopt; moral ignorance is inexcusable. Value-impact forecasting could help make clear the nature of the moral choice being made each time a line of research is opened, a project funded, or an innovation released from the laboratory.

The project described here does more, however, than call attention to the need for this new profession. It provides some of the intellectual apparatus needed by its practitioners. The "conceptual machine tools" offered here by Baier, Rescher, Helmer, Gordon and the others, represent, despite their still primitive character, a key contribution to the birth of this profession of the future.

When this profession comes into being—and this writer, at least, thinks it will—its members will soon find themselves located at the hot center of decision making. They will also quickly learn that they are not merely describing present and future states of the value system, but actively intervening in the process of value change. Their work will inevitably help raise the level of man's self-consciousness. And this change may prove to be of a fundamental nature. For the combination of high-powered technology with a scientific understanding of values will create a new kind of leadership for society. It is to this end that the project here summarized makes its most important and original contribution.

# PART I  ANALYSIS

# FUNDAMENTAL CONSIDERATIONS

# What is value?
# An analysis of the concept

## *Kurt Baier*

### Outline of the problem

It seems no exaggeration to say that "Americans currently face a period in which few institutions, beliefs, or values can any longer be taken for granted. All are under strain; all are challenged. Basic transformations of man and society are now underway, and many vital choices of values must be made."[1] These are vital choices because the values people have are important factors in the determination of their behavior. But how can we make such vital choices? The values we already have, now serve as the rational determinants of our choices. When we choose one course of action in preference to another we do so because we have reason to think that it, rather than the other course, will help to realize at least some of our values. If someone's dominant values are, let us say, communion with nature, clean air, and rock climbing, then (other things being equal) it would be more rational for him to accept a position somewhere in Colorado than in Chicago. But if his values themselves must be chosen, then he has to find some other touchstone by which to select them. But what other, better, or more fundamental touchstones are there?

This is not an imaginary problem. Every day our powers increase, including the power to determine human personality. Soon we shall discover the factors which causally determine changes in a person's values. Every such increase in our knowledge and power at the same time increases the range of our responsibilities. It becomes more urgent to ask: Which of our values *should* be modified and in what direction should they be developed? We simply must question the soundness of the values to which we now subscribe.

Three basic tasks therefore suggest themselves: To identify those developments which constitute the realization of our currently dominant

1. Robin M. Williams, *American Society: A Sociological Interpretation* (New York: Alfred A. Knopf. 1951).

values; to isolate those factors which tend to preserve or undermine the values themselves;[2] and lastly to provide a technique for determining their soundness or unsoundness. For in the absence of such a technique, though we may know how to modify some of our values in this direction or that, we do not know in which direction we should modify them.

These tasks are important and urgent, but we are not well prepared to undertake them. Success depends on our ability to detect and specify a person's or society's values, value structure or value orientation, and any changes therein. However, there is no agreed or even promising method for finding out and stating what changes in the values of an individual or group have taken place during a given period, or what these values are at a given time.[3]

Some of the blame for this unsatisfactory state of affairs can undoubtedly be laid at the door of philosophy. For in the field of human values, respectful attention has been paid to typically philosophical arguments to the effect that we cannot, from the empirically ascertainable facts alone, derive the value of things or what we ought to do. In fact, for a very long time now, the dominant philosophical doctrine about value judgments has also been the reigning dogma in the social sciences. This is not, perhaps, surprising. Few people are shaken by typically philosophical arguments to the effect that all motion is illusion, that there are no causal connections in nature, or that we cannot know the past or the future. Few are shaken because we obviously do know much of the past and do know that there are causal connections in nature, and so on. So it can hardly be true that one can never know these things. By contrast, we really *do not know* how to determine our obligations or the value of things. It is therefore much more plausible to contend that we *can never know* these things. For these and other reasons, most social scientists accept the philosophers' sharp distinction between factual statements and value judgments. And like philosophers, they regard value judgments as essentially normative; and since such judgments are therefore likely to reflect the user's own personal values, they are not suitable for inclusion in a science.[4]

2. If one of our values is affluence, then a rise in living standards will be a move in the direction of the realization of our values. But the very same development may make a further increase in our living standards seem less important and so be a factor tending to undermine this value of ours. For a discussion of this sort of change, cf. the essay on value change by Nicholas Rescher in this volume.

3. For details see N. Rescher's contribution to this volume.

4. Classical treatments of this problem can be found in: Max Weber, *The Methodology of the Social Sciences*, ed. Ed. A. Shils and Henry A. Finch (Glencoe: The Free Press of Glencoe, 1949). Gunhar Myrdal, *Value in Social Theory* (New York: Harper & Brothers, 1958). Charles Morris, *Varieties of Human Value* (Chicago: The University of Chicago Press, 1956). G. H. von Wright, *Varieties of Goodness*, and *Norm and Action* (New York: Humanities Press, 1963). Also Ernest Nagel, *The Structure of Science* (New York: Harcourt, Brace, 1958), especially chs. 13, 14.

ANALYSIS

*What is value? An analysis of the concept*                                          55

The problem is even more far-reaching, however. For value judgments seem to reach deeply into apparently factual ones. We can *a priori* distinguish between value judgments and statements imputing values to a person or a society, the latter appearing not to involve any value judgments by the investigating scientist. But when it comes to actually imputing values, even detached scientists find it difficult to keep out their own personal value bias. Social scientists may not be as unsubtle about it as, for example, Louis Bromfield in his listing of the values of an "egghead."[5] But can *anyone* be quite certain that his own values have not colored his imputations of values to others?

What can be done to still this doubt? We need in the first place an analysis which clearly separates evaluative from nonevaluative elements so that value imputations themselves may be genuinely value free in the desired way. We need a terminology for stating what a person's values are which in no way reflects the speaker's own values. In the second place, if, as seems certain, the range of a person's values is at least partly dependent on his own value judgments, our terminology should lay bare this evaluative element in his values, as well as making clear wherein his holding these values consists.[6]

Where can we find such a terminology? It does not take long to discover that sociology is not a good source, not yet at any rate. In fact, sociologists employ a bewildering profusion of terms, ranging from what a person wants, desires, needs, enjoys, prefers, through what he thinks desirable, preferable, rewarding, obligatory to what the community enjoins, sanctions, or enforces.[7]

5. "Egghead: A person of spurious intellectual pretensions, often a professor or the protege of a professor. Fundamentally superficial. Overemotional and feminine in reactions to any problem. Supercilious and surfeited with conceit and contempt for the experience of more sound and able men. Essentially confused in thought and immersed in mixture of sentimentality and violent evangelism. A doctrinaire supporter of Middle-European socialism as opposed to Greco-French-American ideas of democracy and liberalism. Subject to the old-fashioned philosophical morality of Nietzsche which frequently leads him into jail or disgrace. A self-conscious prig, so given to examining all sides of a question that he becomes thoroughly addled while remaining always in the same spot. An anaemic bleeding heart." Quoted by Richard Hofstadter, *Anti-Intellectualism in American Life* (New York, Alfred A. Knopf, 1963), pp. 9–10.
6. Details will be given below, and cf. also Appendix.
7. For a pessimistic view of the present state of the inquiry, cf. Harold Fallding, "A Proposal for the Empirical Study of Values." *American Sociological Review*, vol. 30 (1965), pp. 223–233.
   I mention a few of the more popular definitions to show the great variety and looseness of terms employed.
   "A thing has or is a value if and when people behave toward it so as to retain or increase their possession of it." (George Lundberg)
   "Anything capable of being appreciated (wished for) is a value." (Robert Part and E. W. Burgess)
   "Values are the obverse of motives . . . the object, quality, or condition that satisfies the motivation." (Richard T. LaPiere)

[*Continued on next page*

Much more helpful are the writings of economists. For economists have attempted to develop precise theories of rational human behavior based on the assumption that such behavior is at least partly determined by human values. Moreover, economists draw the indispensable distinction (largely lost to sociologists) between, on the one hand, the *value* of things, and on the other, the *values* of individuals or societies. Even so, a brief survey will demonstrate the insufficiency, for our purpose, of the terminology developed by economists. This of course in no way detracts from their truly remarkable achievements.

The concept of value, in the sense used in "the value of a thing," is central to traditional economic Value Theory. The value here investigated is of course the so-called exchange or market value of a commodity. Value Theory attempts to give a model of the interaction of all the forces which determine the fluctuations of the market value or price of commodities in a given market. Now, while such a theory would (if sound) be for many purposes of enormous practical importance, it would not say anything about what we ordinarily mean by *the value* of things. In fact, economic Value Theory deliberately sets out to by-pass that question and is wholly successful in doing so. Instead of telling us the value of a commodity, it tells us its price, that is, the quantity of resources a person must relinquish if he is to secure this commodity, and so secure the benefits its possession can yield. But, it is only if one already knows, at least roughly, what the value of a thing is, that

"Values are any object of any need." (Howard Becker)

"A desideratum or anything desired or chosen by someone, at sometime—operationally: what the respondent says he wants." (Stuart C. Dodd)

"By a social value we understand any datum having an empirical content accessible to the members of some social group and a meaning with regard to which it is or may be an object of activity." (Znaniecki)

"(A value is) a conception, explicit or implicit, distinctive of an individual or character-istic of a group, of the desirable which influences the selection from available means and ends of action." (Clyde Kluckhohn)

" 'Values': = : 'the desirable end states which act as a guide to human endeavor or the most general statements of legitimate ends which guide social action'." (Neil J. Smelser)

"The noun 'value' has usually been used to imply some code or standard which persists through time and provides a criterion by which people order their intensities of desiring various desiderata. To the extent that people are able to place objects, actions, ways of life, and so on, on a continuum of approval-disapproval with some reliability, it appears that their responses to a particular desideratum are functions of culturally acquired values." (William R. Catton, Jr.)

" 'Values': = : 'normative standards by which human beings are influenced in their choice among the alternative courses of action which they perceive'." (Philip E. Jacob and James J. Flink)

For an interesting survey and clarification of various conceptions of values used in social science research, cf. Allen Barton, "Measuring the Values of Individuals," *Review of Recent Research Bearing on Religious and Character Formation* (Research Supplement to *Religious Education*, July/August, 1962). *Organizational Measurement* (New York, 1961). This also has a useful short bibliography.

ANALYSIS

*What is value? An analysis of the concept* 37

knowledge of its price can help him to act rationally. If he does not know its value, he may be willing to pay more than it is worth.[8]

Welfare Economics comes much closer to central value problems than does traditional Value Theory. In this field, the word "value" occurs typically in phrases such as "a person's values" or "a society's values," and it there means much the same as a person's preferences or tastes. Given a knowledge of his resources, his prospects, and his tastes, a person is thought to be able to allocate his resources in a way which will realize his values. Now, any such allocation which he himself will not regard as a mistake (a mistake being an allocation which, had he known the outcome, he would have preferred not to make) increases his welfare. Starting from these premises, welfare economists confront a serious problem. To recommend an economic policy capable of increasing the society's welfare, they must define *the idea of social welfare* in such a way that it is related in an inevitable or at least unobjectionable way to the welfare, and thus to the values of the individuals who make up the society. But how is this to be done, if as may and in fact frequently will be the case, an economic policy which brings about some social state of affairs constitutes an increase in the welfare of one individual but a decrease in that of another? This problem has so far proved surprisingly intractable. The difficulty may well be due at least partly to unsuitable definitions of "value" and "welfare."[9]

In view of the very partial and limited interests of economists in the field of values and the difficulties encountered even in these most rigorously developed areas of the social sciences, we felt it necessary to obtain a coherent overview of the whole field, before developing a terminology suitable for a detailed and precise description of people's values. In the course of this investigation, it became quite clear that many of the problems which perplex researchers in this field grow out of misconceptions about the nature of evaluation, its role in rational action, its connection with imputations of values to individuals and societies, and the part evaluation plays in the determination of the soundness or unsoundness of our values.

8. Cf. e.g., Jerome Rothenberg, "Values and Value Theory in Economics" in *The Structure of Economic Science* (Englewood Cliffs: Prentice-Hall, 1966); Neil J. Smelser, *The Sociology of Economic Life* (Prentice-Hall, 1963); Adolph Lowe, *On Economic Knowledge* (New York: Harper & Row, 1965).
9. For a discussion of these problems, see K. J. Arrow, *Social Choice and Individual Values* (New York: John Wiley & Sons, 1957). Robert A. Dahl and Charles E. Lindblom, *Politics, Economics and Welfare* (New York: Harper & Brothers, 1953). David Braybrooke and Charles E. Lindblom, *A Strategy of Decision* (New York: The Free Press of Glencoe, 1963). James M. Buchanan and Gordon Tulloch, *The Calculus of Consent* (Annarbor: Ann Arbor Paperbacks, 1965). Jerome Rothenberg, *The Measurement of Social Welfare* (Englewood Cliffs: Prentice-Hall, 1961). Sidney Hook, ed. *Human Values and Economic Policy* (New York: University Press, 1967).

## Preliminary elucidation of the idea of value

The value of something, such as a work of art, a social practice (purdah), or a state of affairs (full employment) is a certain sort of property of it. The possession of this property by a thing, and its magnitude, are determined by an empirical examination of a certain kind, whose generic name is appraisal. The two most important types of appraisal are ranking and grading. Teachers, for example, appraise their students by ranking them, grading them, or both.

Ranking consists in assigning to each of a given set of entries a place in a hierarchical list of places. Each of the places has an identifiable position within the list. The assigning of entries to a place in the list is carried out on the basis of the greater or lesser extent to which the entries satisfy a given set of criteria. Each ranking is a self-contained competition in which all the entries are compared with one another in respect of that set of criteria, and a place is assigned to each of the entries. Since the competition is self-contained, the place assigned to an entry in one competition carries no implication about how that entry would fare in another competition using the same criteria but ranking different entries. Each entry can be ranked, i.e., assigned a place in the list, only as part of a complete allocation of places to all entries. The position assigned to each depends on the position assigned to every other. It makes no sense to rank a single entry.

Grading is like ranking except that the entries are ordered by reference to a pre-existing known and relatively fixed place list. In grading, the relevant competitors are a much larger group than the entries on a particular occasion. Hence, one can grade a single student. A student's grade (unlike his rank) establishes his place in a fixed hierarchy, not in one determined by the qualifications of his current competitors. If Smith has *top* rank in a course in 1965, nothing follows about what his rank should be in the same course and for the same work in 1966. But if Smith has *a B grade* in 1965, then he should also get a B grade for the same work in 1966. If Jones has an A grade in that same course in 1966, then this implies that if Smith were in his class in 1966 he should be ranked below Jones.

Appraisals are similar to other types of *ordering* based on the magnitude of properties possessed by things, such as ordering on the basis of height, strength, brightness, or hardness. The main difference is that in appraisals the ordering criteria determine an *evaluative* property, not an evaluatively neutral one. A property is evaluative if the criteria are selected on the basis of *desiderata*, that is, features *wanted in* the thing rather than simply found in it, whether wanted or not. Thus, we can order people according to the speed at which they can or often do run. This would be an ordering on the

ANALYSIS

*What is value? An analysis of the concept*

59

basis of an evaluatively neutral property. But when we order *runners* in this way, we normally assume that speed is a desideratum, and that a person who can run faster than another is therefore *a better* runner. When we consider someone as a runner, speed is a desideratum. It is part of the very meaning of calling someone "a runner" that, if it comes to grading him in this capacity, speed *is to be* treated as a desideratum, not as something evaluatively neutral. We can then argue from speed to excellence.

Of course, in many cases of appraisal, the appropriate desiderata are not as easily discovered nor as generally accepted as in the case of runners. One of the reasons for this is that some types of appraisal depend on the diverse *tastes* of the appraisers. In some beauty contests, the statistics of the Venus of Millendorf might score more highly than those of the Venus de Milo, whereas in others it would surely be the other way round. However, even where the criteria are not a matter of taste, as with speed for runners, safety for cars, or honesty for servants, one can and should raise the question of how we establish the appropriateness of a criterion. How do we know that in some cases the criteria are a matter of taste and therefore not further subject to correction? And how do we know that in some cases they are not a matter of taste; and, where they are not a matter of taste, what they are a matter of; and how, in such cases, do we know when, and in what manner, the selection of criteria is further subject to correction?

The answer to these questions is easily seen if we bear in mind the purpose for which we undertake appraisals. We rank and grade things in order to know the extent to which they satisfy the demands we make on them. Why do we want this information? Obviously, because knowledge of this is helpful when making rational choices involving these things. When we have this information, then we know which one of them to pick when things with greater capacities of this sort are wanted or needed by us. When we need models to advertise bathing suits or airline services, the ranks received in beauty contests will be relevant. If we ourselves want to obtain such positions, knowledge of the observable properties (qualifications) necessary for a high score of this sort will be useful to us. The existence of a given type of appraisal is thus explained by the fact that a knowledge of the ranks or grades things get in these appraisals helps in the rational selection of things. That is to say, it helps people allocate their resources in ways likely to increase their success rate in their various endeavors, and to organize and reorganize their endeavors in ways likely to make their successes add up to a life more satisfactory as a whole.

To appraise something, we said, is to ascertain its evaluative properties and to determine its magnitude. That magnitude is the measure of the extent to which this thing, if entered in a certain sort of competition, would satisfy the desiderata set up for that competition. The range of existing competitions i.e., the desiderata we set up and appraise things by, is determined by the kinds of things people want to achieve and to get out of their lives. There is in existence a great variety of such appraisals. Unfortunately, even those appraisals which philosophers and social scientists have concentrated on for such a long time are not well understood. Their mutual interrelations are largely unexplored. However, ordinary usage gives some hints of the areas and considerations which might be more closely examined. Thus, many of the evaluative properties whose possession by various things is a matter of common interest have at least been identified by special names. Thus in appraising materials or substances of various kinds (cloth, tobacco, steel), we typically assess their *quality*; in appraising an applicant or an application, we typically assess his or its *merit*; in the case of an effort or contribution by someone, we assess his *desert*; in the case of a new gadget, its *usefulness*; in the case of some treatment or measure, its *beneficiality*; in the case of some method or technique, its *efficiency*, and so on.[10]

Now, *the value* of something is also an evaluative property, if a very complex and central one. It is the thing's capacity to confer a benefit on someone, to make a favorable difference to his life. The magnitude of its value is the measure of that capacity. Such a measure cannot be developed very far until there is a great deal of relevant knowledge available; e.g., knowledge about the kinds of benefit that can be conferred, the kinds of favorable and unfavorable difference that can be made to a person's life, the causal role which various things can play in the making of such differences, and the circumstances in which they make these differences. When that knowledge is available we can begin the more complex task of appraising these things in respect of that capacity, i.e., assessing the evaluative property we call their value.

The *value* possessed by things must be distinguished from the *values* held by people. The former is an *evaluative property* whose possession and magnitude can be ascertained in appraisals. The latter are *dispositions to behave* in certain ways which can be ascertained by observation. The former are *capacities* of things to satisfy desiderata. The latter are *tendencies* of people to devote their resources (time, energy, money) to the attainment of certain ends. The value of a thing may be great or little, lasting or ephemeral. A particular value among a person's values may be strong or weak, genuine or pretended. The mistakes one can make about the value of a thing include overvaluing or undervaluing the thing, and misjudging wherein it consists. The mistakes one can make about the values people hold include imputing

10. For a somewhat different account, see G. H. von Wright, *The Varieties of Goodness, op. cit.*, Ch. III.

ANALYSIS

*What is value? An analysis of the concept*                                        41

to them values they do not hold or failing to notice values they do hold, and misjudging the strength (or weight) of the values they hold.

If this were the whole story about values, the distinction would be quite sharp and straightforward, though one might wonder why these dispositions should be called *values*—why not just behavior dispositions or attitudes? There is, however, a complicating factor which blurs the sharpness of the distinctions and explains the connection between the value of things and the values people hold. Values have a further property about which one may be right or mistaken, namely, their soundness or unsoundness. It is this property which links values with value. A person's dispositions to devote his resources in certain ways constitute his values if he takes them to be beneficial, to be good ways of expending his resources, or to make his life better than other ways would.

With this brief outline of the idea of values as our guide, we can now more thoroughly examine the nature of appraisals. Various types of specifications are available for assessing the value of a thing. We can indicate the magnitude of this property in a rather rough way, e.g., by saying that the thing's value is nil, insignificant, considerable, great, exceptional, incomparable, immeasurable, or unique; or in a more precise way, e.g., by stating its dollar value. Whatever specification we use, it is clear that in stating the magnitude of the value of something, we are either ranking or grading it in respect of its capacity to confer a benefit on someone. Our next task must therefore be to explain more fully the facts and principles underlying this way of ranking and grading.

## Value and the excellence of a life

Let us call "melioration claims" all assertions to the effect that something confers a benefit on someone. We can then distinguish two elements in such melioration claims: That a benefit is conferred on someone, and that a certain thing plays a certain causal role in the conferring of that benefit. If a useful body of knowledge about melioration is to be built up, we shall have to develop greater specificity for each of these two elements. Some rough distinctions are, however, already available. Thus concerning the second or causal element, we already have the rough distinctions between being *beneficial, useful,* and *of value.*

The claim that *beneficial* rains fell in Georgia or that a change of air was *beneficial* for Jones says that under the conditions prevailing at the time in question, the changes mentioned (rains, change of air) sufficed to confer certain implied benefits (improved harvest, health) on certain persons (Georgia's farmers, Jones). If the rains were merely *useful*, then they did not

suffice to confer benefits of the magnitude conferred by beneficial rains, but
they were helpful; they were instalments of drenchings which would suffice;
contributing factors to the greater benefits which are here obviously desired
or needed. Again, that the road map and the guidebook proved useful to us,
means that our having and using them *facilitated* our accomplishment of our
aims the accomplishing of which conferred a benefit. That the road map and
the guidebook were *of value* to us means much the same as that they were
useful or came in handy. However, whereas their having been useful to us
leaves open the question whether or not we in fact accomplished the aim for
the accomplishment of which they came in handy, and whether its accomplishment was in fact a benefit, their having been of value to us implies an
affirmative answer: that we did accomplish our aim, that it was a benefit
and even that it was an important one.

Such claims can be generalized. We may claim, e.g., that in cases of
sciatica, massage is beneficial, or useful, or of value. By this we mean that
under these conditions, massage plays one or other of these causal roles
(being the whole or a part of what is sufficient) to bring about a certain
improvement in someone's life. Or, if more generally still, we maintain that
*massage* (as such) is beneficial, useful, of value, we mean that, as things are,
there are frequent occasions on which massage would play such a causal role.

These claims differ from one another not merely in that they assign
different causal roles to these things, or in the extent of the benefit supposedly
conferred, but also in the nature of that benefit. Since all appraisals ultimately
depend on the magnitude of the benefit conferred, the appraisal of a change
as a benefit is epistemologically basic. We must therefore devote some space
to its elucidation. The basic idea is that of *a favorable change* in a person's
life. Any change of which a person can be appraised, may be ranked in
respect of how that change affects the excellence of that person's life; whether
it raises that excellence, lowers it, or leaves it unaffected. Appraising such
changes in a person's life consists in comparing them with the change which
is expected or demanded there and then on the basis of a legitimate pattern
or path of life. The excellence of a life as a whole is assessed on the basis of the
actual life's approximation to the expected or demanded ideal pattern.[11] This
ideal pattern determines (more or less sharply), for each state of life, an ideal
level of attainment and an ideal direction of change by comparison with
which the actual level of attainment and the actual changes can be ranked.
On this basis, a given change can be ranked as a raising, a lowering, or a
leaving unaffected of the excellence of that life, according as the change has

11. For a discussion of life patterns, see Charles Morris, *op. cit.* Also, Charles Morris, *Paths
of Life* (New York: George Braziller, Inc., 1956). Cf. also the essays in this volume by
David Braybrooke, Kenneth Boulding, J. K. Galbraith, Sonia Gold, John Powelson, and
David Lewis.

ANALYSIS

*What is value? An analysis of the concept*

43

brought the person's condition closer to, taken it further away from, or left it at the same distance from, the ideal pattern. What we normally call "the good life" is our idea of the ideal life pattern against which a given person's life is supposed to be judged; and what we call "a good life" or "a bad life" is our favorable or unfavorable appraisal, on the basis of some such ideal life pattern, of the actual life of some particular person.

There are three main points of view from which changes in a given life, or lives, as wholes can be ranked or graded. The evaluative property "excellence" therefore correspondingly varies in meaning. The three points of view and the corresponding respects which determine how a given change is to be ranked or graded in this scale of the excellence of a given life, may be called (without too much straining of their natural meaning) *worthwhileness*, *worthiness*, and *worth*, respectively. Only what a given person legitimately regards as worthwhile or the opposite, is relevant to the question of whether a change in his life is a favorable or unfavorable one. Some changes may also raise the excellence of a person's life, in the sense of its worthiness or its worth, but they would not *ipso facto* be *favorable* changes in our sense, the sense related to the derivation of a benefit.

The *worthwhileness* of a life as a whole is determined on the basis of the extent to which the life approximates the life pattern from whose realization the person in question (rightly or legitimately) expects to derive those satisfactions, rewards, or "payoffs," which would incline him to say that the life as a whole was worthwhile. A life which conforms to a person's own ideal pattern of this sort, may be said to cater fully to his tastes. A person will find his life the more worthwhile the more fully it caters to his tastes. Of course, a person may be quite mistaken about what occurrences would cater fully to his tastes, or whether one of two alternatives open to him would cater more fully to his tastes than the other. In such a case, the demands he will make on his life will be misguided. The things he is working for will disappoint him when he gets them. He will not find worthwhile what he expects to find worthwhile. But if he is not in this way misguided, then his life really is the more worthwhile and the more excellent, the more fully it caters to his tastes, the more fully he gets what he is asking from it. And any change in his life is a favorable change, which makes his life cater more fully to his tastes than it did before.

The *worthiness* of a life as a whole is determined on the basis of the extent to which it satisfies the legitimate demands others may make and expect to have satisfied. They are the demands which can be made on anyone, though only after making due allowance for his special liabilities, handicaps, gifts, resources, and opportunities. In this scale of excellence the widow's mite weighs more heavily than the rich man's gold.

The *worth* of a life as a whole is determined on the basis of how much it contributes to the excellence of the lives of others. In this scale of excellence we weigh the benefactors of mankind. Here the rich man's gold weighs more heavily than the widow's mite.

Although the excellence of a given life, in the sense of its worthiness or worth, are not directly relevant to the question under discussion, namely, that of determining whether a change in a given life is favorable or not, it is plain that these excellences are indirectly relevant. For a person may come to find worthwhile, some changes in his life which increase its worthiness, or its worth, and come to do so because of this. To the kind-hearted or high-principled philanthropist, giving will often be as blessed as receiving (or taking), at least as long as it does not force him down into an unpalatably low tax-bracket.

So far, our standpoint has been that of a person examining how a given life as a whole, or a particular actual change in it measures up when tested against certain criteria. This is essentially a passive, backward-looking, judge's point of view. An active, forward-looking, agent's or adviser's point of view, requires us to regard the changes in a person's life as subject to his own control; as the outcome of his choice. If, as we may assume, most people often want favorable changes to occur in their lives, they will also want to know how to make such changes come about. For this purpose, then, they will need to have the relevant meliorative knowledge; to have information about the helpful causal role played by things in the bringing about of favorable changes in someone's life; and information about what these causal roles are, under what conditions these things play these roles, and what the favorable changes are which they bring about thereby. With such knowledge at his disposal, a person can use his resources to *intervene* in the course of events so as to bring that course closer than it would otherwise be to his ideal of the good life.

Let us say of a thing that it makes a *favorable difference* to a person's life whenever it plays a helpful causal role in bringing about a certain change in a person's life, as a result of which that life is more worthwhile *than it would otherwise have been*. Thus, whereas something has made a favorable *change* if, as a result of it's playing its causal role, the life in question after the change is more worthwhile than before; the same thing has made a favorable *difference* if, as a result of its playing its causal role, the life in question after the change is more worthwhile than it would have been if that thing had not played its causal role. In the first case, we compare the *actual* life *before* and *after* the change due to the causal impact of a certain thing. In the second case, we compare the *actual* life after that change with the *hypothetical* life as it would have turned out to be but for the causal impact

ANALYSIS

*What is value? An analysis of the concept*

45

of that thing. Thus a favorable change may be an unfavorable difference, since but for the causal impact in question the change might have been still more favorable. And conversely of course an unfavorable change may be a favorable difference. In our declining years, sometimes the best we can hope for are favorable differences, not favorable changes.

Among the "things" playing such causal roles, making favorable or unfavorable changes or differences to people's lives, the most important are of course persons, making causal impacts through their deliberate actions. It goes without saying that everybody can make such causal impacts also on his own life, thereby trying to improve it. If we had no knowledge of the kind formulated in melioration claims, we should depend solely on chance for a reasonably tolerable life. We could do nothing to protect ourselves against dangers or to take advantage of opportunities. We would be reduced to helplessly recording the ups and downs in the excellence of our lives, and our friends could only rejoice or commiserate with us, as Fortune smiled or frowned on us. As things are, our steadily increasing meliorative knowledge enables us to use our resources to help ourselves and others.

This ability to make favorable differences to our own lives is itself an important element in their excellence though not of course their worthwhileness. For in addition to the *actual* favorable changes and differences which various things are making to our lives, thereby more fully catering to our tastes, we must now list those *potential* favorable changes and differences which consist in increases in *our ability* to make favorable changes and differences, thereby increasing our ability to cater to those of our tastes we most want catered to.

That ability can be increased in various ways. It can be done by improving the environmental conditions in such a way that, with the same powers and resources, a person can now attain a much larger range of ends whose attainment constitutes favorable changes and differences in his life. One way of thus increasing his ability is to improve what might be called *the climate of life*, i.e., the degree of orderliness, predictability, security, and trustworthiness of individuals and institutions in the society. The climate of life is the better, the more reliably one can expect the social and personal guarantees of life, liberty, property, and contractual undertakings to be respected. Those who are today concerned about the increase in organized crime, juvenile delinquency, strikes, racial disturbances, and so forth, worry about the deterioration in our climate of life. Another way of increasing a person's ability to make favorable differences to his life is to improve what might be called *the quality of life*. I have in mind the natural and cultural *amenities*, the variety and quality of the goods and services made available to the members of a given society.[12] Those concerned about the welfare of the underprivileged are not concerned primarily about their happiness or the extent to which their tastes are catered to, but rather about the quality of life in the environment in which they are compelled to live. Clearly, the worthwhileness of an individual's life depends to a very large extent on both the climate and the quality of life in his society.

A person's ability to make favorable changes or differences to his life can also be increased by directly increasing *his own power* to do so, without any intervening change in the cultural or natural environment. Increasing a man's health, wealth, skills, knowledge, and even physical strength can achieve this. Through such increases in his own powers he is then in a better position to take advantage of the amenities already made available in his society for those adequately equipped.

Similarly, we must include among the favorable differences the possession of such *defenses* (walls, locks, armor) as would, or of such *powers* (arms, karate, money) as could be used to, prevent something which would *lower* the excellence of a person's life. And lastly, we must include those factors which bring about the satisfaction of the conditions *necessary* for the continuation of a person's life (his basic needs),[13] such as adequate food, drink, air, shelter, and medicine.

From this lengthy discussion three main conclusions emerge. The first is the undeniable existence of meliorative knowledge,[14] that is, the sort of knowledge which is expressed in melioration claims. Such knowledge provides information about the causal roles played by events, things, and human endeavor in the bringing about of improvements in people's lives. Such knowledge, involving as it does the appraisal of changes in a person's life, can be properly called evaluative. Yet, such knowledge is clearly empirical, based on what people *find* worthwhile and the opposite. Of course, in a sense it is not based *on observation* alone but rather on what is often called *feeling*. But it is empirical knowledge nonetheless. It is as much based on experience as is a burnt child's learning from experience, the *bitter* experience of the burn. What makes the experience "bitter" and thereby an important element in the learning, is not however, something found by

12. Cf. Bertrand de Jouvenel, "*A Better Life in An Affluent Society*," *Diogenes*, vol. 10 (1961), and also his "Efficiency and Amenity," Fortieth Earl Grey Memorial Lecture (London, 1960).

13. Cf. David Braybrooke, "Let Needs Diminish that Preferences May Prosper" in *Studies in Moral Philosophy* (Oxford, 1968; *American Philosophical Quarterly* Monograph No. 1).

14. For a statement of the view that in matters of value there can be no knowledge, cf. A. J. Ayer, *Language, Truth, and Logic* (New York: Dover Publication, 1952). Charles L. Stevenson, *Facts and Values* (New Haven: Yale Paperbacks, 1963). R. M. Hare, *The Language of Morals* (Oxford University Press, 1952). R. M. Hare, *Freedom and Reason* (Oxford University Press, 1963). For a survey of these views, cf. Mary Warnock, *Ethics Since 1900* (Oxford University Press, 1960).

ANALYSIS

*What is value? An analysis of the concept* 47

observation, i.e., by the child's seeing or hearing, say, his own anguished cries.

The second conclusion is that although the core of such knowledge is based on people's tastes and so yields truths which are person-relative, this is no obstacle to genuine knowledge. Features, such as IQ, height, or eye color, are person-relative, but that is no obstacle to genuine knowledge about them. Person-relativity of tastes is no obstacle whatever to establishing what things in fact cater to a person's tastes, and what things don't. In fact, even though of course there are interpersonal differences in taste, the difference must not be exaggerated: lovers' and torturers' handbooks have a remarkable universality of application.[15]

The third conclusion is perhaps practically the most important. For, as we have seen, there are many classes of change in a person's life which, unlike those based on his tastes, are not person-relative at all, but are favorable changes in his life quite independently of his tastes. Thus, whatever his tastes may be, providing him with nourishment and shelter is making a favorable difference to his life, robbing him of it an unfavourable difference.

## Assessing the value of things

In the preceding section I introduced the idea of melioration claims and of meliorative knowledge. Melioration claims purport to give information about the various ways in which things can and do favorably affect people's lives. I distinguished four such ways and called them making an actual or a potential favorable change or favorable difference. We can think of these four ways of favorably affecting a life as species of the genus, "conferring a benefit on a person," and we can think of each of these four types of effect as species of the genus, "improvement in a life." Meliorative knowledge comprises knowledge of the capacity of things to confer benefits on people, and of improvements in people's lives.

Meliorative knowledge is practical, applied knowledge. The greatest triumphs in this field of knowledge have been achieved in the fields of medicine and engineering: how to repair the human body and how to build mechanical aids. We must include in this type of knowledge also the knowledge of various forms of destruction, including the destruction of human beings, since such knowledge often enables us to remove obstacles in the way of making favorable differences to our own lives. In these areas, our knowledge relates to potential rather than to actual favorable changes and differences; increases in our know-how rather than in our know-what. Compared

15. For a short history of the controversy concerning the objectivity of values, see for instance, Risieri Frondizi, *What is Value?* (Chicago: Open Court, 1963).

to our present state of meliorative know-how, the state of our knowledge of actual favorable changes and differences is no doubt rather limited, crude, and unsystematic. But there is every reason for expanding and deepening such knowledge and no reason to think that it cannot be done.

One such advance, if a comparatively small one, would be a perfecting of the type of appraisal we call assessing the value of things. As already mentioned, such appraisals are rankings and gradings of things in respect of their capacity to confer benefits on people. Unlike melioration claims of the kind discussed, value assessments tell us which things have this capacity in a higher and which in a lower degree. Knowing the value of things will thus often be more useful than merely knowing whether things have or do not have that capacity at all. For such knowledge enables us to make rational choices *between* things all of which have this capacity, and all of which are therefore capable of conferring *some* benefit on us.

What are the desiderata on which such appraisals are based? Starting with the lives to be affected, obviously our demand is for the greatest possible improvements. To ensure the occurrence of these improvements, we must find those factors (such as changes in the environment, social institutions, human practices, and individual actions) which reliably bring on their occurrence; and also those things whose presence is an aid or help to people trying to bring about the occurrence of these improvements. Next we must try to single out from among these things those over whose occurrence or presence we have control, for then we can, at will, satisfy those conditions whose satisfaction suffices to set in motion the processes or actions which reliably produce those changes which are improvements in the lives to be improved.

When we talk, vaguely and summarily, of the value of things, we have in mind assessments on the basis of an overall aggregation of a thing's capacity to satisfy the desiderata mentioned. A book, a lecture course, an invention, a suggestion has greater value than another if it satisfies more fully than the other thing the listed desiderata: if it is generally easier to satisfy the conditions under which it can or will play its characteristic causal role (being available for reading, attending, etc.); if it more reliably brings about or is a greater help in bringing about certain intended changes in the lives of people, or brings them about in more lives, or in a larger proportion of lives to be improved; and if the changes brought about constitute a greater improvement.

Of course, such overall, summary assessments are necessarily vague, the criteria often conflict, and the resulting assessments therefore often contain compromises between conflicting criteria. It is easy to be superior or despondent about these facts. The natural and the social sciences operate

ANALYSIS

*What is value? An analysis of the concept*                                              49

deliberately with concepts which are descriptive, taste-independent, and interest-neutral. For this reason, they do not contribute to our stock of meliorative knowledge. Yet, it is of course generally admitted that the value and very purpose of accumulating such scientific knowledge, lies in the aid it can give us in improving our lives. By the self-denying ordinance of excluding evaluative properties from our conceptual scheme, we can avoid the difficulties inherent in these concepts. But by this fiat, knowledge so acquired is condemned to irrelevance at the heart of things.

There is, however, no need for this self-denial. Even in the present neglected state of meliorative knowledge, various devices are available for making value assessments less indeterminate than those alluded to in the previous paragraph.[16] We can indicate the respect in which we rank or grade a thing's capacity to confer a benefit. When we speak of survival, surprise, shock, preventive, prophylactic, explanatory, curative, or nutritive value, we indicate the nature of the benefit by naming the goal state through whose realization the improvement in the relevant lives is to be made, and in the realization of which the appraised thing plays a certain causal role. When we speak of the high survival value of protective coloring we assess the value of protective coloring as high compared with other (unspecified) things playing a comparable causal role in the bringing about of the same goal state, namely, survival of the species in question. This assessment of protective coloring gives a measure (of course a very rough one) of the extent of the success, due to the appraised factor (protective coloring), in reaching the goal state (survival) and of the magnitude of the benefit thereby conferred.

Not all qualifying expressions qualify in quite exactly the same way as those listed in the previous paragraph. This is the cause of frequent and sometimes serious confusions. In view of the widespread use of these qualifying expressions, not only in newspapers and popular writings, but also in serious works of social science, and the absence of any other clearly superior and widely known terminology, it may be helpful if I briefly unravel some of the ambiguities.

Some of these qualifying terms, e.g., political, pedagogic, or commercial, indicate the relevant goal state in only a generic way. Whereas to speak of great survival, surprise, shock value, etc. is to imply that the relevant goal state is survival, surprise, shock, the claim that Mr. K's support has great political value does not imply that the relevant goal state is politics. It implies rather, that the goal state is a political one, that is, one of those typically pursued in political contexts: to gain votes, popularity, influence, power,

16. For a useful discussion of the techniques of appraisal, see Michael Scriven, *The Methodology of Evaluation*. Publication # 110 of the Social Science Education Consortium (1966).

patronage. Some of the terms qualifying value indicate the goal state not by naming it but merely by giving a classification of it.

Another set of qualifying terms, such as snob, news, documentary, artistic, aesthetic, literary, entertainment, and others typically indicate the relevant goal states neither by naming nor by classifying them, but rather by stating *the role* in which the thing appraised helps to bring about various goal states and so confers a benefit on people: *as* news, *as* a document, *as* a work of art, etc.

It would undoubtedly be best if the qualifying expression "intrinsic value" could be altogether banned from the literature. It has caused more trouble than any other technical term and has not, to my way of thinking, advanced our comprehension of value one bit. But there is little hope of this happening. Instead, the best we can hope for is to make its ordinary meaning crystal clear and so remove the temptation to use it in other confusing and misleading ways. Ordinarily, we speak of intrinsic value when we want to contrast the value of a thing in its characteristic or most important role with its value in other secondary roles. Thus, no doubt, the "Face on the Barroom Floor" has little intrinsic value though a great deal of value as a tourist attraction. To understand this contention, we must know that the "Face on the Barroom Floor" is the name of a painting on the floor of a certain famous hotel bar. Its intrinsic value is therefore its value *as a painting*, as a work of art. To know what kind of value intrinsic value is, we must know the intrinsic nature of the relevant thing: we must know that it *is* a painting, and that the intrinsic nature of a painting is being a work of art. Similarly, an old map of Pittsburgh has little intrinsic value, i.e., *as a street guide of Pittsburgh*, but it may have considerable *historical* or *decorative* value. A prayer for rain may have little intrinsic value, i.e., *as a method of making rain*, but it may have psychological value of some sort.

## Value and norm

Knowledge of the value of things will be relevant, not to say indispensable, to anyone who wants to know what he should do. For such knowledge tells him what contribution towards the improvement of his life he may expect from the alternatives open to him. However, while relevant or indispensable, such knowledge is not sufficient. For there is a wide logical gap between knowing the value of things and knowing what one should do. I may know the value of a healthy appetite and of a sound university education without being able to infer from this what Jones or anyone else including myself should do. If a clear sense could be given to "knowing the value of *everything*," then perhaps such knowledge would be sufficient for answering

ANALYSIS

*What is value? An analysis of the concept*

51

what a person should do. But apart from the obvious impossibility of anyone's ever acquiring such knowledge, it would clearly include a great many items which are unnecessary for that question. What, then, must we know in addition to knowing the value of things to be able to answer questions about what someone should do? We may group this knowledge under three main heads: Price, Priority, and Duty.

The *price* or *market value* of a thing, say, a house or a painting or a car, is the quantity of resources one must part with in order to secure control over it, so that one can, at will, satisfy those conditions under which the house etc. will play the causal role in which it confers its characteristic benefit on someone, for the sake of which one wants to secure control over it. This information by itself raises but does not answer the question of whether this thing is *worth its price*, i.e., whether the benefit which it confers repays, or is commensurate with, the resources it takes to secure. Obviously, this is not a question which can be answered by intuition or any other form of direct *inspection*. It has to be *worked out* on the basis of whether alternative resource allocations would yield greater benefits.

The idea of *priority* is based on the fact that the avoidance at a given juncture of certain kinds of harm ensures greater overall benefits than the securing of certain other immediate benefits of great value. The satisfaction of needs, the prevention of the arising of dangers or the provision of protection against them once they have arisen, belongs in this category. The fact that these kinds of harm are *emergencies*, that they must be met immediately or not at all, gives them a greater urgency and so a higher priority of claim on our resources.

The idea of *duty* is based on the fact that the climate of life, and through it the quality of life, and through that the excellence of everyone's life would suffer unless people imposed on themselves certain restrictions in the pursuit of their goals, in whatever way these goals come to be theirs. The psychological mechanisms by which this comes to pass have often been described and need not be spelled out here, in detail. It must suffice to say that whenever one person's goal is such that his reaching it will *ipso facto* thwart that of another, this will tend to give rise to mutual hostility, suspicion, and violence, and through this to a wasteful and mutually detrimental allocation of individual resources. Limitations on permitted ways of selecting and pursuing ends, designed to minimize such friction, obviously confer benefits on all concerned, though not necessarily equal benefits. What we in our society call moral duties, are those limitations which we believe to confer *equal* benefits on all concerned. It is, of course tempting for anyone to set aside these limitations in his own case—for in so doing he benefits doubly from ignoring the restrictions himself and from other people's respecting them. Yet at the same time, because of the harm done someone by every such violation and because of the benefit conferred on everyone by general compliance, we feel that the community is justified in taking whatever steps are necessary and sufficient to ensure general compliance with these limitations, even force.

Now, if a person has this additional information, then he can answer questions about what this or that person, including himself, should do in a certain situation. Given a knowledge of his *tastes*, of his overall *life plan* for the purpose of best catering to them, of the place he has reached in his journey, of *the duties* limiting his freedom to choose, of *the priorities* of claims on his resources, of *the price* of things (including alternative courses of action), and *the value* of things involved in the alternatives before him, and finally a knowledge of *the resources* at his disposal, he is then set to work out which of the alternatives open to him is the one on which *he should* enter. There are many formulae he can use. One that takes into account all the relevant considerations goes something like this: choose that course of action which will employ your resources so as to make the greatest possible difference to the excellence of your life; where this requirement takes notice of *all the legitimate* claims on one's resources including the avoidance of emergencies, the claims of other people, and the pinpointing of "best buys."

Even with such a formula and vastly improved sources of knowledge, it would still be difficult, if not impossible, for anyone to perform for himself the required labor of calculation. The advantage of simple reliable guidelines to obviate these calculations would obviously be very great. In every society there are in fact some simple guidelines of this sort, designed for situations which frequently recur. They sum up the practical (conventional) wisdom of the group. Such wisdom is usually couched in the form of general instructions, precepts, or commandments. It is these which philosophers and sociologists primarily have in mind when they speak of *norms*. The function of such norms is to provide guidance for those who are trying to solve practical problems, that is, to answer questions about what someone ought to do. Such problems involve working out a course of action which would improve the life of the person whose problem is under consideration. Any solution to such a problem must point to such a course of action. Statements formulating such solutions must outline a course of action *as* a course which if followed will improve the life of the person concerned. Such statements are *sound* if they are what they purport to be, namely, solutions to the practical problem in hand, i.e., outlines of a course of action which really would improve the life of the person concerned. Such statements may be general e.g., "One ought not to break the law" or "Thou shalt not kill"; or particular, e.g., "You

ANALYSIS

*What is value? An analysis of the concept* 53

should marry that girl." Statements such as "You *should have married* that girl there and then" purport to give the solutions to a problem that has arisen in the past.

If, as is perfectly natural, we class all those particular and general statements purporting to give guidance to those trying to solve practical problems as *normative* statements, then normative statements, though closely related to value assessments, are nevertheless different from them, and there is no *logical* connection between them.[17] The assessment of the value of a thing does not, by itself (i.e., in the absence of additional and logically independent statements about other matters, such as a person's duties, his resources, the high-priority claims on him, and so on) imply that any one should do anything. And conversely, a statement to the effect that someone should do a particular thing does not imply any statement about the value of anything. However, this mutual logical independence of particular statements of these two kinds goes hand in hand with epistemological dependence of normative statements on value assessments: every normative statement requires some appraisal as its backing, and value assessments can and typically do function in this way. Of course, as already mentioned, when a value assessment is supplemented by various other types of statement, such as a person's duties, resources, and so on, then we can sometimes deduce a normative statement about that person from these premises, and thereby conclusively establish that normative statement. We have then derived a normative statement from various kinds of evaluative ones.

There is thus no plausibility to those widely held skeptical views about value and norm which identify value judgments with normative ones, and explain both as expressions of feelings or emotions, or as exhortations to have feelings, or as commands, prescriptions or other forms of telling people to do things.[18] Telling people the value of something is not any of these things, though it is relevant when people want to know what they should do. Again, telling people what they should do is not telling or exhorting them to do it, nor of course is it expressing one's feelings or emotions or attitudes relative to their doing it. But it is purporting to give them sound solutions to their practical problems. Such remarks are not themselves in any natural sense value judgments, though statements of the value of things are suitable backing for them.

17. For a similar view of the difference between Values and Norms, see Neil J. Smelser, *Theory of Collective Behavior* (New York: Free Press of Glencoe, 1963). Cf. also von Wright, *Norm and Action* (Humanities Press, 1963) and for a discussion of moral norms, my article, "Moral Obligation," *American Philosophical Quarterty*, vol. 3 (1966), pp. 210–226.
18. For a good discussion of these views, see George Kerner, *The Recent Revolution in Ethics* (New York and Oxford: Oxford University Press, 1966).

## The values to which we subscribe

We can now finally consider the sense of "value" central to this inquiry. I mean the sense in which it occurs in what I call value imputations, that is, claims imputing values to people. We impute certain values to Smith when we maintain that keeping up with the Jones', conformity with his country's mores, decency of language, and cleanliness are among Smith's values. Such claims are typically, though not always, made from the sociologist's point of view. "Smith *believes* that the earth is flat" is also typically, though not always, made from the sociologist's point of view. When Smith makes this remark *about himself*, he cannot add without absurdity, "but he is wrong—actually the earth is round." If he were speaking simply as a sociologist of his own views, no absurdity could arise. Similarly, if Smith imputes to himself the values we just imputed to him, namely, cleanliness and the rest of them, then he cannot add without absurdity, "but these values are quite unsound—cleanliness has never done any good to anyone." Having values is, in this respect, like having convictions about, or like valuing (in the sense of cherishing, treasuring, prizing) something: it is what might be called an essentially appraisal-dependent attitude. That I believe or value something *consists in* my having a certain attitude or behavioral disposition: I am disposed to act on my belief, to take protective action in defense of what I value.[19] If I *believe* the sign "Road closed," I do not take the road. If I value your friendship, I do something to protect it when it is threatened. But *what* I believe or value is dependent on the relevant appraisals. If I am rational, I do not believe things for whose falsity I have overwhelming evidence; similarly I do not value things for whose valuelessness I have overwhelming evidence. And the same is true for the values I hold: If I am rational I do not have a favorable attitude towards cleanliness when I believe that cleanliness never did any good to anyone.

The connection between value assessments and value imputations is thus a complicated one. Value imputations are typically made from the sociologist's point of view and so are typically noncommittal, detached. We may impute values to someone else while at the same time holding them to be sound, or holding them to be unsound, or altogether suspending judgment. But when it comes to imputing values to ourselves, we cannot without absurdity impute to ourselves values which we ourselves declare to be unsound. We can no more be satisfied with holding unsound values than we can be satisfied with holding false beliefs, however attached we may be to them. In our own case, the adoption of the sociologist's point of view is

19. For the important distinction between one's valuing something and something's being one of one's values see the Appendix to this essay.

ANALYSIS

*What is value? An analysis of the concept* 55

justifiable only up to a point: as a necessary preliminary to meliorative change. We cannot without absurdity maintain permanent detachment from ourselves. That way lies schizophrenia.

The great importance attributed to the question of what our values are and how, under the impact of this or that causal factor, they might come to change, is due to the perfectly rational fear of some that the *sound* values we now have will be replaced by other less sound ones. It is, however, also due to the irrational fear of others that some of the values we now have and to which they are inordinately attached, will be discovered to be *unsound*, replaced by others, and perhaps never missed.

It is most important not to allow these irrational fears to interfere with the systematic study of our values and their soundness or unsoundness if we are to derive the hoped-for benefits from these investigations. It is, however, quite impossible to find out which of our values we should happily kiss good-bye and which of them we should protect and preserve, and at what cost, unless we can determine what are the values of an individual, and those of a society. We would expect an individual's values to be organized to a considerable degree. We would expect them to be arranged in an order, and we would expect there to be immediate changes in some aspects of this order if there are changes in others. We expect a person's values to be grouped or bunched in certain ways so that a certain characteristic value profile or value orientation or value structure emerges which shows itself in characteristic responses to dangers and threats, opportunities and windfalls in his life. No doubt it will be useful to have at our disposal concepts referring to groupings, arrangements, or emphases of this kind. However, prior to defining workable concepts on so large a scale, we should have a clearer account than is now available of the particular values which we already name and recognize (e.g., cleanliness, thrift, social justice), and which compose those larger wholes, such as value profile and value orientation which social scientists need for their purposes.[20]

20. For a discussion of these, see for instance, William Catton, Jr. "A Theory of Value," *American Sociological Review*, vol. 24 (1959), pp. 310–317. Florence Kluckhohn, "Dominant and Variant Value Orientations" in *Variations in Value Orientations*, ed. by Florence Kluckhohn and Fred Strodtbeck (Illinois: Row, Peterson and Company, 1961, pp. 1–48). Clyde Kluckhohn, "Values and Value-Orientations in the Theory of Action: An Exploration in Definition and Classification," in *Toward a General Theory of Action*, ed. by Talcott Parsons and Edward A. Shils (New York: Harper Torchbooks, 1962). Alex Inkeles, "Industrial Man: The Relation of States to Experience, Perception, and Value," *The American Journal of Sociology*, vol. 74 (1960), pp. 1–31. Salomon Rettig and Benjamin Pasamanich, "Changes in Moral Values Among College Students: A Factorial Study," *American Sociological Review*, vol. 24 (1959), pp. 856–863. Seymour Martin Lipset, "The Value Patterns of Democracy," *American Sociological Review*, vol. 28 (1963), pp. 515–531. Herbert H. Hyman, "The Value Systems of Different Classes: A Social Psychological Contribution to the Analysis of Stratification" in *Class, Status, and Power*
[*Continued on next page*

Such particular value imputations are to the effect that someone has, holds, or subscribes to some particular value, $V$ (e.g., achievement, work, altruism, comfort, equality, thrift, friendship). When we say this sort of thing of an individual or a whole society, we impute to that individual or to that society *a favorable attitude* towards the realization of *various states of affairs*; we vaguely indicate these states of affairs by the value name, "*V*"; and we imply that he has this favorable attitude because he expects (more or less explicitly) that the realization of these states of affairs makes some favorable difference to someone's life, not necessarily that of the value holder himself.

Clearly, these two types of assertion, value imputations and value assessments, make different and logically independent claims. When Jones says that the political value of friendship with Mr. K is great, he *assesses* the political value of that friendship, but he does not thereby impute to *himself* or anyone else the value, friendship, political success, or any other value. Conversely, when Jones claims that friendship is one of Smith's values, he is not thereby himself assessing the value of friendship, or implying that Smith has *made* such an assessment—though he does imply that Smith at least *takes* having friends to confer benefits of some kind and magnitude.

Even the meaning of the word "value" is different in these two kinds of claim. Assessed value is the measure of the *capacity* of some sort of thing to make favorable differences to people's lives. Imputed values are measures of *tendencies* of persons (and *only* persons) to promote certain ends *because* they take the attainment of these ends to make a favorable difference to people's lives. The former gives relevant information about, and grades things as aids to, the betterment of people's lives. The latter gives relevant information about people's actual allocation of resources when guided by their conception of the good life and of how to attain it.

The values of a group are thus part of its conventional wisdom.[21] They are those settled habits of, and attitudes towards, resource allocations which are *essentially appraisal-dependent* in the sense explained:[22] the community is ready to modify these habits and attitudes in the face of what they would themselves recognize as very strong evidence to the effect that these resource

21. I use this expression in the sense made famous by J. K. Galbraith in *The Affluent Society* (New York: Mentor Books, 1958), Ch. II.
22. For further details see the discussion above, p. 54.

---

ed. by Bendix, Reinhard and Seymour M. Lipset (New York: The Free Press of Glencoe, 1953), pp. 426–442. The widely used Allport, Vernon, Lindsey Test (*Study of Values*. Test Booklet, Houghten Mifflin Company. 1960) "aims to measure the relative prominence of six basic interests or motives in personality." The classification is based on Edward Spranger's *Types of Men*. The result of the test is called "A Profile of Values."

ANALYSIS

*What is value? An analysis of the concept*                                    57

allocations do not confer the expected benefits. The *values* of the group differ from its *beliefs* in that, unlike the latter, their subject matter is the good life and how to come closer to it. They differ from the group's *norms* in that instead of spelling out courses of action to be followed in certain circumstances, they point to goal states for whose realization the group is ready to strive because it believes that their realization would confer benefits. The two may be closely related, of course. "Justice" may be one of the group's norms as well as one of its values. The norm, "Be just," indicates (vaguely) what a person should do—namely, give to everyone his due—and in what circumstances (when there is a question of satisfying the claims of desert). The group value indicates a state of affairs (one in which everyone follows the norms of justice and everyone as a result gets his deserts) for whose realization the group is ready to strive because of the benefits which, as it dimly recognizes, its realization confers on all its members.

To see at a glance what role, if any, is played in a particular value imputation by an appraisal, we must set out the elements contained in such imputations. Suppose we impute to Smith the following values: achievement, work, diligence, honesty, social acceptance, clean living, and travel. Of any one of these things it is then true that it is one of Smith's values. Let us abridge this as, "*V* is one of *S*'s values." The three main elements of such a claim can then be set out as follows:

1) "*V* vaguely points to or indicates possible states of affairs

2) towards whose realization *S* has a favorable attitude

3) because *S* believes, explicitly or implicitly, that their realization makes a favorable difference to the life of someone, not necessarily *S* himself."

It is clear that (3) indicates the nature and role of the appraisal involved. I have given some account of this above, and I need not repeat it here. However, a great many important questions of detail remain. Exactly what is it for a person to believe or to take it that the realization of the state of affairs indicated by the value name (e.g., "achievement") makes a favorable difference to someone's life? How would we find out whether he does believe it? Who is the person, if not the agent himself, to whose life the realization of these states of affairs must make a favorable difference? How would we tell whether that belief really *is* the reason why Smith has a favorable attitude towards the realization of these states of affairs? For those interested, I have set out, in an Appendix, detailed answers to some of the more obviously troublesome questions left unanswered in this essay. Of course, even these detailed answers will not satisfy everyone, if indeed they will satisfy anyone. But, given the present confused state of our knowledge of this field, they should be acceptable at least as a beginning.

### APPENDIX

The brief account, in this chapter, of subscribing to particular values is necessarily sketchy and imprecise. It would give little assistance to anybody trying to ascertain whether someone actually subscribed to a given particular value or not, or even to anybody trying to construct a psychological test for that purpose. Some of the gaps holding us back from the latter task can, however, be remedied by a comparatively small effort. In this Appendix, I offer this remedy for those who may be interested.

My account above makes use of four rather large-scale ideas: (1) A possible state of affairs; (2) Someone's having a favorable attitude toward the realization of that state of affairs; (3) His belief that that realization will make a favorable difference to someone; (4) His having that favorable attitude *because* of his having that belief. I must assume that for my purposes of preliminary clarification, my brief remarks about essentially appraisal-dependent attitudes in the last section of the main paper are adequate to make clear the idea of point (4). The ideas in points (1)–(3), however, obviously are in need of considerable expansion.

1.1)

   *Indicating the state of affairs.* What is a possible state of affairs? It is a possible feature, aspect, or state of the world around us, such as American Big Business being free from cramping restrictions, German housewives being thrifty, corporation managers being innovative, and the like. If the world changes in such a way that these possible states of affairs are realized, then the corresponding assertions, "Big Business is free . . .," "German housewives are thrifty," and "managers are innovative" are true, otherwise they are false. These assertions are *made* true by these changes in the world. We may raise the question whether states of affairs are part of the world or part of the linguistic apparatus in terms of which we talk about the world.[23] The answer is that they are part of the world: they are features, aspects, or states of the world selected, referred to, or spoken of by means of our linguistic machinery. By a change in a state of affairs, such as the realization of a possible state of affairs not previously realized, we clearly mean a change in the world. But *what* changes in the world we can refer to, or talk about, is determined by the linguistic apparatus at our disposal: Consider the state of affairs of German housewives being thrifty: that state of affairs is not an English one—if anything it is German—but the fact that *some* change in

23. For a discussion of this problem, cf. P. F. Strawson, "Truth," *Aristotelian Society Supplementary Volume*, 1950, pp. 129–156. J. L. Austin, "Truth" and "Unfair to Facts" in *Philosophical Papers*, by J. Austin ed. by J. O. Urmson and G. J. Warnock (Oxford University Press, 1961).

ANALYSIS

*What is value? An analysis of the concept* 59

the world *constitutes* the realization of *that* possible state of affairs is due to the availability, *in English*, of this way of characterizing the world.

1.2)

    *Specifying the value domain.* How does the value name, $V$, indicate or point to a given state of affairs and how can this method of pointing be made more precise?

    "$V$" indicates a state of affairs in the following rather indirect and indeterminate way. The value name, "$V$", allows us to construct an assertion of the form, "Some individual, $X$, is characterized by "$V$," whose truth would involve the realization of a corresponding state of affairs. That state of affairs is the one indicated by "$V$". Thus, if "$V$" stands for thrift, and $V$ is one of Jones' values, then "$V$" allows us to construct an assertion, "$X$ is characterized by thrift (is thrifty)," whose truth would involve the realization of a state of affairs, $X$'s being thrifty. This then is the state of affairs indicated by "$V$".

    This way of indicating a state of affairs is admittedly rather unhelpful. It gives no clear indication of what we are to substitute for $X$. Exactly what or who is this $X$ whose having the value property, $V$, is favored by $S$? Is it $S$ (the value holder) himself, or perhaps his family, his city, his state, someone, everyone? Clearly, each of these possibilities constitutes a very different state of affairs, and so a very different value.

    Let us call "value bearer" whatever it is that is properly substituted for $X$. Then, if we are to do more than *vaguely* indicate the relevant state of affairs, we must indicate more clearly who or what the value bearers are. Let us call that, "specifying the value domain." How, then, could we go about specifying the value domain?

    A first step in that direction is to give *the type* of value bearer, that is, the type of entity whose being or having $V$ constitutes the state of affairs favored by $S$. I distinguish three such types, individuals, institutions, and environments. To specify in this way the domain of one of someone's values, we simply add one of the adjectives, "individual," "institutional" or "environmental." Thus, "thrift is one of Jones' *individual* values" means that Jones has a favorable attitude towards the realization of a certain state of affairs, namely, one constituted by certain individuals being thrifty. "Equality of opportunity is one of Jones' *institutional* values" means that Jones favors the realization of a state of affairs, namely, one constituted by certain institutions granting or affording equality of opportunity to its members. "Spaciousness is one of Jones' *environmental* values" means that Jones favors the realization of a state of affairs, namely, one constituted by certain environments being spacious.

However, such claims are still rather vague about the value bearer. We still have to speak of "certain individuals," "certain institutions," and "certain environments." Further specification of the value domain is achieved by determining the intended set of value bearers. The most obvious technique would be to state the characteristics, possession of which determines that set. If the domain is individuals, the intended value bearers might then be identified by sex, age, education, or social role, e.g., women, teenage girls, co-eds, professional women, and so on.

Another common way in which to determine the domain of someone's value would be to specify his "perspective," that is, to state whether he thinks of the value bearers as all those belonging to some "in-group" or some "out-group." If he thinks of them as an "in-group," he will characterize them in a way which makes them members of a class of which he too is a member; if as an "out-group," then of a class of which he is not a member. Thus if $V$ is "knowing their place," $V$ will tend to be an "out-group" value, if $V$ is "freedom from restrictions" or "universal franchise," it will tend to be an "in-group" value.

Much the same applies, *mutatis mutandis*, to institutional and environmental values. In the case of institutions also, the domain can be further specified by stating class characteristics which make it possible to identify the particular institutions intended, e.g., governments, corporations, clubs, universities, and so on. Here, too, we can specify the value holder's perspective. Thus universal adult franchise, honest and secret elections, respect for democratic procedures, may be among Jones' institutional in-group values whose domain more specifically are sovereign states; Jones, an American, let us say, favors these states of affairs only in what he thinks of as Western and technologically advanced societies, but not in underdeveloped countries.

## 1.3)

*Aspiration level.* Although it is now clear *whose* being thrifty is favored by $S$, it is still unclear what would constitute a realization of the favored state of affairs, because it is not clear *how* thrifty they have to be. To remove this vagueness, we must specify "the aspiration level" of that value. By this we mean the degree of $V$, the value property, which must be reached if we are to speak of the realization of the state of affairs which $S$ favors because $V$ is one of his values. Suppose one of Jones' values is universal compulsory education or the eradication of poverty. Then the aspiration level at which he subscribes to the former of these values, is the level of education whose achievement by everyone would constitute the realization of the state of affairs which he favors; and the aspiration level at which he subscribes to the latter of these values is the level of affluence (say, an annual income of $3000

ANALYSIS

*What is value? An analysis of the concept*                                     61

per family with two children) whose attainment by everyone would constitute the state of affairs he favors.

1.4)

*Limitations on the value domain.* What is the permissible range of the value domain? The major significant restriction appears to be that the indicated state of affairs should be something about which an individual (logically) can believe that its realization would make a favorable difference to someone's life, and that it (logically) can be realized. It is not necessary that the realization should actually make such a difference or that it should actually be capable of realization. Universal celibacy appears to have been one of the values of the members of the Harmony Society founded by George Rapp, even though celibacy did not in fact make the difference they would seem to have hoped for, namely, eternal life, nor as far as one can tell any other favorable difference; and even though eternal life, whose actual realization might well be a favorable difference, be quite incapable of realization by *any* methods, even vastly more powerful ones than celibacy.

Another less obvious restriction relates to the delimitation of the value domain: it cannot be delimited in an arbitrary way. We can illustrate this by the logical differences between $S$'s *valuing V* and *V's being one of S's values*. As already noted, Jones may value Smith's friendship even though *friendship is not one of Jones' values*, and conversely friendship may be one of his values even though he does not value Smith's friendship. We can now add that *Smith's friendship even cannot be* one of Jones' values. For "Smith's friendship" would restrict the domain of that value in a wholly arbitrary manner. If $V$ is one of your values, then $V$ must be able to do three connected things: point to a *possible* domain for $V$, give rise to a belief that the realization of a state of affairs of that domain would make a favorable difference to someone's life, and justify the delimitation of that domain by its beneficial results. Thus, if one of Jones' values is friendship, then *no special delimitation* of the domain is suggested. If friendship with politicians is one of his values, then the domain is restricted to friendships in which one partner is a politician. Such a restriction must then be grounded in a belief in the dependence of the favorable difference on such a delimitation; in a belief that friendship with nonpoliticians is not as beneficial, advantageous, elevating, etc., as friendship with politicians. Obviously, a restriction of the domain to Smith can hardly be justified in this way. For why should not friendship by Jones with people other than Smith, or by people other than Jones with Smith, or by people other than Jones with people other than Smith, make the same favorable difference to the relevant lives? It is of course peerfecly possible that, for Jones, only friendship with Smith makes that favorable difference: because Smith has influence with the Board of Trustees or with the Draft Board. But such considerations *extraneous to* the nature of friendship, while relevant to whether one values friendship with a certain person and why one values it, are not relevant to whether friendship is among one's values, or why it is so.

2.1)

We can now turn to the question of how we tell whether someone has a favorable attitude toward a given state of affairs, or an unfavorable attitude, or a neutral one. We can distinguish four dimensions along which someone's attitude toward a state of affairs manifests itself:

(i) How his choices are affected by the prospect (or expectation) of the realization (or cessation), as a result of his behavior, of the given state of affairs. We should say that he has a favorable attitude toward the realization of a state of affairs if, when he thinks that doing $x$ will help to realize it whereas not doing $x$ will do nothing toward its realization or actually help prevent its realization or bring about its termination, he is inclined to do $x$ rather than not to do $x$. And we should say that he has the stronger favorable attitude the more strongly he is so inclined.

(ii) What he thinks of its realization, prevalence, and termination. By this we mean mainly what favorable or unfavorable difference he expects from its realization, prevalence, and cessation and for whom he expects it. He has a favorable attitude toward the realization of a state of affairs if he expects its realization to make a favorable difference to those he wishes to be thus benefited, and if he expects it to harm those he wishes to be harmed.

(iii) What proportion of his resources he sets aside for the realization of this state of affairs. He has a favorable attitude toward the realization of a certain state of affairs, if he devotes some of his time, energy, skill, and money to trying to realize that state of affairs. Conversely, he is indifferent to it if he does nothing toward its realization. He has an unfavorable attitude, if he devotes some of his resources to trying to prevent or retard its realization or to terminate its prevalence or to lower the level of aspiration at which it is currently realized.

(iv) How he feels about the realization, prevalence, or termination of the state of affairs: whether he welcomes and is glad about its realization, content or satisfied with its prevalence and upset by or sorry about its termination, whether he is indifferent as between the realization, prevalence, or termination of the state of affairs, or whether he is upset by or sorry about its realization, discontented and dissatisfied with its prevalence, or welcomes and is glad about its termination.

Normally, when a person has a favorable attitude toward the realiza-

ANALYSIS

*What is value? An analysis of the concept*                                    63

tion of a given state of affairs, this will show itself in all of the four dimensions listed. However, we shall say that Jones has a favorable attitude towards a certain state of affairs if he has a favorable attitude in dimensions (i) and (ii); if, that is, he manifests that favorable attitude on those occasions in which he believes that some course of action open to him would help to realize the state of affairs in question by tending (other things being equal) to enter on that course of action, and if he thinks that the realization of the state of affairs makes a favorable difference to some people. In our view, it is quite possible that a person should have a favorable attitude toward a state of affairs without (iii) and (iv), i.e., without *manifesting any feelings* toward the realization of the state of affairs or *going out of his way* to promote or maintain that state of affairs.

2.2)

There are two main ways of telling precisely which are the states of affairs toward whose realization a certain person has a favorable attitude. The first is to determine these states of affairs on the basis of the *observed reactions* (manifest favorable attitudes) by that person toward states of affairs: either favorable reactions toward states of affairs whose realization he is witnessing; or observed unfavorable reactions toward states of affairs whose termination or prevention he is witnessing. The second is to determine these states of affairs on the basis of certain *expressed opinions* by that person: what, *in his opinion*, are the states of affairs he is bringing about, making possible or making probable, by what he is doing. In regard to both of these ways, it may be difficult to determine the precise nature of that state of affairs: to specify the dimensions we have called the type of value bearer, the domain of the value, and the aspiration level of the value. It will normally be helpful *to ask* the person himself just what the specification of these dimensions should be. However, it must be remembered that in these matters a person may conceal the truth not only from others but also from himself. Hence what he says may conflict with what he does. A man may think that his values include racial equality, social justice, and equal opportunity for all, yet he may oppose desegregation in the school to which he sent his daughters, oppose equal pay for women or Negroes, and oppose the improvement of educational facilities for the children of the poor. In such cases, we must first make clear exactly wherein (that is, in the realization of precisely what state of affairs) the realization of his professed values *would* consist, and then try to elicit from him precisely what is the sate of affairs (type of value bearer, domain of value, and aspiration level) toward whose realization he has a favorable attitude, and ascertain by observation whether his manifest reactions, his deliberate choices, and the expenditure of his resources bear out his own judgment of what states of affairs he favors.

3.1)

   We have already said enough on the question of what it is for something to make a favorable difference to the life of someone. We must now make clearer what it is for someone to *believe* this, explicitly or implicitly.

   The main problem here is just how to determine whether a person does hold such a belief. The difficulty for the investigator lies in finding a situation such that a person's readiness to act on a certain belief must show itself in readily observable behavior. It would be helpful if such behavioral tests could be supplemented by the person's own answers to direct questioning about whether he holds such a belief. For it would seem that the believer himself is often, perhaps most of the time, in a better position than anyone else to formulate the beliefs he holds, and to say whether or not he holds a certain belief. Investigators cannot always rely on such answers, however, for the person questioned may be lying. But since people normally do not lie unless they have reasons to deceive someone, investigators can use answers to questions given at least on occasions and on topics when motives for concealment and deception are absent. With the assistance of certain aides, such as truth-drugs, lie-detectors, and the like, we may even be able to tell whether a person is lying or telling the truth. Even when not lying, however, a person may be giving a false answer. He may have *misunderstood* the question, perhaps understanding something different by "a favorable difference" from what we understand by it; or he may simply *be mistaken in thinking* that he really believes the matter in question. Thus, if we rely on a person's own answers to questions about what he believes, we will do well to make sure that he clearly understands what belief we are inquiring about, that he is not mistaken in thinking that he believes it, and that he is not lying. Misunderstandings are especially likely to occur in this case, since both "belief" and "favorable difference," the key words in our question, are vague and difficult for anyone to understand. Thus, when we ask Jones whether he thought that the Pass Road was closed, he may (misunderstanding the meaning of "thought that") take us to be asking whether the thought The Pass Road is Closed, had entered his mind. If it has entered his mind, this is not of course sufficient to show that he believed that the road was closed, nor if the thought had not entered his mind sufficient to show that he did not believe it. Such minor sorts of misunderstanding can be avoided by careful formulations of the question.

   More serious are the difficulties and ambiguities attending the meaning of "making a favorable difference," "kind of favorable difference" and "identity of person to whom that difference is made." Let us, for the sake

ANALYSIS

*What is value? An analysis of the concept*                                                      65

of brevity, substitute the terms, "benefit," "kind of benefit" and "identity of the beneficiary." Enough has been said about these ideas above. It will, however, be helpful to say a little more about further ways of specifying who are, in the opinion of the value holder, the beneficiaries of a given value of his. The availability of such ways of identifying the beneficiaries might help us become clearer in our own minds about what exactly our values are, and whether they are sound.

For purposes of determining the soundness of our values the most useful classificatory system would be one which specifies beneficiaries by their relation to the value domain. On this basis, we can distinguish three classes: those which are *domain-internal*, those which are *domain-transcending*, and those which are *domain-external*. A given value is domain-internal, if the beneficiaries are persons entirely within the value domain; domain-transcending if some of the beneficiaries are within, some without the value domain; and domain-external if all the beneficiaries are persons outside the value domain. Thus, to begin with values whose bearers are persons, let us assume that thrift and family loyalty are among Jones' values, and that the domain of these values is Jones' own family, including himself. We can then distinguish three different beliefs concerning who the beneficiaries are. We can say that these two among Jones' values are domain-internal if he believes that only members of his family are the beneficiaries; domain transcending if he believes that members of his family as well as others are the beneficiaries; and domain-external if he believes that only nonmembers of his family are the beneficiaries. Suppose that *exclusiveness* and *racial purity* are among Jones' values, and that the domain of these values is best defined as Jones' in-group schools and clubs, perhaps, those to which he and his class belong or aspire to belong. Then these values may be domain-internal (if he believes that only members of his class are beneficiaries); domain-transcending (if he believes that members of his class as well as members of other classes are beneficiaries); and domain-external (if he believes that only non-members of his class are beneficiaries). Parallel distinctions can be drawn for values whose bearers are institutions or environments.

Two further distinctions may help a man get clearer about the beliefs he holds concerning what benefits accrue to whom upon the realization of a certain state of affairs. The first is especially important in the case of a person's values which he regards as moral values, *or at any rate as morally important ones*. Jones may for instance regard thrift and family loyalty as moral values but be in doubt about whether they should be so regarded, and in doubt about whom he expects to benefit from their realization. Let us assume that thrift and family loyalty are among Jones' individual, in-group, domain-internal values, that is, values from whose realization he expects benefits only for persons within the domain who are also members of one of Jones' in-groups. We may then distinguish between two important sub-classes of these values, those which are *reflexive* and those which are *distributive*. Such a domain-internal value shall be called reflexive if the value holder expects *any* person within the value domain to benefit from being the value bearer. Thus, thrift and family loyalty are reflexive values of Jones' if Jones believes that *anyone* in his family who is thrifty and loyal to the family will benefit from being so, irrespective of whether or not anyone else is so too. By contrast, these values of his are distributive, if he believes that the benefit will accrue to some member of the domain other than the member who is thrifty or loyal. Thus, Jones' values, thrift and family loyalty, are distributive if he believes that any one family member's being thrifty or loyal will benefit some other member of the family. This distinction, it should be noted, applies only to domain-internal values, and it is not ex-clusive: values may be both reflexive and distributive.

Distributive values are particularly important for the maintenance of morality. They tend to give rise to a demand that every member of the domain *should* subscribe to the value, and hence to a favorable attitude to-ward those members of the domain who do, and an unfavorable attitude toward those who do not subscribe to that value. Distributive values in other words give rise to psychological pressures in the direction of uniformity of values. The pressure will tend to be the more insistent the greater the benefit conferred on the beneficiary and the greater the sacrifices made on the part of the value bearers (those who are thrifty and loyal). The more the persons within the value domain desire the benefit which the realization of a distributive value confers on them, the more strongly they will tend to insist on its full realization throughout the value domain. The more they suspect that the beneficiaries desire the benefit, the more they will insist on recipro-city, refusing to become value bearers unless others within the value domain do so as well. The insistence on reciprocity, "playing the game," "doing one's bit," "pulling one's weight" and so forth, which is so characteristic of values which are regarded as moral, is thus typically a mark of the distributiveness of a value. It differs from simple "égoisme à deux" (typified by cooperative activities such as making love) in that there is not necessarily the happy coincidence between any and every (normal) move being both reflexively and distributively beneficial. Universal (distributive) beneficiality is achieved, not by anyone doing as he pleases or as he thinks will benefit himself, but only by everyone doing his (assigned) bit (casting his bread on the waters) even though this will not directly (reflexively) benefit him.

The second important distinction divides values, from the perspective of the value holder, into *self-interested* and *disinterested* ones. We may speak of self-interested values when the value holder believes he is the only beneficiary; of disinterested ones when the value holder believes he is not one of the beneficiaries. Supposing again that thrift is one of Jones' domain internal values, we can say that it is a self-interested value insofar as it is reflexive (since then Jones' being thrifty would in his opinion confer a benefit on himself); a disinterested value insofar as it is distributive (since then Jones expects his being thrifty to confer a benefit on some other person within the domain). However, if Jones insists on reciprocity or exerts pressure on others to play the game and do their bit, then thrift is only a partly disinterested value of Jones', even though it be distributive.

This chapter grew out of regular discussion meetings during the summers of 1965 and 1966, attended by David Braybrooke, Nicholas Rescher, John Robison and Jerome Schneewind. I am deeply indebted to all the participants, but especially to David Braybrooke who has drawn my attention to important writings in the fields of economics and sociology which I would have overlooked and who read and substantially improved many of the earlier drafts of this paper. He has saved me from many errors, but of course is not responsible for any that remain. I have also greatly benefitted from regular discussions with four graduate students, Bliss Cartwright, Louis Kort, Michael McDonald, and Stephen Norris who acted as Research Assistants.

# FUNDAMENTAL CONSIDERATIONS

# What is value change?
# A framework for research

## *Nicholas Rescher*

*A methodological examination of the problem with special reference to fore-seeable changes in American values induced by social and technological change over the next generation*

### Modes of value change: a preliminary typology

We shall not attempt to delineate the concept of a *value* here. This essential preliminary task has been dealt with elsewhere.[1] It should be said, however, that we shall here construe the term "value" in a very extended sense. Sometimes "human value" is restricted to the area of personal values (of character and personality). But we take it to include not only what the individual may prize in himself and his associates, but also what he prizes in his society, his nation, his culture, his fellowmen in general, and his environment. We thus view this idea extended over a very broad domain—ranging from *individual* to *social* and *universal* values.

The present discussion of value change proceeds within the framework of a cluster of basic concepts regarding the nature of value change which must be explained at the outset. These concepts relate to the explication of what a *value change* is, and the clarification of the different sorts of things that are at issue here.

### *Value subscription*

A person who subscribes to (i.e., has, accepts, holds, is dedicated to, gives his adherence to, etc.) a certain value will be characterized as a sub-scriber to this value. This idea can obviously be applied to a group of persons

1. See K. Baier, "What is Value?" above, and N. Rescher, *Introduction to Value Theory* (Englewood Cliffs, 1968).

ANALYSIS

*What is value change? A framework for research* 69

as well. "*Dietary propriety*," for example, is a value[2] for Catholics (orthodox Jews, Muslims, etc.—all, to be sure, in different ways), but not at all for Protestants.

### Value acquisition and abandonment

When a person begins to subscribe to a value to which he did not previously give adherence, we shall say that he has *acquired* this value. In the reverse case, when he gives up adherence to a value to which he previously subscribed, we shall say that he has *abandoned* this value. Value acquisition and abandonment is the most radical sort of "change" with respect to a given value on the part of an individual value subscriber; it is not a matter of more or less, of degree, but rather turns on the yes-no issue of a given value's entering or exiting from a person's set of accepted values. This is the sort of thing one thinks of in connection with a religious or ideological conversion.

### Value redistribution

A given value is more or less widely distributed throughout a group according as a larger or smaller proportion of members of the group subscribe to it. We may speak of a *value redistribution* when there is a change in the extent or in the pattern of its distribution in the society. A very common way in which a value becomes a "value of a society," that is, becomes successively more and more generally diffused (i.e., more and more extensively distributed) throughout this society in that most or virtually all of its members subscribe to it—is to start out as the value of some dedicated minority who successfully manage to promote its increasingly widespread acceptance. This has been the history of many of our national values (e.g., "*tolerance*").

### Value emphasis and de-emphasis

A situation may develop in which a value, even when not affected by other modes of value change, may suddenly come to be emphasized (or de-emphasized), because changes in the life environment force it to our attention. If a value is securely established, for example, we may no longer (need to) pay it much heed—though presumably we would if it were "threatened." The course of events renders some values operatively *topical*—having lain dormant before, they are now in the spotlight and resource-demanding— while other values more or less negligible (at any rate *pro tem.*).

---

2. That is, a religious value—the medical values of dietary adequacy and safety are not now at issue.

## Value rescaling

The set of values to which a person (or group) subscribes can generally be compared on a value scale of higher and lower, and to some extent can even be arranged in a strict hierarchy.[3] This does not turn on the yes-no issue of whether a subscriber does or does not adhere to certain values, but on the *extent* of his commitment to them. The height of a value on the scale is determined by a multiplicity of factors such as the tenacity of maintaining and preserving the value, preparedness to invest energy and resources in its realization and propagation, and the attachment of high sanctions to the value (i.e., how much compliance is expected and how much reproach heaped upon the transgressor), etc. The reordering of such a value scale by mutual reranking of its components in a "revaluation of values" is among the more drastic varieties of value change. One finds this sort of thing, for example, when there is a widespread reorientation in the sources of identity and self-worth in a changing society (particularly in the wake of some extensive loss of social stability).

## Value redeployment

A value is inevitably held in the context of a domain of application, the range of cases that are held to come within the purview of this value: the objects or occasions for value implementing action or appraisal. (Paradigm example: driving a car within the speed limit lies within the domain of application of the value *"law abidingness."*) The operative arena of the ideals of legal and political equality were gradually extended to include the American Negro and the American Indian, but this does not mean that these values as such were given a different or higher niche in the shrine of American values—simply that we began to apply them over an enlarged domain with changed boundaries of application. One of the most profound value changes in Roman history was the bringing of the provincials within the precincts of Roman citizenship; for the Roman politician and jurist this was clearly a matter of redeployment of existing values—rather than turning upon the acquisition of new values, it involved redefining the area of application of old ones. (Think also of the Apostle's conception of some gentiles as "circumcised of the spirit.") Thus Senator Eugene McCarthy has noted in a recent article[4] that only for a short time now has the right to an opportunity to secure suitable employment and the right to educational opportunities come to be recognized as *"civil rights."* He remarks that "[Barry Goldwater] as a candidate used to say regularly that the Constitution of the United States says nothing about education." Noting that this is quite

3. The ordering at issue here is not a strict but a *partial* ordering in the mathematicians' sense.
4. "My Hope for the Democrats," *Saturday Review*, November 5, 1966, p. 50.

**ANALYSIS**

*What is value change? A framework for research* 71

correct, McCarthy goes on to observe that, however, the constitution "says a lot about human dignity and human happiness and certain inalienable rights." These concepts, McCarthy holds, are nowadays to be so interpreted or reinterpreted that education and employment fall within their purview.

### Value restandardization

A mode of value change that is particularly sensitive to and reflective of changes in the social, economic, and technological environment is a change in the *standard of implementation* of a value, the guidelines for assessing the extent to which a value is attained in particular cases within its domain of application. Here there are two possibilities: the changing of existing standards, and the introduction of new ones. The airplane passenger has not changed the high importance he places upon the values of *"safety,"* *"speed,"* *"reliability"* and *"comfort"* with respect to his mode of transportation since the 1920's, but he expects these value desiderata to be realized in a heightened degree: he brings a different set of standards to bear in judging the degree of their attainment, especially in settling the question of whether they have been sufficiently or *minimally* realized.[5] (It is in this sense that we generally speak of the "raising" and "lowering" of standards.) A more dramatic example is that of the *standard of living*—a century ago economists thought of a worker's earning his "livelihood" in terms of *survival* for himself and his family; today we think of it in terms of a share in "the good life" which the economy makes possible for all and the society expects for everyone. This restandardization of the value of *"public welfare"* has been matched by a corresponding escalation of the value of *"public health,"* which was formerly regarded in essentially negative terms (the absence of diseases and injuries) but has now come to be viewed in an essentially positive way (physical, mental, and social well-being, or even the optimal development of human potentialities). In an era of technologically luxuriant affluence one is no longer content to set value standards at the low point of catastrophe prevention. In such cases we have a restandardization of the value in question, a changed concept of the minimally acceptable degree of their attainment. Also, new standards can be added, as in this age of pesticides we add standards of consumption safety to the usual standards of palatability in evaluating fruit.

### Value implementation retargeting

A value realization target is a specific goal or objective adopted by a value subscriber in the interests of making progress in the realization of

---

5. It is useful to distinguish between *minimal standards* of this basic requirement on the one hand, and on the other *optimal standards* of what one would ideally aspire to have.

the value at issue. For example, a person on whose value scale "the promotion of international understanding" rates high may in consequence set for himself the specific target of serving abroad in the Peace Corps. Now once he has done this—or found that he cannot do it—he may move on to adopt some other target for implementing the value at issue, and this is what we shall call value implementation retargeting. (Example: female suffrage, Negro suffrage, voter-qualification age of 18, poll-tax abolition, English-literacy test abandonment, one-man one-vote doctrine as targets for the value of *"voting equality."*) When a series of successive targets has been set as accepted for sequential attainment, we have a *priority schedule* in terms of the successive "orders of business" on the agenda of implementing the value at issue. The *revision* of such a list of priorities is a significant form of value change, albeit a mild one. An even milder version of this mode of value change is the resetting of a target date, the deadline for attaining the specific value target at issue. (Example: the Soviet Union and the transition from socialism to genuine communism.)

### Upgrading / downgrading

We distinguish systematically between modes of upgrading and corresponding modes of downgrading in terms of the preceding varieties of value change, as follows:

| Modes of Upgrading | | Modes of Downgrading |
|---|---|---|
| value acquisition | 1 | value abandonment |
| increase redistribution | 2 | decrease redistribution |
| rescaling upwards | 3 | rescaling downwards |
| widening redeployment | 4 | narrowing redeployment |
| value emphasis | 5 | value de-emphasis |
| restandardization by a raising of standards | 6 | restandardization by a lowering of standards |
| retargeting by adding implementation targets or by giving higher priority to existing ones | 7 | retargeting by dropping implementation targets or by giving lower priority to existing ones |

The point is that the modes of upgrading represent very diverse ways in which heightened acceptances of or emphasis upon a given value can occur: The modes of upgrading all represent higher valuations of the value, and the modes of downgrading represent a devaluation of it.

## Some ways in which value change can come about in a society

The preceding section dealt with some of the principal modes or types of value change from the *conceptual* angle of classification and, in particular, distinguished these from the standpoint of (1) the person or group affected

ANALYSIS

*What is value change? A framework for research*

73

(e.g., in value redistribution) and of (2) the mode of affectation (e.g., the rescaling vs. the redeployment of a value). We now turn to a consideration of the sources in the sense of the *causal* origins of such changes. Our aim is to make a systematic survey of at least some of the most important causal factors which provide the motive power for the dynamical process of value change in persons and societies.

What are the values *of a society*, and how is one to determine them? They are values so generally acknowledged and widely diffused throughout the society that explicit, overt appeal to them can well be expected from publicly recognized spokesmen for values: newspaper editorialists, graduation exercise speakers, religio-moral sermonizers, political orators, and the like. What sense does it make to deal with values at this level of generality? The proof of the pudding is in the eating. The enterprise makes sense only insofar as it illuminates recognizably significant aspects of the society at issue. No doubt many features of societies must be studied in finer detail, but —societies having the sort of cohesion they do—there is every reason to expect that some of their value phenomena can usefully be studied at a fairly high level of generality.

A value change can come about either *derivatively* or *directly*. It is derivative when, for example, the value at issue is *subsidiary* or subordinate to some other value and changes because this other value does so. For example, think of a complex value cluster (e.g., *"economic justice"*) and a subordinate value that represents a constituent element of this cluster (say *"equality of opportunity"*). Then a change in the fate of the one will generally involve a corresponding change in the fate of the other. A second important species of derivative value change exists in the content of a means-value that is *instrumental* to some larger scale end value. When one value (e.g., *"cleanliness"*) is bound up with another (*"health"* or *"social acceptance"* or *"godliness"*) in a strict means-end relation, then an upgrading or downgrading of one will call for a corresponding change in the hierarchical status of the other.

A value change is *direct*, in contrast to *derivative*, when it comes about under the direct, immediate operation of causal factors, rather than coming about as the result of other value changes. Direct value changes are best classified according to the type of causal impetus that induces them. Here there are, of course, a vast number of alternatives. By way of explanation and illustration, let us consider a few examples.

### Value change induced by a change of information

Here the root cause of the change is of a purely cognitive character of the sort typified by value changes brought about by discoveries in the sciences. Suppose, for example, that Smith values $x$ (say, *"frugality"*) and values it instrumentally, i.e., largely or wholly because he believes it to be a means to *y* (say, *"the economic prosperity of the country"*). If something (the findings of economists) persuaded him of the incorrectness of this presumed means-end relationship, Smith would almost certainly downgrade the instrumental value in a suitable way. (Something much of this sort seems to have happened in the 1960–1966 era to the "automation hysteria" that prevailed in the U.S. at the outset of the period.) Perhaps the most drastic way in which this sort of change could affect contemporary American values would be through the discovery of a supercivilization in a not too remote part of our galaxy: all of our values instrumental to human welfare and self-esteem would have to undergo an agonizing reappraisal.

### *Value change induced by ideological and political change*

Here the root cause is a matter of value indoctrination. There is a wide range of possibilities with respect to this source of value change. It can take the gradualistic form of conditioning, advertising, propaganda and "promotion." Or it may take the form of an ideological steam roller as with Islam and the Bedouin in the 8th century or the Evangelical movement in England in the last century. One of the more drastic ways in which this mode of change could come about in the America of the near future is by a collapse of the center in political life (erosion of consensus, a revolt against reason, upsurge of extremism) in response to disaffection as "rising expectations" outgrow the limits of the attainable, leading to a victory of an extremism of the right or the left.

### *Value "erosion" induced by boredom, disillusionment, and reaction*

Here the root cause is one of a wide spectrum of sociological factors that are significantly operative in American society. The status of a value can be eroded away when, in the wake of its substantial realization in a society, the value "loses its savor" and comes to be downgraded by disenchantment and disillusionment. Some examples would be: *"efficiency"* in the era of automation, *"progress"* in our age of anxiety, *"economic security"* in a welfare state, and *"national independence"* for an "emerging" nation in socio-economic chaos. Some erosion of the status of a value comes about through the mere passage of time in our evolution-minded and change-oriented society. It has been aptly noted that whereas "almost anywhere in the world outside the industrial areas, most types of change are considered undesirable" in our society change has, *per contra*, come to be regarded as almost a good in itself.[6] And this generic phenomenon of course affects values too. The very

6. E. M. Albert, "Conflict and Change in American Values," *Ethics*, vol. 74 (1963), pp. 19–33; see p. 29.

ANALYSIS

*What is value change? A framework for research*                                         75

fact that a value has been accepted for some time is a point in its disfavor. Contrast the connotation of "of the past," "old fashioned," "outmoded," "dated," and "passé" with that of "of the future," "new," "novel," "up-to-date," "recently introduced." (And note the demise in recent American usage of "new-fangled" as a pejorative term and its lapse as an epithet of derogation.)

We turn now to a consideration of that causal source of value change which has greatest relevance for our investigation, to wit:

### *Value change induced by economico-technological change and changes in demographic factors*

This is the category of value changes of basic importance for our purposes, and will form the central topic of the remaining parts of this paper. It is clear that change in this sphere has enormous repercussions for values— providing tremendous opportunities for the enhancement of some of our traditional ideals and aspirations, and great threats to the realization of others.

It is appropriate to note one significant difference from the methodological point of view between this last item and its predecessors. This is the inherently greater tractability to investigation of value changes that root in changes in the economic/technological/demographic sphere as contrasted with value changes stemming from some of the other sources we have considered. It is harder by at least an order of magnitude to predict changes in information (scientific progress) and in the ideologico-political sphere than it is to predict changes which root in factors that (like those of economic, technological, and demographic sphere) alter themselves in a relatively evolutionary rather than revolutionary way, so that their forecasting is— barring a major war—relatively reliable, calling in large measure on the extrapolation of existing trends, and thus less sensitive to the introduction of wholly new developments.

## A methodological framework for analyzing induced value changes

We must now examine in detail the basic question: How can a change in the economico-technological or the demographic sector be expected to work to induce a change in the schedule of values? Since our orientation is to the future, what we need is an essentially predictive mode of analysis. But what methodological tools are available for the study of value change? Three sorts of predictive techniques are clearly relevant:

*Extrapolation* of historical experience. This consists in the projection of current trends and tendencies.

*Analytical forecasting* models of the sort familiar from other disciplines (especially economics).

*Questionnaire techniques* designed to elicit from well-informed persons their considered judgments about future developments—particular efforts being made (by information "feedback" techniques or in other ways) to establish some sort of consensus results.

We have elsewhere applied[7] the questionnaire methodology to the study of our problem. Our present problem is: How can one best apply the extrapolation and analytical forecasting techniques (or some combination thereof) to the study of value change in a society?

One important key to this question lies in a consideration of the fact that values can come into conflict with one another, not of course in the abstract, but in the competing demands their realization and pursuit make upon man's finite resources of goods, time, effort, attention, etc. Thus when a change occurs in the operating rationale that constitute the operative framework within which a value is pursued in a given society, we may expect a series of stresses upon our scale of values militating for a rescaling in their ordering or a change of the value standard, etc. But how is one to predict the character of this value response? Here key factors lie in two considerations: *cost* and *benefit*.

### The cost of maintaining a value

As was just said, the pursuit of the realization of a value requires the investment of various resources. The extent of the requisite investment will be affected by changes in the environment: *"Cleanliness"* comes cheaper in modern cities than in medieval ones, and the achievement of *"privacy"* costs more in urban environments than in rural ones. The maintenance of a value will obviously be influenced by its cost. When this becomes *very* low, we may tend to depreciate the value as such. When it becomes high, we may either depreciate the value in question as such (the "Fox and the Grapes" reaction)—or rather more commonly—simply settle for lower standards for its attainment. (Think here of *"peace and quiet"* in this era of jet screams, sonic booms, and auto sirens.)

### The felt benefit of (or need for) maintaining a value

Any society is likely to have a group of values that occupy a commanding position on its value scale. These are the values to which it is most fundamentally committed in the various relevant modes of commitment, such as the tenacity of maintaining and preserving the value, preparedness to invest energy and resources in its realization and propagation, the attach-

7. See Ch. V below. For a further discussion of predictive methodology see Appendix 5, especially pp. 104 ff.

ANALYSIS

*What is value change? A framework for research*

77

ment of high sanctions to the value (i.e., how much compliance is expected and how much reproach heaped upon the transgressor, and the like). These most deeply held values are viewed to be relatively unchangeable and virtually "beyond dispute."

In most modern, Westernized societies—and certainly in the U.S.A.—these dominant values prominently include: (1) the *SURVIVAL* of the society, (2) the *WELFARE* of the society, (3) the *ADVANCEMENT* of the society, and (4) *REALITY-ADJUSTMENT* of the society. The first is, of course, not only a matter of the *mere* survival of the society, but as its survival as the sort of society it is; the holding of this value is thus a matter of a kind of homeostasis. We mean the welfare of the society to be concerned largely in the manner of the economists, having to do with the standard of living in the society, the set of goods and services available to its members, but also calling for a reasonable degree of attainment of its various (non-materialistic) ideals. The third value, progress, is primarily a matter of the improvement of the state of affairs obtaining under the two preceding heads. Finally, reality-adjustment is a matter of accepting things as they are, and adjusting to them or changing them, rather than seeking false security in some fantasy-realm myth or magic. If the pursuit of the realization of a value somehow becomes much more difficult or costly so that one must (*ex hypothesi*) "settle for less" one can either (1) adjust and "accept the inevitable," or (2) keep the lamp of aspiration burning bright, possibly even giving this value a greater emphasis. A culture heavily committed to "reality adjustment" would by and large tend to the first mode of resolution, except where its dominant and basic values themselves are concerned.

Now when we speak of the "benefit of" or the "need for" maintaining a certain value in our society, we mean this to be thought of in terms of its inducing to realization of the four dominant values just indicated. Thus, for example, "*pluralism*," a value which plays a prominent role in contemporary U.S. Catholic thought, answers to a "need" precisely because it conduces to the interests of the group in helping it to adjust to the constraints of its environment. Again "*scientific and intellectual skill*" and the various values bound up with this are of late coming to be upgraded on the American value scale precisely because of society's increased need for these skills in the interests of survival, welfare, and advancement under contemporary conditions. Much the same can be said for "*innovation*," as witness the really very modest degree of worker resistance to technological change in recent years.

The illustrations just given have gotten us ahead of our place; before turning to such items of concrete detail we must resume our topic of predictive method. What we are proposing to do is to examine pressures upon American values in terms of the following line of methodological approach:

1) We begin with an environmental change in the operative context of a value represented by an economico-technological or a social or demographic change that increases the cost of pursuing the realization of a certain value.

2) We examine the nature of this increased cost to see what sorts of stresses and strains it imposes upon the pursuit of the value at issue.

3) We consider the likely resolution of the stresses and strains in the light of the needs of the society, construing "need" in terms of its continuing pursuit of its basic values.

We thus begin with trend or tendency of economico-technological or social or demographic character that makes for changes in the costs of pursuing an existing scheme of values; we note the difficulties or opportunities that such a cost-change creates; and then we examine how these difficulties are likely to be resolved (or opportunities capitalized on) effectively, assuming that certain basic values provide the relatively stable centers around which the resolution of value conflicts will pivot. Given a change in the pattern of the *costs* of the value pursuit we ask—how most effectively can the society derive *benefits* therefrom—i.e., how best can "needs" of the society (construed in terms of an accommodation of its most basic values) be accommodated? Put in a nutshell, the proposed method of inquiry is an extension into the area of value studies of the cost-benefit or cost-effectiveness approach of economic analysis.

It should be stressed that even major technological changes can be such as to have very little effect upon values. For it is important to distinguish between a *value* as such on the one hand, and the means for its realization on the other. A technological change that affects the latter may leave the former substantially unaffected. (Think of the few relevant values apart from *"convenience"* affected by the switch from manual to electric typewriters.)

## The rationale of the cost-benefit approach

In saying that $x$ is one of $N$'s values ("Patriotism is one of Smith's values") we underwrite, *inter alia*, the inference to two conclusions:

1) $N$ is prepared to devote some of his resources (money, time, effort, discomfort, etc.) to the implementation of $x$—i.e., in furthering the extent of its realization in the world. And moreover,

2) He does so *in the belief*—and indeed *for the reason*—that the increased realization of $x$ will benefit ("prove advantageous for," "promote the

ANALYSIS

*What is value change? A framework for research*                79

interests of") certain individuals—either $N$ himself or others to whose interest he is attached.

A brief comment on each of these points is in order.

First consider point (1). When we say (seriously say) that $x$ is one of $N$'s values we are prepared to claim that $N$ would take his subscription to $x$ into due account in making relevant choices, with the result that the outcome of these choices, viz. $N$'s actions, significantly reflect $N$'s commitment to $x$. Thus we may view $N$'s investment of resources (money, time, etc.) in those of his actions explicable in terms of his espousal of $x$ as an indispensable part of this acceptance of $x$. Authentic adherence to a value implies *some* commitment to the pursuit of its realization, and this, in turn, calls for at least some investment of resources (advocacy and verbal support at the very minimum). The extent of this requisite investment will be dependent upon—and will be affected by changes in—the working environment: *"Peace and quiet"* costs more in an urban environment than in a rural one.

As regards point (2), it is of the essence of $x$'s serving in the role of *a value* for $N$ that he views the realization of $x$ as beneficial (for someone, not necessarily himself). Moreover, this benefit will have to be of such a kind as to be a benefit ("a thing of positive value") from $N$'s own point of view. Some benefits will be more fundamental than others, subsidiary benefits, and the most basic and fundamental benefits will be associated with dominant values (including survival, security, health and pleasure in the case of individuals, and survival, security, welfare, and progress in that of modern Western societies).[8]

This dual aspect of costs and benefits provides the key to the single most important type of stresses and strains that work upon values. For it renders them susceptible to an evaluation procedure of the cost-benefit type familiar from economic analysis. In the case of any value we can make a kind of balance sheet of (1) the balance of benefits—i.e., advantages over disadvantages—inherent in its realization, as contrasted with (2) the various sorts of costs that would be entailed by the endeavor to bring this realization about. The following possibilities obviously arise in the context of a cost-benefit analysis of this sort: In the circumstances of a given operating environment:

A) $N$ may "oversubscribe" to $x$, the value at issue, either because (Ai) he has an exaggerated conception of the benefits involved, and

8. Of course there are many different types of benefits, just as there are many different kinds of investments of resources or *costs* (e.g., money, time, effort, discomfort). And different people can assess these benefits differently—just as they can assess different costs differently. None of these sorts of complexities need concern us for the moment.

accordingly "invests" too much in the value, or (Aii) he has a correct conception of the benefits involved, but nevertheless makes a larger than proportionate investment towards securing these benefits (i.e., "overpays" for them).

B) $N$ may "undersubscribe" to $x$, the value at issue, either because (Bi) he has an unduly deflated conception of the benefits involved, and accordingly "invests" too little in the value, or (Bii) he has a correct conception of the benefits involved, but nevertheless makes a less than proportionate investment towards securing these benefits.

A survey of possibilities of this sort indicates the sort of pressures upon values that can build up from the direction of a cost-benefit point of view.

When we consider the constellation of value commitments of a person or a society, the soundness or "realism" of a value can be assessed—not abstractly, but—*in context*. We can test the value economy at issue against the background of the concept of a spectrum of well-ordered modes of life, each one of which is characterized by an appropriate and viable balance of value commitments. In extreme instances, the entire value economy that is built into the framework of a life-history ideal can become obsolete by becoming infeasible under changed circumstances (e.g. the knight-errant, the master-craftsman).

This brings out the contextual nature of this mode of value criticism— its dependence on the setting of a complex of value commitments held under certain specific conditions and circumstances. It is clear that value criticism of this sort would never result in the verdict that a certain value (i.e., genuine value) is inappropriate as such. But it could maintain that a person, leading his life in a certain particular setting, oversubscribes or under- subscribes to a given value, given the nature of this setting. Such criticism, then, does not address itself to values directly and abstractly, but rather to the holding—and consequent concrete action upon—certain values under specifiable conditions. In the face of grounds for criticism of this sort, the value at issue becomes subject to a pressure for change.

It is important to notice that social and technological change in a life environment can thus centrally affect the stability of values from this cost- benefit point of view. For on the one hand, such change can alter the costs involved in realizing a value (either downwards, as with air-travel *"safety"* in recent years, or upwards, as with urban *"privacy"*). And on the other hand, such changes in the life environment can also alter the benefits derivable from realizing a value (as, e.g., the benefits to be derived from wealth decline in an affluent society).

This perspective highlights the idea of the *relevance* of values to the

ANALYSIS

*What is value change? A framework for research* 81

specific life environment that provides the operative setting within which a value is espoused. For with a change in this setting, a certain value may be greatly more or less *deserving* of emphasis, depending on the changes in the nature and extent of the corresponding benefits in the altered circumstances. Or again, the value may be greatly more or less demanding of emphasis depending on changes in the cost of its realization in a given degree. In extreme cases, a value can become *irrelevant* when the life setting has become such that the historically associated benefits are no longer available (e.g., knight-errantry, chivalry, and—perhaps—*noblesse oblige*), or it can even become malign when action on it comes to produce more harm than good (as with certain forms of *"charity"*).

## Some illustrations of our cost-benefit method in the American context

We come now to the *raison d'être* of the conceptual and methodological considerations that have gone before it: The utility for these abstract considerations lies with the systematic guidance they can afford in regard to the concrete actualities. In the remainder of this paper we shall try to exhibit their applicability to a series of illustrative cases. The reader is urged not to lose sight of the forest for the trees and to bear in mind that these cases are not adduced for their novelty or intrinsic interest: They are compiled from a strictly functional perspective as illustrations of the workings of the conceptual and methodological approach outlined above.

The examples given are closely related to a questionnaire on value change in the United States over the next generation (i.e., to around 2000 A.D.) which has been reported on elsewhere.[9] To a large extent the discussion of these examples is guided by the questionnaire, and is an attempt to systematize and to provide—within the framework of our cost-benefit approach—a coherent rationale for its results. Moreover we seek to picture these value change trends anticipated by the respondents to the questionnaire against the backdrop of those socio-economic and technological developments that exert a productive influence in their realization.

Let us turn, then, to a consideration of some specific American values and how they are likely to be affected by predictable patterns of economico-technological change as it will foreseeably develop over the next generation.

CASE 1: *Nationalism and the national image*
The point of departure is fixed by three considerations: (1) the advance

9. See Ch. V below.

of complex technology—especially military technology—in many lands, (2) the role of nuclear weapons as a "great equalizer" among nations, and (3) the enormously sharp rise in marginal costs for keeping significantly ahead of "the field" in military technology. The upshot is an enormous costliness in maintaining a wide gap in military power between our nation and others. This is bound to affect our national self-image and the character of our nationalism—and that of other lands also, of course. The pattern of the future for the United States and other current super powers may well lie in the direction of a scaling down of international *"grandeur"* through readjustment to the Sweden-Switzerland style of happy self-sufficiency emphasizing domestic welfare. The locus of national pride thus may tend to shift from the economic-military sector to that of science, learning, and the arts, with the Muses as successors to Mars. The days of the Era of Manifest Destiny, transformed by Teddy Roosevelt from the continental to the international sphere, are clearly numbered. A concomitant of this decline of nation-oriented values is a corresponding upgrading of cultural and mankind-oriented values (internationalism, humanitarianism).

CASE 2: *Materialism*

There is little question that the tremendous productivity of America's industry will continue and accelerate. Our economy will keep grinding along at a fast and furious pace and its even more efficiently produced products must be used up. The corresponding vision of the good life based on the concept of mass and massive consumption—steadily blazoned forth in radio and TV and printed advertising—will no doubt entrench and extend itself to a heretofore undreamt of extent. Gadgetry will move on to heights of which the self-vibrating toothbrush is but a pale foreshadowing.

One further aspect of this phenomenon is worth noting in detail: In the course of time the "made in USA" character of this materialistic ethos will fade away: it will become part of the general culture of technically developed societies throughout the world. Thus despite the strengthening of material values in the America of days ahead, our society will be less "different" in this respect than is and has been the case. (This also bears on Case 1 above.) Moreover, it is not unlikely that under the influence of "realization erosion" a disillusionment with material values in general—and *"economic security"* in particular—will come about in the long run. The doubling of per-capita (real) income since 1920 has already had a significant effect along these lines. Greater security of job-tenure and pay soon comes to be taken for granted to an extent that leads to sharp de-emphasis on the values at issue.

ANALYSIS

*What is value change? A framework for research*                                    83

CASE 3: *Independence*

With the growth in size both of our population and of the productive units of our economy we penetrate deeper and deeper into an age of masses: Born in a mass hospital and educated in a mass school we work for a mass employer while living in a mass urban complex and so continue our lives supplied by mass shopping units, informed by mass media of information and opinion, and entertained by mass entertainment, until we achieve burial in a mass graveyard. Movement outside the herd-tracks of some mass phenomenon comes to be difficult and expensive; our activities become geared to mass needs in just the way that it is easier to maintain a 1965 Ford than the rather simpler machine of 1935. (There is almost always a "systematic inexpense" in running with the mass.) This tendency to increased massiveness obviously has major implications for the traditional American value of independence. (Ever since the Declaration of Independence, *"independence"* has always been one of the key concepts of American life.) These implications are so ramified that they must be considered under several heads:

ECONOMIC INDEPENDENCE It requires no elaborate explanation to show that the economic independence of the small unit operating with a minimum of environmental constraints is pretty much a "thing of the past," rendered economically unviable by the mechanisms of massive innovation (and large-scale research), mass production, and mass marketing. In a complex urbanized society fewer and fewer people are capable of functioning independently of "the economy" intertwining their actions with those of others. This is a trite point and does not need to be elaborated.

PERSONAL INDEPENDENCE The welfare state has unfairly been the whipping-boy here—the real problem is that of the *mass* state under modern conditions (military service for many, college education for most, mass communication, pervasive organization for a high standard of living, central data collection for taxation and other purposes, etc.). The threats to authentic individualism—under the conditions of central planning that arise here— have been discussed to a point where they need not be dwelt on here. As it becomes harder and harder for an individual to go his own way in the things that count, the traditional value of personal independence is increasingly threatened. It may well yield ground to group conformism as a positive value in some guise that will make a pale thing of the *"social adjustment"* of Deweyite memory. The decline of individual values will doubtless be accompanied by a corresponding rise in group values—though the group may well be not the society as a whole but some preferred sub-group of it. (In this regard, as in others, we may consider the Southern California of today as setting the pattern for the America of the future.)

NATIONAL INDEPENDENCE The increasingly close interlinkage of nations by modern methods of transport and communication and the inter-relationships of national economies in such a way as to link the welfare of each state with that of others have already created pressures upon this traditional value. But perhaps the key factor is the clash between national sovereignty and public safety in the era of conveniently deliverable multi-megaton weapons. The obstacles that lie in the way of national independence in the sense of a go-it-alone noninterdependence will be such that one can confidently look for a depreciation of this value.

CASE 4: *Social accountability*

The crowding of the avenues of action in modern life increasingly puts the individual into a position not so much of interacting with other individuals as individual agents but of reacting to them as a mass comprising a complex "system." Many of the things that go wrong are best looked at—at any rate from the standpoint of their victims—as *system malfunctions*. It seems probable in this context that we will less and less treat such failures as matters of individual accountability. If $X$ cheats, burgles, or inflicts motor vehicle damage upon $Y$, the view will increasingly prevail that $Y$ should not have to look to $X$ for recovery from loss but to a depersonalized source— viz. some agency of the society. We will not improbably move increasingly towards the concept of a "Veteran's Administration" for the victims of the ordinary hazards of life in our society. Individual responsibility and personal accountability has suffered some depreciation in American life over the past two decades, but it seems likely that in the years ahead social accountability will become an increasingly prominent value.

CASE 5: *Creative and intellectual achievement*

As the complexity of the structure and the machinery of our economy and the society in general increases, there comes about an increased need for persons with certain particular traits and qualities—for example, especially those concerned with skills in the sciences and engineering, and economic and managerial matters. The result is that a higher premium will be put upon the values traditionally bound up with these particular traits and qualities. Intelligence and inventiveness for example, are values that will probably be in the ascendant for many years ahead. (Already today, Academe has made peace with the business community and *Babbitt* is no longer the answer to an English instructor's prayer.) Consequently the value

*What is value change? A framework for research*          85

**ANALYSIS**

of good education is also securely placed, although there may be certain strains and stresses here caused by (a) direct pressures upon the school population itself (with 10,000,000 Americans in college by the year 2000), and (b) a certain value erosion about education itself as its slips increasingly in status from a surplus asset to a minimal requirement.

Think also of the remarkable extent to which forecasting and planning have become respectable in many sectors of the American institutional scene in the last decade, a fact itself in large measure due to technical progress.[10] Many believe that the values of *"hard work"* and *"pride of workmanship"* are in the descendant in an era of automation, but this conclusion strikes me as dubious. (The society may choose to go not the way of idleness but that of selective production of highly labor-intensive goods and services.) Moreover, there seems little doubt that in the better-taught and more leisure-oriented America of the year 2000, artistic creativity and the arts (creative and performing) generally will occupy a far more important and influential place than they do today.

CASE 6: *Organization and institutionalization*

Although America has in the past been able to achieve prodigies of progress on the basis of a large measure of individual effort and individual initiative, the value of organization in common effort for the public good has been recognized since the days of Benjamin Franklin as the natural channel of individual effort. The value of common action through association and institutionalization has always been accepted—despite a strong strain of independence of the "No thanks, I'll go my own way" type. But in days ahead with an increasing dependence on and need for (and thus augmented —though at first no doubt ambivalent—respect for) institutions we may reasonably expect an increased respect for institutions and an upgrading of institutional values and the social ethic generally. The economists' classic example of a "free good," namely fresh air, is already sufficiently scarce as to fall into the public domain of regulation (smoke-control, etc.)—control in cases of this sort being a pretty much inevitable step in the public interest. The decline of independence remarked on above may be looked upon to undermine the traditional individualistic (and even anarchaic) strain in American life with its concomitant duality towards laws, rules, and law abidingness. Our increasing reliance on institutions will upgrade and strengthen institutional values. The present-day "revolt" of the American Negro, for example, is not so much a rebellion against American institutions

10. Thus, to take one example among many, Richard Goodwin remarks that "the creations of our genius—science and inventive skill—are poisoning our rivers and our air, devastating the nature which once fed the spirit"—and then immediately finds the remedy in adequate and comprehensive planning.

as a protest on the part of those who look on themselves as outsiders excluded from them. Note that the current remedies to the exclusion problem (e.g., the "War on Poverty" and the Job Corps) are of a strictly institutional character. So are various of the means to solve the problem of youth anomie by creating institutional means for helping the young to find "meaning in life" by socially useful service (e.g., the Peace Corps). (Such ventures represent an institutionalization of idealism—they represent a scaling down in individual ambition, a shift from playing a part on the big stage oneself to being a small cog in a big venture.) Some values have, of course, long been institutionalized as regards the standard *modus operandi* of the pursuit of their realization (*"law and order"*—the police; *"justice"*—the courts), and this phenomenon is becoming sharply intensified.

CASE 7: *Public service*

Over the past generation there has been a marked tendency in American life—one whose continuation and intensification can confidently be looked for—to shift from the Protestant Ethic of "getting ahead in the world" to the Social Ethic of "service to one's fellows"—from the gospel of profit and devotion to Mammon to the gospel of service and devotion to Man. Many forces have produced this phenomenon—ranging from spiritual causes such as a decline of traditional religious orientation on the one hand, to material causes such as the rise of the welfare state on the other ("God helps those who help themselves" perhaps—but the state is not so exclusive about it, and so it is less urgent in our affluent society to "look out for oneself"). There has thus been in many sectors of our national life—including the industrial—a distinct elevation of the historic American value of public service. And by "public service" here one must not think of just the traditional political arena, but *service* of a very different kind. Think, for example, of the Peace Corps and the phenomenon of a very rich man's son helping supply water to a very poor man's house. The "social engineering" of which the poverty program is only a first and modest forerunner, will become an increasingly prominent phenomenon of the future. And our society's housekeeping problems are already very extensive (one in seven workers works for the government—federal, state, or local).

CASE 8: *Self-advancement*

The prospect of self-advancement has been an important American value in the past. America has traditionally been thought of—perhaps not rightly but nevertheless actually—as the "land of opportunity," the land of unlimited horizons where the "American dream" of self-improvement and self-advancement opens up prospects of vast success for those who have

ANALYSIS

*What is value change? A framework for research*  87

the requisite pluck and luck. With the virtually inevitable increase in the socio-economic rigidity of American life as the automation-revolution comes to a head and the present triads to economic and socio-political egalitarianism continue to unfold themselves, we shall reach the end of an era in this regard. As the Horatio Alger vision becomes harder and harder of realization, it will become a reality for increasingly few and will stop being a vision for the mass. Social adjustment and the acceptance of a value-pattern based on socio-economic realities may well prevail over the older vision of a heroic drive towards outstanding achievement. The group-adjustment point of view may well be expected to predominate over the historic American value of self-advancement to a place of outstanding prominence.

CASE 9: *Individualism*

The pressure of demographic forces on American society has received much discussion. Not only is there increasing crowding in the land generally and its population centers in particular, but there is the especially unstable side effect of "category crowding": we have to deal not just with more people, but with more "senior citizens," more teenagers, more college students, more scientists, etc., etc. We move in environments saturated with people. The sheer volume of people filling our institutions, cities, arteries of transportation, stores, public parks, etc. has a seriously erosive effect on a whole list of American values ranging from *"privacy"* to the cherished right to be treated as a person rather than being "processed" as part of a herd. (Think of the Berkeley affair and the battlecry, "Do not fold, staple, or mutilate!") Note here also the tendency to physical grouping—largely for reasons of economic convenience—that results in segregation by age (all the "young marrieds" in one neighborhood and the "senior citizens" in another). Perhaps the main impact of these trends is upon the traditional value of individualism. Note here the desperate effort to preserve the façade of "counting" in a mass society. (Think of the "one-man one-vote" doctrine: It would not be surprising if even the US Senate as such should come under fire by liberals within the foreseeable future.)

CASE 10: *The domestic virtues*

Various tendencies ranging from the contraceptives to the welfare state's case of the helpless in an affluent society can reasonably be expected to make deeper inroads upon family values and the domestic virtues (family loyalty, prudence, thrift, etc.). (In the urban Negro ghetto the family is well on the way to extinction.) It is even possible that in a few decades the multi-generation continuing and tightly cohesive family unit (parents living with grown children, annual family reunions, family traditions handed down from generation to generation, etc.) may become— outside the Catholic orbit—a status symbol of the especially affluent, much as with the multiplicity of wives in the Islam of today.

CASE 11: *Comforts and amenities*

In the US today some 70 percent of the work force is employed in the service industries. We are clearly in the midst of an "amenities revolution" with the bulk of work-effort no longer devoted to the production of things needed to make life livable, but diverted to the production of amenities to make life pleasant. As such, "amenity resources" become more and more extensively developed. There is little doubt that an erosion will take place among the relevant values with lessened emphasis upon various aspects of "welfare," especially in its remedial aspects. (This, of course, also creates a situation in which events consequent upon the realization of one value may lead to an added emphasis upon others—so that the realization of economic security may create "insecurities" in other sectors.)

## Conclusion

We have tried here to achieve three objectives: (1) to analyze the nature of value change and to elucidate some of the ways in which value change can come about in a society, (2) to present a methodological frame-work for the predictive analysis value changes, and (3) to provide some illustrations of the application of the method to value changes under the impact of social and technological forces that will unfold foreseeably over the next generation. An important qualification must be stressed. We have treated the value changes of item (3) as isolated examples without attempting to interrelate them into a composite and synoptic picture of "the new value pattern" for the America of the year 2000. This task of synthesis remains undone, although some steps are taken towards its consideration in Appendix 4 on "Some Possibilities for Future Value Change in America."

By way of conclusion it will perhaps not be deemed inappropriate for us to list here in a summary way some important historic American values that will in all likelihood be subjected to severe stresses and strains in the remaining years of this century, stresses and strains that will in some cases eventuate in a probable upgrading and in others downgrading:

ANALYSIS

*What is value change? A framework for research*                    89

| Upgrading | Downgrading |
|---|---|
| mankind-oriented values (humanitarianism, internationalism) | nation-oriented values (patriotism, chauvinism) |
| the intellectual virtues | the domestic virtues |
| reasonableness and rationality | responsibility and accountability |
| the civic virtues | independence (in all its senses) |
| group acceptance | self-reliance and self-sufficiency |
| social welfare | individualism |
| social accountability | self-advancement |
| order | economic security |
| public service | property rights (and personal liberty generally) |
| aesthetic values | progressivism (faith in progress) |
| | optimism (confidence in man's ability to solve man's problems) |

NOTE: "Upgrading" and "Downgrading" here are used in the generic *technical* sense explained above. (They do not refer specifically to what is there called *value rescaling*.)

It should be noted that we have been dealing with phenomena in the mainstream of American values. The possibility of radical divergencies from and reactions to some of these developments on the part of radical and disaffected minorities (political minorities, beatniks and teenagers, intellectuals, etc.) is not only not to be ruled out, but can actually be expected to come about.

The writer is indebted to his associates in the Pittsburg Values Project for helpful discussion of some of the ideas presented in this paper.

# Glossary on value change

(NOTE: Nine various modes of value change have been indicated by an asterisk*)

*value subscriber:* A person who subscribes to (has, holds, accepts, adheres to) a certain value.

*value acquisition* *: A person's commencing to give adherence to a value to which he did not previously subscribe.

*value abandonment* *: A person's ceasing to give adherence to a value to which he previously subscribed.

*value distribution* (in a given group): determined by the pattern of subscription to this value by members of the group. (Usual dimension: more vs. less diffused.)

*value redistribution* * (in a given group): Change in the pattern of distribution of the value within the group.

*value emphasis* (or de-emphasis): Determined by the extent to which the course of events renders a value topical ("in the spotlight" for attention and the investment of resources) or the reverse.

*value scale* (of a person): Comparative (and generally hierarchical) ordering of the values subscribed to with respect to higher or lower.

*value rescaling* *: Reordering of the values comprising a value scale.

*domain of application* (of a value): A set of cases taken to lie within the purview of the value in that subscription to the value calls for a certain position in regard to these cases.

*value redeployment* *: A change in the boundaries of the domain of application of the value (e.g., of politico-legal *"equality"* to include the Negro).

*value standard:* Guidelines for measuring the extent to which a value is attained (realized) in particular cases within its domain of application. (Minimal adequacy standards are of special significance.)

*value restandardization* *: Change in a value standard; frequently characterizable as a "raising" or "lowering" of the standard. (Escalation or relaxation of minima.)

*value implementation target:* A specific set of desired circumstances set up as

ANALYSIS

*What is value change? A framework for research*                                                91

a concrete, definite goal for progress in the realization of the value  at
issue (e.g., value—*"civic improvement"*; target—clearance of a
certain slum area).

*value implementation retargeting\**: A change in the target that has been set
for implementing the value at issue. (Note: one might not change targets
but merely the *resetting of a target date.\**) Sequence of successive
targets: *priorities and revision of priorities.\**

# *A tentative register of American values*

NOTE: We deal here with overtly espoused and publicly appealed to values to the exclusion of (1) unconscious motives (e.g., conformism, culture insecurity vis à vis Europeans) and (2) traits of national character (e.g., love of novelty). The factors included in the register are such that explicit or overt appeal to them can well be expected from publicly recognized spokesmen for values: newspaper editorialists, graduation exercise speakers, religio-moral sermonizers, and political orators. Such values can be extracted by "content analysis" of the pronunciamentos of such sources. The values now at issue are those generally acknowledged and widely diffused throughout the society and not those specific to some group (physicians, Catholics, Chinese-Americans, Westerners). Moreover they are all socially general values in that those who espouse them do so so as to value them not only personally (for themselves) and societally (for people in general). In short we are concerned to list *genuine values* adherence and dedication to which is at this writing widely diffused throughout virtually all sectors of American society. The scheme of classification turns on the issue of the setting at issue in the maintenance of the value (oneself, one's group, the society, the nation, all of mankind, the environment).

## I. *Self-oriented values*
1. personal "material" welfare (the right to life and the pursuit of happiness)
   a. health (physical and mental well-being)
   b. economic security and well-being ("materialism" and the American way of life)
   c. personal security (stability of the conditions of life)
2. self-respect (the right to be treated *as a person* and *as a member in good standing of the community*; honor, honorableness)

ANALYSIS

*What is value change? A framework for research*                    93

3. self-reliance (self-sufficiency; rugged individualism and the pioneer tradition)
4. personal liberty (the right to endeavor to "shape one's own life," to work out major facets of one's own destiny and to go one's own way)
    *a.* freedom (from interference)
    *b.* privacy
    *c.* property rights
5. self-advancement ("success," ambition, diligence)
6. self-fulfillment (and "the pursuit of happiness")
7. skill and prowess
    *a.* the intellectual virtues (intelligence, education, know-how, realism, practicality, versatility, etc.)
    *b.* the physical virtues (strength, dexterity, endurance, good appearance, cleanliness, etc.)
    *c.* the virtues of the will (strengths of character)
        1. readiness for hard work (industriousness)
        2. toughness (fortitude, endurance, bravery, courage)
        3. initiative and activism (the "go getter" approach)
        4. self-control (temperateness, sobriety)
        5. perseverance and stedfastness
    *d.* competence (pride of workmanship)
    *e.* inventiveness and innovativeness
    *f.* initiative (the "self-starter")
    *g.* well-informedness (access to information, being "in the know")
    *h.* faith ("believing in something" including "having a sense of values")
    *i.* appreciation and appreciativeness (of "the good things of life")

II. *Group-oriented values*
1. respectability (group acceptance, avoidance of reproach, good repute, conformity, the "done thing" and the "herd instinct")
2. rectitude and personal morality (honesty, fairness, probity, reliability, truthfulness, trustworthiness—the "man of honor")
3. reasonableness and rationality (objectivity)
4. the domestic virtues (love, pride in family role, providence, simplicity, thrift, prudence, etc.)
5. the civic virtues (involvement, good citizenship, law-abidance, civic pride—the "greatest little town" syndrome)
6. conscientiousness
    *a.* devotion to family, duty
    *b.* personal responsibility and accountability

    *c.* devotion to principle (especially of one's religion—"the godfearing man")

7. friendship and friendliness
     *a.* friendship proper
     *b.* loyalty (to friends, associates)
     *c.* friendliness, kindliness, helpfulness, cooperativeness, and courteousness (the good scout; "getting along with people")
     *d.* fellow-feeling (compassion, sympathy, and "love of one's fellows")
     *e.* gregariousness
     *f.* receptivity (openness, patience, "the good listener")
     *g.* personal tolerance ("live and let live," "getting along with people")
     *h.* patience
8. service (devotion to the well-being of others)
9. generosity (charity, openhandedness)
10. idealism (hopefulness in human solutions to human problems)
11. recognition (getting due public credit for the good points scored in the game of life; success and status)
12. forthrightness (frankness, openness, sincerity, genuineness; keeping things "above board," the fair deal)
13. fair play (the "good sport")

## III. *Society-oriented values*

1. social welfare (indeed "social consciousness" as such)
2. equality
     *a.* tolerance
     *b.* "fair play," fairness
     *c.* civil rights
3. justice (including legality, proper procedure, recourse)
4. liberty (the "open society"; the various "freedoms")
5. order (public order, "law and order")
6. opportunity ("land of opportunity" concept; the square deal for all)
7. charity (help for the "underdog")
8. progressivism optimism (faith in the society's ability to solve its problems)
9. pride in "our culture" and "our way of life"

## IV. *Nation-oriented values*

1. the patriotic virtues (love of country, devotion to country, national pride)
     *a.* national freedom and independence
     *b.* national prosperity and national achievement generally
     *c.* patriotism and national pride

ANALYSIS

*What is value change? A framework for research* 95

*d.* concern for the national welfare

*e.* loyalty (to country)

*f.* chauvinism (nationalism, pride in national power and preeminence)

2. democracy and "the American way"

3. "public service" in the sense of service of country (the nation)

### V. *Mankind-oriented values*

1. the "welfare of mankind"

    *a.* peace

    *b.* material achievement and progress

    *c.* cultural and intellectual achievement and progress

2. humanitarianism and the "brotherhood of man"

3. internationalism

4. pride in the achievements of "the human community"

5. reverence for life

6. human dignity and the "worth of the individual"

### VI. *Environment-oriented values*

1. aesthetic values (environmental beauty)

2. novelty

# Possible developments to 2000 A.D. with major implications for American values

A. Military
   1. major (i.e., all-out, central) war
   2. chronic and large-scale limited warfare
   3. a Russo-Chinese war
B. International Politico-Economic
   1. major nuclear proliferation
   2. massive growth in international economic disparities
   3. massive diminution in international economic disparities
   4. revival of nonbilateral balance-of-power politics
C. Domestic Political
   1. demise of the two-party system
   2. collapse of the center (death of the consensus government in the U.S.)
   3. civil war and the police state
   4. utter stabilization in socio/economic/political life (with a mild form of police-statism)
   5. triumph of isolationism
   6. triumph of internationalism
D. Socio-Psychological
   1. widespread disillusionment, malcontentism, alienation
   2. decline of traditional social values (normlessness, anomie, desperate value seeking)
   3. demise of the family as a continuing unit across lifespans
   4. widespread insecurity (instability of conditions of life)
   5. growth of aesthetic consciousness
E. Demographic
   1. massive urban sprawl and urban crowding
   2. massive category-crowding
      *a.* the teenagers
      *b.* the oldsters

ANALYSIS

*What is value change? A framework for research*                                        97

F.  Economic[11]
1.  automation and the solution of the (domestic) problem of production
2.  creeping egalitarianism and the solution of the (domestic) problem of distribution

G.  Educational
1.  continuing crisis over educational objectives
2.  large-scale use of teaching machines and computerized (depersonalized) education
3.  large-scale production of educated misfits (disparity between personal qualifications and social needs; e.g., women right now!)
4.  education as a way of life—in 1976 28 percent of our population will be in school: will it be 50 percent by 2000?

H.  Technological
1.  major innovations
    *a.* weather control
    *b.* education by direct brain-inputs
    *c.* wholly new sources of food and power (e.g., ocean farming, controlled thermonuclear power)
    *d.* selective death-deference
    *e.* genetic control of progeny
2.  large-scale spread of existing techniques
    *a.* computerization of practically everything
    *b.* equalization of medical facilities
    *c.* world-wide TV
    *d.* rationalization of transport technology
3.  the back-fire problem (backlash from large-scale interference with "nature")

I.  Medical
1.  supersimple contraception
2.  thought-control drugs (and advanced "brain washing")
3.  genetic control of offspring ("genetic engineering")
4.  bio-prosthesis, transplant, life prolongation and selective death-deference (to age 200?)
5.  rejuvenation
6.  computerized public health and preventive medicine

J.  Religious
1.  ecumenism run rampant

11. The "new economics" will not be concerned so much with the traditional economic issue of material welfare—let alone the classic problems of productive scarcity—as with matters of "social engineering" towards "the good life."

    2. religiosity by pill ("consciousness expansion")

    3. major popular revival of *theological* (contrast here with "social") religion

K. Space

    1. multi-generation space travel

    2. planetary colonization

    3. discovery of a super-civilization in space

# Some possibilities for future value change in America

NOTE 1: Possible value changes are listed under the causal factor (social, economic, technological) primarily operative in tending towards its production.

NOTE 2: This is not a list of value changes that inevitably *will* happen but of one that plausibly *may* happen.

NOTE 3: Here, of course, one can only list the more or less "foreseeable" consequences of the various "causal factors." And it must be recognized that developments often have very unexpected, and pretty well *unexpectable* effects upon the values of a society. (Think of the enormously wide range of variation of the effects on American values of the automobile.)

NOTE 4: Here we are concerned to look at the possible effects of various (primarily technological) developments upon values. To take this standpoint is not to deny the (obviously true) thesis that the process of causal influence is also reciprocal; i.e., values in guiding our choices importantly condition the ways in which technological innovations are introduced and utilized.

A.  The (Domestic) Population Explosion and Urban Crowding
    1. devaluation of privacy
    2. strengthening of small-group values (fraternal organizations, participation sports) to provide foci of "identity"
    3. upgrading of physical security, stability, public order
    4. upgrading of tolerance
    5. upgrading of beauty (natural and artistic), heightening of aesthetic values

B.  Improvement in Means of Transport and Communication
    1. upgrading of mankind-oriented values (and to some extent a corresponding devaluation of nation-oriented ones)
    2. growth of cosmopolitanism and strengthening of internationalism

C. Politico-Economic Equalization and the Increase in the Realization of Social Equalitarianism
   1. downgrading of equalitarian values (economic, political, etc.) due to disillusionment (with the benefits of social integration, etc.) since their increasing realization will bring home the fact that they just are not high roads to the millenium
   2. erosion of idealism, in part due to the preceding and in part due to the demise of the "myth of unlimited opportunity"
D. The Advance of Automation
   1. downgrading of progress and of material values generally (partly because the things at issue will come to be taken for granted, partly because their increasing realization will markedly fail to bring on the millenium)
   2. upgrading of handicrafts, workmanship, and skilled and unskilled services generally (revaluation of labor-intensive means of production; potential explosion of the "problem of leisure" myth and the "spectre of mass technological unemployment")
E. The Expansion of the Welfare State
   1. devaluation of economic security as such (by realization erosion)
   2. erosion of initiative (the "man in the grey-flannel suit"; rise of testing and counseling)
   3. flight from responsibility ("let George do it"; Miss Genovese and the 27 witnesses)
   4. growing ambivalence to authority (increasing dependence thereon and resentment thereof)
   5. rising expectations (possible unrealism with inherent danger of revolution)
   6. ambivalence to physical comfort (growing dependence but dislike to admit it)
   7. reappraisal of public service (higher valuation growing further down the line: police, postal service)
F. Onset of the "Big Brother" State (UDB—the "universal data bank"; social engineering; centralized power and control)
   1. probable upgrading of democratic values (in face of obvious threats thereto, demanding greater investment)
   2. ambivalence to authority
   3. threat to personal status (dehumanization) as our fate is increasingly in the hands of—not people, but—machines
G. The Proliferation and Sophistication of Modern Weapons of Mass Destruction
   1. downgrading of the characteristic species of national pride

*What is value change? A framework for research*

ANALYSIS

101

    2. upgrading of mankind-oriented values
H.  The Advance of Medical Techniques
    1. weakening of family values (contraceptives)
    2. weakening of value defenses against the unpleasant contingencies of human life (diseases rarer; deaths later)
I.  The Advance of Education
    1. disillusionment with education of such (it will no longer be looked on as the panacea to social ills)
    2. intensification of value stresses due to gap between educational fitness and "life"

# The future as an object of research

## Introduction

The theme of this discussion is the foreseeing or forecasting of changes in human affairs. Our interest is in *the future*, or at any rate the sort of picture of the future that we can draw for ourselves today. We shall not attempt to consider the future in its awesome totality, but shall limit the perspective to two sectors of particular interest alike to makers of public policy and to reflective citizens in the modern world: science and technology on the one hand, and our human and social environment upon the other.

Such a theme poses not simply a project, but a problem. It does so because it is far from clear to what extent and *by what methods* we can today draw a picture of tomorrow's world in these areas. And even if we can do so reasonably well for literally *tomorrow's* world—the prospect becomes increasingly clouded as we proceed beyond the morrow towards the era a generation hence, the world of the year 2000 at the dawn of the 21st century.

## The future is now in fashion

Since the early 1960's, the future has blossomed forth into a topic of increasingly widespread concern and interest. This may not seem surprising —as somebody has remarked, it is only natural that one should be interested in the future, since we're all going to spend the rest of our lives there. But it has not always been so—even quite recently a scientist who concerned himself with futuristic questions may well have found himself regarded by his colleagues as something of a renegade: a cross between a Nostradamus-like seer and a science-fiction writer. In recent years, however, the future has come into its own.

The most visible showing has been made by men of affairs who rub shoulders with academics. The pattern has been set by such books as Bertrand de Jouvenel's *Art of Conjecture* (original French edition, Monaco, 1964; English translation, New York, 1966), Dennis Gabor's *Inventing the Future* (London, 1964), Theodore J. Gordon's *The Future* (New York, 1965), and

ANALYSIS

*What is value change? A framework for research* 103

also articles by Daniel Bell in his and Irving Kristol's journal *The Public Interest*. These American publications have been matched by a spate of books and articles in French and German—with such themes as Fritz Baade's *Der Wettlauf zum Jahre 2,000* (Oldenburg, 1960)—which we shall not trouble to detail here.[12]

Behind this essentially publicistic effort lay the less widely bruited work of what might be called *The Advice Establishment*: clusters of hard and soft scientists working on advisory boards, study groups, and information-gathering commissions: the idea-producers for the policy-makers of our society. I think here of the Commission for the Year 2000 (a study-group chaired by Daniel Bell working for the American Academy of Arts and Sciences), the studies conducted by Resources for the Future in Washington, D.C. and the work of the National Planning Association, the studies completed last year by the Automation Commission (the National Commission on Automation, Manpower, and Technological Progress), the study currently in progress in the Civic Affairs Department of the National Industrial Conference Board, and the work of the Futuribles group in France, among others. All of these groups alike have the same fundamental objective: to provide guidance about the future as background for policy formulation.

A number of serious journalists have been sufficiently impressed by this spate of future-oriented studies to take up the cause. One may mention here the excellent article on "The Future as a Way of Life" by Alvin Toffler in the summer, 1965, issue of *Horizon* magazine, as well as a feature article in *TIME*, which coined the term "the futurists" for those who have been prominent in establishing and promoting this area of research. There is Walter Cronkite's recently-launched television series on "The Twenty-First Century." The January, 1967, issue of *Fortune* magazine contains an article on the future by Max Ways in which he speaks of "the new style" in forecasting and planning. Indulging in the futures game himself, he ventures the prediction: "By 1977, this new way of dealing with the future will be recognized at home and abroad as a salient American characteristic."

A project is undergoing serious exploration of founding in the U.S.A. an Institute for the Future—an organizational center for future-oriented studies somewhat along the lines of such non-profit research institutions as the Institute for Research in the Behavioral Sciences at Stanford or The RAND Corporation. Such an organization already exists on a very modest scale in Europe in the Institut für Zukunftsfragen in Vienna. A "World Future Society" was launched in Washington, D.C., in 1966 with a newsletter called *The Futurist* first issued in February, 1967.

12. For further details as to publications in the area see the Bibliography at the end of the book.

This whole constellation of activities, in the aggregate massive in scope and diversified in approach—comprises what might be called *The Futures Industry*. The activities of this industry go on at an increasingly intensive pace in dozens of institutions in the U.S.A., and in many corners of the world.[13]

The key to this new attitude towards the future lies in the idea of planning. For "planning" is nowadays no longer an idea with pejorative connotations, somehow reminiscent of communism, but a concept whose key importance is recognized in virtually every department of modern affairs: in government, in education, in research, in industry, in labor affairs. The value of planning has been brought home to everyone by the problems posed for our society by the strains of the phenomena of economic fluctuations, of automation, of educational inequities, of urban congestion, of the pollution of air and water—all of which can be removed or relieved by the use of foresight, in the planning of preventive measures. The premium put on planning by the increasingly high price that must—in the current context— be paid for by the traditional policy of meeting difficulties as they arise and "muddling through" has given a new-found respectability to future-oriented studies.[14]

## The problem of predictive methodology

The issue of a *specific methodology of prediction* has largely been neglected by methodologists and philosophers of science, who have concerned themselves primarily with considerations relating to explanation. This procedure is justifiable as long as one believes that explanation and prediction are strict methodological counterparts. However, this belief is one that has in recent years been increasingly under attack, and there is good reason to reject it—especially so with respect to the social sciences.[15] Consequently, it behooves us to take a brief look at the predictive instruments that are available.

13. For a comprehensive survey of the area see Erich Jantsch, *Technological Forecasting in Perspective* (Paris, 1966; Working Document for the Organization for Economic Co-operation and Development), and the Abt Associates, *Survey of the State of the Art: Social, Political, and Economic Models and Simulations* (Cambridge, Mass., 1965; Report for the National Commission on Technology, Automation, and Economic Progress). The former of these documents, despite its title, does not restrict its range to strictly scientific and technological issues, but concerns itself also with their social implications. Moreover, it contains an extensive bibliography, and makes a comprehensive survey of organizations and institutes in Europe and the U.S.A. that concern themselves with forecasting in these fields.
14. For an incisive description of the new attitude towards the future see Olaf Helmer, "New Developments in Early Forecasting of Public Problems: A new Intellectual Climate" (Santa Monica, 1967; RAND Corporation Research Paper P-3576).
15. For a detailed discussion of the issues adverted to rather allusively in the present paragraph see O. Helmer and N. Rescher, *On the Epistemology of the Inexact Sciences* (Santa Monica, 1960; RAND Corporation publication R-353).

ANALYSIS

*What is value change? A framework for research* 105

Basically three items of predictive methodology are at our disposal: the extrapolation of historical experience, the utilization of analytical models, and the use of experts as forecasters.

Little need be said about the first of these methods, the extrapolation of historical experience. Everyone is familiar with the essentials of this type of projection into the future of current trends and tendencies. Everyone is well aware both of the usefulness of this method, and also of its drastic limitations. These are particularly significant in the areas at issue in the present discussion. The rapid pace of scientific and technological change in our times (and consequently its social impact) is so great that the method of extrapolation can be said, almost on general principles, to be ineffective. And this is especially true in the case of scientific change, since innovation in this sphere involves, almost by definition, a sharp break with the consolidated experience of the past.

The standard method of prediction in most cases—ranging from astronomy to meteorology and economics—is the analytical model. Here we have to do with a description (given, in the most familiar cases by sets of differential equations) of the phenomenology of the processes representing the functioning of a system. In the presence of such descriptive machinery the process of prediction becomes simple: We feed in the requisite data regarding the present state of the system, grind the cranks of the analytical mechanism, and obtain results about its future state.

This sounds idyllic, but all is not so easy. The principal trouble, of course, is that no one has yet devised analytical models for the processes that are relevant in the present context of discussion. The processes of scientific innovation, technological invention and diffusion, and the unfolding of patterns of social change are lions still waiting to be tamed by analytical model-builders. As yet we know little enough about which parameters are to be used in describing these processes, let alone being able to interrelate these parameters in analytical models.

We arrive now at the third of the aforementioned predictive methods—those which involve the systematic use of experts. The rationale of this procedure must be considered at least briefly.

For a predictive understanding of the course of human affairs, the concept of "nascent causality" represents a key factor. A *nascent* cause is one whose efficacy is as yet only beginning to make itself felt, so that its workings are subtle and masked by a host of other, currently more prominent factors.[16] A nascent cause is not a trend, but a significant causative

16. See Michel Massenet, "Methods of Forecasting in the Social Sciences" in *Three Papers Translated from the Original French for the Commission on the Year 2,000* (Brookline, Massachusetts, 1966; American Academy of Arts and Sciences).

factor in a trend of the future. But how is such a factor to be identified prior to—or in the incipient stages of—its actual impact? This is one of the principal points for the rationalization of expertise. The expert is able to bring to bear his background information in a way that is not systematized in a predefined analytical model but involves informed judgment based on inarticulated data. He is thus able to base his assessment not only upon overt trends, but also upon underlying regularities and a general, informed appraisal of the phenomenology at issue.

Granted that the expert has the generalized understanding necessary to provide insight into "nascent causality," how is this information to be extracted from him? Here a wide spectrum of procedures opens up before us, including questionnaires and interviews, brainstorming sessions, Delphi techniques (iterated questionnaires with information feedback) and operational games which provide a focussed structure to intellectual interaction. The details of these procedures do not concern us here.[17] The point to be stressed from the angle of our considerations is that the systematic (and preferably structured) utilization of expert opinion and speculation is perhaps the principal and most promising forecasting tool in the technological-scientific-social domain with which we are concerned.

## Some major difficulties for prediction

Among the considerations that indicate the need for more research on the problems of predictive methodology in the sphere of the human sciences is the existence of certain substantial (but readily identifiable) difficulties in this sphere. It is well worth while detailing a few of these.

### Feedback

Predictions in human affairs, once they become appropriately public, can readily stimulate a reaction. If, for example, some undesirable development is foretold, preventive measures to assure its nonrealization can be taken, thus falsifying (or at any rate suspending) the initial prediction. Or again, if some prominent scientist designates some problem as a significant focus of future research his declaration itself may serve as a stimulus, giving his prediction an element of self-fulfillment. This type of phenomenon is well known in connection with election forecasts, which can themselves generate a significant reaction from the electorate: the candidate whose victory is indicated may either gain added support (the "bandwagon effect")

17. For further details regarding such procedures—and a more general justification of the predictive use of expert judgment—see O. Helmer and N. Rescher, *On the Epistemology of the Inexact Sciences* (*op. cit.*).

ANALYSIS

*What is value change? A framework for research* 107

or his rival may do so (the "underdog effect"). Various methodological mechanisms exist by which difficulties of this type can in certain cases be accommodated.[18] But in general such reactivity to predictions creates special difficulties in the human sciences, and demands special attention in the context of future-oriented research.

## Chance

In human affairs factors which are *prima-facie* so small in proportion as to be virtually negligible can become amplified to the point of making an enormous difference in the course of events. Such developments represent the intervention of "chance" not because they do not fit within the general cause-and-effect matrix of events, but because their effects are disproportionately large when judged in the context of the way in which affairs usually proceed in this area of operation. Chance thus becomes the significant entry on the stage of highly improbable, and thus unpredictable, developments. A good example would be the assassination of a key political figure. Other illustrations of such "chance" events that have a major impact will doubtless leap to the reader's mind. It is clear, however, that various domains can differ sharply in the scope that they provide for chance developments to make a major impact: it is obviously larger in the area of scientific discovery than in the demographic sphere, and larger in the political area than in either of these. The element of chance is particularly significant for the study of predictive methodology, because chance sets limits to our capacity for specific prediction. To the extent that developments result from causes that come into operation through "chance," they are (almost by definition) impossible to predict.[19] One of the tasks of a methodology of prediction would be to determine the relative extent of the *Spielraum* of chance perturbations, and, moreover, to analyze the mechanisms through which "chance" developments can make an impact in various areas.

## Fashions

In human affairs—and not only sartorial, but scientific, intellectual, cultural, and political as well—the role of *fashion* is highly significant. As a social as well as a rational animal, man tends to conform his activities to those of selected fellows, and of course the substance of these conformities alters over time. We know a great deal about the generic mechanisms through which changes in fashion will become operative (the desire

18. See H. A. Simon, "Bandwagon and Underdog Effects" in *Models of Man* (New York, 1953).
19. That is, though one can always make the generic prediction that this type of development is *possible* one could not have made the specific prediction that in the case at issue this possibility would be *actualized*.

for novelty, the pull of the taste-maker, the urge to be *au courant*, etc.). But the specific *content* of future fashions is something much harder to foresee. We have little difficulty in substantiating the thesis *that* there will be such changes, and are well informed about the *why*—the causative factors —of these·changes. But just *what* the new foci of emphasis will be is something about which we are, in most instances, pretty much in the dark. The systematic study of the formation of intellectual and social fashions would be yet another important task for the development of an adequate predictive organon for future-oriented studies.

### Values

Many corners of man's environment, and virtually all facets of his actions reflect the fact that people make choices. These choices manifest their preferences which, in turn, mirror their values. Man's technological and social environment in the future will thus in significant measure be the reflection of his future values. Yet not only is scientific and technical progress itself difficult to predict, but the issue of its implementation imposes yet another stratum of difficulty for such progress presents us with opportunities, but just how—and indeed whether—we capitalize upon these opportunities will depend upon what these values will be. The scientific study of values is a recent and still very underdeveloped discipline. The predictive instrumentalities for the study of value change are sadly lacking at present. Progress in this area is a requisite for significant advances in the study of the human environment of the future.

## The problem of data

One very important consideration that cannot be overstressed in a discussion of predictive methodology relates to "the data" of the field. Prediction in the areas that have concerned us here—in the sphere of science and technology and in that of social phenomena—is an enterprise that is still in its infancy. (This is why great stress is to be placed in this sphere upon methodological considerations.) Now the point to be stressed in this connection is that here, as elsewhere, theory must march hand-in-hand with data, and cannot successfully develop until our grasp on the "facts of the matter" improves.

When one thinks of the current relative success in economic forecasting and the great progress that has been made in the U.S. over the years in this area, one must bear in mind also the great bodies of enormously elaborate data compiled by various information—gathering activities—above all the Bureau of Labor Statistics. Such fact-finding resources can and should be

ANALYSIS

*What is value change? A framework for research*                                                 109

broadened into the areas with which this discussion has been concerned. Matching the President's annual Economic Report, there should each year be a Social Report, and a report on Science and Technology. If the data needed for such reportage are ever developed, one can confidently expect that in the wake of this the predictive instrumentalities in these domains will improve dramatically.

## Conclusion

This discussion has concerned itself with the human ecology of the future—the question of our scientific, technological, human, and social environment at a substantial remove from the present. Neither the desirability nor the actuality of extensive researches in this sphere can at this time of day be regarded as genuinely open to question. But the *scientific standard* of such investigations represents an issue that is still in significant measure far from settled. The level of craftsmanship of forecasts in this sphere will not be as high as it can and should be unless such efforts are infused by a high degree of substantive adequacy and methodological sophistication. The main purpose of this discussion has been to urge the contention that progress towards this desideratum calls for two as yet only fragmentarily fulfilled requisites: explicit research on the methodological problems of forecasting in the "soft" sciences, and a substantial improvement upon the current means of gathering data in the relevant areas.

# LOOKING BACKWARD

# Technology, ways of living, and values in 19th-century England

## *J. B. Schneewind*

Fox hunting became the major hunting pursuit of the English aristocracy and landed gentry during the 18th century, when it replaced stag hunting.[1] By the end of the Edwardian era the great days of hunting were over: despite occasional magnificent runs, "the packs . . . were enjoying an Indian summer, the more glorious in retrospect for the nearness of the war which was to change their society beyond recognition or reclaim."[2] The sport had begun to have its troubles during the last quarter of the 19th century. Trollope lists a number of them, when he describes a group of hunters talking over the perils of hunting "in these modern days" (this is 1880):[3]

not the perils of broken necks and crushed ribs . . . but the perils from outsiders, the perils from new-fangled prejudices, the perils from more modern sports, the perils from over-cultivation, the perils from extended population, the perils from increasing railroads, the perils from indifferent magnates (sc., who won't keep up their woods and fox coverts as they ought) . . . and that peril of perils, the peril of decrease of funds and increase of expenditures!

It was a matter of more seriousness, perhaps, than we would first allow. For the city dweller who kept a hunting box and a couple of horses in some convenient location and came down once or twice a week to hunt under the local Master, hunting was a pastime, as expensive as it was thrilling. For the country resident it was more than that. Foxhunting, we are told,[4] was

1. J. L. and B. Hammond, *The Village Labourer*, London, 1948, vol. II, p. 14.
2. John Arlott, "Sport," in *Edwardian England 1901–1914*, ed. S. Nowell-Smith, Oxford, 1964, p. 453.
3. A. Trollope, *The Duke's Children*, Ch. LXII.
4. F. M. L. Thompson, *English Landed Society in the Nineteenth Century*, London, 1963, pp. 144–145.

perhaps the most real and fundamentally influential element in country society. The brotherhood reached far beyond the loyalities bred by estates and embraced men from a great many stations in life, for alongside the lord, the squire and the parson, the farmer, the doctor, the solicitor and even the village sweep could all be seen at the meet; the labourer alone had no representative here . . . the fox did more for the unity and strength of the landed interest than rent rolls.

And, the historian adds, "barbed wire did more to destroy the ties of the country society than death duties." Developed after the invention of the galvanizing process, barbed wire was introduced from the United States in the early 1880's,[5] at first—oddly enough—to protect fox coverts, later of course for more general fencing. It added a peril to Trollope's list and thereby assisted in the destruction of that traditional order of country society in which hunting played so important a role.

This is an example of one way in which technological innovation may hamper an established way of living and thereby challenge a familiar embodiment of accepted values. Examples will readily come to mind of ways in which technological innovations have assisted the formation of new ways of doing things. I mention one which is not, perhaps, familiar. In the development of urban recreation for the working classes, the brass band movement played an important role. Beginning about mid-century at around the same time as the start of mass spectator sport it grew, especially in the North of England, until by the beginning of the twentieth century it was estimated—with some exaggeration—that in Yorkshire and Lancashire alone there were between four and five thousand such bands. Since the workmen in factories, collieries and mills formed their own bands, they could not have afforded extremely expensive instruments. Hence brass technology undoubtedly contributed something to the movement. An improved method of making brass tubing was patented in 1838, and a year earlier a method was found of compounding copper and zinc so as to provide larger brass sheets of far greater workability than had earlier been available. These two improvements cut the cost of instruments, and a specifically musical invention was at hand to complete the task. Valveless brasses were extremely difficult to play, and almost totally unable to produce genuine melodies. In the early 19th century, however, valves were introduced and this, says our authority, "removed the physical drawbacks and gave the horns and trumpets an enormously increased utility. All notes were quickly available, and the brass instruments became capable of melody—*any* melody within their compass."[6]

5. On barbed wire, see Singer *et al.*, *History of Technology*, Oxford, 1958, vol. V, p. 625.
6. On brass, see Singer, *op. cit.*, pp. 607–608, 625. On the musical aspects see Percy Scholes, *Oxford Companion to Music*, 9th. ed., Oxford sub. title "Brasses" and "Brass Band". Cf. also S. G. Checkland, *Rise of Industrial Society in England*, New York, 1964, p. 268.

Changes such as these seem trivial taken by themselves. Cumulatively, however, a sufficient number of them constitute a change in the whole fabric of men's experience. If values guide choices, indicate the significance of action, and give direction to lives, then a study of ways of living and their changes is of considerable importance for an understanding of changes in values. For the patterns of life that are feasible, and the directives that are relevant, given one set of established ways of living, may be impossible or irrelevant under changed conditions. And it is interesting to ask what happens to values when this sort of stress is put on them.

To clarify what is meant by "values" in this context is a matter of some difficulty. It is important both that a reasonably precise terminology be available, and that the terminology be reasonably close to the language which we all use in our everyday discussions of values. In the present paper I shall use the account of value presented by Kurt Baier in his essay "What Is Value," together with one or two additions.

(a) Following Baier, we distinguish value imputation from value assessment. To impute a value to someone is simply to claim that that person (or group) holds or has the value: he is called the value holder. It is not to say anything about the reasonabless of holding the value or about the soundness of the value itself. Evaluation and criticism of values is value assessment, and in historical investigation of values it is not of primary concern. (b) When we impute a value to some person, we are claiming that there is some possible state of affairs, roughly indicated by the term naming the value, towards the existence or realization of which the person has a favorable attitude, for the reason that, so he believes, the existence of realization of the state of affairs would confer a benefit on someone or other. This state of affairs I shall speak of as the embodiment of the value. (c) Baier analyzes the state of affairs which is the embodiment of a certain value into a subject, the value bearer, and a predicate, the value property. Thus if "thrift" is one of my values, then the state of affairs which is the embodiment of this value is Smith's being thrifty, Morgan's being thrifty, Blank's being thrifty, etc.: Smith, Morgan, and Blank are the value bearers; and being thrifty the value property. Baier classifies value bearers into three groups—individuals, institutions, and environments—and these in turn may be further classified, but the subdivisions here are not of major importance for us. (d) Finally Baier suggests that we specify roughly the degree to which the state of affairs indicated by the name of the value must be realized before the value holder thinks that the world is reasonably satisfactory with respect to the value in question. This is a matter of what Baier calls the value holder's aspiration level. A correlative term might be useful for the situation with respect to the bearer. One might speak of the realization level to refer to the degree to which the bearers of a value do in fact realize that value.

These definitions all refer to the attitudes, beliefs, and reasonings of the value holder, not to those of the observer or historian. Thus what counts as a benefit, when we say that the value holder must believe that the realization of a certain state of affairs would confer a benefit on someone, is entirely a matter of the value holder's opinion. Because of this relativity to the value holder, the above account of values leaves a great deal of room for irrationality or nonrationality, even though it distinguishes value attitudes from other active attitudes by classifying them as attitudes held for a reason. A value is not just the same as a personal taste, liking, or whim. But a value imputation can be true even if the beliefs it involves about benefits are false; even if the belief about benefits, whether true or false, is ill-grounded, from a scientific point of view; and even if the value holder clings to his beliefs, and his attitude as based on them, in the face of conflicting evidence or criticism of his reasoning.

How, then, are we to use this abstract scheme of concepts to interpret the enormous bulk of material made available to us by the work of historians of England in the last century, and to fit it in with the vast literature of self-interpretation produced by Victorian essayists, novelists, poets, philosophers, and social critics? Baier's analysis of value immediately suggests three points at which value change might be investigated. (a) We might try to investigate changes in those *beliefs* of value holders which are relevant to the values they hold. Where a state of affairs is valued because of the value holder's belief, and the belief changes, his attitude toward the state of affairs may very well change. If he really held the value for the reason contained in the belief, and if there is no other reason for it, then presumably the attitude will change, and if it does not, then the value holder will be displaying irrationality of some sort—stubbornness, prejudice, etc. There are numerous examples of changes in values induced at least in part by changes in belief during the Victorian period. Some of them will be noted later. A study of these rationales for values, their changes, and the extent to which changes in any given rationale was effective in changing the given value to which it lent support, would thus be one possible approach to the problem of value change. (b) We might try to investigate changes in *attitude* without concerning ourselves greatly about the changes in belief which may or may not have produced the changes. It is of course possible that two persons might have different attitudes, one favorable, the other not, toward the same thing, even though their relevant beliefs about them are, so far as one can tell, the same. Differences of attitude between country dwellers and city dwellers, between first generation city-dwellers and their children, between first generation factory workers and second generation factory workers, might well be investigated, in a variety of ways, as a means of dealing with the problem of value change. (c) We might, finally, in terms of Baier's scheme, investigate changes in *value bearers* in the range of individuals, institutions, and environments toward which value holders can and do direct their favorable or unfavorable attitudes and with which they must live and act. This is an avenue of approach which may seem unhelpful. It is natural to think of change in the things and people and activities around us as *subject to* evaluation, not as being itself change in values. But this natural way of looking at the matter oversimplifies it. Three factors enter into consideration here.

i) In a society which is to a large degree "traditional" in Max Weber's sense of the term, so that there is a strong "belief in the everyday routine as an inviolable norm of conduct,"[7] any change in habitual modes of activity will tend to be viewed as being directly and of itself a change in values. England during the beginning of the 19th century was still in this way "traditional" in considerable sectors of its population, and there is at least some trace of this attitude in all societies.

ii) The names of most important values are fairly abstract or general: that is, there are numerous imaginable classes of bearers of the values for which they stand. But at a given time any one society presents only a comparatively few types of bearers of a specific value. These embodiments are naturally treated by members of the society as paradigm cases of the value in question, so that the abstract term is understood best in terms of the specific bearers it has in that society. If these change, then the interpretation put on the value by value holders is likely to change.

iii) Because values are meant to be guides to conduct, it is natural to think of change in values as giving rise to changes in patterns of action, and not the other way around. And there is no doubt that the process often goes in this direction. Values may be changed as a result of religious conversion, or of intellectual conviction, and the value holder's behavior may be altered to conform to his new beliefs. But our interest is in the ways in which technological change affects values. And while technological innovation may perhaps produce, by itself, religious conversion—for the ways of God are after all mysterious—this does not seem to be the typical source of such occurrences. And though the effects of technology on more purely intellectual convictions are no doubt numerous, they are largely confined to beliefs about technology itself, and have little if anything to do with

7. Max Weber, "The Social Psychology of the World Religions," in *From Max Weber*, trans. H. H. Gerth and C. W. Mills, New York, 1958, p. 296.

immediately altering values. It is easier by far to see how technology changes ways of living than to see how it changes beliefs or attitudes. If we can show how changes in ways of living may bring about changes in values, we shall have a more effective tool for discussing the impact of technology on values.

Without, therefore, denying the importance of studying changes in the beliefs and attitudes of value holders, I wish to suggest that for an understanding of the impact of technological change on values an investigation of changes in the embodiments of values is of at least equal importance. I propose to discuss the embodiments of value primarily in terms of ways of living, rather than in terms of objects, people, or institutions. For ways of living involve all three of these classes of value bearers, closely related.

Nothing is to esoteric to be understood by the concept of a way of living. At any given time in a society people in roughly similar life-situations will be living lives of roughly similar patterns and carrying on their activities in ways which are readily recognizable as the same. School children go through their education in similar ways, people go to work and behave at work in one of a smaller number of similar ways, professional courtesy is exercised in much the same way in dentists', lawyers', and funeral directors' offices all over the country, indeed even ways of picking fights or quarreling are pretty similar throughout groups of similarly situated people. Of course individuals vary the style of a given type of performance, sometimes in crucially important innovative ways. But the widespread ability to pick out odd, unusual, eccentric, or "deviant" ways of doing things testifies to the existence of an enormous body of generally accepted ways of doing things which are usually assumed in a traditionalist manner, to be "the ways one does things." If we consider now not so much a single person's performance of roles in a whole life as the component parts by which the person accomplishes the various tasks that arise for him in the course of his life, we can see a similar sort of social patterning. How one cooks, how one dresses, how one gets to and from work, how one makes a table or repairs a leaky pipe, how one decorates one's house or celebrates one's festivals, worships or refrains from worships, participates in public affairs or fails to do so—these ways of doing things also enter into what I have in mind in speaking of ways of living. The concept is left vague quite deliberately. One might in the end think of it as covering all learned behavior. For learning how to do things is learning a rule or something like a rule, living in a certain way, like following a rule, is something which many people can do at different times and in different manners. There are two features of ways of living which are significant for our inquiry.

i) Ways of living and doing things are inextricably connected with implements and deliberately maintained procedures. Most of the things we do cannot be explained without some reference to tools, machines, gadgets, techniques and processes, or to social roles, complex institutions, and rule-defined statuses. It needs no saying that all men's lives are largely shaped by their work and that work would not be what it is without the tools and techniques it involves. Even leisure is shaped by products of technology: the environments and implements of play open or close the possibilities for employing free time, and shape the uses that can be made of it.

ii) Ways of living are liked or disliked. People may be contented or discontented, satisfied or dissatisfied with the various available ways of doing things, and they may accept or reject the ways of living which their surroundings and their abilities enable them to choose, or try to force upon them.

These two obvious features of ways of living indicate how it is that technology can make an impact on values through them. On the one hand they are intricately interwoven with the existing technology of a society, and readily changed by any change in it. On the other hand they are prime objects of the basic value creating response of humans: liking and disliking. In being like rule-directed action—that is, in being general or repeatable modes of action—they have a feature which makes them similar to objects of value assessment, value assessments are favorable or unfavorable judgments accepted *for a reason*, and where a reason for such a judgment is given, there is implicit the generalization that anything sharing the feature indicated in the reason would (so far, and other things being equal) be a proper object of the same, favorable or unfavorable, attitude.

The general hypothesis of the present essay is then that the main way in which technological change influences values is through its influence on ways of living. The process can be abstractly sketched as follows. Technological changes bring about changes in ways of living, because of the innumerable ways in which tools and techniques are bound up with them. Insofar as these changes are minor, they can be accommodated to the existing structure of values without much strain or distortion. As changes in ways of living accumulate, either intensively as a result of radical change in limited activities, or extensively as a result of affecting a much larger group of people or activities, one of several kinds of strain is put on the value system.

i) If the destruction of old ways of living, or the new ways which replace them are unacceptable to large numbers of people, then because the technology which compelled these changes was itself sanctioned or not prohibited by the existing system of values, there will be pressure for revision of the value system. This might consist in abandoning certain values altogether, in upgrading some already held value with respect to others, or in introducing new values which might if widely held lead to mitigation of the undesirable conditions.

ii) If the new ways of living are acceptable, and yet are at odds with the value system then there will be a tendency to reject that portion of the value system which gives rise to the conflict, to search for new value concepts in terms of which the favored features of the new ways of living can be articulated, or to readjust, within the old value system, the relative importance of various values. Neither the rejecting nor the revising process will be rapid or unresisted. There will be a tendency to defend the old system against negative criticism by attempting to show that the unacceptable happenings imputed to it are not really to be blamed on it, or that they are even merely temporary, or that they are negligible, or that they bring such benefits that the costs are justified. And there will be attempts to defend the old system against innovation by arguments showing that the new ways of living are really already sanctioned by it, that there are precedents under it for them, that the values in it have been too narrowly understood and that they still offer useful guidance. These pressures may lead to extension or revision of the old value concepts while keeping the old names, and an accommodation with new conditions may be reached. But it is a sign of more serious value change if no accommodation can be reached and an old value name is dropped, so that the ways of living subsumed under the concept it stood for come to be thought of as falling under a different concept (if indeed they have not themselves disappeared). At this point numerous additional factors enter into the process. There is a question of the availability of ideological alternatives to the old concepts or systems. Much will depend on the extent to which value holders are used to talking and thinking about their values, rather than accepting them implicitly and unquestioningly. And there are considerations of the degree to which the value system is bound up with other systems of thought and belief, e.g., religious or political commitments, racial or nationalistic beliefs. Because elements of this sort enter into value change, the impact of technology on ways of living cannot be considered to be the only, perhaps not even the decisive factor. Technology affects large areas of the life-experience to which values must be relevant and for which they must provide guidance, but those areas alone do not determine the values men hold.

There are some interesting analogies between the pressures leading to value change indicated above and pressures which lead scientists to revise their conceptual schemes.[8] These are worth noting briefly, since they

8. I am indebted here to Thomas Kuhn's *The Structure of Scientific Revolutions*, Chicago, 1962.

suggest that there is less irrationality in changing values to accommodate new ways of living than might at first appear.

(a) Scientific concepts, involving laws or law-like generalities in their meanings, may be seen as summing up and predicting a great many particular happenings. Their acceptability rests in large part on the accuracy with which they reflect the facts about particular events. It also rests, however, on the case with which they can be used to predict future happenings accurately. Value concepts, involving rules or rule-like directives in their meaning, may be seen as reflecting a shared sense of the value or legitimacy (or, of course, if they are negative value concepts, of the lack of value or the illegitimacy) of a group of actions, and as directing more actions of the same sort, in appropriate circumstances. Their acceptability rests in large part on the acceptability of the particular actions which they indicate. It rests also on the ease with which these concepts and the rules of action embedded in them can be used to derive guidance for future acceptable actions. There is thus a parallel between the discovery of a large body of factual data running counter to the expectations derived from a scientific theory, and the introduction under a value system of a large number of ways of doing things which people find intolerable. In either case there is reasonable pressure for change.

(b) Scientific systems are frequently defended against empirical evidence which seems to refute them by making adjustments within the system. It may be allowed that laws have classes of exceptions, to be explained by special hypotheses: or evidence may be dismissed as too slight, or poorly gathered; or it may be allowed that there are apparent anomalies, but claimed that these will be explained at some time within the framework, so that it need not be changed. Similarly defenses for value systems under attack may be made, as indicated above. Such moves are by no means entirely irrational, or evative. Where a system has functioned well for a long time, there is some reason for defending it in these ways and for keeping it at least until one has an equally useful replacement.

(c) Empirical information may be fitted into more than one scientific system. Consequently, when data conflicting with one system begin to outweigh the data fitting it, it is possible to construct a new system which will include both sets of facts: the best-known illustration of this is of course the history of the development from Ptolemaic to Copernican theories of the heavenly motions. Similarly, ways of living may be seen as falling under different value concepts or as belonging to different systems of values. Hence even if there is radical change in values it is nonetheless possible to preserve some of the older ways of living, by seeing them as bearers of different values.

In this connection one further point might be made. Some philosophers of science have suggested that radical changes in scientific theory require not only a large amount of data conflicting with established theories, but the existence of a fairly well developed alternative to the older theory as well: otherwise the cost of abandoning the old theory is too high. Whether this is true or not, it is at least interesting to speculate on parallel phenomena with respect to values. The existence of large numbers of identical histories, schemes for social regenerations, utopian plans, etc. during periods of social change would then seem to be a response to a genuine need in the thought of the times and to be, in this respect at least, quite a reasonable response. While it would be necessary to pursue this point further in a full study of value change, it need be noted here only as an indication of the limitations of a study confining itself to the impact of technology on values.

In illustration of the general outlook presented above, I propose to discuss some changes that took place during the Victorian era in England. "The Victorian age" an early Edwardian observer wrote, "will be stamped in record of the future as an age of hurrying changes. In many respects that change has resulted in a profounder transformation than had been effected by all the preceding centuries."[9] This attitude is to be found in innumerable other writers, earlier as well as later. The Victorians themselves were aware of the rapid and extensive changes through which they were living and saw their times as in some special way transitional.[10] There were perhaps numerous ages which liked to think of themselves as in some special way transitional or revolutionary, yet historical retrospection may well sympathize with the Victorian claim above others. Thus Peter Laslett, in his recent study *The World We Have Lost* treats the 19th century as if it showed for the first time on a large scale the features of the world we have gained to replace the lost world of the 17th century and earlier whose features he so interestingly portrays.[11] In terms of growth of population, expansion of industrialization, and involvement with other nations around the world, the developments which began in the half century or so before 1830 reached, in the seven decades following, astounding proportions. If the nature and place within the national life of industry, agriculture, religion, and government had begun to alter before Victoria came to the throne, it was during her reign that the changes became entrenched everywhere and

9. C. F. Masterman, *In Peril of Change*, New York, 1905, p. 303.
10. For example of Victorian comments on this point see Walter E. Houghton, *The Victorian Frame of Mind*, New Haven, 1957, pp. 1–2, and the entries indexed under "transition."
11. New York 1965. See e.g. p. 204: ". . . English society (was) different in order from anything which had ever gone before, in Europe or in the whole world. . . . the process of social and industrial transformation which we call *industrial revolution* was already virtually complete."

their results everywhere inescapable. "The typical town worker of the decade 1820-1830," Clapham writes, "was very far from being a person who performed for a self-made employer in steaming air, with the aid of recently devised mechanism, operations which would have made his grandfather gape."[12] "It is doubtful whether in this period (sc., up to the 1840's) . . . we can speak of a proletariat in the developed sense at all, for this class was still in the process of emerging . . ." Hobsbawn tells us.[13] But within the next few decades the proletariat emerged and the worker generally was doing jobs his grandfather could not have understood. Corresponding changes were occurring in the other classes of the society, though in none of them was there so drastic and painful an adjustment to be made as in the working classes. It would be surprising if changes of this magnitude in men's ways of living did not affect the commonly held values, and even a slight acquaintance with Victorian social and intellectual history suggests that there was indeed value change of a thorough-going and even radical sort. It is an indication of the change that so many words standing for central Victorian values now seem rather quaint and "dated." We no longer praise manliness, frugality, or piety as many Victorians did, nor do we recommend that persons should abide in the station in life to which they were born and do its duties with a becoming deference to their superiors. Whatever the extent and directions of the value changes as a whole, we may here consider simply some ways in which *technology* affected them. I shall discuss two central topics: centralization of government and work.

One of the most important and most frequently discussed changes in Victorian England was the shift from extreme dislike of and resistance to regulative and constructive action by the central government on any and all social problems, to a willingness to admit the necessity and even the positive desirability of such action. While opposition to an active central authority was by no means universal—working men sometimes appealed to ancient laws and traditions involving the government in the regulation of working conditions, and they were not without support from members of other classes—the value which supported objections to centralization made a deep appeal to almost every section of the country. "Local rights and customs were cherished against the encroachment of the State by Gentry and common people alike," Thompson says, and the working man shared with the aristocrat a deep belief in the values suggested by the phrase "the free born Englishman."[14] It was these values, standing together under the

12. J. H. Clapham, *An Economic History of Modern Britain*, Cambridge, 2nd ed., corrected, 1939, p. 74, and cf. vol. II, 1932, p. 22.
13. E. J. Hobsbawn, *Labouring Men*, London, 1964, p. 276.
14. E. P. Thompson, *The Making of the English Working Class*, New York, 1963, paperback ed. 1966, p. 82.

concept of freedom which were most affected by the movement toward strengthening the central government.

"One of the most curious peculiarities of the English people"; Bagehot says,[15] "is its dislike of executive government. . . . The natural impulse of the English people is to resist authority." He gives substantially the same reason for this as J. S. Mill gives, in the opening pages of *On Liberty*, tracing it to the political situation in previous centuries, which called for resistance to the encroachments of tyrannical monarchs. The Englishman's independence was embodied in the numerous ways in which he was left alone by the government,[16] rather than in ways in which he was given powers or abilities to do things. Prior to industrialization the conditions of life and the absence of changes in them made this a feasible state of affairs. Population was small, cities were small and few, agriculture was primarily carried on for subsistence, manufacturing was on a small scale, and there was little communication among the innumerable minute communities of rural England. Within those communities authority was exercised by members of the great web of nobility and gentry and by the ministers of the local parish churches.[17] The central government did little, press gangs and unusual taxes during wartime excepted. In 1832, when the population of England and Wales had risen to the unprecedented level of about fourteen million, the central government still employed only some 21,000 persons (exclusive of the army and navy), and of these over 15,000 were employed by the Customs and Excise Services. Administration was the work of about 5,000 justices of the peace, drawn from the resident nobility, gentry, or clergy, and of a variety of office holders in over 15,000 parishes and 200 chartered boroughs.[18] Each unit was responsible for its new roads and bridges, its own water, sewage, poverty and disease, its own emergencies due to flood, food shortage, or plague, its own police, and its own education. These ways of doing things were accepted as being immemorially old, but they had already begun to show their unsuitability to the kinds of administrative problems which by the 1830's were already prevalent. As the unsuitability became more evident, the amount of interference by central government in the activities and choices of subjects increased. Two types of growth may be distinguished. There is first the kind that arises directly out of needs coming from population growth, technological innovation and the related changes in conditions of work, increased mobility of the population, and

15. Walter Bagehot, *The English Constitution* (1867), "Conclusion." Cp. E. P. Thompson, *op. cit.*, Ch. VIII.
16. The free-born Englishman "claimed few rights except that of being left alone": E. P. Thompson, *op. cit.*, p. 81.
17. Peter Laslett, *op. cit.*, Ch VIII.
18. David Roberts, *Victorian Origins of the British Welfare State*, New Haven, 1960, pp. 9–20.

similar alterations in traditional ways of living. There is second the kind of growth which is due to the tendency of any agency to expand in order to do adequately the task it is set, and to find new aspects of its work which had not previously been considered, but which require additional authority and personnel.

The first kind of change in the role of central government is perhaps most dramatic in connection with the needs arising from urbanization. Here the changes in ways of living became appallingly evident.[19]

The suddenness with which the people of England appeared for the first time to acquire a sense of sight and smell and realize that they were living on a dung heap, was due to the impact of industrial change. By the 1840's, the slow procession of piecemeal alterations in the modes of production and ways of life had produced a qualitative change visible to all. England was rich. England lived in towns. England worked in factories, and travelled by rail. And as these economic techniques offered the possibility of revolutionizing the sanitation of towns, they also made the need for such remedies more acute.

The growth of government control over public health shows how changes in value bearing ways of life together with changes in value supporting beliefs combine to produce important changes of attitude in one apparently limited area after another, with the cumulative effect of bringing about a basic alteration of values. Resentment of public regulation of water supply systems, sewage and garbage disposal methods, graveyards, slaughterhouses and markets, public rooming houses, and other sources of disease and annoyance, was motivated in large part by private interest in the profits obtainable from supplying these necessaries,[20] but it was given justification by appeal to the traditional dislike of interference together with the belief that nothing but good could come of being left to do these things locally. The enormous rise of the death rates in large cities in the 1830's, by which time population accumulation began to outstrip the existing methods of administration and sanitation,[21] showed that the old ways were not viable for the new cities. The new cities themselves were the result of changes in methods of production and transportation, with the steam engine playing a major role by freeing factories from the need for waterpower. But the bare existence of the problems they posed, though it was a necessary condition of the changes in administration which were meant to solve them, was not a sufficient condition. In relation to public health a vast campaign of public education had to be carried out, and the changes in belief produced by the shocking revelations of the various commission and parliamentary reports

19. S. E. Finer, *The Life and Times of Sir Edwin Chadwick*, London, 1952, p. 212.
20. *Ibid.*, pp. 434 ff.
21. *Ibid.*, pp. 213–215.

was a prime mover in altering public values. At practically every stage the reformers had to face violent opposition. More than monetary interest was at stake: the individual was told that he was to be prohibited from throwing refuse away as he had always done; that his house was to be inspected to make sure the drains had traps; that he was to pay for services which he had no option but to accept; that he was not to bury his dead where they had always been buried—it is no wonder that these violations of privacy and self-determination aroused opposition. But the opposition, shaken by the revelations of the consequences of leaving things alone, was further weakened as actual trial of new methods showed that benefits accrued from them, in the forms of lowered death rates, lowered sickness costs, and longer and healthier lives, and that they did not seem to have the expected drawbacks. At least as important as this was the simple passing of time. "The 'spirit' of politics is most surely changed," Bagehot remarks,[22] "by a change in the generation of men," and what is true of politics is true of every other area in which public opinion plays an important role. A generation for which there is a presumption that interference will be harmful and destructive of liberties is replaced by one which makes no such presumption because it has been brought up living with sanitary inspectors, public water supplies, public sewage systems, centrally run poor-houses, etc., and has not suffered the evils from them that their parents feared. For the new generation the new ways of living are the normal ones, to be defended in their turn, perhaps, against another set of innovations.

Similar patterns are found when one examines the history of factory legislation. New ways of living are forced on men by acceptance of new technology for manufacturing. As these spread the problems involved in them come to men's attention, and some shared value—"humanitarian feeling," perhaps[23]—enables a timid first step to be taken toward giving some relief. In one industry after another, often under pleas that the situation is especially difficult, or that interference with children is not really interference with the free men, or that interference for the sake of protecting women is not really interference with the sacred right of freedom of contract, regulations are passed, are improved, and are slowly enforced. Experience accumulates to show that the effects of such legislation are not disastrous.

22. Bagehot, *op. cit.*, Preface to Second Edition (p. 269).
23. The concept of "humanitarian feelings," frequently used by historians, glosses over a number of difficult issues. Ford Madox Brown, in *Fathers of the Victorians*, Cambridge, 1961, discusses some of the difficulties of considering the Evangelicals as motivated by "humanitarian feeling": they held, he says, that "benevolences and philanthropies are virtuous only because of the Christian love in which they are performed and by no means in the mere act of helping the distressed" (p. 104). Moral duty motivated other reformers, and this should no more be confused with humanitarian feeling than the antihumanistic orientation of the Evangelicals.

Thus one finds one of the strongest opponents of early factory legislation saying, in Commons in 1860:[24]

> I have a confession to make to the House. Experience has shown, to my satisfaction, that many of the predictions formerly made against the Factory Bill have not been verified by the result, as on the whole, that great measure of relief for women and children has contributed to the well being and comfort of the working classes, whilst it has not injured their masters . . .

With alteration in belief, attitude tends to alter as well, and when a new generation comes on the scene, the newer beliefs, attitudes, and ways of living are simply part of their understanding of a normal life. It comes to be accepted that the government can and must interfere with freedom of contract under certain conditions. The way is thus prepared for value concepts which will not treat the new ways of living simply as regrettable departures from the proper path, but as an integral part of what ought to be.

The second type of change in the role of central government—that brought about by growth from within of a government office—has been studied in detail in one case,[25] though the processes there analyzed must have been present in other cases. Demands for labor, and fear of famine, produced an enormous increase in the number of emigrants, largely from Ireland, in the years following 1815. Laws governing the conditions of passengers on emigration ships were introduced under plea of urgent necessity, and passed —with a reference to the precedent of the regulation of the slave trade. At first ineffectual, they were gradually strengthened, and finally officials were appointed to work at the relevant locations with an eye to law enforcement. Among these men there grew up the habit of doing whatever was necessary to enforce the laws, and of demanding authorization from Parliament for further powers.

> The supersession of parliamentary processes by delegations of legislative and judicial powers ceased to seem extraordinary but came to be regarded as the mere formalization of the inevitable and indispensible. [There was] a profound change in the presuppositions and bearing of the administrators. In place of a static and purely executive, they developed a dynamic, creative, and expert concept of administration.[26]

This process, essentially the development of the modern idea of government instead of the idea of a government used merely to restore a natural balance and harmony of social action, has obvious affinities with the pressures from outside the administrative sphere leading to increased centralization. And it involved a discovery of considerable importance for the development

24. C. Driver, *Tory Radical*, New York, 1946, p. 518.
25. Oliver MacDonagh, *A Pattern of Government Growth*, London, 1961.
26. *Ibid.*, p. 344.

of modern society—the discovery of efficient techniques of administration and enforcement.

The older values summed up in the concept of freedom did not disappear under the development of centralized government, nor, in one important way, were they downgraded. The Englishman still treasured his rights to freedom of speech and religion, to trial by jury, and to freedom from search and seizures. But since the realization level of those values continued to be thought of as satisfactory—indeed, it improved for members of the working classes, with the repeal of repressive anti-trade-union legislation, the cessation of government persecution of labor leaders, and the granting to more and more workers of the vote—there was less need to worry about them than about other issues. Precisely because men could continue to be free in these ways at the same time that the government was controlling more and more of their activities, the value named "freedom" could cease to imply the total absence of government interference. The sufferings of the working classes, and the general discomforts of city dwellers of all classes, resulting from the new ways of living which technology thrust upon them, made men think about the functions of government in new ways, and forced them to try to formulate new values to guide social action. That enterprise had not yet been completed.

Much has been written about the "protestant ethic" and the work orientation of the Victorians. Certainly the intellectuals were very vociferous about work—whether recommending it on its own merits, or as a held doubt. But it is unclear how far their recommendations reflect widely means of self realization, or as an aspirin for the headaches of religious values. There is little evidence to support the contention that the members of the working classes need relief from religious doubt,[27] for example, though it is quite possible the members of the middle class might have endorsed Bagehot's dictum that "business is really more agreeable than pleasure."[28] But even they had numerous motivations to work hard and succeed over and above any that religion might have given them. The facts are hard to interpret. It may possibly be true that a fairly wide consensus developed with regard to centralization by the end of the century—did not Harcourt say that "we are all Socialists now"?[29] but this would not be true with regard to

27. K. S. Inglis, *Churches and the Working Classes in Victorian England*, London, 1963, suggests that what was prevalent among the workers was not religious doubt, but indifference to religion combined with dislike of the social policies of the churches, both established and dissenting.
28. Bagehot, *op. cit.*, p. 141.
29. See J. H. Clapham, *op. cit.*, vol. III, 1938, pp. 397–400.

values concerning work. The ideology of self-help was preached to, and widely accepted by, the middle classes. It was aimed at the workers too, but there is little evidence to show that it was accepted by them. There were numerous working class leaders of whose views Samuel Smiles could have been proud—Joseph Arch, for example, who formed the first union for agricultural laborers:[30]

> I firmly believe in the apostolic injunction, that if a man will not work, neither shall he eat. The drone, high or low . . . should be forced to work. . . . I teach the farm labourers never to be satisfied while there is a chance of advancing in life. To teach a man to be content to stick in the mud, is to teach a man to curse himself. I think we should increase within his mind a just discontent for every year of his life, to make himself a better man, and go one better every year he lives.

But while the workers seem to have accepted the belief that men must work in order to deserve to eat, they did not all accept the doctrine of the permanent increase of just discontent with one's lot. More importantly, self-help, to the working man, soon turned out to mean—as it did for Arch—mutual aid. The main development regarding work-values during the Victorian period was the spread of class consciousness in its modern form. The spread of this phenomenon is attested by the disappearance of the language which had previously been common in talking about different levels of status, wealth, and power in society—the language of ranks and orders, of degrees and of interests:—and its replacement by the terminology of class, with its emphasis on money as the ultimate determinant of position.[31] The process affected those who remained in the country as well as the city dwellers and factory workers:

> The peasant, under the old system, had a definite independent place in the community. He commanded respect for his skill, judgment, and experience in his own industries. He was not cut off by any distinctions in ideas, tastes, or habits from the classes above. On the contrary, each grade shared almost imperceptibly into the next. Today, the intermediate classes have disappeared. . . . There are in many villages only two categories—employers and employed The gulf . . . has been broadened by the progress of a civilization which is more and more based on the possession of money.[32]

Class consciousness is a complex matter, but at its core there is, not simply an awareness of one's membership in a class, but a tendency to value one's

30. Joseph Arch, *The Story of His Life as Told By Himself*, London, 1898, pp. 262–345.
31. See on this point two interesting articles by Asa Briggs: "Middle Class Consciousness in English Politics, 1780–1846," *Past and Present*, 9 April 1956; and "The Language of 'Class' in early Nineteenth Century England," in *Essays in Labour History*, ed. A. Briggs and J. Saville, London, 1960.
32. Lord Ernle (R. E. Prothero) *English Farming Past and Present*, London, 1922, p. 409. And cf. M. K. Ashby, *Joseph Ashby of Tysoe*, Cambridge, 1961, pp. 276–285.

interests qua member of that class over one's interests qua member of some other group—national, religious, or political. The rise of class consciousness was thus a change in values. And it is plainly a change that had much to do with the conditions under which men worked and the ways in which they were treated, as workers, by others in the community. Obviously technology alone does not explain the growth of class consciousness: political developments, as well as the rise and propagation of new social theories, would have to be brought in for anything like a full account.[33] But for our purpose a brief look of some ways in which technology was involved in the change may be profitable.

One of the most significant and far-reaching of the changes induced in large part by technology was the stripping away from the family of one after another of the activities that had previously been centered in it. In preindustrial Europe generally work was largely done in one's family: "in all occupational groups the union of business and family relationships was a normal feature of this period (sc. up to the industrial revolution) everywhere in the Western world."[34] Spinning and weaving as well as agriculture involved all the members of the family. Laslett has recently spelled out the numerous ways in which even employees were treated as members of the family in and for which they worked: this seems to have been true not only of household servants but equally of apprentices and hired hands.[35] This way of living was deeply rooted in men's habits. During the first decades of the factory system it was maintained, as whole families worked in one factory, often at one machine. But various alterations in the machines, together with the growth of new employment practices, gradually forced the cessation of the system, and brought about the separation of work from family life which is so clear a pattern today. Middle-class work went through similar changes. The family firm, with its paternalistic relations to its few employees, was eventually replaced in large part by bigger firms in which professional managers had important roles, and then, from the 1870's on, even family businesses tended to be "impersonalized under limited liability."[36] The need for highly skilled personnel, resulting in part from technological progress, finally brought about the professionalization of military careers, thus cutting into the connection of work and family among the higher ranks of society. Similar needs in the government resulted in the passing of the civil service acts, which broke the hold of family connection over that area of work. To meet the requirements of the new types of career, and to assist in the social climbing which interested many members

33. Cf. E. P. Thompson, *op. cit.*, p. 194.
34. Kurt Samuelson, *Religion and Economic Action*, New York, 1964, p. 123.
35. Laslett, *op. cit.*, esp. Ch. I.
36. Checkland, *op. cit.*, p. 129.

of the middle class, new educational methods were accepted: the tutor at home and the local school were replaced by the boarding school. People began to look less to the family and more to Friendly Societies, Burial Societies, Insurance Companies, and Cooperative associations for protection against financial distress caused by death, illness or unemployment.[37] Finally, the family had been the source of one's permanent status and the main determinant of one's values. As the possibilities of geographic and social mobility, and the pressures toward it, increased, it became less and less likely that one would live, work, and raise a family where one's family had always done so; less likely therefore that one would form part of a continuous family group: and less likely that family skills, customs, trades, or beliefs would be maintained. These changes add up to the development of a very differrent way of living family life from that prevalent in earlier centuries.

The effects of this change on the development of class consciousness were considerable. The older style of home life and home work bound one closely to a specific locale and to a small group of people of highly differentiated statuses, all working in a cooperative manner for ends each could understand and in some measure share. The sense of attachment to one's locale and to the people one knew was stronger than any sense of attachment to other people working in the same way as oneself and earning the same income. With the disintegration of the older system, and the growth of industrial complexes in which workers were segregated with workers and mangerial personnel with their own kind, any sense of community of interests between supervisors and supervised as belonging all to one craft or trade became hard to maintain.[38]

The condition of work in the new factories reinforced the workers' sense of their common condition. To make the most of machines, it was necessary that men come to work every scheduled day and work uniformly during scheduled hours. Since relations between employer and employees were becoming increasingly impersonal, the only incentives which the employers could manipulate were monetary, i.e., wages and fines. Prior to industrialization neither work nor incentives had been organized in this fashion. Work had been irregular, not only in agriculture, where natural cycles were dominant, but in connection with such manufacturing as there was. Cloth workers in particular had been notorious for lives of

37. The growth of the suburbs should be mentioned here. In large part made possible by technological development, it increases the social distance between workers and managers by increasing the physical separation of their homes. Inglis, *op. cit.*, passim., notes much worry about the emptying of urban churches by the flight to the suburbs.
38. Cf. Checkland, *op. cit.*, pp. 263 ff; and Neil Smelser, *Social Change in the Industrial Revolution*, Chicago, 1959, esp. Ch. IX–XIII.

alternate spells of frenzied, round the clock labor followed by bouts of drinking, idleness, or work on their own farm plots. Age old custom and the natural conditions of life in a predominantly agricultural society were reinforced by the teachings of pastors and masters. Workers were to be content with their lowly station in life as that to which God had called them. They were not to attempt to increase their material well-being beyond certain clear limits.[39] As a result of their habits and their indoctrination, the workers who formed the labor reserve for the factory system were "men who were non-accumulative, non-acquisitive, accustomed to work for subsistence, not for maximization of income."[40] This way of life had to be changed if industrialization was to proceed. The problem of making workers responsive to a cash stimulus was at the core of the problem of factory discipline—the concept itself, we are told, "was new, and called for as much innovation as the technical inventions of the age"[41] and apparently success was rather slight until about the 1840's, after which time an increasing regularity and reliability was noticeable in workers. Compared with the appallingly bad living conditions, the wretched hours and surroundings of work and the general proverty and insecurity of working-class life during this period, the regularization of labor may seem a minor trouble. But in it the break with other ways of living came to one kind of climax, for it made clearer than anything else the extent to which under the new conditions one could not control one's own life.

Signs of the growth of working class consciousness may be seen in various developments. The way in which working men calculated what they would ask for wages, for example, changed only slowly from the old mode in which the amount of the fair day's wage one would ask for a fair day's work was determined in relation to a number of customs and traditions varying from craft to craft and from grade to grade within each craft. "The wage-structure of a developed capitalist economy was not formed in a void. It began," Professor Hobsbawn says, "as a modification or distortion of the pre-industrial wage-hierarchy and only gradually came to approximate to the new pattern."[42] It was not until the decades around the middle of the century that the workers "learned to regard labour as a commodity to be sold in the historically peculiar conditions of a free capitalist economy"[43]

39. Hannah More's various edifying tales illustrate the ideology of contentment with one's lot almost too perfectly: see e.g. "The Shepard of Salisbury Plain." In Arch's autobiography, referred to above, there is an incident involving the ancient attitude toward overly gaudy dress for laborers: cf. p. 51, referring to an incident in the 1840's.
40. S. Pollard, "Factory Discipline in the Industrial Revolution," *Economic History Review*, 2nd ser., Vol. XVI, 1963–64, pp. 245, 259.
41. *Idem.*
42. E. J. Hobsbawn, *Labouring Men*, London, 1964, p. 347.
43. *Ibid.*, p. 345.

and even then they still used noneconomic criteria for settling what amounts to ask. It was not until the end of the Great Depression in the last decade of the century that workers cut free of traditional determinants of wages. But the mid-century change in attitude toward the nature of wages is of interest by itself, as an indication of an abandonment of older ways of thought in favor of a way which, admirably or regrettably, was more in keeping with the facts of the world in which they lived.

A further and extremely interesting insight into the change of attitude may be obtained from noting the differentiated responses of workers to the American Civil War. It is well known that the vast majority of workers in the North of England supported the antislavery side in the Civil War.[44] But influential leaders of the working class supported the South, apparently out of hatred for the American North. Harrison points out that working-class newspapers were all on the side of the South, as were most of the older trade union leaders. His explanation of this is that the American Civil War stood as a proxy for the class struggles in England. There was no unanimity among workers as to "whether the landed oligarchy or the manufacturing capitalists represented the main enemy of Labour." The older leaders, formed in the early days of the labor movement, tended to view the capitalists as the enemy: the younger men, accustomed to the new system, no longer looking to a rural past as the ideal of life, tended to see the landowners as the enemy, because of their opposition to Corn Law reforms. It was the older leaders, whose hostility toward the industrial system "took its point of departure in the old, primitive opposition to modern industry as such, rather than in vision of constituting modern industry on a cooperative instead of a competitive basis"[45] who sympathized with the South. Such men could still talk of cotton as "the great seducer that has deluded our active population from the labour of the fields." These men refused to see any difference between the legal slavery of the Negro workmen and the wage slavery of English Capitalism. But the rising generation of leaders were "coming to terms with Capitalism": their demands were not for a reversal of the trend of a century, but for a better place within the system for the workers.[46] And indeed some of the best of the old Chartist leaders were, with them, opposed to the South. Unlike their pro-Southern former fellow workers, they "had no desire to undo the work of the industrial revolution." They could see how wage slavery was an advance on slavery pure and simple, while admitting the horrors of the former and fighting against them.

44. Royden Harrison, *Before the Socialists*, London, 1965, p. 65.
45. *Ibid.*, pp. 55–56.
46. *Ibid.*, p. 57.

The change in workers' attitudes shown by their mixed reactions to the American Civil War was reflected to some extent in the images and stories in terms of which the workers thought about their problems and their situation. During the earlier decades of the industrialization process, there is strong evidence of persistence of a hankering for return to the older country life among the workers. Thus the appeals made by Richard Castler, one of the greatest of popular speakers among the leaders of the anti-Poor Law and the Tory Act agitations, made frequent use of imagery drawn from an idealized picture of the old life of the rural laborer.[47] Chartist agitators too drew heavily on the golden past:[48]

Here is that we may live to see the restoration of old English times, old English fare, old English holidays, and old English justice, and every man live by the sweat of his brow . . . when the weaver worked at his own loom, and stretched his limbs in his own field, when the laws recognized the poor man's right to an abundance of everything.

The fiction which the workers read also reflects longings for a lost simplicity of the past. "The 'domestic story' lies at the heart of almost all the penny-issue fiction published during the eighteen-forties," we are told, and the theme of the goodness of country life is a deep part of it. In the following years plots centering on the purity of the heroine began to displace the rural-home themes, and "the theme of the family became less and less important to lower-class fiction."[49] What these few facts suggest—and the point needs much further investigation—is that workers persisted in thinking of the new ways of living under the old terms for a considerable period. The myth of a simple life in the country was not merely nostalgic: it was a conceptualization of a way of life which they continued to see as the norm or ideal, and the actualities around them were seen as departures from it, as thoroughly evil conditions to be changed or done away with. Among intellectuals the Disraelian Young Englanders and much of Carlyle's work show a similar state of mind. Along with these older modes of thought new ones were preparing: Owenism had a wide following among working men, as did numerous other advanced or revolutionary thinkers. But it was after the collapse of the Chartist movement that the older ways of thinking began to be decisively displaced. I do not mean that the myth of a golden time in a rural past was completely abandoned—far from it—but it ceased to be the central organizing scheme for working class evaluations of living conditions, for tactics of the labor movement, and for attitudes toward capital and management.

47. Driver, *op. cit.*, pp. 128–129, 428–429 and generally Ch. XXXII.
48. Feargus O'Connor, quoted in E. P. Thompson, *op. cit.*, p. 230.
49. Louis James, *Fiction for the Working Man, 1830–1850*, Oxford, 1963, pp. 99, 102, 109.

It is generally agreed that from about the end of the Chartist movement in 1848 to about the 1880's the workers were acclimatizing to capitalism and accepting industrialism as the basis of the social order.[50] Obviously technology alone could not have brought this about. Political changes, such as the removal of antilabor legislation, the admission of labor to a vote, and the opening of some political offices to working-class men, were necessary, as were improvements in working conditions and in wages, before the new ways of living could be acceptable to the workers. The shift in the ways of living brought about by the massive and uncontrolled publication of new technology first forced the workers into opposition to the value which had produced for them an intolerable existence, and then, when modifications of these values and ways of living had been achieved, provided them with a life experience in terms of which new values of their own made sense and could be accepted. The basis had been laid from which the later developments of the century toward socialism could take place.

The writer wishes to thank Kurt Baier, David Braybrooke, and Nicholas Rescher for their helpful discussions of various ideas presented in this paper.

50. See e.g., G. D. H. Cole, *Short History of the British Working-Class Movement*. London, revised edition of 1948, pp. 6, 7.

## LOOKING FORWARD I

# A questionnaire study
# of American values by 2000 A.D.

## *Nicholas Rescher*

### Introduction

The "Questionnaire on Changes in U.S. Values" at issue in this discussion was drawn up by the writer in the early months of 1966 with the cooperation of members of the Pittsburgh Values Project and Dr. Olaf Helmer of the RAND Corporation. The aim of the questionnaire, as set forth in its Introduction is as follows:

This questionnaire is part of a study of likely changes in American values over the next generation, say to the year 2000. Its aim is to elicit respondents' views concerning two items:
1) Which widely held American values are likely to change under the impact of foreseeable scientific, technological, demographic, and socio-economic change, between now and the last decade of the century?
2) What can be said about the nature, magnitude, causal mechanism, and above all, the *desirability* of such change?
It should be noted that, when we speak of a value's changing, we do *not* think of its being dropped altogether or introduced entirely anew, but primarily have in mind either (a) its being downgraded or upgraded on a person's scale of values, or (b) its being de-emphasized or emphasized, in the sense that (while still holding that value in the same place on the scale) one sets a lower or a higher standard of achievement in realizing the value in the world around one. (In an age of sonic booms we may not value "*peace and quiet*" the less, but just settle for a lower level of its attainment.)

The nature of the questionnaire is best and most simply gathered by an inspection of the document itself, as presented below.

During the spring of 1966, roughly seventy-five copies of the questionnaire were sent out to various persons, a special effort being made to focus upon high-level scientists and science administrators whose interests are significantly future-oriented. It was felt that the impact of technological change on American values could be assessed most effectively and relevantly by the persons best qualified to form a vivid picture of the prospects, possibilities and nature of the technological environment of the future. Moreover, scientifically-oriented people themselves constitute one important channel through which technological changes make their impact on the society in general, and how they *perceive* these effects can prove a significant determining factor.

The composition of the respondent group was as follows:

*I. By Affiliation*

| | |
|---|---|
| IBM Corporation Scientists | 10 |
| NSF Staff Members | 14 |
| RAND Futures Group | 10 |
| Harvard Program on Technology | 8 |
| Pittsburgh Values Project | 10 |
| Miscellaneous | 6 |
| **TOTAL** | **58** |

*II. By Training*

| | |
|---|---|
| Natural Scientists | 29 |
| Social Scientists | 8 |
| Humanists and Educators | 15 |
| Others | 6 |
| **TOTAL** | **58** |

Various cautions must be mentioned and indeed emphasized. The sample is minute and—even within the group of scientists and intellectuals —very definitely biassed in the direction of the "hard" sciences. No weighty "conclusions" can be rested on the outcome of the present round of the questionnaire. It is avowedly a *pilot project* in the study of possible value changes by questionnaire techniques. Its upshot is, at best, (1) to demonstrate the feasibility of this mode of inquiry, (2) to highlight some of the strengths and weaknesses of the specific design features of the questionnaire, and (3) to indicate—in a way admittedly more suggestive than conclusive— some of the likely features of anticipated value change. (From the stand-point of the Pittsburgh Values Project this last feature was of particular interest because of the guidance it gave to our work in the initial phase of the enquiry, and its suggestiveness for future phases of research.)

The purpose of the present chapter is to present the outcome of the questionnaire and to offer some comments upon this by way of tentative interpretation.

## Question 1

The detailed data regarding the responses to this and the ensuing questions are presented in the tabulation of results appended at the end, which provides the backdrop for the present discussion. One of the striking features of the responses to the present question is the large degree of consensus. If we attach significance to an index value of $\geqslant 1/2$ (or $\leqslant -1/2$)[1] then a significant interpretation is possible in six of the eight cases. It is noteworthy that the bulk of the responses tend to the negative. Only two of the items of "folklore"—an increasing emphasis on social values (item 4) and a decreasing emphasis on religious ones (item 5)—are regarded on consensus as true, the latter emphatically so.

The picture emerging from the consensus responses to this question about current "folklore" regarding American values is that of a definitely continuing commitment to American values, very much along present-day lines, except for an increased emphasis upon social and a decreased emphasis upon religious values. The "cocktail party catastrophism" inherent in such changes as those of items 1, 2, and 8 was dismissed by the consensus of the respondents. The large negative score for item 7 (aesthetic values) is interesting and accords smoothly with other parts of the questionnaire— the respondents apparently look to a boom in aesthetic values and by a two-to-one majority they reject the charge of "debasement."

## Question 2

One striking aspect of the responses to this question is the respondent's firm anticipation of substantial changes with respect to the espousal of specific values: With respect to half the items (eighteen of twenty-seven) the consensus is for a probable change. Almost always, the anticipated change is in an upward direction; there are only three exceptions, the subjects of these downward trends being items 7 (*"self-reliance"*), 20 (*"devotion to family"*), and 31 (*"patriotism"*).

A second striking feature of the responses are their optimism: Almost always when a change is anticipated the majority of those who anticipate it regard this as a good thing. This being the rule, there are only three cases of anticipated value changes regarded as desirable by less than half the respondents: items 7 (decline of *"self-reliance"*), 20 (decline of *"devotion to family"*), and 29 (increased emphasis upon *"novelty"*). This last item was the only case in which the increase in a presently held value was viewed as desirable by less than half of those who anticipate its coming about. The only instance of a presently held value whose decline is foreseen with favor is item 31 (*"patriotism"*). (One trusts the respondents construed this with jingoistic overtones.)

Going beyond these results, the picture emerging from the consensus

1. See the Statistical Summary of Results below for an explanation of this "index."

responses to this question about changes regarding specific values indicates certain other conclusions:

(a) A distinct strengthening of "selfish" values viz., items 1 ("*one's own plea-sure*"), 2 ("*physical well-being and comfort*"), 3 ("*economic security*"), 4 ("*con-venience*"), 15 ("*leisure*").
(b) A distinct strengthening of cultural and aesthetic values (items 25, 26, 27).
(c) A strengthening of mankind-oriented values, viz. items 33 ("*social justice*"), 34 ("*peace*"), and 35 ("*internationalism*").

On balance, the idea of a "value erosion" in an affluent welfare-oriented society is decisively rejected by the respondents.

The pattern of results described here support the following hypotheses: the respondents anticipate substantial further economic progress, as a result of which—they expect that—people will have higher standards regarding "*pleasure*," "*comfort*," "*convenience*," "*security*" and "*leisure*." But a lesser effort will be required to secure these items and to distribute them so that everyone has an attractive share—hence less exacting standards of achievement regarding self-reliance and conscientiousness will be involved. Also, more time and resources will be available for the pursuit of "*beauty*" and "*culture*," for "*self-fulfillment*," and for "*service to others*." (Note that in answer to Question 4, item II-6, large increases in human energy and performance levels are expected to lead to increased emphasis both on self-fulfillment and on voluntary service to others.)

## Question 3

Again, it is striking that the respondents firmly anticipate substantial changes with respect to various categories of values: a positive consensus for change obtains in half the cases (eight of seventeen).

In most instances (six of eight) the change is one of increased emphasis on a value: the two exceptions are items 6 ("religious values") and 16 ("parochial values"). To summarize:

| Increased Emphasis | Decreased Emphasis |
|---|---|
| Service and Other-regarding Values | Religious Values |
| Material Values | Parochial Values |
| Aesthetic Values | |
| Social Values | |
| International Values | |
| Intellectual Values | |

Again, the optimism of the group is striking: in *every* case, the majority of those respondents who anticipate the value change at issue view this change positively, regarding it as a desirable one.

The picture that emerges from the response to the question about the trends in various categories of values is perfectly consistent with that of the previous question regarding specific values (strengthening of materialism, broadening of valued horizons from local to international perspectives, greater emphasis on social values, a strengthening of intellectual, cultural, and aesthetic values).

## Question 4

*Category I (political-economic-sociological developments)*

Virtually all of the developments in this category were felt to have significant implications for value change (the fifteen items result in six double-plus outcomes, seven single-plus outcomes, and only two indecisive outcomes). The two indecisive outcomes were items 10 (*"chronic limited warfare"*) and 14 (*"a Chinese takeover in Asia"*). I would conjecture that the respondents felt that the American value scheme had already discounted for the potential effects of these possible developments.

It is noteworthy that one value, viz. item 33 (*"social justice"*) was felt to be positively affected by six of the possible developments of this category and negatively by none. Also in some instances, e.g., item 1 (*"domestic population explosion"*), a development was felt to have both positive and negative implications for one and the same value (viz. item 14, *"privacy"*). (Presumably its being harder to get would on the one hand lead us to put more effort forward in its pursuit, and yet nevertheless have to resign us to doing with less of it, i.e., set a lower level of aspiration.)

*Category II (education and psychotechnics)*

Without exception, all of the developments in this category were felt to have significant implications for value change (the six items result in two double-plus outcomes and four single-plus outcomes).

*Category III (biotechnics)*

The items of this category having to do with aging and with reproduction were felt to have significant value implications. The tabulated data speak for themselves here.

*Categories IV-VIII (various economic-technological developments)*

The results here were one of the really striking features of the questionnaire, that is to say the *negativity* of these results. Of the thirteen items in these categories, only two were felt to have any significant value implications at all, namely items IV-1 (*"automation in commerce and industry"*) and VI-2 (*"discovery of remote intelligent life"*). Weather control and new developments in the production of food, as well as the entire area of transport and communications did not suggest any significant repercussions for values. The only ready account I can give for this negative showing in the value relevance of the technical-technological sector—given that all the respondents were persons whose imaginations could not fail to serve them properly here—is that in their considered opinion the scheme of American values has already discounted for the foreseeable developments in this essentially technico-technological area.

Substantial interest attaches to certain "tension-points" where a change with extensive value implications $(++)$ has value effects of low desirability, e.g., items I-1 (domestic population explosion) and I-2 (massive urban sprawl) with their whole host of attendant adverse value implications.

A word of caution is needed. The inquiry addressed itself to the flow of developments in the mainstream of American values. The possibility, indeed probability of sharp divergencies from the general drift, particularly on the part of radical and disaffected minorities, cannot be ruled out—but indeed seems more than probable.

## Conclusion

This survey of the outcome of the questionnaire has thus brought to light an interesting anomaly that certainly warrants further investigation. On the one hand, the consensus of the respondents looks towards substantial changes in American values over the next generation. On the other hand, various of the most technological phenomena of our era (automation, the revolution in transport and communications, and space) are virtually excluded from causal responsibility for these changes. For the technocrats who formed our respondent groups, technological change does not loom large in its direct value implications—it is overshadowed by social and political developments of a technologically facilitated but not directly technically constituted sort (e.g., the welfare state, the population explosion, and urban sprawl). (The main area of technical effects are seen in the biomedical area of Category III.) Perhaps the best inference is that technological change makes its impact on values in this highly indirect way, by altering the general "climate of life," shaping the framework within which others (social, political) forces have their effect upon values. This problem should certainly feature prominently on the agenda of future research.

In any event, the most striking feature of the questionnaire responses is their clear optimism. One has grown accustomed to virtually endless diatribes against the dangers of technical civilization to human values. This point of view finds a decisive rejection by the consensus of respondents throughout the questionnaire. The point of view of those whom we have characterized as the "cocktail party catastrophists" finds little if any support in the findings we have presented here. One qualifying note should, however, be struck. Among the detailed results for Question 4 there are occasional indications of value adverse developments indicative of a concern about the future for the expression of which no straightforward provision was made in the schedules of items and answers in the earlier questions. (Furthermore, coming last, Question 4 exercised a minimum influence, by way of concrete suggestions, upon the earlier answers.) Thus the optimism of the vaguer context of the earlier answers might have to be qualified in the light of the (adverse) value effects seen for such items as I-13 (nuclear arms proliferation) and II-5 (psychoengineering).

I wish to thank Mr. Douglas Hosler for his help in the interpretation of the questionnaire, and to Professor David Braybrooke for making helpful suggestions on this head.

## QUESTIONNAIRE ON CHANGES IN U.S. VALUES

## INTRODUCTION

This questionnaire is part of a study of likely changes in American values over the next generation, say to the year 2000. Its aim is to elicit respondents' views concerning two items:

(1) Which widely held American values are likely to change under the impact of foreseeable scientific, technological, demographic, and socio-economic change, between now and the last decade of the century?

(2) What can be said about the nature, magnitude, casual mechanism, and above all, the *desirability* of such change?

It should be noted that, when we speak of a value's changing, we do *not* think of its being dropped altogether or introduced entirely anew, but primarily have in mind either (a) its being downgraded or upgraded on a person's scale of values, or (b) its being de-emphasized or emphasized, in the sense that (while still holding that value in the same place on the scale) one sets a lower or a higher standard of achievement in realizing the value in the world around one. (In an age of sonic booms we may not value "peace and quiet" the less, but just settle for a lower level of its attainment.)

Note: Almost all of the questions are "open-ended," and the respondent is invited, and indeed *urged*, to make additions of his own, when he thinks this to be necessary or desirable.

## Question 1

Each of the following is an item of what might be called the "current folklore" about presently operative trends in American values. In each case fill in the blank ( ) with the code letter you regard as appropriate. If you feel the contention to be inadequately or vaguely formulated, please give it the most generous interpretation you can think of to make good sense of it. (In this event, please reword the item in your own way.)

KEY

The contention at issue is

A. definitely true
B. in large measure true
C. in some measure true
D. false
E. the very reverse of the truth
F. entirely meaningless

### Current "Folklore" About American Values

1.     We are losing our commitment to values in general. Nothing is dear to us throughout
( )     our lives—we choose only what momentarily fills the gap.

2.     American values are going to pot. The traditional American value foci (country, honor,
( )     independence, probity, etc.) are becoming things of indifference to us. They are no
        longer upheld or worried about.

3.     We are becoming more and more materialistic. The spiritual qualities of man are no
( )     longer precious to us.

4.     Our values are becoming more and more *social* values, with less and less emphasis
( )     upon *individual* values. (E.g., social injuctices worry us more than individual ones.)

5.     Our values are becoming more and more man-directed ("health," "success," "group-
( )     acceptance") and less and less God-directed ("living God-fearing lives," "doing
        God's work," "accepting what God ordains").

6.     Our traditional commitment to *moral* values are going by the board. Honesty, probity,
( )     etc. are becoming obsolete. Moral indignation is out of fashion. We are less and less
        prone to bring to bear the ideas of right and wrong, and increasingly diffident about
        our ability to make such discriminations.

7.     Our taste and our aesthetic values in general are being debased (by mass-culture,
( )     television, pulp magazines, etc.).

8.     We have lost our attachment to the serious values that reflect genuine human needs
( )     (health, friendships, freedom, etc.). Increasingly we value what is essentially frivolous
        (escape, diversion, amusement).

9.     Respondent's choice (specify):
( )

## Question 2

For each of the listed values, indicate whether the next generation (say to 2000 A.D.) will, in your opinion, see a change in the direction of:

   ++ greatly increased emphasis
   + slightly increased emphasis
   0 little or no change
   − slightly decreased emphasis
   − − greatly decreased emphasis

Wherever you foresee a change (i.e., give an entry other than 0) indicate whether this change is to be regarded, from *society's* point of view, as being:

   D+ very desirable
   D desirable
   0 neutral
   U undesirable
   U− very undesirable

   Note: When we "value something more" (e.g., our physical comfort) this does not necessarily mean that we devote more money, time, or attention to it: we may well not, but may simply "take it for granted." The point is that we would be the *more willing and prepared* to take steps on behalf of its maintenance *if this were to be necessary.*

| Value | Change/Desirability | Value | Change/Desirability |
|---|---|---|---|
| 1 one's own pleasure | ( / ) | 22 law and order | ( / ) |
| 2 physical well-being and comfort | ( / ) | 23 service to others (voluntary) | ( / ) |
| | | 24 idealism | ( / ) |
| 3 economic security | ( / ) | 25 natural beauty (or environment) | ( / ) |
| 4 convenience (in style of life) | ( / ) | | |
| 5 self-respect | ( / ) | 26 culture | ( / ) |
| 6 self-fulfillment | ( / ) | 27 aesthetic beauty (e.g. in architecture) | ( / ) |
| 7 self-reliance | ( / ) | | |
| 8 love and affection | ( / ) | 28 personal beauty ("good grooming," etc.) | ( / ) |
| 9 wealth | ( / ) | | |
| 10 prowess and ability | ( / ) | 29 novelty | ( / ) |
| 11 success | ( / ) | 30 equality and civil rights | ( / ) |
| 12 power | ( / ) | 31 patriotism | ( / ) |
| 13 freedom from interference | ( / ) | 32 democracy | ( / ) |
| 14 privacy | ( / ) | 33 social justice | ( / ) |
| 15 leisure | ( / ) | 34 peace | ( / ) |
| 16 friendship | ( / ) | 35 internationalism | ( / ) |
| 17 intelligence | ( / ) | 36 human dignity | ( / ) |
| 18 reasonableness and rationality | ( / ) | 37 reverence for life | ( / ) |
| 19 prudence | ( / ) | 38 Respondent's | ( / ) |
| 20 devotion to family | ( / ) | 39 Choice | ( / ) |
| 21 conscientiousness | ( / ) | 40 (specify) | ( / ) |

## Question 3

Values can usefully be considered from the standpoint of certain groupings that may be set up for the purpose of contrast and comparison. It is to be recognized that these groupings are loose-textured cross-classifications, and are not neatly compartmentalizing divisions.

The responses to be given to this question are of exactly the same sort as with the preceding. Again we use the same key for grading value changes and evaluating the desirability, from society's point of view, of a presumed change.

*Extent of Change*

++ greatly increased emphasis
+ slightly increased emphasis
0 little or no change
− slightly decreased emphasis
− − greatly decreased emphasis

*Desirability of the Change (for Society)*

D+ very desirable
D desirable
0 neutral
U undesirable
U− very undesirable

*Value Grouping*

*Change/ Desirability*

1. self-regarding values (e.g., prudence, self-advancement) ( / )
2. other-regarding values (e.g., service to others, tolerance) ( / )
3. material (e.g., personal comfort, economic security) ( / )
4. spiritual (e.g., reverence for life) ( / )
5. aesthetic (e.g., attractiveness in design of furniture, etc.) ( / )
6. religious (e.g., piety, self-sacrifice) ( / )
7. personal (e.g., self-reliance, intelligence) ( / )
8. social (e.g., social justice, service to others) ( / )
9. local (e.g., civic pride) ( / )
10. national (e.g., patriotism, national pride) ( / )
11. international (e.g., the brotherhood of man, peace) ( / )
12. prowess (e.g., fitness, physical skill) ( / )
13. intellect (e.g., intelligence, wit) ( / )
14. character (e.g., conscientiousness, reasonableness) ( / )
15. self-oriented (e.g., success, prestige) ( / )
16. parochial (e.g., family-pride, fraternity loyalties) ( / )
17. humanitarian (e.g., "idealism," human dignity) ( / )
18. ⎱ Respondent's ( / )
19. ⎰ Choice ( / )
20. (specify) ( / )

## Question 4

Consider the list given below of probable scientific/technological/demographic/socio-economic changes or innovations, taking place over the next generation (through 2000 A.D.). In each case, four items should be indicated in the appropriate column:

A. Whether, in your opinion, the change will have
        O for *little or no*
        + for *some*
      ++ for *a significant*
    effect upon U.S. values.
B. What value(s) from the list in Question 2 will be primarily affected? (Please list them by number.)
C. Whether the effect is an increased emphasis ( ↑ ) or a de-emphasis ( ↓ ).
D. Whether each of these particular changes is to be viewed, from society's point of view, as being:
        D+ very desirable
        D desirable
        O neutral
        U undesirable
        U− very undesirable

The respondent is not asked to estimate the likelihood of the development's occurrence—but to consider its effects *if it occurs.*

|  | A.<br>Extent of<br>Value<br>Implication | Nature of Value Effects<br>(B \| C \| D)<br>(Value\|Direction\|Desirability) |
|---|:---:|:---:|
| *Possible Development* |  |  |
| **I. [POLITICO-ECONOMIC-SOCIOLOGICAL]** |  |  |
| 1. domestic population explosion | ( ) | ( / / ) ( / / ) ( / / ) |
| 2. massive urban sprawl (supercrowding) | ( ) | ( / / ) ( / / ) ( / / ) |
| 3. rise of extremism in U.S. politics | ( ) | ( / / ) ( / / ) ( / / ) |
| 4. Hawaiinization of race relations in the U.S. | ( ) | ( / / ) ( / / ) ( / / ) |
| 5. rise of super-welfare state in U.S. | ( ) | ( / / ) ( / / ) ( / / ) |
| 6. social restratification in an affluent society | ( ) | ( / / ) ( / / ) ( / / ) |
| 7. rise of the "welfare world" | ( ) | ( / / ) ( / / ) ( / / ) |
| 8. thorough realization of civil rights | ( ) | ( / / ) ( / / ) ( / / ) |
| 9. omnipresent central planning | ( ) | ( / / ) ( / / ) ( / / ) |
| 10. chronic limited warfare | ( ) | ( / / ) ( / / ) ( / / ) |
| 11. greatly increased internationalism and<br>    multinationalism | ( ) | ( / / ) ( / / ) ( / / ) |
| 12. worldwide armaments agreement | ( ) | ( / / ) ( / / ) ( / / ) |
| 13. atomic weapons proliferation | ( ) | ( / / ) ( / / ) ( / / ) |
| 14. a Chinese takeover of Asia | ( ) | ( / / ) ( / / ) ( / / ) |
| 15. a collapse of the U.N. | ( ) | ( / / ) ( / / ) ( / / ) |
| 16. OTHER (please specify) | ( ) | ( / / ) ( / / ) ( / / ) |
| **II. [EDUCATION AND PSYCHOTECHNICS]** |  |  |
| 1. an intensified knowledge explosion | ( ) | ( / / ) ( / / ) ( / / ) |
| 2. upsurge of aesthetic awareness and<br>    sensitivity | ( ) | ( / / ) ( / / ) ( / / ) |
| 3. continuing reeducation for most | ( ) | ( / / ) ( / / ) ( / / ) |
| 4. supersimple education (using drugs) wide<br>    use of sophisticated teaching-machines | ( ) | ( / / ) ( / / ) ( / / ) |
| 5. psychological engineering (e.g., by<br>    socially accepted use of personality-<br>    control drugs) | ( ) | ( / / ) ( / / ) ( / / ) |
| 6. large increases in human energy and<br>    performance levels | ( ) | ( / / ) ( / / ) ( / / ) |
| 7. OTHER (please specify) | ( ) | ( / / ) ( / / ) ( / / ) |
| **III. [BIOTECHNICS]** |  |  |
| 1. artificial organs | ( ) | ( / / ) ( / / ) ( / / ) |
| 2. biochemical general immunization | ( ) | ( / / ) ( / / ) ( / / ) |
| 3. control of aging process (life-prolonga-<br>    tion past 150 for some) | ( ) | ( / / ) ( / / ) ( / / ) |
| 4. fertility control and supersimple<br>    contraception | ( ) | ( / / ) ( / / ) ( / / ) |
| 5. genetic control of progeny (sex, IQ,<br>    physical features) | ( ) | ( / / ) ( / / ) ( / / ) |
| 6. OTHER (please specify) | ( ) | ( / / ) ( / / ) ( / / ) |
| **IV. [AUTOMATION]** |  |  |
| 1. massive automation in commerce and<br>    industry (including management) | ( ) | ( / / ) ( / / ) ( / / ) |
| 2. automation in the home (household<br>    "robots") | ( ) | ( / / ) ( / / ) ( / / ) |
| 3. automation in information (automated<br>    libraries and automatic translation) | ( ) | ( / / ) ( / / ) ( / / ) |

**KEY:**

| *Extent* | *Direction* | *Desirability* |
|---|---|---|
| O little or none | ↑ increased emphasis | D + very desirable |
| + some | ↓ decreased emphasis | D desirable |
| + + significant |  | O neutral |
|  |  | U undesirable |
|  |  | U − very undesirable |

| Possible Development | A.<br>Extent of<br>Value<br>Implication | Nature of Value Effects<br>(B \| C \| D)<br>(Value/Direction/Desirability) | | |
|---|---|---|---|---|
| 4. automation in the professions (law, medical diagnosis) | ( ) | ( / / ) | ( / / ) | ( / / ) |
| 5. OTHER (please specify) | ( ) | ( / / ) | ( / / ) | ( / / ) |

### V. [TRANSPORT AND COMMUNICATIONS]

| Possible Development | | | | |
|---|---|---|---|---|
| 1. the TV-telephone | ( ) | ( / / ) | ( / / ) | ( / / ) |
| 2. near-automatic largescale goods transport | ( ) | ( / / ) | ( / / ) | ( / / ) |
| 3. instantaneous worldwide communication (by satellite) | ( ) | ( / / ) | ( / / ) | ( / / ) |
| 4. super-speedy worldwide transport of people | ( ) | ( / / ) | ( / / ) | ( / / ) |
| 5. global ballistic transport of goods (on small scale) | ( ) | ( / / ) | ( / / ) | ( / / ) |
| 6. OTHER (please specify) | ( ) | ( / / ) | ( / / ) | ( / / ) |

### VI. [SPACE]

| Possible Development | | | | |
|---|---|---|---|---|
| 1. extensive space exploration (Mars landing) and moon colonization (beyond the Antarctica scale) | ( ) | ( / / ) | ( / / ) | ( / / ) |
| 2. discovery of remote intelligent life | ( ) | ( / / ) | ( / / ) | ( / / ) |
| 3. OTHER (please specify) | ( ) | ( / / ) | ( / / ) | ( / / ) |

### VII. [MISCELLANEOUS]

| Possible Development | | | | |
|---|---|---|---|---|
| 1. weather control | ( ) | ( / / ) | ( / / ) | ( / / ) |
| 2. synthetic proteins and ocean farming | ( ) | ( / / ) | ( / / ) | ( / / ) |
| 3. OTHER (please specify) | ( ) | ( / / ) | ( / / ) | ( / / ) |

**KEY:**

| *Extent* | *Direction* | *Desirability* | |
|---|---|---|---|
| O  little or none | ↑ increased emphasis | D+ | very desirable |
| +  some | ↓ decreased emphasis | D | desirable |
| ++ significant | | O | neutral |
| | | U | undesirable |
| | | U− | very undesirable |

## STATISTICAL SUMMARY OF RESULTS

## Question 1

NUMERICAL RESULTS

| Item No. | NUMBER OF RESPONSES (*Response Coding*) | | | | | | No. Ans. | Total No. | Score | Index | Interpretation |
|---|---|---|---|---|---|---|---|---|---|---|---|
| | *A* | *B* | *C* | *D* | *E* | *F* | | | | | |
| 1 | 0 | 3 | 18 | 24 | 5 | 8 | 0 | 58 | —39 | —.67 | Probably false |
| 2 | 0 | 5 | 18 | 31 | 1 | 2 | 1 | 58 | —37 | —.65 | Probably false |
| 3 | 1 | 10 | 18 | 17 | 6 | 3 | 3 | 58 | —11 | —.20 | |
| 4 | 3 | 15 | 21 | 13 | 2 | 2 | 2 | 58 | +28 | +.50 | Probably true |
| 5 | 26 | 24 | 7 | 0 | 0 | 1 | 0 | 58 | +133 | +2.29 | True |
| 6 | 1 | 6 | 23 | 20 | 5 | 1 | 2 | 58 | —17 | —.30 | |
| 7 | 4 | 2 | 15 | 26 | 6 | 3 | 2 | 58 | —39 | —.70 | Probably false |
| 8 | 1 | 3 | 18 | 29 | 4 | 1 | 2 | 58 | —43 | —.74 | Probably false |

PERCENTAGES

| Item No. | NUMBER OF RESPONSES (*Response Coding*) | | | | | | No. Ans. |
|---|---|---|---|---|---|---|---|
| | *A* | *B* | *C* | *D* | *E* | *F* | |
| 1 | 0 | 5 | 31 | 41 | 9 | 14 | 0 |
| 2 | 0 | 9 | 31 | 53 | 2 | 3 | 2 |
| 3 | 2 | 17 | 31 | 30 | 10 | 5 | 5 |
| 4 | 5 | 26 | 36 | 22 | 3 | 3 | 3 |
| 5 | 45 | 41 | 12 | 0 | 0 | 2 | 0 |
| 6 | 2 | 10 | 40 | 34 | 9 | 2 | 3 |
| 7 | 7 | 3 | 26 | 45 | 10 | 5 | 3 |
| 8 | 2 | 5 | 31 | 50 | 7 | 2 | 3 |

*Key to Score and Index*
1. For the *score* count the letter entries as follows: A = +3, B = +2, C = +1, D = —2, E = —3, F = 0.
2. The index is the *mean score*.

*Note:* In the "Interpretation" we gloss an Index value of ≥.5 as meaning "probably true" and one ≤ —.5 as meaning "probably false."

## Question 2

| | NUMBER OF RESPONSES (Response Coding | | | | | | | | | $x$ Total No. Expecting Outcome | $y$ No. Considering Outcome as Desirable | $(y/x.100)$ |
|---|---|---|---|---|---|---|---|---|---|---|---|---|
| Item No. | ++ | + | o | − | −− | Total No. | Score | Index | Probable Outcome | | | % |
| 1 | 14 | 25 | 11 | 4 | 0 | 54 | 49 | .91 | + | 39 | 20 | 51 |
| 2 | 20 | 25 | 9 | 1 | 0 | 55 | 64 | 1.16 | + | 45 | 32 | 71 |
| 3 | 20 | 26 | 3 | 6 | 1 | 56 | 58 | 1.04 | + | 46 | 35 | 76 |
| 4 | 15 | 34 | 4 | 0 | 0 | 53 | 64 | 1.21 | + | 49 | 33 | 67 |
| 5 | 2 | 16 | 24 | 11 | 0 | 53 | 9 | .17 | | | | |
| 6 | 9 | 24 | 11 | 8 | 1 | 53 | 32 | .60 | + | 33 | 32 | 97 |
| 7 | 2 | 5 | 11 | 29 | 8 | 55 | −36 | −.65 | − | 40 | 8 | 20 |
| 8 | 3 | 14 | 30 | 5 | 2 | 54 | 11 | .20 | | | | |
| 9 | 2 | 16 | 15 | 19 | 2 | 54 | −3 | −.06 | | | | |
| 10 | 7 | 22 | 13 | 10 | 1 | 53 | 24 | .45 | | | | |
| 11 | 4 | 14 | 18 | 16 | 0 | 52 | 6 | .12 | | | | |
| 12 | 3 | 9 | 26 | 13 | 0 | 51 | 2 | .04 | | | | |
| 13 | 2 | 14 | 11 | 20 | 8 | 55 | −18 | −.33 | | | | |
| 14 | 7 | 12 | 5 | 18 | 13 | 55 | −18 | −.33 | | | | |
| 15 | 20 | 28 | 4 | 2 | 0 | 54 | 66 | 1.22 | + | 48 | 35 | 73 |
| 16 | 2 | 7 | 35 | 8 | 2 | 54 | −1 | −.02 | | | | |
| 17 | 10 | 30 | 11 | 3 | 0 | 54 | 47 | .87 | + | 40 | 34 | 85 |
| 18 | 2 | 28 | 19 | 4 | 1 | 54 | 26 | .48 | | | | |
| 19 | 0 | 12 | 24 | 17 | 1 | 54 | −7 | −.13 | | | | |
| 20 | 0 | 6 | 15 | 30 | 3 | 54 | −30 | −.56 | − | 33 | 6 | 18 |
| 21 | 1 | 1 | 28 | 21 | 3 | 54 | −24 | −.44 | | | | |
| 22 | 1 | 31 | 9 | 13 | 0 | 54 | 20 | .37 | | | | |
| 23 | 4 | 27 | 14 | 10 | 1 | 56 | 23 | .41 | | | | |
| 24 | 2 | 13 | 21 | 15 | 1 | 52 | 0 | 0 | | | | |
| 25 | 10 | 30 | 4 | 10 | 1 | 55 | 38 | .69 | + | 40 | 38 | 95 |
| 26 | 5 | 31 | 12 | 5 | 1 | 54 | 34 | .63 | + | 36 | 33 | 92 |
| 27 | 10 | 30 | 8 | 5 | 0 | 53 | 45 | .85 | + | 40 | 37 | 93 |
| 28 | 3 | 16 | 30 | 5 | 0 | 54 | 17 | .31 | | | | |
| 29 | 7 | 27 | 12 | 7 | 0 | 53 | 34 | .64 | + | 34 | 10 | 29 |
| 30 | 14 | 34 | 7 | 0 | 0 | 55 | 62 | 1.13 | + | 48 | 47 | 98 |
| 31 | 1 | 3 | 17 | 28 | 5 | 54 | −33 | −.61 | − | 33 | 24 | 73 |
| 32 | 1 | 19 | 23 | 7 | 1 | 51 | 12 | .24 | | | | |
| 33 | 2 | 42 | 9 | 1 | 0 | 54 | 45 | .83 | + | 44 | 43 | 98 |
| 34 | 16 | 20 | 15 | 2 | 0 | 53 | 50 | .94 | + | 36 | 35 | 97 |
| 35 | 23 | 22 | 8 | 1 | 0 | 53 | 67 | 1.26 | + | 45 | 44 | 98 |
| 36 | 4 | 26 | 13 | 9 | 1 | 53 | 23 | .43 | | | | |
| 37 | 6 | 12 | 19 | 17 | 1 | 55 | 5 | .09 | | | | |

**Key to Score, Index, and "Outcome"**

1. For the score count the +/− entries as follows: ++ = +2
   + = +1
   0 = 0
   − = −1
   −− = −2

2. The *index* is the average score.
3. The *outcome* is + if index ⩾.5 and − if index ⩽−.5.

## Question 3

| Item No. | NUMBER OF RESPONSES (Response Coding) | | | | | No. Ans. | Total No. | Score | Index | Probable Outcome | $x$ Total No. Expecting Outcome | $y$ No. Considering Outcome as Desirable | $(y/x.100)$ % |
|---|---|---|---|---|---|---|---|---|---|---|---|---|---|
| | ++ | + | o | − | − − | | | | | | | | |
| 1 | 4 | 15 | 16 | 16 | 1 | 0 | 52 | 5 | .10 | | | | |
| 2 | 6 | 28 | 11 | 6 | 1 | 0 | 52 | 32 | .62 | + | 34 | 33 | 97 |
| 3 | 8 | 34 | 5 | 5 | 0 | 0 | 52 | 45 | .87 | + | 42 | 30 | 71 |
| 4 | 1 | 16 | 16 | 18 | 1 | 1 | 52 | −2 | −.04 | | | | |
| 5 | 2 | 38 | 5 | 6 | 1 | 0 | 52 | 34 | .65 | + | 40 | 40 | 100 |
| 6 | 0 | 3 | 8 | 34 | 7 | 0 | 52 | −45 | −.87 | − | 41 | 22 | 54 |
| 7 | 2 | 20 | 16 | 11 | 1 | 2 | 50 | 11 | .22 | | | | |
| 8 | 5 | 38 | 6 | 3 | 0 | 0 | 52 | 45 | .87 | + | 43 | 43 | 100 |
| 9 | 0 | 13 | 12 | 26 | 1 | 0 | 52 | −15 | −.29 | | | | |
| 10 | 0 | 7 | 26 | 27 | 1 | 1 | 51 | −22 | −.43 | | | | |
| 11 | 4 | 39 | 6 | 3 | 0 | 0 | 52 | 44 | .85 | + | 43 | 43 | 100 |
| 12 | 2 | 15 | 18 | 17 | 0 | 0 | 52 | 2 | .04 | | | | |
| 13 | 7 | 32 | 8 | 4 | 0 | 1 | 51 | 42 | .82 | + | 39 | 35 | 90 |
| 14 | 1 | 13 | 24 | 12 | 0 | 2 | 50 | 3 | .06 | | | | |
| 15 | 3 | 14 | 22 | 13 | 0 | 0 | 52 | 7 | .13 | | | | |
| 16 | 0 | 4 | 14 | 32 | 2 | 0 | 52 | −32 | −.62 | − | 34 | 19 | 56 |
| 17 | 3 | 24 | 12 | 12 | 1 | 0 | 52 | 16 | .31 | | | | |

*Key to Score, Index, and "Outcome"*
1. For the score count the +/− entries as follows: ++ = +2
                                                                                    + = +1
                                                                                    0 = 0
                                                                                    − = −1
                                                                                    − − = −2
2. The *index* is the average score.
3. The *outcome* is + if index ⩾.5 and − if index ⩽−.5.

Key to Question 4

*Key to Score, Index, and "Outcome"*
1. For the *score* count ++ as 2
                                          + as 1
                                          0 as 0
2. The *index* is the average score.
3. The *outcome* is ++ if index ⩾1.25 and + if index ⩽1.00.

## Question 4

| Item No. | ++ | + | o | Total No. | Score | Index | Probable Outcome | Values Affected ↑ | ↓ |
|---|---|---|---|---|---|---|---|---|---|
| **I** | | | | | | | | | |
| 1 | 25 | 21 | 0 | 46 | 71 | 1.54 | ++ | 3, 14 | 7, 13, 14, 25 |
| 2 | 25 | 21 | 1 | 47 | 71 | 1.51 | ++ | 13, 25 | 2, 4, 13, 14, 25, 27 |
| 3 | 20 | 17 | 9 | 46 | 57 | 1.24 | + | 12, 31 | 13,18,30,32, 35 |
| 4 | 22 | 17 | 8 | 47 | 61 | 1.30 | ++ | 30, 33, 36 | |
| 5 | 23 | 18 | 5 | 46 | 64 | 1.39 | ++ | 2, 3, 33 | 3, 7, 13, 14 |
| 6 | 10 | 22 | 9 | 41 | 42 | 1.02 | + | 3, 9, 11, 12, 30, 33 | |
| 7 | 19 | 20 | 8 | 47 | 58 | 1.23 | + | 3, 33, 34, 35 | 7 |
| 8 | 18 | 24 | 5 | 47 | 60 | 1.28 | ++ | 30, 33, 36 | |
| 9 | 15 | 28 | 3 | 46 | 58 | 1.26 | ++ | 3 | 7, 13, 14 |
| 10 | 11 | 23 | 13 | 47 | 45 | .96 | | | |
| 11 | 15 | 27 | 4 | 46 | 57 | 1.24 | + | 33, 34, 35, 36 | 31 |
| 12 | 14 | 20 | 12 | 46 | 48 | 1.04 | + | 34, 35 | 12, 31 |
| 13 | 17 | 20 | 9 | 46 | 54 | 1.17 | + | 12, 31, 34 | 22, 34, 35, 37 |
| 14 | 8 | 24 | 14 | 46 | 40 | .87 | | | |
| 15 | 15 | 18 | 13 | 46 | 48 | 1.04 | + | | 34, 35 |
| **II** | | | | | | | | | |
| 1 | 20 | 21 | 5 | 46 | 61 | 1.33 | ++ | 2, 3, 17, 18, 26 | |
| 2 | 10 | 30 | 6 | 46 | 50 | 1.09 | + | 6, 25, 26, 27, 28 | |
| 3 | 13 | 28 | 6 | 47 | 54 | 1.15 | + | 3, 5, 6, 7, 17, 18 | |
| 4 | 9 | 30 | 4 | 43 | 48 | 1.12 | + | 1, 6, 17 | 17 |
| 5 | 20 | 20 | 5 | 45 | 60 | 1.33 | ++ | 2 | 5, 7, 13, 14 |
| 6 | 15 | 18 | 13 | 46 | 48 | 1.04 | + | 6, 7, 10, 23 | |
| **III** | | | | | | | | | |
| 1 | 10 | 20 | 15 | 45 | 40 | .89 | | | |
| 2 | 8 | 23 | 14 | 45 | 39 | .87 | | | |
| 3 | 19 | 18 | 7 | 44 | 56 | 1.27 | ++ | 1, 2, 6, 15, 37 | |
| 4 | 17 | 20 | 7 | 44 | 54 | 1.23 | + | 1, 3, 8, 20, 36, 37 | |
| 5 | 19 | 15 | 8 | 42 | 52 | 1.26 | ++ | | 36 |
| **IV** | | | | | | | | | |
| 1 | 16 | 21 | 6 | 43 | 53 | 1.23 | + | 2, 3, 15 | 3 |
| 2 | 5 | 22 | 16 | 43 | 32 | .74 | | | |
| 3 | 9 | 18 | 15 | 42 | 36 | .86 | | | |
| 4 | 3 | 22 | 17 | 42 | 28 | .67 | | | |
| **V** | | | | | | | | | |
| 1 | 3 | 16 | 24 | 43 | 22 | .51 | | | |
| 2 | 2 | 19 | 22 | 43 | 23 | .53 | | | |
| 3 | 8 | 26 | 9 | 43 | 42 | .98 | | | |
| 4 | 7 | 25 | 10 | 42 | 39 | .93 | | | |
| 5 | 2 | 12 | 27 | 41 | 16 | .39 | | | |
| **VI** | | | | | | | | | |
| 1 | 6 | 16 | 20 | 42 | 28 | .67 | | | |
| 2 | 17 | 12 | 14 | 43 | 46 | 1.07 | + | 35, 37 | |
| **VII** | | | | | | | | | |
| 1 | 9 | 19 | 15 | 43 | 37 | .86 | | | |
| 2 | 9 | 16 | 18 | 43 | 34 | .79 | | | |

# LOOKING FORWARD II

# The feedback between technology and values

*Theodore J. Gordon*

When we consider the evolving behavior patterns of societies over the past millenia, we are aware of an apparent relationship between values and technology. History is rich with examples of this relationship, from the advent of fire to the exploration of space. Note the contemporary question: "Why go to the moon?—if God had meant us to be there, He would surely have put us there." Even though we can find many examples of the connection between technology and values, the mechanism connecting the two is not immediately obvious. How do the values held by a society affect the technology which that society produces? In what manner does the technology which a society employs affect its values? The answers to these questions are important because our society is beginning to plan the course of its technological development; planning involves goal selection and goal selection involves values. Therefore to aid in planning, and to gain insight into the possible consequences of our decisions it is important to prove the relationships between technology and values.

As a first tentative step in exploring this relationship, a brief study of the potential social uses of certain items of future technology was conducted for this symposium. The potential innovations analyzed and their anticipated social consequences are summarized in the appendix to this paper. This listing will form a starting point for the value simulation to be conducted later on. The technological changes considered were selected from several forecasting studies; to present a manageable package, the test was limited to twenty items which appeared to be "value laden." Each item was first described in terms of the present state of the art. Then in a series of "brainstorming" sessions, each item was reviewed methodically to construct a list of potential social responses to the envisioned development. These responses were categorized as follows: technological, economical, health, educational, political, and social. It was hoped that this breakdown would order the analysis and permit description of as many as possible of the potential applications of technology which might occur in alternative future societies. The study was clearly not exhaustive, either in terms of stated possible future technologies or possible social uses of these tools; yet even this brief glimpse showed that society has tremendous latitude in the application of new devices and techniques.

As an example of the techniques employed, we examined the possible implications of the attainment of a 100-year life expectancy. Clearly the trend in the United States suggests that a 100-year life expectancy will have been obtained just after the turn of the century. The rate of increase of life expectancy has been almost linear, rising from 38.3 years in 1850 to 67.5 years in 1963. Research going on in the country today would seem to indicate that continued improvement can be expected. New organs will become available through transplanting or prosthesis, artificial organs will probably come into much wider use, eventual chemical control over aging may be possible as genetologists reach a deeper understanding of the aging process. The life span of some laboratory animals has been doubled, for example, by tight control over diet. Aging "instructions" may be contained within the nuclei of human cells; genetic manipulation might amend these instructions. Continued research in the mechanisms of bacterial and viral diseases may lead eventually to complete, general immunization. All of these activities led us to believe that a forecast of increased life expectancy would be reasonable.

With this background we ask what this increased life span might mean to various segments of our society. We presumed a socio-political environment generally similar to that which we have at present, and probed possible effects of the development (in this case, 100-year life expectancy). For example, the results of the increased life span which we suggest might be possible are:

*Economic:*
It must be assumed that an increase in life expectancy will also increase the number of years in which a man remains potentially useful and productive. Thus a 100-year life span implies that increasing numbers of people beyond the age of 65 may wish to be employed. Leisure time would increase and expenditures for occupation of this time would also rise.

Our Social Security structure will require revision if economic minima are to be provided to the older citizens of our country.

The "senior citizen" bloc will have unique consumer demands such as: low speed automobiles, perhaps battery powered for urban transportation; artificial organs; picture phones; mass media entertainment; and household robots.

In spite of the presumed vitality of the older population, a maximum age of employment law might be enacted so that the younger people can work. If extensive social security measures were in effect, the young work force would thus be devoting part of its output to the support of the "senior citizen" group.

*Political:*
The older people may form a political group of considerable power and significance. Special legislation may be enacted for the convenience of this group.

*Social:*
A shifting of the median age of the population may be accompanied by greater urbanization.
   Great leisure communities may be formed to resemble periods from the past. This artificial return-to-a-more-gracious-age would provide retired citizens a choice of, for example, colonial or gay nineties cities having modern advantages but requiring strict adherence to the mores and technology of the era.

In preparing this compendium of potential social responses to the twenty hypothesized new technological developments, we asked, "Given this technology, what might society do?" In asking this question, the notion occurred to us that the mechanism relating values to technology

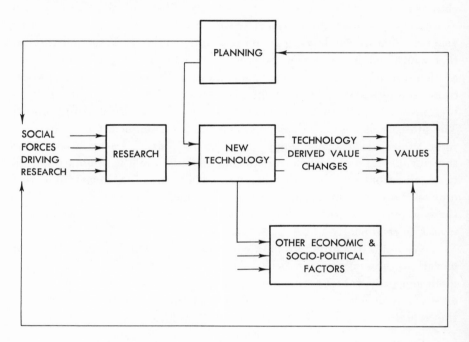

Figure 1

and technology to values was probably a feedback system in which values helped determine the directions of technological development. Once established, technology provided the tools for the pursuit of new values and indeed influenced the new values themselves. The nature of this feedback mechanism and its implication in planning will be discussed in this paper.

   A postulated model of the interface between values and technology is shown in Figure 1. The major elements of the model are: *research* which, when applied, results in *technology*; *values*, which are affected by technology and other factors; and *planning* which serves as a filter in the feedback loop between values and research. The model implies that values influence the forces which drive technology, directly and indirectly. The direct path results from the value systems held by the researchers themselves; the indirect path reflects the impact of external planning on research. This model is obviously qualitative and nonrigorous. Factors which link these major sociological elements have undoubtedly been omitted. However, even this simplified mechanical concept of the complex social operation which forms and modifies our values may have some importance. First, the model at least hints at the possibility of constructing more intricate and accurate models. Even the simplified model concept can serve as a basis for simulation exercises which may be useful in sharpening the concept of the mechanism. Most importantly perhaps, the model permits an ordered inquiry into the factors which drive research, the means by which technology influences values, and the implications of planning as a moderator of the loop.

## Forces driving research

Today, the principal source of inspiration for research is the researcher himself. He works on projects that interest and challenge him and that he considers solvable. Beyond personal motivations there lies the influence of available funding for the project. Now, let us look at how these factors—interest, challenge, solvability, and fundability—influence research.[1]

Interest as a motivation for selection of a research project stems from many sources—academic friendships and associations, for example, or respect for past problems articulated by influential professors. Interest also runs in tides, sweeping across the disciplines in great waves of publications. Although no surveys of recent scientific and technical publications have been run, a general literature scan suggests the tide in the last decade featured elementary particle physics; now the tide is in the biological sciences: biochemistry, the almighty gene, inheritance, and the DNA Code. The next decade or the decade after, it may be in cosmology or geodesy, but as the man in the street might say, "Who needs it? Cure my corns and you'll really have something."

The limits of acceptable challenge and solvability are set by the scientific method. The method permits diverse researchers—separated geographically, philosophically, politically, and ethnically—to work toward common goals. Means of scientific communication are open to these people, so that, more often than not, their work augments one another's to broaden

---

1. The material relating to the factors controlling the directions of technology is drawn from: T. J. Gordon, "Motivations for Engineering Research," keynote paper, *Proceedings of the Conference on Research Enlargement*, Report 66–18, UCLA, March 1966.

the base of understanding in a given discipline. However, the scientific method forces nature into neat conceptual boxes. The boxes contain facts, theories, and methods that are appropriate to the discipline. They form a way of looking at a set of phenomena that has been found to produce predictable and acceptable results. The information in a given box is taught to young scientists in universities; it is the information from which textbooks are constructed and courses are taught. These boxes form constrained views of particular aspects of the world which must be believed as starting points for research. These beliefs are the ticket of admission to the profession of science.

Once these beliefs are stated and accepted, certain legitimate problems are opened to scientific investigation. It is the business of normal research to probe these open questions, to determine significant facts that add to the precision of beliefs, to test the paradigm in a variety of new situations, to resolve the ambiguities in the original context of the rules of the game. In other words, "normal" research, which is the major occupation of most scientists, is not directed towards the novel, but toward the refinement of previously stated positions.

Research outside of the paradigm is valued when the old beliefs fail in precision or prediction, when there is no alternative but to abandon the old ideas. In this environment, new ideas are welcome; but if new ideas are presented before the crisis is clearly in evidence, they will be rejected, since scientific business is being conducted well enough on the old principles. This view of the structure of science comes from the brilliant work by Thomas Kuhn, *The Structure of Scientific Revolutions*.[2]

Funding brings inhibiting limitations of its own. Aside from the massively funded government projects such as the Apollo lunar landing program, or the 200 BEV particle accelerator, "little science" funding is derived from mission-directed government agencies, private corporations, and universities. Today, over 60 percent of the nation's research funds for individual investigators comes from the government.[3] This funding is distributed by agencies with specific goals; thus innovation goals are set by the mission of the funding agency. We should note here exceptions to this pattern. The National Science Foundation issues its government grants without mission-oriented strings attached; but these funds account for only a very small part of the total research in the country.

Capital seems to be available in rather concentrated pockets. As the interest of researchers runs in tides so do the interests of capital. Research

2. Chicago, The University of Chicago Press, 1962.
3. *Basic Research and National Goals: A Report to the Committee on Science and Astronautics,* U.S. House of Representatives, Washington, D.C. 1965.

which is clearly associated with national security is easier to fund and can be funded to higher levels than, for example, research into artificial life.

Some "little scientists" work directly for industry. Here the long-range goals of corporations set the objectives for the research. The scientists in their company laboratories work ultimately toward the profit goal. There are some corporations, however, that allow their researchers to tackle any project which interests them on the theory that (1) it creates a good corporate image; (2) maybe something of value will come out of it; and (3) it's deductible anyway. Thus these factors of *personal interest, challenge, solvability*, and *fundability* set our research patterns and establish our technological future. The direction of research today is, in effect, determined by the interests of government and industry; the patterns of interest of individual scientists; and, the scientific method itself, which declares only certain fields of investigation fair game.

Note that the list of factors which drive technology does not include values *per se*. Yet, to a degree, all of these factors interrelate with value concepts. *Personal interest* comes from a lifetime of education at the hand of parents, society and teachers. Education must certainly include learning what society considers important, beautiful and meaningful, and applying this knowledge to one's work. While project *funding* is derived primarily from mission-directed agencies, some of these promote currently held values. The National Institute of Health, for example, is sponsoring research into the aging process with a view toward increasing life span. While the scientific method sets the limits of *solvability* and *challenge*, value directed research is not excluded from normal science. Clearly, our value structure today supports research and advancing technology. We are dedicated to national survival; in the age of status quo, technological preeminence is a political tool. Among the list of attributes of society which we generally consider "good" are: increasing personal comfort, advancement for the sake of advancement, knowledge: all of these values indicate that society today endorses technological progress. It is through these and similar mechanisms that currently held values impinge on the molding process of research, and in its turn, technology. More direct mechanisms seem to be rare. Research is seldom initiated simply to preserve values; the chastity belt may be the last case on record.

## Technology-derived value changes

While the effect of values on research seems to be largely implicit, the effect of technology on values seems to be more direct. Values apparently change to fit the world which technology presents. This change seems to occur through a number of mechanisms including: enhanced attainment, novelty, redistribution, restandardization, and increased information.[4]

The attainment of values brings individual satisfaction, happiness, in the past, today, or in the future. Changing technology clearly changes the means available to the individual and society for attaining value derived goals. For example, the value "friendship" today includes friends made via short wave radio. "Economic security" is enhanced by high speed ticker tapes and computers. "Pleasure" tomorrow may be drug induced or a sensation evoked by the electrical stimulation of portions of the cortex. In applying new technology to old value achievement situations, the values themselves may change subtly. Picture a future age in which complete biochemical immunization against viral and bacterial diseases is possible. In that world a head cold might be an unequaled mark of distinction, a cause for rejoicing. It might bring a week of nostalgia and evoke fond memories of the time of the aspirin and hot water bottle.

As pointed out by Rescher, some value changes are induced by sheer weight of boredom, by disillusionment and reaction. Changing fashions in clothing, and the length of teenage hair may be examples of this mode. New technology, all sparkling and chromed, is an antidote to boredom. Novelty, in itself, has become a value. We seem to be experimenters, testing this, trying that, always reaching for "the experience." I have heard the statement, perhaps I have even said it myself, "I'd like to try everything at least once." Technology gives us a never-ending parade of things to try in the unbounded search for the meaning of self, which after all, may be the base of all values. In the environment, anything new might be "in," or anything so far "out" it might be considered "in," and being "in" or "out," becomes a value for some. What could be "in" tomorrow? Green skin induced by genetic engineering, freezing of bodies after death and attempted resuscitation when the cure for death has been discovered, learning from a computer by direct connection with its memory, battery powered automobiles, hermaphrodism; almost anything you can think of.

Redistribution refers to that aspect of technology which promotes rapid spread of values. Television has been remarkably effective in supplying our new generation with a unified set of values. Technology will soon make this diffusion world-wide. Television and direct broadcast satellites in synchronous orbit, will carry words and images of what is right and proper and valuable to most people in the world. What one community does, perhaps others will desire to do. Automobiles have also promoted this diffusion through greatly increased mobility; technology is about to extend the jet

4. Part of this discussion follows the reasoning developed by Nicholas Rescher in his discussion of "The Dynamics of Value Change."

airplane to the supersonic transport. Ballistic rocket transports will permit travel to any point in the world within thirty minutes, if we could ever solve the problem of how to get to the rocket port. With these new tools coming, what's "in" will be quickly known, and known across the world.

Technology brings value restandardization. Values are usually satisfied only to some degree. No matter how much "security" someone has attained, there is more to be sought; the jug of "power" can never overfill. Technology changes the framework of value satisfaction. Freedom meant something a little different to the founders of our nation than it does to us. A hundred years ago, privacy meant a hundred acres between your house and your neighbor's; today it means the absence of telephone bugs. Beauty, pleasure, wealth, power, social justice; the meaning of all of these words is evolutionary and can be defined only at a particular point in time, in view of the technological framework in which they are set. Tomorrow, technology will restandardize our concepts of mother love with ova and sperm banks, our concepts of self with experience and pleasure amplification, and perhaps our concept of individual rights as automated abundance permits us to guarantee certain economic minima to all people.

Advancing research and technology will bring new information. This data will undoubtedly affect our inventory of values in degree and content. Here new values spread, not from the "in" group, but from the *cognessetti* to the rest of society. These changes are likely to be lasting over relatively long periods since they will affect some of the basic tenets of our reality. Our concepts of God and creation will change with the advent of laboratory created self-replicating molecules, the discovery of extra-terrestrial intelligence, and attainment of a higher degree of understanding of the mechanism of the formation of the solar system and the universe.

Thus, while the effect of values on research and the course of evolving technology seems to be minor, the effect of that technology on future values seems to be great. This sociological feedback loop can be compared to a giant audio amplifier in which part of the output is connected to the input. If the tuning of the feedback is proper, the amplifier is stable and the music is pure and undistorted; if the feedback is of improper phase or amplitude, wild oscillations can result and the concert can end in screeching failure. One wonders if our value feedback system is stable.

## Planning and value feedback

Planning in our time of rapid technological change is essential. Without adequate knowledge of the possible effects of our actions, technology may bring inadvertent calamity to the world. In the last decade there has been a growing realization that planning is important and possible in fields lying outside of the bounds of absolute scientific causality, and powerful planning tools have been developed. These include operations analysis, utility theory, gaming concepts, and systems engineering. All of these approaches to planning share certain common features: definition of the problem, statement of possible alternate solutions, and establishment of criteria for evaluation of the possible consequences and their alternate paths of action. It is in this last area, criteria evaluation, that future technology and current values interact. A planner must base his recommended course of action on certain values. "If we do thus and so, the results are apt to be 'better'." "Better" here means better for the company, the nation, or the individual depending on the problem being analyzed. Obviously the term "better" connotes certain implicit value judgments on the part of the planner; where the effect of technology on society is involved, the values must be sociological values. Thus the act of planning imposes the planner's judgment of future values on his conclusions.

If planners use today's values in their planning they imply that values will be or should be static, yet values are evolutionary. Do we know what's right for tomorrow? If we do not, how can we plan effectively? If we think we do, what freedom have we left for them?

Just as unexpected scientific uses appear for apparently useless scientific discoveries, so will pleasing uses be found for what we consider potentially odious developments today. Cases in point: atomic energy, born in terrifying destruction, can save us from power extinction which may accompany the depletion of our hydrocarbon resources; the music of Stravinsky has become pleasing; bathing, we have found, does not cause disease and loss of skin.

In the age of efficient fertility control and threatening over-population, sexual enjoyment may be separated from reproduction. This may be a lovely, beautiful, part of the natural order of things tomorrow. Today it seems wrong. Tomorrow may consider our worst vice, righteousness; our worst misery, happiness. They may be nearer the truth, since after all we and all the generations before us have not found the answers to the world's ghettos and wars, bigotry and injustice.

Take drugs for example. Most of us feel that there's danger here and would, if we could, guard our children from this vice.

The use of personality-control drugs looms as one of the major potential problems or blessings of the future. The spectrum of worlds which can crystallize around this technological development include these three possibilities: a subjugated Huxleyan society, dominated and soothed by dulling *Soma*; a hedonistic, over-leisured, drug addicted noncivilization:

or finally, a prosperous world where drugs bring memory, knowledge, and experience of self. Perhaps we fear a world where drugs are readily available because we are not sure values will remain strong enough to avoid the trap of hedonistic self-indulgence. Dr. Timothy Leary, an advocate of consciousness expansion through the use of LSD, has likened this worry to the fear felt by some at the birth of automotive transportation. He wrote:

The claim was made in 1900 that the motor carriage, accelerated to speeds several times that of the horsedrawn vehicle, would revolutionize society. . . . First of all, we object to the dangers: high speed will snap nervous minds, gas fumes are fatal, the noise will prevent cows from giving milk, horses will run away, criminals will exploit the automobile.

Then the puritanical objection: people will use cars for pleasure, for kicks.

Then we question utility: what can we do with speedy carriages? There are no men to repair them. There are no roads, few bridges. There are no skilled operators. The supply of fuel is small; who will sell you gas?

Then we raise the question of control: who should be allowed to own and operate these powerful and dangerous instruments? Perhaps they should be restricted to the government elite, to the military, to the medical profession. . . .

Now consider consciousness-expanding drugs. . . . No language. No trained operators. Lots of blacksmiths whose monopoly is threatened. A few people who do see an inevitable development of a new language, a transfiguration of every one of our social forms. And these few, of course, the ones who have taken the internal voyage. . . .

The political issue involves control: "Automobile" means that the free citizen moves *his* own car in external space. Internal automobile. Auto-administration. The freedom to expand your own consciousness—cannot be denied without due cause.[5]

Is Leary right? The attempted prohibition of alcohol, a drug certainly as dangerous in some respects as LSD, failed. The underlying value judgment on which prohibition was based either did not sample the real values of the people, or values changed with time. Could the same series of events take place with LSD? Today's legislation may not prevent its use, as legislation did not prevent the use of alcohol. Tomorrow's voters, attuned to the joys of personality control drugs, may repeal inhibiting laws, and shake their heads in wonder about the prudes who would have denied them the freedom to simply relax and enjoy life.

What is the answer? In planning we are striving to protect our children by guaranteeing the preservation of our values. Yet our children may not be happy with our values, and, left to their own devices may find value systems which put ours to shame. Somehow, planning must find a premise more encompassing than preservation of our values; I suggest that premise

5. Timothy Leary, "The Politics of Consciousness Expansion," *The Harvard Review*, Summer, 1963, pp. 36–37.

is the preservation of personal liberty, where the definition of liberty includes preservation of creativity and the right to initiate change. Note that liberty is not defined primarily as the right to pursue happiness, the right to satisfy values, because in a behavioristically controlled world, happiness may be found in subjugation. If we plan for an environment which preserves personal liberty our progeny will have the chance to use their judgment, not ours, in the application of our technological legacy.

# *Forecasts of certain technological developments and their potential social consequences*

## Index

## FERTILITY CONTROL

EVENT   World wide acceptance and use of oral contraceptives or other simple and inexpensive means of fertility control.

BACKGROUND   The major incentive for developing techniques of fertility control is to limit population levels. There seems to be general agreement that expanding, exploding population levels are undesirable. An extrapolation of today's increasing rate of growth would place world population at over nine billion within the next sixty years. This tripling of population implies a tripling of food, power, and resources production to maintain current per capita consumption levels. This will be very difficult to accomplish. Furthermore, increasing population levels apparently inhibit the rate of economic growth of developing countries since major portions of available resources must be devoted to sustenance and cannot be diverted to other segments of the economy such as industrialization.

Fertility control is possible today through chemical and mechanical means. Governments have generally recognized the dangers implicit in unchecked population increases, and have begun to propagandize for control, and, in some countries, have furnished contraceptive devices to all who request them. In many countries legalized abortion has materially reduced birth rates.

## Implications

TECHNOLOGY   As demand for fertility control increases, available devices will become more efficient.

A seriously over-saturated population level may result in greater pressure for space colonization of habitable planets.

Motivational research will identify the basic factors driving the population to saturation.

ECONOMY   Achievement of effective fertility control will result in more rapid emergence of the underdeveloped nations.

Overcontrol, that is a diminishing population level, could result in economic starvation—production without consumers.

HEALTH   Failure to gain control could result in wide-spread starvation, the Malthusian limit.

The incentive for the extension of life-span would diminish if the world overcrowds.

Overcrowding will produce unequaled problems in allocations of resources and in waste disposal. Some scientists have predicted that the earth will be doomed, eventually, by smog.[6]

Overcrowding can lead to social pathology in which abnormal behavior patterns are developed. In experiments with rats, overcrowding led to abandonment of progeny, hypersexual and homosexual behavior, cannibalism and other aberrations.[7]

6. See *Los Angeles Times*, August 8, 1965. Prediction made by Morris Neiburger of UCLA.
7. John B. Calhoun, "Population Density and Social Pathology," *Scientific American*, vol. 206 (1962), pp. 139–146.

EDUCATION   In the absence of control, education will become increasingly difficult. A tripling of population would imply a tripling of the world's schools and teaching staffs to maintain current levels of education. This would imply a change in techniques to achieve more efficient methods including teaching machines, television grammar schools and high schools, reliance on canned material, etc.

SOCIAL   These conditions have been predicted for the overcrowded world of the future:[8]

a. Highways are one constant traffic jam.
b. The government has rigid control over the number of cars produced; a new one can be produced only when an old car is taken out of circulation. There is no more room for roads.
c. A birth certificate is the government's permit for birth; one cannot be issued until a death is recorded.
d. A maximum age bill is enacted; when this age is reached, a man may no longer be dependent on society for food or shelter.
e. The world's political factions are the "juniors" and "seniors." The juniors believe the world belongs to the young; the seniors advocate eugenics, sterilization, and abortion. The final world war may occur between these factions.
f. Cannibalism breaks out.

Extension of the practice of birth control among the minority races in the United States might decrease the social dependence of these groups and tend to reduce discrimination.

In the age of fertility control sexual enjoyment may be separated from reproduction. Reproduction will be the result of choice rather than chance.

Diminishing of crowding might remove lack of food lebensraum as a cause for war.

POLITICAL   The world's population will not accept contraceptive practices in unison. Rather, there will be regional and geographic differences in rates of acceptance. This imbalance may well have political consequences, if, for example, our population stabilizes while that of Africa and China continues to increase. The span between the haves and have-nots would widen; population pressures would be greatest where they could be least afforded.[9]

Tax structures may be modified to favor smaller families.

Direct government intervention is a possibility. Dr. Homi Bhabha,

8. T. J. Gordon, *The Future*, New York, St. Martin's Press, 1965.
9. *Ibid.*, p. 22.

President of the Indian Atomic Energy Commission, has suggested that contraceptive agents might be added to a widely used staple such as grain or salt.[10] Vogt has suggested that the answer might lie in adding an aphrodisiac to a contraceptive pill.[11]

The possibility of adding contraceptives to staple commodities suggests that surreptitious contamination of water supplies with contraceptive agents might be a weapon system of the future.[12]

## 100-YEAR LIFE SPAN

EVENT   100-year life expectancy for white male babies born in the United States.

BACKGROUND   In 1850, the life expectancy of a newborn white male in the United States was only 38.3 years. Through medical advances and improvement in our environmental conditions, this figure has climbed to 67.5 years in 1963. The rate of increase has been almost linear in recent years and the trend suggests that by 2030, a white male baby born in the United States will have a 100-year life expectancy.

This increase in life span will probably be the result of several bio-medical and technological advances. New organs will become available through transplanting or prosthesis. Artificial organs may be used, employing metal, plastic and electronic components and powered by electrical impulses generated by the body itself. Eventually chemical control over aging may be possible as gerontologists reach a deeper understanding of the aging process. The life span of some laboratory animals has been doubled, for example, by tight control over diet. Aging "instructions" may be contained within the nucleii of human cells; genetic manipulation might amend these instructions. Continued research in the mechanisms of bacterial and viral diseases may lead eventually to complete, general immunization, which would, of course, increase life expectancy.[13]

## Implications

ECONOMY   It must be assumed that an increase in life expectancy will also increase the number of years in which a man remains potentially useful

10. Vogt, *People*, New York, William Sloane Associates, 1960, p. 229.
11. *Ibid.*                    12. *Ibid.*
13. See *Los Angeles Times*, November 12, 1965, for a report on the doubling of the life span of rotifers by cutting down on diet and lowering temperature of the water in which the animals lived. This work was accomplished by Dr. C. H. Barrows and Dr. N. W. Shock of the National Heart Institute.

and productive. Thus a 100-year life span implies that increasing numbers of people beyond the age of 65 may wish to be employed. Leisure time would increase and expenditures for occupation of this time would also rise.

Our Social Security structure will require revision if economic minima are to be provided to the older citizens of our country.

The "senior citizen" bloc will have unique consumer demands such as: low speed automobiles, perhaps battery powered for urban transportation; artificial organs; picture phones; mass media entertainment; and household robots.

In spite of the presumed vitality of the older population, a maximum age of employment law might be enacted so that the younger people can work. If extensive social security measures were in effect, the young work force would thus be devoting part of its output to the support of the "senior citizen" group.

POLITICAL  The older people may form a political group of considerable power and significance. Special legislation may be enacted for the convenience of this group.

SOCIAL  A shifting of the median age of the population may be accompanied by greater urbanization.

Great leisure communities may be formed to resemble periods from the past. This artificial return-to-a-more-gracious-age would provide retired citizens with a choice of, for example, colonial or gay nineties cities having modern advantages but requiring strict adherence to the mores and technology of the era.

# PERSONALITY CONTROL DRUGS

EVENT  Widespread and socially widely accepted use of nonnarcotic drugs (other than alcohol) for the purpose of producing specific changes in personality characteristics.

BACKGROUND  Tranquilizing drugs are already in wide use today, and so-called truth drugs as well as hallucinatory drugs (LSD, etc.,) are in existence. It seems quite probable that a large variety of drugs will be obtainable in the "liquor store of the future," such as anti-gloom and anti-grouch drugs, esthetic, perception, and pleasure intensifiers that will transform a person's outlook and personality to fit any desired mood or meet any undesired vicissitude.

Magical mushrooms can be traced back thousands of years. Hundreds of other hallucinogenic drugs are in religious and social use today. To this natural inventory can now be added mescaline, a derivitive of Peyote; psilocybin, the synthetic analog of the Mexican mushrooms; and LSD, a synthetic resembling a rye fungus. LSD's symptoms are widely known; it is very powerful, an ounce will provide 500,000 doses; it is simple to manufacture, it is ostensibly being made in covert laboratories in large quantities. The Food and Drug Administration may take action to outlaw its wanton use.

## Implications

TECHNOLOGY    Research in personality control drugs may lead to a new psychotechnology by which predetermined moods, responses, perhaps even intelligence levels may be obtained through the use of drugs.

ECONOMY    Could pill production for social use become big business?

The ready availability of anxiety reducing drugs may make leisure a pleasurable, perhaps hedonistic continuum of escape.

Persons addicted to the new drugs, either physiologically or psychologically, will be withdrawn from the work force. If the movement becomes widespread, the nondrug workers (perhaps softened to their task by other drugs) may have to produce for the idle.

HEALTH    While hallucinogenic drugs are not apparently, in the strictest sense, habit forming, there can be psychological addiction.

The insight gained in psychodrug research could result in an order of magnitude increase in the number of cases amenable to chemical therapy.

EDUCATION    Experiments conducted by McConnell of Michigan, Jacobsen at UCLA and many others indicate that memory may somehow be stored in molecules of ribonucleic acid (RNA). While widely contested, the possibility exists that in the future, memory pills, even intelligence pills, may become available.

POLITICS    The Huxlian view of *Soma* is perhaps the best example of politically inspired, government controlled use of drugs. In this view, the government issues drugs in order to placate the population. Anxiety-removal pills would be available free, everywhere; a happy people are free from revolt.

Drugs which distort reality may be developed too. These may have important political uses, particularly if combined with psychochemicals which open the user's mind to suggestion.

Drugs which destroy the will to resist, or remove or enhance courage, may become important weapons.

SOCIAL   Prohibition may come again.

Will there be "good kid" pills for the children? "No crime" pills for habitual criminals?

Timothy Leary, a former Harvard professor, has advocated the use of consciousness expanding drugs. After leaving Harvard, he molded "the experience" into a religious setting. Hallucinogenic drugs can provide a shortcut to Nirvana. Will the religion of the future be based on drug-induced, extra-personal insight? Experiments conducted by Dr. Leary with divinity students indicate that this may happen. Almost all reported very deep religious revelations under the influence of LSD.


# INCAPACITATING RATHER THAN LETHAL WEAPONS

EVENT   Use of incapacitating weapons to form a decisive portion of the arsenals of major nations.

BACKGROUND   The nations of the world have already begun to build arsenals of weapons designed to incapacitate rather than kill. Tear gas has been used for decades. Many more advanced weapons can be added to this group. A RAND Long Range Forecasting Study estimated that incapacitating chemical agents could be available by 1970; biological incapacitating agents, shortly thereafter.[14] Contemporary experimentation with these agents seems to indicate that many predetermined responses may be evoked by specific psychochemicals. For example, certain agents produce cowardice. Depriving the brain of monkeys of amine causes them to lose agressiveness; administering the drug causes viciousness.

Water-hose cannons, electric spark canes, noise generators, and other possible riot control weapons fall into this class of incapacitating device.


## Implications

TECHNOLOGY   Incapacitation suggests the control of behavior, and advanced systems may grow out of the present research into the mechanisms

14. T. J. Gordon and O. Helmer, *Report on a Long Range Forecasting Study*, September 1964.
    P–2982.

of behavior. For example, the RAND study suggested that mass hypnotic recruitment of forces from the enemy population may be possible by the year 2020.

SOCIAL   Elimination of killing in war might result in a socially acceptable form of conflict.

These devices could provide means for completely effective crowd and riot control and eliminate mobs and civil insurrections.

POLITICS   The advent of incapacitating weapons, combined with their possible surreptitious use might change the character of warfare. These weapons might find particular use in crowd control or brush fire wars. Efficient covert methods of delivery might permit war in a situation in which only the aggressor knew that war was under way. The vanquished nation might awake one morning to discover that while it had slept, over the past week, an invasion had occurred. Furthermore, they might feel nothing but honor, euphoria, and contentment (chemically induced) about their situation. In a world where such wars are possible, what will status-quo mean?


## SOPHISTICATED TEACHING MACHINES

EVENT   Widespread use of sophisticated teaching machines.

BACKGROUND   Conventional teaching machines are based on the use of "open loop" programs; i.e., a course of instruction is programmed, the student reads these instructions, and is then immediately tested on his comprehension. A correct answer leads to further instruction; an incorrect answer leads to a repetition of the misunderstood material presented in an alternate form.

Sophisticated teaching machines will be based on computer devices having large memories and sensing systems which detect certain physiological reactions of the student. If an incorrect answer is given, the machine might search its memory to determine the reason why such answers were given in the past, and based on a statistically optimum approach, vary the next programmed instruction. Increasing anxiety of the student could be detected by measurement of skin resistance and the course of instruction altered to present the information in a less demanding fashion. These advanced teaching machines might be linked to homes or schools by very wide-band communications systems, giving a large number of people efficient access to instruction.

It is to be expected that these systems would greatly speed the learning process.

## Implications

TECHNOLOGY  Research in specialized computers for teaching will increase.

The technology of learning will be extended. Physiological instrumentation will become more accurate and efficient.

Input-output devices for computers might eventually permit the teaching machines to operate in a conversational mode.

ECONOMY  More people knowing more facts should enhance the rate of increase of our economy.

SOCIAL  Home instruction via TV link to central computers may be accepted as the norm in education.

Wider education may result in diminishing of racial barriers.

POLITICS  These machines can be programmed to teach more than facts; attitudes, abstract ideas, politics and policies can be taught as well. Since the techniques of programming will be controlled by a relatively few people in the country, the exact ideological content of the course of instruction will not be accessible to PTA groups for review and critique. What is taught will be right by definition. Who will program the programmers?

EDUCATION  Widespread use of sophisticated teaching machines could affect the form and substance of schools.

The machines may be linked in the home via wide-band communications systems and thus make college education generally available.

Key professors may spend full time with computer programmers rather than classes.

Increased efficiency of learning may reduce time to educate to a given level by 30 percent.

## OCEAN FARMING

EVENT  Economically useful exploitation of the ocean through farming, with the effect of producing at least 20 percent of the world's food.

BACKGROUND   Two types of ocean farming are generally contemplated: cultivation of plankton and other small plants and animals; and the raising or trapping of meat-fish herds as livestock. It may be possible to use plankton directly as food, or as fodder. It is apparently quite palatable, tasting like shrimp, lobster, or vegetables.[15] At the present time, the density of plankton is too low to make its harvesting profitable except in special circumstances. Seaweed is consumed as food today, of course. It is used in salads or as a vegetable and forms the basis of the gelatin agar-agar. About 50 million tons of fish are taken from the ocean each year, and this catch is growing at the rate of about 8 percent per year over the past few years. While the per capita consumption of sea food in the United States in only 11 pounds per year, it ranges to as much as 130 pounds per year in Japan.

As the population of the world increases it will become important to develop and exploit new sources of food. Perhaps one of the least difficult methods of increasing food supply is through the extension of ocean food productivity. Estimates vary as to the amount of food which the oceans can ultimately yield, but some have held that the oceans can produce enough food annually to supply a world population of thirty billion people.[16]

## Implications

TECHNOLOGY   Advanced fishing gear will be required. This may include electronic fish detectors similar to sonar, electrical trawls and traps, underwater sensors, and telemetry buoys. New food processing techniques may be required to convert sea borne protein into more palatable forms. These processing units may be floating factories.

ECONOMY   The US fishing industry has maintained an almost level rate of production over the last ten years despite a rapid increase in world productivity and modernization of fishing fleets of other nations. As our own more conventional food sources become more expensive, perhaps demand and consumption of sea food will increase in the US and the importance of conventional agricultural produce will diminish.

HEALTH   Ocean food may be necessary to avoid widespread starvation as the world population mounts. If conventional means are relied upon to meet the needs of the increasing numbers of people, formidable problems

15.  Lionel A. Wolford, *Living Resources of the Sea*. Ronald Press, New York, 1958.
16.  Van Camp Sea Food Company. *Potential Resources of the Ocean*. Long Beach, California, January 1965, pp. 12–22.

will be encountered in the provision of farm land and in the production and distribution of fresh water and fertilizer.

SOCIAL   The cowboy of the future may ride a submarine; the farmer, a barge. Cetaceans may be trained to herd fish much as sheep dogs presently herd their flocks.

New ocean farming jobs will diminish unemployment.

Increasing conflict between private and national ocean farming interests may lead to the modern equivalent of piracy.

POLITICS   Serious legal disputes have already occurred between countries, states, and commercial enterprises. These legal problems may ultimately require that nations act to bring portions of the ocean under their direct national sovereignty.

International agreements may be made to farm the oceans cooperatively.

Availability of food from the ocean may diminish the probability of war.

## CONTROLLED THERMONUCLEAR REACTIONS

EVENT   Means found to control thermonuclear reactions.

BACKGROUND   Experimental work is currently being conducted at Livermore and elsewhere in this country and overseas to determine means for producing controlled thermonuclear reactions. These reactions, similar to those on the sun, consume hydrogen at very high temperatures and yield helium and nuclear energy. It has been estimated that sea water deuterium expended in controlled fusion power generators could meet man's increasing energy needs for billions of years.[17] Power producing plants employing thermonuclear power will not generate radioactive wastes. The major technological problem at present is the technique for containment of the ionized plasmas which exist at millions or billions of degrees.

### Implications

TECHNOLOGY   Fusion reactors hold the promise of producing electrical energy very economically, directly from heat with no moving parts. Since a major impediment to the development and use of desalination systems is

17. Richard F. Post, *The Fourth State of Matter*, brochure published by the University of California, Lawrence Radiation Laboratory, Livermore, California.

the availability of cheap electrical power, the advent of controlled thermonuclear power might also trigger implementation of large scale sea
water conversion projects.

Continued research in plasma physics can be expected to add to our
knowledge of interplanetary space since plasmas pervade this domain.

These reactors can be packaged in light compact units, and may
provide the solution to power production on lunar and planetary bases and
thus make indefinite stays practical.

Solution of the thermonuclear gas containment problem might lead
to new forms of space propulsion based on the high speed ejection of ionized
plasmas.

POLITICS  Widespread use of these power systems would suggest proliferation of sophisticated thermonuclear technology, convertible, perhaps,
into weapons technology.

The possibility of atmospheric contamination may become an international political issue.

Supplying TN power systems to underdeveloped nations might
become a form of foreign aid and result in another form of competition
between the US and USSR.

ECONOMICS  Since these systems will probably be government built and
operated, government vs. private power may become a heated issue.

Low cost power will probably increase our GNP.

Competing power systems will diminish in importance, causing some
economic instability in these industries, but reducing the drain on some
of our natural resources.

## CONTINUED AUTOMATION IN COMMERCE AND INDUSTRY

EVENT  Increase by a factor of ten in capital investment in computers
used for automated process control.

BACKGROUND  The great labor-saving advantages of automation have
revolutionized computational and data handling techniques, as well as
in-process manufacturing control and almost every other area where
machines and men interact. Extended use of automation has been forecast
including: the establishment of a credit card economy, air-traffic control—
a positive track on all aircraft at all times, advanced forms of teaching
machines, automation of office work and services perhaps leading to the

displacement of a significant portion of the current work force, automated libraries, automated medical diagnosis, language translators, automated rapid transit, widespread use of automatic decision making at management level for industrial and national planning, electronic prosthesis, robot services, high IQ machines which comprehend standard IQ tests and scores above 150, automated highways, remote facsimile newpapers, man-machine symbiosis, enabling man to extend his intelligence by direct interconnection with computing machinery, centralized (possibly random) wire tapping. This spectrum of possibilities and opportunities is undoubtedly incomplete. Experts have disagreed about the social and economic effects of this extension of automation, but in one study[18] at least, almost all participants agreed that the problem of unemployment resulting from automation was a serious one. It is possible that social upheavals will accompany this progress.

The National Commission on Technology, asked by Congress to evaluate the effect of technological change on the US since World War II, found the output per manhour increased at an overall rate of 2 percent per year from 1909 to 1947. From 1947 to 1964 the rate was 3.1 percent per year. Current gross national product growth is 3.5 percent per year; the commission estimated that it would have to grow at a rate of 4 percent per year in order to absorb the growing labor force. Hence they recommended certain anti-unemployment measures which included: establishing the government as an employer "of last resort," negative income tax, two years of compulsory education, and free college.

## Implications

TECHNOLOGY  Electronic miniaturization, sensing systems, memory devices, simplified access, verbal input and output systems; all of these and associated devices will be developed.

ECONOMY  Investment in these systems will grow. Over the next decade, capital equipment associated with automation or automatic process control may grow by an order of magnitude. These machines, in turn, will permit increasing production. The machines themselves may be used to determine what products are needed, by whom, and the proper price of the product.

Automation will create demand for new types of employment.

Unemployment may grow.

Some countermeasures to the possible social upheavals which may occur as a result of continued automation are:

18. Gordon and Helmer, *op. cit.*

    a. Protection of certain jobs such as household and other services from automation.

    b. Lowering retirement age by five years.

    c. Massive WPA type programs.

    d. Shortening the work week by 20 percent.

    e. Two years compulsory post-high school education.

    f. Massive aid to underdeveloped regions (including portions of the United States).

    g. All-out government sponsored retraining programs.

POLITICS  Automation will improve the efficiency of controlled and planned economics. In the USSR, for example, automation will improve the planning of resource allocation, the distribution of goods to meet consumer demands, and the setting of prices. In democracies, computers will extend the scope of bureaucracies, possibly at the expense of privacy.

Means may be found for equitable distribution of overabundance to raise the level of the underprivileged nations.

SOCIAL  Alternatives to work will become important. Education may become an important leisure time pursuit. Expenditures for leisure will increase.

Computers may move into the home, performing services such as keeping books, programming food preparation, ordering supplies, remembering birthdates, etc.

The extension of automated productivity may create a new demand for personal services and handmade products, even mechanical products. Perhaps tomorrow we will prize handmade lawnmowers and automobiles.

Computers will enter and affect private lives. Possible marriage partners may be selected by computer (as is being practiced today, on a small scale), and taxes will be collected and monitored automatically.

It seems clear automation will increase productivity and leisure. How people will use leisure remains unanswered. The spectrum of responses seems to include:

    a. increasing GNP making a better life for all, with acceptable uses found for extra leisure.

    b. increasing GNP but with growing national guilt accompanying unproductive leisure.

    c. increasing GNP but with an appreciable portion of the population occupied in hedonistic, idle and unproductive pursuits.

## ARTIFICIAL LIFE

EVENT   Creation of a primitive form of artificial life (at least in the form of self-replicating molecules).

BACKGROUND   Many scientists believe that the creation of life was a chance occurrence which resulted from a fortuitous combination of chemicals. In the laboratory, short duration tests (Urey-Miller) have already produced complex prebiological molecules such as amino acids. In these experiments, compounds thought to be present on the primordial earth were excited with gentle heat, ultraviolet radiation, and electrical discharge.

In 1955 Dr. Fraenkel-Conrat separated a tobacco mosaic virus into its constituent, nonliving parts. These were shown to be inert. Yet when recombined, a small amount of the original virility was restored to the virus.

DNA probably represents nature's simplest self-replicating molecule. Watson and Crick have pictured the molecule as a dual helix, with each half of the helix forming the basis of daughter molecules. The arrangement of organic chemicals along these helical chains is the subject of extensive laboratory and analytic analysis. It is thought that the arrangement of molecules holds the key to heredity, and represents, in fact, the genetic information passed in the process of reproduction.

Some scientists, such as Dr. Cyril Ponnamperuma, have formed nucleotides, the chemicals which make up the DNA chains, artificially in the laboratory by processes thought to duplicate those which occurred naturally on the earth several billions of years ago. Other scientists have already formed portions of the DNA chain in sequences which exist in living cells.

## Implications

TECHNOLOGY   Continued research directed toward creation of artificial life may finally identify the source of life on earth. Furthermore, this technology will undoubtedly add great expertise to genetic engineering, in which hereditary defects may be controlled through manipulation of genes. (See our discussion of Genetic Control above.)

SOCIAL   If artificial life is created, organized religion may have to remove life as a supernatural phenomenon. Eventually, it may have to offer a set of ethics and rules for living and modify its scope of "creation." With creation identified as a chemical process, will morality degenerate?

## WEATHER CONTROL

EVENT    Feasibility of limited weather control, in the sense of substantially affecting regional weather at acceptable cost.

BACKGROUND    A special panel of the National Academy of Science has investigated the results of cloud seeding over a period of years. Their report stated in part: ". . . we find some evidence for precipitation increases of as much as 10 or even 20 percent over areas as large as 1000 square miles over periods ranging from weeks to years." Shortly after this report, on February 4, 1966, Senator Clinton Anderson introduced a bill directing the Department of the Interior to "conduct a comprehensive program of scientific and engineering research, experiments, tests, and operations for increasing the yield of water from atmospheric sources." This marked the beginning of government sponsored weather control, and includes rain making, snow making, and hail, hurricane, tornado, fog, and lightning suppression.

Many commercial operators are already in the business of cloud seeding, and judging from the NAS report, are meeting some success. Experiments (Simpson-Malkus, Scientific American, December 1964) have also been conducted in modifying the severity of hurricanes through silver iodide crystal seeding. A French meteorologist has created artificial tornados. Jean Dessens of the University of Clermont formed twisters by generating heated vertical columns of air using 100 oil burners.

Our weather satellites in orbit are permitting more accurate weather predictions on a global scale. The Tiros and Nimbus series provide pictures of cloud cover from orbit using television images, read out to ground stations on command. Study of this data will lead to a deeper understanding of the mechanisms of global weather.

## Implications

TECHNOLOGY    When weather can be produced to order, hydroelectric power may become competitive with thermonuclear power.

World-wide weather engineering and control stations may be required.

It may prove efficient to control weather from orbiting space stations which "bomb" the atmosphere with seeding chemicals.

An orbiting mirror, at high altitude, could direct sunlight to dark portions of the earth to control the night and illuminate areas for rescue operations.

Small manipulations may trigger relatively large planetary reactions; therefore complex analysis, observational networks, and computer predictive systems will be required when weather control is initiated on a larger scale.

ECONOMY    Simple weather *prediction* could have important economic consequences. President Johnson has stated that five day accurate predictions could result in savings of $2\frac{1}{2}$ billion dollars to agriculture, 45 million dollars in the lumber industry, 100 million dollars in surface transportation, 75 million dollars in retail marketing, and 3 billion dollars in water resources management, in the United States alone. Weather *manipulation* will probably be relatively inexpensive; its economic effects will be tremendous. Certain areas of the country could be designated, for example, sun zones. Others could be set up for particular agricultural requirements: a rice zone, a cotton zone, etc. An orbiting mirror could produce heat where required for habitation or agriculture.

POLITICS    Weather control obviously can be an important weapon. Accurate control can deprive nations of water or create floods, without identification of the aggressor nation.

Within the government we have already seen a struggle for the funds associated with this new research. If weapons of weather are produced, which agency will control them? The Strategic Air Command?

An orbiting mirror, brought to focus on a point on the earth could be a frightening weapon.

Since weather modification will have global consequences, international agreements may be required to foster this work, and these agreements may promote international cooperation between nations and world law.

SOCIAL    Will citizens of the future select their weather by referendum? Will there be lobbyists advocating the weather of their preference?

Daylight may be a purchasable commodity.

There may be a growing tendency to blame bad weather on the government.

## GENERAL IMMUNIZATION

EVENT    Large scale biochemical general immunization against bacterial and viral diseases.

BACKGROUND    A virus, typically, is constructed of protein surrounding a nucleic acid core. In attacking a cell, the protein coating of the virus attaches to a healthy cell and opens a path for the nucleic core. Once inside the cell, the nucleic acid of the virus takes command of the cell's manufacturing process, and instead of manufacturing normal life needs such as amino acids, the cell starts manufacturing more viruses, complete with protein shells, ready to attack other healthy cells. Thus reaching an understanding of the function, the cell and the DNA and RNA within it may lead to a new technique of immunization by which viruses are either denied entry into healthy cells or are made incapable of taking over the cell's functions.

Bacteria are microscopic unicellular plants which may be pathogenic. The parasitic types can cause disease in humans; however, since the time of Pasteur, vaccination with antitoxins has provided immunity against certain types of bacteria. Recently chemotherapy has utilized various antibiotics which act as a direct poison to the bacteria, but not their host.

Research in the functioning of the cell, particularly its reproductive mechanisms, and continued work with antibiotics offers promise of the development of effective general immunization agents which will prevent viral and bacterial diseases in all men. The World Health Organization, under the auspices of the United Nations, provides a means of the dissemination of the information and material required to effect this immunization program.

## Implications

TECHNOLOGY Having accomplished general immunization, medical research staffs would be free to attack other medical problems not associated with bacteria and viruses such as: transplantation of limbs and organs, genetic engineering, stimulation of the growth of new organs and limbs, and aging.

POLITICAL A "senior citizen" block of political significance may accompany the shift in the median age.

Effective immunization techniques might well eliminate the possibility of bacteriological warfare.

The world health organizations might receive wider acceptance and achieve even greater responsibility in executing this immunization program,

ECONOMY With fewer people afflicted with common disease, and thus more available to work, unemployment would be likely to rise.

Leisure time expenditures would increase.

HEALTH The major cause of death would be old age. Senility might become more common.

EDUCATION   The increased life expectancy, combined with extra leisure might provide extra emphasis to education as a means of using leisure time.

SOCIAL   The shift of the population median age may be accompanied by a trend toward greater urbanization, or specialized communities.

Death rate would decrease, resulting in shift of the age center of gravity toward old age.

Perhaps immunization would be rejected by a significant portion of the world's population on religious grounds.

TECHNOLOGY   Implicit in the eradication of viral diseases is the solution to the problem of back contamination; the transmittal to the earth's biosphere of pathogenic organisms from alien planets.

## GENETIC CONTROL

EVENT   Feasibility (not necessarily acceptance) of chemical control over some hereditary defects by modification of genes through molecular engineering.

BACKGROUND   Drs. Watson and Crick were awarded the Nobel Prize in 1962 for their description of the DNA molecule. Most biochemists believe that the double helix strand of DNA contains the cell's genetic information. This molecule is located in the cell's nucleus. Although the molecular mechanisms are not known completely, it is believed that the strands of the double helix are held together by intermolecular electrostatic forces. Where compounds on one strand "stick out," there are "holes" on the other strand. If the strands separate, "dead" compounds floating nearby are attracted by the electrostatic unbalanced forces and fall into the "empty" holes. The new chain now forms the other half of a new DNA dual helix; where there were once two intertwined strands there are now two groups of two strands: genes are now available for a new cell. In a similar manner, transfer RNA molecules line up with the DNA molecules and carry the alignment information through the cell's nucleus into the outer portion of the cell. There, other chemicals are aligned by the electrostatic forces inherent in the RNA chain. These alignments produce chemicals which are, in effect, the output of the cell. Thus the arrangement of chemicals on the DNA helix controls the manufacturing process of the cell. The output of a cell may be, typically, amino acids, or proteins.

Scientists are now in the process of determining the sequence of chemicals which produce specific manufacturing processes. Once these codes are determined, the information will be at hand by which control over a cell's genetic and manufacturing instructions may be influenced.

## Implications

TECHNOLOGY   Identification of the codes will open new, vast engineering possibilities. Specific proteins may be manufactured by proper coding of cells *in vitro*. In all of man's history, he has had to rely on animals or plants for food. Protein synthesis through DNA controlled cellular processes will give man the opportunity to manufacture his food supply.[19]

Genetic engineering may become important. As specific codes become known and as tools for manipulation become perfected, it may be possible to intervene in the cellular inheritance process and manipulate the instructions transmitted from one cell to another. Thus a new profession may be born.

HEALTH   Control over genetic process may make it possible to intervene in the heredity process and influence defects normally transmitted by this process. This type of genetic surgery may also be applied to "normal" characteristics so that specialized human beings might be produced to order. Will we create all men equal or will we order special athletes for the "games"; research scientists with IQ's of 200 and diminutive bodies; and finally, the eternal model of youth for sex?

Starvation might be eliminated as a cause of death, since genetic processes could be used to manufacture proteins as outlined above, and genetic control of agricultural products could be expected to greatly increase conventional yields.

With the elimination of inherited disabilities, life expectancy would increase. Furthermore aging itself may be found to be a genetic property.

Understanding of the genetic process may lead to the ability to control the antibody rejection process and thus permit the ready transplantation of foreign organs and limbs.

It has been theorized that each cell contains in it the data required to construct an entire human being. This is certainly true of a single ovum and sperm cell. Perhaps, someday, it may be possible to trigger a single cell into a process of replication so that a "clipping" from an individual would be sufficient to recreate the individual. This type of experiment has already been performed successfully with plants.

19. Chinese scientists have constructed a protein, according to recently published reports.

Genetic process may be employed to trigger the body's construction of new organs and limbs.

EDUCATION   If organisms can be grown in the pattern of previous genetic models, why couldn't memories be preprogrammed? Could we regrow Einsteins, complete with their experience and knowledge?

The ability to learn; almost certainly IQ; and what Jung called the "collective unconscious," the racial inheritance, can be influenced by genetic surgery.

Fertility, perhaps even aging itself, might be influenced with proper genetic intervention.

POLITICS   Who will choose the model for mankind?
Who will select the defects to eliminate?
Who will select the parents who will receive the genetic operation?
Who will select the individual to be replicated?
Whose politics will be programmed?

SOCIAL   Racial characteristics may be eliminated or modified through genetic processes.

## MAN-MACHINE SYMBIOSIS

EVENT   Man-machine symbiosis, enabling man to extend his intelligence by direct electromechanical interaction between his brain and a computing machine.

BACKGROUND   Two distinct fields of research may merge sometime in the future. The first deals with identification of the functions performed by various portions of the brain, the second with the anthropomorphic similarity between man, computers and mechanisms.

Fine electrodes have been inserted into the brains of animals and men; when these electrodes are supplied with electrical voltage the reactions of the organisms can be predicted and depend solely on the voltage applied and the location of the wires in the brain. Cats and chickens, carrying radio controlled receivers, can be remotely commanded to cluck, scratch, or cower by a transmitted electrical signal. Severe cases of depression in humans have been treated by self-initiated "pleasure center" stimulation of the cortex.

In the mapping of the brain, Dr. Wilder Penfield evoked complete recall reactions when electrically stimulating certain portions of the brains of humans. The reaction in some patients was a "tape playback" replay of previous experiences, indicating that memory could be stimulated by artificial means. These experiments suggest that the process might be reversible; i.e., perhaps "memory" could be imposed by external devices.

Machines are being designed to closely follow human commands. The requirements for handling dangerous radioactive materials, for example, resulted in the design of manipulators which follow the remote hand motions of operators. Beyond this, machines have been designed to follow eye motions, respiratory cycles and heart beat.

Man-machine symbiosis refers to a direct linking of human intellect with computers; to a linking of human muscles with task-performing machines.

TECHNOLOGY    The mapping of the functions of the brain will lead to an understanding of brain mechanisms; this in turn may lead to more efficient, adaptive computers and programs which function in a "reasoning" manner.

Machines which multiply human energy, force and dexterity, and respond to thought rather than switch-throwing may be possible, permitting extension of the environments in which humans may function. For example, a remote controlled Mars surface robot may be possible which presents 3D-TV images to the operator on earth, and responds to the body motions and amplified thought commands of the earth-bound explorer.

EDUCATION    Learning may eventually be programmed through a process of computer directed recordings on the brain.

POLITICS    Who will write the programs for the direct-recording education? Will it be politically motivated?

HEALTH    Robot mechanisms may become part of human beings, an amputee may have a brain directed mechanical arm or leg.

SOCIAL    Computers may become colleagues in a real sense.

Certain human intellects may prove more favorable for machine direction. Only the best minds may be selected for machine control functions.

## HOUSEHOLD ROBOTS

EVENT    Use of computer programmed automatic household labor in the average American home.

BACKGROUND   Every housewife has robots working for her today including —garbage disposals, washing machines, automatic defrosters, dishwashers, etc. Unquestionably, additional labor-saving machines can be invented and utilized. These might include:

1. Household computers for memorizing appointments and birthdays, telephone numbers, and budgets; computing tax; programming appliances and ordering groceries.
2. Remote controlled lawnmowers and vacuum cleaners.
3. Language translators.
4. Teaching machine-tutors.
5. Picture-phones.
6. Air conditioners, purifiers, perfumers, exchangers.
7. Cooks.
8. Masseurs.
9. Baby sitters.

There is no question that these devices could be built; whether they will be built and placed in wide operation depends on economic motivation.

## Implications

POLITICAL   Robots will to a degree replace human services.

In the face of increasing unemployment pressures, anti-robot legislation may be enacted to protect certain services from machine take-over.

HEALTH   Robots will create human leisure, and perform menial and odious tasks.

SOCIAL   What will the relationship be between people and their machines?

The profession of robot repair and servicing may gain status.

ECONOMY   Robots will create new markets. Will they have built-in obsolescence? Will handmade robots (a status symbol) be more desirable than those produced by other robots?

Computers in the home will facilitate conversion to a credit card economy.

## PRESERVATION OF PRIVACY

EVENT   Legislation enacted to prevent establishment of national data banks which might contain extensive personal information about citizens without their consent.

BACKGROUND    Advancing technology has made snooping cheap, easy, and efficient. Private parties can purchase miniature listening devices; in fact these have been advertised in the public press.[20] Diplomatic olive pits and listening eagle insignias have been discovered and are old hat. Just how wide industrial bugging has spread is anyone's guess. One Southern California private investigator estimated that more than 20 percent of his firm's time is spent in hunting for concealed microphones in corporate board rooms and legal offices.

In addition to the bugging devices, computers, with their tremendous memory and versatility, will add to the coming lack of privacy. Computers, for example, will increase the scope of business transactions accomplished by credit. Our entire economy could go on computer controlled credit, virtually eliminating currency. Upon completing a transaction in a store, the purchaser's bank would be signalled by the seller that the purchase had been made, over closed communication circuits. The depositor's account would be automatically scanned and if the proper balance were present, credits would be transferred from the buyer to the seller. Employers would not pay their employees, they would transfer credits to their account. If overdrawn, the bank would automatically advance credit to their overextended depositors.

In order to speed this streamlined economic credit system, some bankers have suggested that all people in the United States be identified by their Social Security number. This number would identify their telephone, their bank accounts, and their birth and death. "After all," argues the banker, "two people can have the same name, so a unique number personally identified by the individual would increase rather than decrease privacy."

If such a system were established in response to economic pressures, it could be easily extended to compute income tax automatically (bills would be sent periodically by the government), military service, training, skills; even fingerprints could be recorded and transmitted on-call.

Some scientists have projected an eventual marrying of bugging devices with the large memory population-identification computers. These systems could provide police analysis of randomly sampled telephone conversations. The bugs would feed computers programmed to detect key criminal or possibly subversive words. Big Brother would be watching.[21]

## Implications

TECHNOLOGY    There is no doubt that miniaturization of electronic circuits will continue. Computer memories will expand and the imple-

20. *Los Angeles Times*, December 29, 1965.
21. Gordon and Helmer, *op. cit.*, p. 21, item 25.

mentation of the economic credit transfer system will become a matter of desire rather than feasibility. Word recognition devices have already been used in primitive form; these will undoubtedly become more exact.

The implementation of the credit transfer system would provide a tremendous impetus to the development of large memory computers.

Conducting business by wire would lead to the development of other associated electronic gadgetry such as picturephones.

ECONOMY   Computers with access to the flow of transactions throughout the country might be employed to make economic projections which could be the basis of resources allocations, price setting, profit fixing, and import and export taxation. Taxation of individuals could be keyed to detailed national need and ability to pay. Tax monies could be transferred automatically, from personal credit accounts to the government.

Personal social security numbers could be used to index the data files in the computer central.

HEALTH   The organized personal data could be scanned in a number of ways. Statistical health trends in the population could be determined with greater rapidity and accuracy. For example the relationship between cigarette smoking and lung cancer might be established without question by a single computer routine.

EDUCATION   School records would be filed in data central. Special skills could be recorded and retrieved on demand by the government or potential employers.

POLITICS   Big Brotherism, the state monitoring its population, is possible.

Bureaucracies could increase in scope and accuracy with the data supplied by central computers. VA, FHA, Bureau of the Budget, Council of Economic Advisors, Civil Aeronautics Board, Federal Power Commission, U.S. Civil Service Commission, National Labor Relations Board; in fact, all of our bureaucratic service organizations would benefit from the use of the collected data.

As public indignation grows, specific legislation may be enacted to prevent further government intrusion into personal matters.

SOCIAL   If bugging were to become a popular pastime, we might find new ways to use leisure, but we would probably also have to invent new ways to insure privacy. For example, we might have houses with invasion-proof rooms, special anti-tamper telephone lines (at a higher rate, of course) and a bug removal service as regular as the gardener.

As computers extend their scope, will we become more immune to receiving their impersonal instructions?

## WIDE-BAND COMMUNICATIONS SYSTEMS

EVENT    General use of communications systems which carry at least 100 video and information channels into average homes.

BACKGROUND    The amount of information which can be carried on an electromagnetic communication channel is a function of its carrier frequency. At low frequencies, one megacycle per second or so, radio can carry voice information. Television is transmitted at higher frequencies, typically 100 megacycles per second and higher; at still higher frequencies, typically those of high frequency microwaves or lasers, literally hundreds or thousands of TV channels could be accommodated simultaneously.

It is technically feasible to employ today's wide-bandwidth communications systems in home television service. If such a system were implemented, programming techniques would certainly change. For example, out of the many hundreds of channels available, perhaps half could carry college level curricula. Some would still be used for entertainment, undoubtedly; others would be devoted to local advertising (thus replacing or augmenting the merchandising function of regional newspapers). Some of the remaining channels might be devoted to automated voting.

In one possible concept, the home viewer-voter (or specially selected voters?) would watch the debate relating to the item under consideration on the special channel. Then using his telephone, his vote would be registered on special large memory computers. The tele-voting circuit would involve dialing a special number, for example, and then dialing in the voter's identification code number. The computer would scan the number for authenticity, take the vote (probably also in dialed code), then tabulate it and forward it to the national central computer. The system could also be used for vote-taking on local issues or even nonpolitical issues.

## Implications

TECHNOLOGY    The implementation of wide-band communications systems for home service use would lead to the development of inexpensive microwave communications receivers.

Automated voting procedures would require new telephone switching equipment if accomplished over telephone lines, and would spur the development of very large memory computers located regionally and capable of communicating with each other.

ECONOMY  Availability of a large number of TV channels might affect newspapers and magazines greatly, particularly if the home TV sets were equipped with video tape recorders or facsimile printers. One channel might carry only local news; another, world and national news; a third, human interest and feature stories. One station might cover the stock market (automated stock purchasing?)

Use of some of this channel space might replace local newspaper advertising. Perhaps the voting machines could be used to place orders for merchandise.

The new devices associated with this development would spur the electronics and automation industries.

EDUCATION  Ready and cheap availability of excellent curricula (combined perhaps with increased leisure) might make education a respectable and common pastime.

Canned lectures by eminent professors may make TV teaching superior to that in resident institutions.

University degrees will be extended to viewers who complete their courses solely on TV. Residency requirements may disappear.

Automated voting apparatus in the home could be used in conjunction with the educational courses in a remote teaching machine mode, so the live lecturer could get real time feedback on the interest, impact, and absorption of his material. Where a point was not properly understood, the lecturer might amend his text and reiterate the point from a different aspect.

POLITICS  In the scenario described, automated anarchy is possible with each national issue being determined by plebiscite. Issues might be determined by popular appeal rather than national good. Every election, from presidential to dog catcher, would take the form of a great debate. Personality and appearance would become even more important in elections.

SOCIAL  Automated voting could provide a grand national game which could be leisure-filling. Electing Miss America could become important.

Easy education could result in a new class of savants, dedicated to learning as an end in itself.

## CONTINUED SPACE EXPLORATION

EVENT   Budgeting of the civilian space program at levels exceeding one percent of the GNP.

BACKGROUND   The United States is committed to land a man on the moon before 1970. A five billion dollar per year industry has been built up in the accomplishment of this objective. The facilities and resources developed in the lunar landing program will have much wider applicability; the Saturn vehicle and the Apollo spacecraft can be the basis of continued interplanetary exploration through the seventies and eighties. The Air Force has also embarked on a space program which will place a manned orbiting space station aloft in the early seventies. For reasons of national security, demonstration of technological preeminence, economic stimulation, scientific curiosity, and the direct contributions which can be made to man's life through orbital observations; the space program will continue. Military men will be placed in orbit around the earth; scientific exploration will continue on the lunar surface and in the vicinity and eventually on the surface of nearby planets.

### Implications

TECHNOLOGY   The technology involved in continuing the exploration of space is convertible into military technology. As skills in designing vehicles and transporting personnel develop, commercial rocket transport vehicles may become possible which can reach any point on earth within 30 minutes. A base on the moon could serve as a point of departure for a manned Mars mission, particularly if propellant production on the moon proves possible.

    Some manufacturing process may be well suited to function in orbit or on the lunar surface. For example, processes that require low gravity or are enhanced by vacuum environment may occupy part of the lunar station. Telescopes in orbit or on the moon would escape the obscuring atmosphere of the earth; radio telescopes on the lunar surface could be very large and would be isolated from the man-made radio noise of earth.

ECONOMY   The growing GNP will probably permit an extension of the country's investment in space projects in the years to come. A cutback in this field without immediate conversion of the talent and capability to other allied areas would have serious economic impact.

HEALTH  It has been suggested that the orbital and lunar stations might serve as sanatoria for stroke and heart patients since the low gravity would probably prove beneficial to their recuperation.

POLITICS  Space may prove an alternative to war. It provides heroic goals which are nondestructive.

The use of space for military purposes excludes the underdeveloped nations and thus tends to preserve the bipolar status quo world.

Space provides an internal national goal which, at least in the case of the Apollo program, has proved unifying.

Space missions may continue to provide a visible demonstration of technological preeminence.

Our space programs provide a means for drawing other nations into our political orbit by permitting their participation in the national programs.

EDUCATION  Space has captured the imagination of some young students. Astronauts will continue to be worthy heros.

SOCIAL  Observations made from earth orbit can materially add to man's comfort on earth. For example, plankton distribution, location of meat-fish herds, diseased orchards, crop growth patterns as observed from orbit can materially add to the earth's food production.

As population grows on the earth, waste disposal may become a significant problem. Perhaps solar probes can be used to rid the earth of noxious wastes by shooting these packages to the surface of the sun.

Perhaps the day will also come when we seek to minimize our population pressures through colonization of nearby habitable planets. Depletion of the earth's resources may cause us to look to space for replenishment.

The global communications systems possible through the use of space satellites will bring the nations closer together and illustrate, hopefully, that men are still men the world over.

## ADVANCED TECHNIQUES OF OPINION CONTROL, THOUGHT MANIPULATION AND PROPAGANDA

EVENT  Use of advanced techniques of opinion control, thought manipulation and propaganda in combating crime, rebellious populations in time of civil upheaval, and in wartime.

BACKGROUND  Behavior of people can be directed in three ways: direct physical manipulation, chemical intervention, and finally, psychological control. Research in these three fields is currently providing deeper insight into mechanisms of human behavior.

*Physical* manipulation techniques are centering around cortex stimulation by small electrodes. In this process electrodes are implanted in the brain at predetermined, precise, locations. When excited by small electrical impulses, predictable motor and emotional responses are evoked. Drs. J. Delgado, W. E. Roberts, and N. E. Miller, writing in the *Naval Research Review* wrote:

> Under the influence of electrical stimulation of the brain the cats and monkeys performed like electrical toys. Depending on which "button" was pressed by the investigators, one of a great variety of motor responses was evoked. These involved movements of virtually all parts of the body. . . . Even if we tried to impede the response by holding the animals, they struggled to free themselves in order to follow the command. . . .[22]

Humans have also been wired. A patient at the Massachusetts General Hospital, dying of cancer, was given relief from his pain by a transistorized stimulator which could send a weak current through his thalamus whenever he pressed a button.[23] Other patients have been wired successfully to avoid psychological disturbances.

In a rather well known experiment, "pleasure points" in the brain of rats were excited through a circuit the rats themselves could close. They found the sensation irresistible. One rat pressed the button 8,000 times an hour and paused for food only when absolutely necessary.

The operation required to implant electrodes in the brain is simple, and the small plug can be hidden cosmetically.

*Chemical* intervention techniques may utilize a battery of drugs that typically destroy the will to resist, invite forgetfulness, provoke artificial courage, and distort perceptions. For example, Dr. Guy Everett, of the Abbott Laboratories, reduced the level of amine in monkeys and found their natural aggressiveness and viciousness diminished. The animals could be returned to normal by injections of the chemical. When the chemical was administered to mice, they attacked anything in sight.[24]

Psychological techniques for behavior control include hypnotism, imprinting, conditioning, and brainwashing. As an example of these techniques, imprinting is the process by which young animals may learn certain aspects of social behavior. Apparently modification of the environment at a critical time in the imprinting process, can have important be-

22. Quoted by Robert Coughlan, "Behavior by Electronics," *Life*, March 8, 1963, p. 99.
23. *Time*, October 1, 1965.
24. *Los Angeles Times*, December 29, 1965.

havioral consequences. Dr. E. H. Hess of the University of Chicago exposed ducklings without previous experience to artificial mothers. In some experiments the surrogate mother was a wooden duck decoy. It was found that 16-hour animals showed less imprinting.[25]

Modification of behavior through hypnotism is well known. Recent experiments have indicated that hypnotic suggestion can be transmitted by television. Russian reports have indicated that it may even be possible to transmit hypnotic suggestion telepathically.[26]

## Implications

TECHNOLOGY  The behavioral sciences have lagged behind the natural sciences. Continued work in this field will undoubtedly lead eventually to deeper understanding of the mechanism of behavior. A drug, stimulation of a known point in the brain, a psychological procedure: these will all be used in the future to produce a fine control over behavior. The research leading to this control will provide better understanding of motivations, brain functions, body chemistry, learning processes, and memory.

ECONOMY  Will advertisers use TV hypnosis to promote sales? Are they using it already?

HEALTH  Reaching an understanding of behavioral processes should lead to efficient treatment for psychoses; with further insight, perhaps psychosis-provoking situations can be avoided. But without anxiety will there be ambition?

EDUCATION  The implications here are obvious; the desire for education can be implanted. Facts can be manipulated into the brain. Who will write the educational programs when experience has been supplanted with forced feeding?

POLITICS  The Nazi regime, under Hitler, was striving for this sort of control. Will Big Brother achieve it?

The use of these techniques in warfare, hot or cold, will be tremendously important, not only for influencing enemy troops and population, but for control and motivation at home as well.

Understanding of behavior mechanisms and control can lead to prevention of crime and war.

25. Eckhard Hess, "Imprinting in Animals," *Scientific American*, March 1958.
26. Experiments were conducted by Professor Leonid L. Vasiliev of Leningrad University.

SOCIAL   People in some future society may wish to have the social operation of electrode implantation because to be wired is *right* and to be right is
to be happy. These electrodes could be energized by small receivers. Who
will run the transmitters and push the buttons?

## CONTINUED TREND TOWARDS URBANIZATION

EVENT   Eighty percent of the population of the United States living in
cities.

BACKGROUND   The percentage of the American population living in
cities has been steadily climbing. In 1880 there was only one city containing
one million people; now there are five. In 1800 approximately 5 percent of
the total population of the country lived in urban communities; by 1960,
69.9 percent lived in areas classed as urban; an extrapolation of the rate of
growth shows that by 1986, 75 percent of our population may live in cities.

Some city planning efforts have anticipated this potential growth.
City cores are being designed as wide grass malls that exclude automobiles.
Leisured strolling and shopping along these malls provide a logical end to
strangling traffic. As the population continues to grow, the cities will fill,
and building will grow, probably vertically. According to some architects,
these new buildings will be constructed of new, ultralight materials and
will be multipurpose containing, perhaps, living quarters, service shops,
parking, helicopter terminals, office space, schools, hospitals, communications
centers; living, working, and leisure may be conducted on a vertical plane
rather than horizontal.

## Implications

TECHNOLOGY   Concentrations of population will increase problems of
waste disposal.

New forms of automotive transportation will be required for city
travel.

ECONOMY   Grouping of population centers will ease conversion to a credit
card economy in which computers keep track of transactions.

HEALTH   Overcrowding can cause abnormal behavior patterns. However,
proper design of the new vertically oriented city should minimize apparent
crowding.

Central air-conditioning systems will make it simple to filter or add aerosols to the air for inconspicuous immunization and decontamination.

EDUCATION  Schools can be centralized. Classes can be handled on electronic distribution systems built into the buildings.

POLITICS  These city cores may become political entities in themselves. For example, an integrated building may have its own mayor, police force, fire services, library, etc.

SOCIAL  It may be possible to be born, live a full childhood, receive an excellent education, work profitably and finally die in a single environmentally controlled building.

With the further concentration of population, crime may increase.


# OVA/SPERM BANKS ESTABLISHED

EVENT  Commercial operation of ova and sperm banks.

BACKGROUND  Dr. Jerome K. Sherman of the University of Arkansas and other researchers have conducted tests in which sperm of a donor male is frozen, stored, then later thawed and used for artificial insemination. In an epic experiment, two women have been successfully inseminated with human sperm which had been stored at liquid nitrogen temperature for two months.

Dr. E. S. E. Hafez of the University of Washington has conducted experiments in which hormones are used to cause ripe eggs to be released in large quantities from a cow's ovaries. These eggs are fertilized through artificial insemination. The embryos, perhaps as many as one hundred, are flushed from the mother and implanted in other cows to complete their gestation period in a normal manner, but with the genetic properties of its true parents.


## Implications

SOCIAL  Dr Hafez has speculated that in 1980, it might be possible "for a housewife to walk into a new kind of commissary, look down a row of packets not unlike flower-seed packages, and pick her baby by label. Each packet would contain a frozen one-day-old embryo, and the label would tell the shopper what color of hair and eyes to expect as well as the probable size and IQ of the child. After making her selection, the lady could take the packet to her doctor and have the embryo implanted in herself, where it would grow for nine months, like a baby of her own."[27]

Furthermore, it may be possible for the lady shopper to have her baby artificially inseminated using sperm contributed by a genetically suited donor, perhaps a great man of the past.

As suggested by Dr. Sherman and other scientists, semen banks may be established in the future. Spermatozoa deposited in these banks will be preserved by freezing. A husband, going away to war, might wish to deposit his seed. Possibilities for the use of such banks in eugenic programs are obvious. If these banks were shielded from nuclear radiation, destructive genetic mutations which might otherwise occur during a nuclear war would be avoided.

Dr. D. Petrucci of Bologna, Italy, and other scientists in the United States, have succeeded in fertilizing ripe ova *in vitro*. Reports have indicated that Dr. Petrucci's embryos grew for fifty-nine days at which time he terminated the experiment. Perhaps this type of work will lead, someday, to the Huxlian picture of mechanized pregnancy, babies produced in glass wombs, freeing mothers from discomforts of natural pregnancy and providing the fetus with an ideal, optimum environment.

The author wishes to acknowledge the valuable discussions, comments, and critiques about this paper furnished by Marv Adelson, Olaf Helmer, Bob Prehoda, Nicholas, Rescher, and John A. Wright.

27. Quoted in "Will Man Direct His Own Evolution," by Albert Rosenfeld. *Life*, October 1, 1965, p. 98.

## LOOKING FORWARD III

# Simulating the values of the future

### Olaf Helmer

*A simulation exercise for the study of future values as conducted in Pittsburgh in September, 1966*

## Introduction

My discussion will present a brief description of the design of a simulation workshop conducted as part of a conference at the University of Pittsburgh on the subject of the effects of technological change on American values. This simulation exercise was devised by the writer in collaboration with Theodore Gordon, and we are grateful to Nicholas Rescher for constructive suggestions. The exercise commenced with the presentation of a paper by Gordon, entitled "Interaction of Technology and Values," and addressed itself to a set of twenty potential future technological and environmental developments described in an appendix to that paper.

The experiment is designed to accommodate the participation of approximately thirty persons, not all of whom need be active at all times during the five-hour duration of the exercise.

The workshop opened with the following introductory remarks, which explain the intended purpose and the structure of the undertaking:

## Text of introductory statement

"We are about to ask your indulgence in participating with us today in a trial exercise concerned, as is this entire conference, with the potential value structure within our future society. The framework within which we propose to do this with your cooperation is somewhat unconventional. It cannot be described as a scientific experiment, nor is it a mere exercise in round-table philosophizing. Rather, we may think of it as an operations-analytical workshop. Operations analysis typically is decision-oriented, and so will be today's exercise. Moreover, it will employ, in a rudimentary fashion, two operations research techniques: simulation, and the systematic use of expert judgment.

The subject of values, since it deals with highly intangible matters, is a most elusive one, especially if we are talking about future rather than present-day values. Consequently it seems at first sight well-nigh impossible to approach it in an operationally meaningful way. We shall attempt to do so, all the same, not by asking you to judge values in the abstract, but by eliciting statements of your preferences when you are presented with a simulated decision-making situation. Thus we shall be dealing not with future values directly but with potential future environments against which a future values structure is to be judged. In particular, we shall involve you in a simulated planning process, in which you will be asked (a) to make decisions affecting the character of our environment, (b) to estimate the societal consequences of your decisions, and (c) to evaluate the desirability of these consequences.

What we are trying to carry out is, strictly speaking, only a simulation of a simulation, in the following sense. We are inviting you to take a critical look at the method of simulating the process of social planning as a means of arriving at a moral evaluation of alternative futures. To perform such a simulation properly would take much more time and effort than can be compressed into a few hours. Hence all we can attempt to do today is to go through a brief pilot study of such a simulation, in the hope to convey some of the flavor that a full-scale study might have. What we shall do here is merely the first step in a procedure that properly should be iterated a number of times and that should go into more detail than we can consider in the brief time at our disposal. Thus we shall merely simulate a simulation of a social decision-making process.

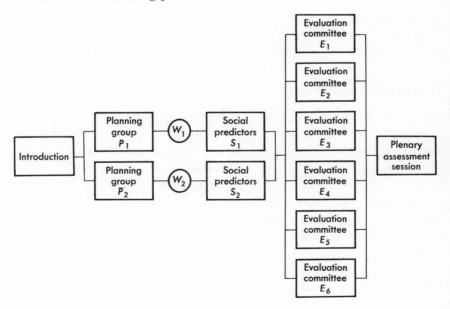

The procedure for today's exercise is illustrated by the chart on the opposite page.

The conferees are to be divided up into ten groups, as indicated, and eventually meet in plenary session. We begin with sessions in parallel of two planning groups, $P_1$ and $P_2$. Each of these will be given a different set of objectives, with which in mind they will be required to simulate longrange planning at the governmental level. Their decisions will help determine the technological and environmental features of two future worlds, $W_1$ and $W_2$, as of the year 2000. Each of these worlds will then be examined as to the implied social consequences by $S_1$ and $S_2$ respectively, who represent groups of social predictors. The descriptions of both worlds, $W_1$ and $W_2$, including their predicted social aspects, will then be referred to six committees of evaluators, $E_1$ to $E_6$, who will make comparative evaluations of $W_1$ and $W_2$ from the respective simulated viewpoints of six major sectors of American society as of the year 2000:

| | |
|---|---|
| $E_1$ = Teenagers | $E_4$ = Persons over 65 |
| $E_2$ = Housewives | $E_5$ = Cultural elite |
| $E_3$ = Middleclass employed | $E_6$ = Persons in lowest income decile |

The findings of these evaluation committees as to their preferences between Worlds $W_1$ and $W_2$ will be submitted to the final, plenary, session. There the conferees will be asked to assign appropriate weights to the opinions of the population sectors simulated by these committees, on the basis of which their six preference statements will be combined into one overall expression of preference between the two alternative futures under consideration.

This sketch of today's scenario will later be augmented with detailed instructions to each group as it begins its session.

In conclusion one general remark on the purpose of this workshop may be in order. Its intent is to provide a constructive approach to future values in operational terms, by creating a simulated decision-making situation in which the participants are given a chance to express their value preferences among specific alternative futures. We do not wish to make exaggerated claims regarding the utility of this activity. Yet, when we are all done, it may be hoped that at the very least the participants will feel that —even if the exercise had little intrinsic value—it was a thought-stimulating cooperative conference technique; at best they may agree that —although only a pilot experiment—the workshop will have conveyed the glimmering of a new truly interdisciplinary way of approaching otherwise highly intangible problems.

## The planning groups

The two planning groups, $P_1$ and $P_2$ are to meet simultaneously. Each will consist of five members, plus a member of the experimental control group acting as chairman.

An opening statement by the chairman will be as follows:

"We would like you to think of yourselves in this session as high-level planners within the federal government, concerned with planning decisions that may affect the technological and environmental character of our society around the coming turn of the century.

You have before you brief descriptions of twenty major possible developments that may take place by the year 2000, together with current estimates of the probabilities of their occurrence. These probabilities can be raised by appropriate governmental action; in some cases this can be done easily, in others this is harder to achieve. The 'degree of difficulty' indicated in each case is intended to be a measure of how relatively difficult it is to raise the probability by a given amount.

This committee is to decide how to allocate ten points (representing a special effort by the federal government) in order to raise the stated probabilities. The degree of difficulty indicates how many of your ten points must be used in order to raise the probability of an item by 20 percent. (Exception: If an item has an 80 percent probability, this probability is raised to 95 percent.) Points may be expended so as to raise a probability by more than one notch; but once a probability is either 90 percent or 95 percent it cannot be raised any further.

In deciding how to allocate your points we want you to be guided by the desire

| ($P_1$) | ($P_2$) |
|---|---|
| to raise the gross national product to the highest expected level. | to create a world in which values prevail, that, if anything, are better than those of today; in particular, individual liberties should be curtailed as little as possible. |

We first ask each of you to make this allocation of ten points independently, by filling in the 'Initial' column in your list of Potential Developments.[1] Later we shall try to arrive at a group consensus."

The chairman, on his Group Planning Form,[2] notes all five responses

1. See Appendix A.        2. See Appendix B.

in the "Initial" column, including zeros when there is no allocation. Whenever the response of four out of five is the same, he enters that response in the "Final" column. If these responses happen to add up to ten, the group's planning procedure is thereby terminated. Otherwise the (positive or negative) excess of points must still be allocated (by addition or subtraction) as follows. The chairman invites a brief debate regarding items where a consensus is lacking, in the approximate order of decreasing dissent. Each member then independently distributes the excess points (positive or negative) among the items not yet having firm allocations, using his "Second" column. The chairman now continues the firming up of final allocations on the basis of these returns, using equal decisions by four out of five first and the medians next. If the result still is either deficient or in excess of ten, items are reconsidered where two out of five had recommended respectively a higher or lower allocation, and a choice among these is made by a voice vote of preference or, if that fails, at random.

The allocations of points thus obtained lead to "new probabilities," entered in the column thus headed on the Group Planning Form.

## Random projection

The new probabilities just obtained by $P_1$ and $P_2$ are further modified by taking certain anticipated correlations among potential developments into account. If the probability of an event has just been raised, the number of that event is circled wherever it occurs in the "influenced" columns of the Group Planning Form; each such circle indicates that the probability is to be raised (or lowered) by 10 percent. (Exception: 90 percent is raised to 95 percent if at all; 95 percent is not raised further.)

These adjusted probabilities are now used to decide, by means of a random device (such as a table of random numbers) which of the twenty potential developments is to be a feature of the world of 2000. These random decisions, however, are not carried out independently for Worlds $W_1$ and $W_2$: If, as the result of the planning process, an event received the same probability, it is decided equally for both worlds; if it received different probabilities, it is decided by independent random processes for the two worlds, except that an outcome is rejected if the event turns out to be true in the world where it had the smaller probability and false in the other.[3]

The result of this procedure, then, is the description of two worlds, $W_1$ and $W_2$ in terms of which of the twenty potential developments considered here are, or are not, true in them.

3. Strictly speaking, in order not to affect the probabilities of the event in each of the two worlds, it is necessary to replace its probabilities, say $x$ and $y$ (where $x \geqslant y$), by $xy/(1-x+xy)$ and $y/(1-x+xy)$ respectively, before applying the above procedure.

## Social-prediction phase

Among the materials required for this exercise are a number of replicas of a deck of twenty cards, labelled "Potential Social Consequences," one for each of the twenty potential developments considered above.[4] From each of a set of such decks, those cards which correspond to the events true in $W_1$ are abstracted; and similarly for $W_2$.

The two groups of social predictors, $S_1$ and $S_2$, each consisting of five persons, plus a member of the control staff acting as chairman meet simultaneously. Their meetings may well begin before the meetings of $P_1$ and $P_2$ are over, so that each member can spend some time familiarizing himself with the contents of the twenty descriptive vignettes which appear as an Appendix to Gordon's paper.

As soon as the subdecks of Potential Social Consequences have been prepared, each member of $S_1$ is given a deck corresponding to $W_1$, and each member of $S_2$ one corresponding to $W_2$.

The chairman then makes the following opening remarks:

"In this session your role is that of social predictors. You have in front of you brief descriptions of technological and environmental developments that you are to assume to have taken place by the year 2000. For each such development, certain potential consequences for our society have been listed; others may occur to you if you try to imagine a world characterized by the developments that have been stipulated.

Please consider each development listed in the deck in front of you. First of all, if any one of you thinks that there is an additional social consequence that deserves consideration, led it be added to each person's sheet. Now, for each potential social consequence listed, this group is to state its opinion as to how likely it is to be an actual consequence of the development in question and, if it indeed were a consequence, how importantly it would affect the nature of our society.

Each of you is first to give his estimates of likelihood and importance independently, using percent probabilities from the range ten, twenty, . . . , ninety for the former, and one of the numbers one, two, three to express negligible, slight, or considerable importance respectively, and entering these in the two 'Initial' columns. Later we shall try to arrive at a group consensus."

The chairman records these responses on a Social Predictions sheet,[5] circles in each case the median probability and the median importance, and enters their product, all under the "Initial" heading. If the product is 120 or more, he enters a "+" in the "Accept-or-Reject" column, and if it is eighty or less, he enters a " − " there.

---

4. See Appendix C.          5. See Appendix D.

On the remaining items, he invites a brief debate, and at its conclusion asks each member independently to revise his former estimates, using the "Final" columns.

Again the chairman records the responses (where they are different), notes the medians, and enters their product. If now the product is less than 100, the consequence is rejected ("−"), if it is more than 100 it is accepted ("+"). In cases where it is equal to 100, it is accepted if the total number of other accepted consequences is fewer than three, and rejected otherwise.

The results of the sessions up to this point are processed as follows: Those features which pertain to World $W_1$ but not to $W_2$, and likewise those that pertain to $W_2$ but not to $W_1$ (in other words the features in which $W_1$ and $W_2$ differ), are entered by number on eighteen copies of the World $W_1$/World $W_2$ Comparison sheets,[6] for use by the evaluation committees. In addition, both the common features and the differentiating features of $W_1$ and $W_2$ are displayed in verbal form on the walls of the plenary-session conference room (which is also used for simultaneous sessions of the committees $E_1$ to $E_6$):

| Distinct Features of $W_1$ | Common Features of $W_1$ and $W_2$ | Distinct Features of $W_2$ |
|:---:|:---:|:---:|
| DEVELOPMENTS | DEVELOPMENTS | DEVELOPMENTS |
|  |  |  |
| SOCIAL CONSEQUENCES | SOCIAL CONSEQUENCES | SOCIAL CONSEQUENCES |
|  |  |  |

## Evaluation phase

Each of the six committees of evaluators, $E_1$ to $E_6$, will consist of three persons, seated at separate tables in the room later used for the plenary session. Each member receives one of the World $W_1$/World $W_2$ Comparison sheets.

An opening statement is made to all participants in this phase, as follows:

6. See Appendix E.

"The purpose of this session is to arrive at a comparative evaluation of two alternative futures. Displayed on the wall are descriptions of two worlds, $W_1$ and $W_2$, of the year 2000: technological and environmental developments assumed to have taken place by the end of this century, and estimated consequences of these developments for our society.

Each of the six assembled committees is to evaluate these alternative worlds from the point of view of the best interests of a different sector of our society as of the year 2000. For example, the committee labelled 'teenagers' is to try to reach an understanding of the values which will be held by teenagers in the year 2000 in each of the worlds $W_1$ and $W_2$; it is then to decide whether the social conditions stipulated for $W_1$ or for $W_2$ are preferable, by virtue of giving greater satisfaction to these projected values, and to state by how much they prefer one to the other, and for what reasons; and similarly for the other five committees.

The opinion of each committee will later be reported to a plenary session of all conferees. For this purpose we have asked one member of each committee to serve as its reporter. The reporter will also take responsibility for recording the individual responses as well as the group consensus on a $W_1:W_2$ Evaluation sheet.[7]

The first thing we would like each of you to do now is to consider each social consequence stipulated only for $W_1$, and later similarly for $W_2$, and to indicate whether, from the viewpoint you are simulating, you regard it as highly undesirable ('$-2$'), mildly undesirable ('$-1$'), essentially indifferent ('0'), mildly desirable ('$+1$'), or highly desirable ('$+2$'), by writing the appropriate figures in the 'Initial' columns. This is merely a preparatory step, intended to make it easier for you to make an overall intuitive comparison of $W_1$ and $W_2$ from your simulated viewpoints. The result of this comparison should then be expressed by splitting 10 points between $W_1$ and $W_2$ to indicate your relative preference ('10:0', '9:1', . . . , or '0:10').

The individual appraisals will later be combined into a group opinion."

Each group's reporter records these initial responses on his $W_1:W_2$ Evaluation form. He then invites a discussion aimed at exploring the reasons for differences of opinion among the three members of the committee; reference to their previous numerical evaluations of each world's special features may here be helpful. At the end of the discussion, each member is again to make an independent, revised evaluation. The result again is recorded by the reporter, the median of the three responses is noted and taken to be the committee's consensus. The three World $W_1$/World $W_2$

7. See Appendix F.

Comparison sheets are collected by the reporter, to aid him in making a report to the plenary session later.

## Final assessment

The final plenary assessment session is to open with a statement by the chairman (Theodore J. Gordon) in which he will summarize the features of the two worlds $W_1$ and $W_2$, using the prepared wall displays.

Each conferee will then be handed an Assessment slip,[8] on which he is to indicate what weight, in his opinion, should be given to the evaluations by the population sectors represented by the six committees, $E_1$ to $E_6$. He does this by distributing a total of sixty points over the six committees (with the constraint, however, that no more than twenty points be allocated to any one entry).

These responses are collected and their means computed. These means will be used to weight the opinions presented by the six committees.

Each of the six committee reporters in turn is asked to report his committee's $W_1:W_2$ evaluation and briefly to summarize the reason for their finding. These $W_1:W_2$ evaluations are entered on an Evaluation wall display, which looks as follows:

PREFERENCES BETWEEN WORLDS $W_1$ AND $W_2$

| | Committee | $W_1:W_2$ | Weight | Product |
|---|---|---|---|---|
| $E_1$ | Teenagers | | | |
| $E_2$ | Housewives | | | |
| $E_3$ | Middleclass employed | | | |
| $E_4$ | Persons over 65 | | | |
| $E_5$ | Cultural elite | | | |
| $E_6$ | Poor | | | |
| | | | $\frac{1}{100} \times$ Total: | |

After the six reporters have been heard, the weights based on the conferees' assessments are entered, the product is computed for each line, and the products are added up to determine which world is preferred and by how much.

The session terminates with a dual post-mortem, giving the participants an opportunity (a) to comment on the substantive outcome of the exercise and (b) to vent their criticisms of the method used.

Since the entire workshop is intended to be merely a pilot simulation,

8. See Appendix G.

Part (b) of the post-mortem, in particular—if it is reasonably constructive—may be a valuable contribution to the development of simulation methods in the general area of the inexact sciences. It is to be hoped, after all, that this very tentative experiment will provide some insights as to better ways of dealing both constructively and interdisciplinarily with so problematic an issue as that of the system of social values of the future. For a brief report on (and critique of) the actual run of this exercise, see pp. 9–12 of Alvin Toffler's Introduction.

# APPENDIX A

| Potential Development | Proba- bility | Diffi- culty | Initial | Second | Final | New Probab. |
|---|---|---|---|---|---|---|
| 1. *FERTILITY CONTROL*—World wide acceptance and use of oral contraceptives or other simple and inexpensive means of fertility control | 50 | 2 | | | | |
| 2. *100-YEAR LIFE SPAN*—100 year life expectancy for white male babies born in the United States | 30 | 1 | | | | |
| 3. *PERSONALITY CONTROL DRUGS*—Widespread and socially widely accepted use of non-narcotic drugs (other than alcohol) for the purpose of producing specific changes in personality characteristics | 50 | 1 | | | | |
| 4. *INCAPACITATING RATHER THAN LETHAL WEAPONS*—Use of incapacitating weapons to form a decisive portion of the arsenals of major nations | 40 | 2 | | | | |
| 5. *SOPHISTICATED TEACHING MACHINES*—Widespread use of sophisticated teaching machines | 80 | 1 | | | | |
| 6. *OCEAN FARMING*—Economically useful exploitation of the ocean through farming, with the effect of producing at least 20% of the world's food | 30 | 3 | | | | |
| 7. *CONTROLLED THERMONUCLEAR REACTIONS*—Means found to control thermonuclear reactions | 50 | 2 | | | | |
| 8. *CONTINUED AUTOMATION IN COMMERCE AND INDUSTRY*—Increase by a factor of 10 in capital investment in computers used for automated process control | 80 | 2 | | | | |
| 9. *ARTIFICIAL LIFE*—Creation of a primitive form of artificial life (at least in the form of self-replicating molecules) | 20 | 1 | | | | |
| 10. *WEATHER CONTROL*—Feasibility of limited weather control, in the sense of substantially affecting regional weather at acceptable cost | 30 | 2 | | | | |
| 11. *GENERAL IMMUNIZATION*—Large scale biochemical general immunization against bacterial and viral diseases | 30 | 2 | | | | |
| 12. *GENETIC CONTROL*—Feasibility (not necessarily acceptance) of chemical control over some hereditary defects by modification of genes through molecular engineering | 20 | 1 | | | | |
| 13. *MAN-MACHINE SYMBIOSIS* — Man-machine symbiosis, enabling man to extend his intelligence by direct electromechanical interaction between his brain and a computing machine | 10 | 1 | | | | |
| 14. *HOUSEHOLD ROBOTS*—Use of computer programmed automatic household labor in the average American home | 60 | 1 | | | | |
| 15. *PRESERVATION OF PRIVACY*—Legislation enacted to prevent establishment of national data banks which might contain extensive personal information about citizens without their consent | 20 | 1 | | | | |
| 16. *WIDE BAND COMMUNICATIONS SYSTEMS*—General use of communications systems which carry at least 100 video and information channels into average homes | 50 | 2 | | | | |

|  | | | POINT ALLOCATION | | | |
|---|---|---|---|---|---|---|
| *Potential Development* | *Proba-bility* | *Diffi-culty* | *Initial* | *Second* | *Final* | *New Probab.* |
| 17. *CONTINUED SPACE EXPLORATION*—Budgeting of the civilian space program at levels exceeding 1% of the GNP | 60 | 3 | | | | |
| 18. *ADVANCED TECHNIQUES OF OPINION CONTROL, THOUGHT MANIPULATION, PROPAGANDA*—Use of advanced techniques of opinion control, thought manipulation and propaganda in combating crime, rebellious populations in time of civil upheaval, and in wartime | 40 | 1 | | | | |
| 19. *CONTINUED TREND TOWARD URBANIZATION*—90% of the population of the United States living in cities | 50 | 3 | | | | |
| 20. *OVA/SPERM BANKS ESTABLISHED*—Commercial operation of ova and sperm banks | 40 | 1 | | | | |

# APPENDIX B

GROUP PLANNING FORM

| | | | POINT ALLOCATIONS | | | | POS.   NEG. | | |
|---|---|---|---|---|---|---|---|---|---|
| *Potential Development* | *Prob.* | *Diff.* | *initial* | *second* | *final* | *New prob.* | *influenced by* | *Adj. prob.* | *W i* |
| 1. Fertility Control | 50 | 2 | | | | | 11 12 20 | | |
| 2. 100-year Life Span | 30 | 1 | | | | | 1 6 | | |
| | | | | | | | 11 12 | | |
| 3. Personality Control Drugs | 50 | 1 | | | | | 11 | | |
| 4. Incapacitating Weapons | 40 | 2 | | | | | | 12 | |
| 5. Teaching Machines | 80 | 1 | | | | | 2 8 | | |
| | | | | | | | 13 16 | | |
| 6. Ocean Farming | 30 | 3 | | | | | | 1 | |
| 7. Controlled Th-Nuclear Power | 50 | 2 | | | | | | | |
| 8. Continued Automation | 80 | 2 | | | | | 5 13 14 | | |
| | | | | | | | 16 19 | | |
| 9. Artificial Life | 20 | 1 | | | | | 12 20 | | |
| 10. Weather Control | 30 | 2 | | | | | | | |
| 11. General Immunization | 30 | 2 | | | | | | | |
| 12. Genetic Control | 20 | 1 | | | | | 9 | | |
| 13. Man-Machine Symbiosis | 10 | 2 | | | | | 8 | | |
| 14. Household Robots | 60 | 1 | | | | | | | |
| 15. Preservation of Privacy | 20 | 1 | | | | | 8 12 18 | | |
| 16. Wide-Band Communications | 50 | 2 | | | | | 8 14 19 | | |
| 17. Continued Space Exploration | 60 | 3 | | | | | | | |
| 18. Opinion Control | 40 | 1 | | | | | 3 5 13 | | |
| 19. Continued Urbanization | 50 | 3 | | | | | 2 18 | | |
| 20. Sperm Banks | 40 | 1 | | | | | 12 | | |

## APPENDIX C

1.A. **FERTILITY CONTROL**—WORLD WIDE ACCEPTANCE AND USE OF ORAL CONTRACEPTIVES OR OTHER SIMPLE AND INEXPENSIVE MEANS OF FERTILITY CONTROL.

|  | *Likelihood of Consequence* | | *Importance of Consequence* | |
|---|---|---|---|---|
| *Potential Social Consequences* | *Initial* | *Final* | *Initial* | *Final* |

1. Improvement of the economic status of currently under-developed nations
2. Over-control, resulting in diminishing population levels
3. Increasing imbalance between have and have-not nations resulting from disparity in the rate at which certain nations accept birth control measures
4. Increasing life span
5. Diminishing of discrimination as a result of extension of the practice of birth control among minority races in the U.S.
6. Reduction in the probability of war
7. Relaxation of sexual mores
8. Use of surreptitious contraceptive seeding of enemy staple commodities in war
9. Other

1.B. **CONTINUED POPULATION EXPLOSION**—POPULAR REJECTION OF BIRTH CONTROL MEASURES.

|  | *Likelihood of Consequence* | | *Importance of Consequence* | |
|---|---|---|---|---|
| *Potential Social Consequences* | *Initial* | *Final* | *Initial* | *Final* |

1. Increasing starvation as the malthusian limit is approached
2. Development of behavior patterns currently considered abnormal, including abandonment of progeny, hypersexual homosexual behavior and cannibalism
3. Anti-population legislation including birth licenses, revision of tax structures to favor small families, and limited education
4. Direct government intervention, controlling population levels by adding contraceptive agent to widely used staples
5. Increasing bureaucracy made necessary by growing requirements for resource allocations
6. Increasing probability of war
7. Lowering of educational levels
8. Other

2. **100-YEAR LIFE SPAN**—100-YEAR LIFE EXPECTANCY FOR WHITE MALE BABIES BORN IN THE UNITED STATES.

|  | *Likelihood of Consequence* | | *Importance of Consequence* | |
|---|---|---|---|---|
| *Potential Social Consequences* | *Initial* | *Final* | *Initial* | *Final* |

1. Revision of social security structure to provide economic minima to senior citizens
2. Development of special devices and services for the aged including low-speed automobiles, perhaps battery powered, artificial organs, mass media entertainment, and household robots
3. Enactment of legislation limiting maximum age of employment to provide work for the younger segment of the population
4. Emergence of a "senior citizen" political bloc
5. Increasing urbanization
6. Increasing unemployment
7. Other

3. **PERSONALITY CONTROL DRUGS**—WIDESPREAD AND SOCIALLY WIDELY ACCEPTED USE OF NON-NARCOTIC DRUGS (OTHER THAN ALCOHOL) FOR THE PURPOSE OF PRODUCING SPECIFIC CHANGES IN PERSONALITY CHARACTERISTICS.

|  | Likelihood of Consequence | | Importance of Consequence | |
|---|---|---|---|---|
| *Potential Social Consequences* | *Initial* | *Final* | *Initial* | *Final* |

1. Widespread physiological addiction to hallucinogenic drugs
2. Degeneration of leisure into hedonistic escape from reality
3. Government use of drugs for population-wide behavior control
4. Socially accepted use of drugs to obtain predetermined moods in the manner in which alcohol is employed today
5. Use of drugs in warfare to increase the courage of friendly troops and removing the will to resist of enemy troops
6. Use of drugs by the church to promote extra-personal religious insight
7. Use of drugs to promote:
   a. Learning
   b. Memory
   c. Suggestion
   d. Minimize crime (anti-crime suggestions to habitual criminals)
8. Increasing unemployment
9. Anti-drug legislation
10. Other

4. **INCAPACITATING RATHER THAN LETHAL WEAPONS**—USE OF INCAPACITATING WEAPONS TO FORM A DECISIVE PORTION OF THE ARSENALS OF MAJOR NATIONS.

|  | Likelihood of Consequence | | Importance of Consequence | |
|---|---|---|---|---|
| *Potential Social Consequences* | *Initial* | *Final* | *Initial* | *Final* |

1. Elimination of killing in war resulting in socially acceptable conflict
2. Evolution of covert war techniques permitting surreptitious and undiscovered warfare
3. Effective crowd and riot control eliminating mobs
4. Other

5. **SOPHISTICATED TEACHING MACHINES**—WIDESPREAD USE OF SOPHISTICATED TEACHING MACHINES.

|  | Likelihood of Consequence | | Importance of Consequence | |
|---|---|---|---|---|
| *Potential Social Consequences* | *Initial* | *Final* | *Initial* | *Final* |

1. Changing form and substance of schools
2. Increasing teaching efficiency resulting in reduction of time to educate by 30%
3. Acceptance of home instruction by teaching machines as the norm
4. Political control over programmed courses
5. Increasing GNP
6. College education for all
7. Reduction in racial discrimination
8. Other

6. **OCEAN FARMING**—ECONOMICALLY USEFUL EXPLOITATION OF THE OCEAN THROUGH FARMING, WITH THE EFFECT OF PRODUCING AT LEAST TWENTY PERCENT OF THE WORLD'S FOOD.

| *Potential Social Consequences* | *Likelihood of Consequence* | | *Importance of Consequence* | |
|---|---|---|---|---|
| | *Initial* | *Final* | *Initial* | *Final* |
| 1. National territorial claims extending into the oceans | | | | |
| 2. Increasing availability of ocean products leading to the diminishing importance of conventional agricultural produce | | | | |
| 3. International agreements to farm the ocean cooperatively, and thus avoid wide-spread starvation | | | | |
| 4. Increasing conflict between private and national ocean farming interests leading to a modern equivalent of piracy | | | | |
| 5. Increasing life span through avoidance of widespread starvation | | | | |
| 6. Reduction in probability of war | | | | |
| 7. Reduction in unemployment | | | | |
| 8. Other | | | | |

7. **CONTROLLED THERMONUCLEAR REACTIONS**—MEANS FOUND TO CONTROL THERMO-NUCLEAR REACTIONS.

| *Potential Social Consequences* | *Likelihood of Consequence* | | *Importance of Consequence* | |
|---|---|---|---|---|
| | *Initial* | *Final* | *Initial* | *Final* |
| 1. Supplying of thermal nuclear power systems to help under-developed nations | | | | |
| 2. Application of sophisticated thermonuclear technology into weapons technology | | | | |
| 3. Implementation of large scale water conversion projects leading to irrigation of arid areas in this country and elsewhere | | | | |
| 4. Social pressures leading to the inhibition of further development of thermonuclear power systems on the basis of suspected atmospheric contamination | | | | |
| 5. Increasing GNP | | | | |
| 6. Government rather than private ownership and operation of thermonuclear power stations | | | | |
| 7. Other | | | | |

8. *CONTINUED AUTOMATION IN COMMERCE AND INDUSTRY*—INCREASE BY A FACTOR
OF 10 IN CAPITAL INVESTMENT IN COMPUTERS USED FOR AUTOMATED PROCESS CONTROL.

| | Likelihood of Consequence | | Importance of Consequence | |
|---|---|---|---|---|
| *Potential Social Consequences* | *Initial* | *Final* | *Initial* | *Final* |

1. Increasing unemployment
2. Anti-automation legislation including:

   a. Protection of certain jobs from automation
   b. Lowering the retirement age by five years
   c. Massive WPA type programs
   d. Shortening the work week by 20%
   e. Two years of compulsory post high school education
   f. Massive aid to underdeveloped regions (including parts
      of the United States)
   g. All-out government sponsored training programs
3. Creation of new types of employment
4. Derivation of means for equitable distribution of overabundance, to raise the level of the under-privileged nations
5. Establishment of the government as an employer "of last
resort," guaranteeing an annual wage through negative
income tax
6. Increasing acceptance of education as an important and
acceptable leisure time pursuit
7. Rising demand for handmade products and personal
services
8. General acceptance of diminishing privacy and intrusion
by increasing efficient bureaucratic organizations
9. Increasing GNP making a better life for all, with acceptable
uses found for extra leisure
10. Increasing GNP but with growing national guilt accompanying unproductive leisure
11. Increasing GNP but with an appreciable portion of the
population occupied in hedonistic, idle and unproductive
pursuits
12. Other

9. *ARTIFICIAL LIFE*—CREATION OF A PRIMITIVE FORM OF ARTIFICIAL LIFE (AT LEAST IN THE
FORM OF SELF-REPLICATING MOLECULES).

| | Likelihood of Consequence | | Importance of Consequence | |
|---|---|---|---|---|
| *Potential Social Consequences* | *Initial* | *Final* | *Initial* | *Final* |

1. Decline in the importance of the concept of supernatural
creation
2. Attacks on the experiments in the manner in which evolutionary theory was attacked
3. Church acceptance of the experiments resulting in gradual
construction of an ethical, rather than punitive and supernatural, morality
4. Other

10. **WEATHER CONTROL**—FEASIBILITY OF LIMITED WEATHER CONTROL, IN THE SENSE OF SUBSTANTIALLY AFFECTING REGIONAL WEATHER AT ACCEPTABLE COST.

| *Potential Social Consequences* | *Likelihood of Consequence* | | *Importance of Consequence* | |
|---|---|---|---|---|
| | *Initial* | *Final* | *Initial* | *Final* |

1. Acceptance of U.N. regulation of weather manipulation
2. Growing tendency to blame bad weather on inefficient government
3. Introduction of the means for weather control into the strategic weapons arsenal
4. Lobbyists and special interest groups petitioning for weather of their choice
5. Weather selected by referendum
6. Establishment of weather controlled geographic zones for the production of certain agricultural crops
7. Other

11. **GENERAL IMMUNIZATION**—LARGE SCALE BIOCHEMICAL GENERAL IMMUNIZATION AGAINST BACTERIAL AND VIRAL DISEASES.

| *Potential Social Consequences* | *Likelihood of Consequence* | | *Importance of Consequence* | |
|---|---|---|---|---|
| | *Initial* | *Final* | *Initial* | *Final* |

1. Rising unemployment as the result of fewer disease initiated disabilities
2. Social acceptability of drafts and wet feet
3. Emergence of a senior citizen "social force" of increasing importance as a result of the shift in minimum age
4. A trend toward greater urbanization, or specialized communities, resulting from the shift of population medium age
5. Elimination of bacteriological warfare
6. Wider acceptance and importance of the world health organizations under the auspices of the United Nations
7. Rejection of immunization by large segments of the world's population as "ungod-like"
8. Other

12. **GENETIC CONTROL**—FEASIBILITY (NOT NECESSARILY ACCEPTANCE) OF CHEMICAL CONTROL OVER SOME HEREDITARY DEFECTS BY MODIFICATION OF GENES THROUGH MOLECULAR ENGINEERING.

| *Potential Social Consequences* | *Likelihood of Consequence* | | *Importance of Consequence* | |
|---|---|---|---|---|
| | *Initial* | *Final* | *Initial* | *Final* |

1. Elimination of inherited defects through molecular engineering
2. Tailoring of inherited characteristics to adjust IQ, physique, and other attributes according to the order of parents
3. Application of genetic control to agricultural processes and protein manufacturing to provide more significant food supply
4. Legislation controlling the application and practice of genetic operations
5. Increasing pressure to apply the principles of genetic engineering to the problem of aging
6. Widespread practice of transplanting organs and limbs
7. Construction of duplicate human beings from single cell source material
8. Growth of new organs and limbs using genetic processes
9. Elimination of racial characteristics resulting in greatly diminished discrimination
10. Other

13. *MAN MACHINE SYMBIOSIS*—MAN MACHINE SYMBIOSIS, ENABLING MAN TO EXTEND HIS INTELLIGENCE BY DIRECT ELECTROMECHANICAL INTERACTION BETWEEN HIS BRAIN AND A COMPUTING MACHINE.

| *Potential Social Consequences* | *Likelihood of Consequence* | | *Importance of Consequence* | |
|---|---|---|---|---|
| | *Initial* | *Final* | *Initial* | *Final* |
| 1. Public acceptance of teaching techniques which will involve computer directed recording on the brain | | | | |
| 2. Public acceptance of wiring man into machines to provide for controlling functions | | | | |
| 3. Use of computers as colleagues | | | | |
| 4. Emergence of computer controllers as a prestigious professional group | | | | |
| 5. Other | | | | |

14. *HOUSEHOLD ROBOTS*—USE OF COMPUTER PROGRAMMED AUTOMATIC HOUSEHOLD LABOR IN THE AVERAGE AMERICAN HOME.

| *Potential Social Consequences* | *Likelihood of Consequence* | | *Importance of Consequence* | |
|---|---|---|---|---|
| | *Initial* | *Final* | *Initial* | *Final* |
| 1. Increasing use of machines to replace human services | | | | |
| 2. Anti-robot legislation to guarantee certain services to human workers | | | | |
| 3. Elevating the social position of machine repair men | | | | |
| 4. People exhibiting real affection for their machines | | | | |
| 5. Rise of credit card economy | | | | |
| 6. Other | | | | |

15.A. *PRESERVATION OF PRIVACY*—LEGISLATION ENACTED TO PREVENT ESTABLISHMENT OF NATIONAL DATA BANKS WHICH MIGHT CONTAIN EXTENSIVE PERSONAL INFORMATION ABOUT CITIZENS WITHOUT THEIR CONSENT.

| *Potential Social Consequences* | *Likelihood of Consequence* | | *Importance of Consequence* | |
|---|---|---|---|---|
| | *Initial* | *Final* | *Initial* | *Final* |
| 1. Enactment of associated legislation which guarantees personal privacy including outlawing of bugging and wire tapping | | | | |
| 2. Establishment of limited scope data banks by mission oriented government bureaus | | | | |
| 3. Credential requirements established for access to stored personal information | | | | |
| 4. Diminishing of size and scope of bureaucracies | | | | |
| 5. Other | | | | |

15.B. **DECREASING PRIVACY**—ESTABLISHMENT OF NATIONAL DATA BANKS CONTAINING EXTENSIVE PERSONAL INFORMATION ABOUT CITIZENS WITHOUT THEIR CONSENT.

| *Potential Social Consequences* | *Likelihood of Consequence* | | *Importance of Consequence* | |
|---|---|---|---|---|
| | *Initial* | *Final* | *Initial* | *Final* |
| 1. State control over human behavior approaching big brotherism | | | | |
| 2. Growing bureaucracies increasing in scope and accuracy with the aid of central computers | | | | |
| 3. Bugging becoming a national pastime | | | | |
| 4. Increasing use of privacy-assuring devices | | | | |
| 5. Use of social security numbers for universal identification: school records, telephone numbers, bank accounts, income tax, draft, etc. | | | | |
| 6. Acceptance of intrusion into privacy as the norm of government | | | | |
| 7. Legislation against intrusion into personal matters | | | | |
| 8. Central computers making resource allocations, and fixing profits and taxation | | | | |
| 9. Central computers used to determine statistical information from personal data storage including—census, health records, migration, advertising effectiveness, actuarial data, etc. | | | | |
| 10. Other | | | | |

16. **WIDE BAND COMMUNICATIONS SYSTEMS**—GENERAL USE OF COMMUNICATIONS SYSTEMS WHICH CARRY AT LEAST 100 VIDEO AND INFORMATION CHANNELS INTO AVERAGE HOMES.

| *Potential Social Consequences* | *Likelihood of Consequence* | | *Importance of Consequence* | |
|---|---|---|---|---|
| | *Initial* | *Final* | *Initial* | *Final* |
| 1. School classes conducted in the home via television | | | | |
| 2. Automated voting in the home approaching automated plebiscite | | | | |
| 3. Use of facsimile printers to produce magazines and newspapers in the home | | | | |
| 4. Automated purchasing from the home via communicating links associated with TV advertising | | | | |
| 5. Granting of university degrees of viewers who complete the courses solely on TV | | | | |
| 6. An emerging class of savants dedicated to learning as an end in itself | | | | |
| 7. Canned lectures by eminent professors making TV teaching superior to that in resident institutions | | | | |
| 8. Other | | | | |

17. **CONTINUED SPACE EXPLORATION**—BUDGETING OF THE CIVILIAN SPACE PROGRAM AT LEVELS EXCEEDING ONE PERCENT OF THE GNP.

| *Potential Social Consequences* | *Likelihood of Consequence* | | *Importance of Consequence* | |
|---|---|---|---|---|
| | *Initial* | *Final* | *Initial* | *Final* |

1. Acceptance of space adventures as an alternative to war
2. Use of orbital and lunar stations as sanitarium for stroke and heart cases
3. Selection of national space goals providing unifying direction to the U.S. economy and industry
4. Acceptance of astronauts as national heroes
5. Elimination of some international barriers to understanding through spaceborne devices such as communication satellites
6. Colonization of habitable planets
7. Reduction of unemployment
8. Use of solar probes to dispose of earth's noxious wastes
9. Use of orbital stations to provide direct economic benefits such as detection of diseased crops, aid to shipping, weather observations, etc.
10. Continued use of space exploits as a demonstration of technological preeminence
11. Other

18. **ADVANCED TECHNIQUES OF OPINION CONTROL, THOUGHT MANIPULATION PROPAGANDA**—USE OF ADVANCED TECHNIQUES OF OPINION CONTROL, THOUGHT MANIPULATION AND PROPAGANDA IN COMBATING CRIME, REBELLIOUS POPULATIONS IN TIME OF CIVIL UPHEAVAL, AND IN WARTIME.

| *Potential Social Consequences* | *Likelihood of Consequence* | | *Importance of Consequence* | |
|---|---|---|---|---|
| | *Initial* | *Final* | *Initial* | *Final* |

1. Use of hypnosis on television
2. Use of physical, chemical and advanced psychological techniques for speeding education and enhancing learning
3. Adding of behavior control devices to the tactical weapons arsenal including, for example, chemicals which destroy the will to resist
4. Growing use of electrical devices which stimulate portions of cortex and permit certain physiological responses on command
5. Use of behavior control techniques to minimize crime and war
6. Other

19. **CONTINUED TREND TOWARD URBANIZATION**—NINETY PERCENT OF THE POPULATION OF THE UNITED STATES LIVING IN CITIES.

| *Potential Social Consequences* | *Likelihood of Consequence* | | *Importance of Consequence* | |
|---|---|---|---|---|
| | *Initial* | *Final* | *Initial* | *Final* |

1. Establishment of a credit card economy in which computers keep track of transactions
2. New types of buildings vertically oriented, environmentally controlled, with integrated services such as schools, hospitals, stores and so on
3. City cores becoming political entities; for example, an integrated building may have its own mayor, police force, fire services, library, etc.
4. Exclusion of automobiles from city cores
5. Increasing crime
6. Increasing atmospheric pollution
8. Other

20. *OVA/SPERM BANKS ESTABLISHED*—COMMERCIAL OPERATION OF OVA AND SPERM BANKS.

| *Potential Social Consequences* | Likelihood of Consequence | | Importance of Consequence | |
|---|---|---|---|---|
| | *Initial* | *Final* | *Initial* | *Final* |

1. Large spread acceptance of techniques of ova implantation whereby the prospective mother can select an embryo for implantation in herself
2. Widespread acceptance and practice of artificial insemination
3. Use of sperm banks in genetic programs, particularly to preserve the sperm of genetically gifted donors and to provide a nuclear shielded environment for human genetic material
4. Acceptance and practice of mechanized pregnancy in which ova are fertilized *in vitro* saving mothers from discomforts of natural pregnancy and providing the fetus with an optimum environment
5. Other

## APPENDIX D

### SOCIAL PREDICTIONS RECORD

| # of Dev | # of Solo | INITIAL | | | INITIAL | | | Accepted or Rej'd. |
|---|---|---|---|---|---|---|---|---|
| | | *Proba.'s* | *Importances* | *Prod.* | *Proba.'s* | *Importances* | *Prod.* | |

## APPENDIX E

| WORLD $W_1$ | | | | WORLD $W_2$ | | | |
|---|---|---|---|---|---|---|---|
| # of Development | # of Consequence | DESIRABILITY | | # of Development | # of Consequence | DESIRABILITY | |
| | | *Initial* | *Final* | | | *Initial* | *Final* |

| | Initial | Final |
|---|---|---|
| Preference Ratio $W_1 : W_2$ | : | : |

## APPENDIX F

$W_1 : W_2$ EVALUATION
                    *By Committee* .........

| Committee Member | Initial | Final | Median |
|---|---|---|---|
| Person at left of Reporter | | | |
| Person at right of Reporter | | | |
| Reporter | | | |

WEIGHT ASSESSMENT

| Population Segment | Weight |
|---|---|
| $E_1$: Teenagers | |
| $E_2$: Housewives | |
| $E_3$: Middleclass Employed | |
| $E_4$: Persons over 65 | |
| $E_5$: Cultural Elite | |
| $E_6$: Persons in Lowest Income Decile | |
| Total: | 60 |

Name: ..................................................

# PART II INTERACTION

# THE POWER OF VALUES I

# Technology as a means

## *Bertrand de Jouvenel*

We live in an Age of Opportunity. Our modern civilization is far superior to any other in terms of power, and thereby we enjoy undreamed of possibilities to foster the good life not for a tiny minority, as in earlier societies, but for the multitude. This is a wonderful privilege; nonsensical therefore is the attitude of those who regret not having lived at some former epoch: no matter that their personal circumstances might have been better, their means of improving the circumstances of their fellowmen would have been slighter. It is right to rejoice in the greatness of these means: it is proper to feel responsible for their personal and optional use.

We should be aware of two important features which qualify our Age of Opportunity. First the Opportunity—and to stress it I use the capital —is primarily a collective, a social Opportunity, and not primarily an individual opportunity in the sense of "Go West, young man." It is true enough that the powers of Man, in advanced countries, have been multiplied by a factor of a hundred; but the statement would be obviously untrue applied to the individual; we have not become, severally, so many Hercules. This new wealth of powers pertains to societies, it is managed by the managers of great organizations, we only get individually the benefits of these forces, benefits the nature of which depends upon the judgments of their managers. Thus the conditions and style of life of individuals depend upon the management of the social Opportunity.

The second qualification is more difficult to express but it is of capital importance. We can quite confidently expect that the increase of our collective powers shall continue and the probability of its acceleration is great. However, we should not confuse the gross increase in powers with a net progress of Opportunity. In every realm there exists a relationship between past and future action, past action placing constraints upon future action. In so far as these constraints are of a psychological nature, we are apt to regard them as capable of being broken. But there is another aspect: the changes wrought by action in the environment. As long as human action

217

was an insignificant scrabbling of rare and feeble insects, this did not mortgage future action. Indeed there is an essential difference between American history and that of Europe or the far longer history of Asian civilizations: the migrants who came to America from Europe, bearers of a relatively advanced technology, found unlimited natural resources unaffected by any previous uses. But as we grow capable of ever heavier actions which ever more profoundly modify the environment, such modifications become more important data for future actions. Therefore even though we can think of our powers as due to increase, it does not follow that we can think of the Opportunity afforded to each generation of our successors as allowing to each progressively greater latitudes of choice. Whether such latitude shall in fact increase or decrease we cannot say for certain. This we should think of as a function of increasing means and increasing constraints. What we may call "the balance of net Opportunity" is very favorable in our day; we must at least envisage the possibility of its being less favorable in terms of what might lead to our descendants judging that we have handicapped their moving toward a good life by our improvident use of an exceptionally favorable balance of Opportunity.

I take it that our concern is to place our descendants in circumstances conducive to the flowering of *la pianta uomo*, according to the expression of the poet Alfieri, which strongly suggests the dual aims of prosperity and quality, as indeed the Roman salute *vale* implied wishes both of good fortune and of worthiness. Strongly felt and unclearly conceived, this concern inspires to men of good will the advocacy or the performances of "moves" which are seldom rationally related to an overall view of the social system and an understanding of its many internal links, and which are often fertile in undesired after-effects and side-effects. Unwanted effects wax in importance as the moves become heavier and as we are packed closer. Of this we have grown quite sharply aware: therefrom the many laudable efforts of our day to take a general view of Society, to speculate upon the improvements which can be contrived within one generation, and to provide so to speak a general picture within which we can place the initiatives and innovations.

Of major importance is the placing in this picture of "scientific and artificial aids to man" to use the felicitous expression introduced by Robert Owen in 1820.[1] Alvin Weinberg rightly stresses that we can often employ "technological fixes" to deal with social problems rebellious to treatment by attention to alteration of human behavior; thus so to speak calling in the technologist to cut the Gordian knot we cannot untie.[2] This approach is to

1. Robert Owen: *Report to the County of Lanark*, Part 1 (Glasgow, 1821).
2. Alvin Weinberg, Acceptance speech for the University of Chicago Alumni Award, June 2, 1966. Published in French in *Analyse et Prevision*, October 1966.

be welcomed because it represents techniques as means to achieve social ends, means to be consciously employed. And this is their true nature. Unfortunately they are currently seen or sensed quite otherwise.

Life in Western society is a new fatalism, a feeling that our future is determined for us by the autonomous course of a super-human agency, whose god-like nature is acknowledged by the reverent use of the capital: Technology. It showers upon us benefits of its own choosing, it makes demands we may not deny. It blazes the trail of the future like a mythical Juggernaut's chariot, it drives us down if we stand in its way, and bears us from success to success if we cling to its side. Thus Technology is represented as an idol which richly rewards its servants who do not question its course.

This attitude displays our natural bent toward superstition, which seems in no way abated by our partaking of a scientific civilization. Indeed we prove more naive than the primitives; when they made idols of natural forces it was at least true that these were outside their control and generated in a manner they could not understand, which is of course not true of Technology.

It would be hard to find a phenomenon more dependent upon human decisions than the evolution of techniques. Indeed while the current decision as to its autonomy comes from the quickening of its pace, this acceleration itself manifests more conscious and deliberate decision making.

That the evolution of techniques depends upon human decisions, this is the pivot of my paper. If so, then how are these decisions made, by whom, and on what grounds? What above all are the values which enter into such decision making and determine the choices? Recognizing that the system moves under the impact of a great variety of decisions made by a variety of groups, and that it can not be otherwise, the values which inspire discrete decisions assume a decisive importance. To what degree are the values taken into account here and there consistent with one another and with ultimate values regarding the condition of *la pianta uomo*? If the consistence is doubtful, how can it be improved? How can the ultimate values be injected to a greater degree into the discrete decisions? These are the questions I wish to raise. These are questions which are not meant to be answered, whose function is to become a demanding presence in our minds.

But first of all I must solidly establish the pivotal proposition.

At all times in every state of society the material existence of men rests upon the practice of reliable modes of operation. These reliable modes we called "arts" up to the 18th era or century: for instance I can find in my library "the art of the charcoal burner," "the art of the candlemaker," "the art of the bricklayer" and so forth.[3] A new word crept in as a mere

3. I refer to the *Description des Arts et Metiers* published from 1761 to 1769 in Paris, Duhamel du Monceau et al.

adjective: technical. Technical meant what pertains to the arts; then "technique" comes to displace "art," a displacement correlated with the increasing role played in the performance of operations by machinery and especially machinery moved by nonanimal energy.[4] Note that when Europe came into regular communication with China, and to a far greater degree with India, we found the arts (in the extensive and traditional sense) in most aspects more advanced in those parts of the world than in our own: our best informers, the Jesuit missionaries, marvelled at the skill of Asian workers using instruments of amazing lightness and cheapness. The taste which Europeans, at least since the Germanic invasions, have shown for heavy instruments—in peace or war—was to us a handicap until the intervention of new motive powers[5] turned it into an asset. Enough thereupon: the point I am concerned to make is that techniques are properly ways of doing things which depend essentially upon resort to powered machinery.

This is a very important point: because it follows therefrom that the introduction of a new technique depends upon the provision of the adequate machinery, in other words upon an *investment*. Nobody would deny this but many will forget when discussing how society will be moulded by technological progress, and such forgetfulness justifies my stressing the obvious.

In those activities which we still call "arts," and which require no significant capital expenditure[6] one may speak of a spontaneous course of change. Someone does a thing differently or does a different thing, and others imitate it. This is called progress by those who prefer the new style. Such changing in the arts (in the narrow sense) depends upon individual actions and reactions. At no time is there a massive input, subject to a decision made by wielders of collective resourses (no matter whether it be a private or a public collectivity).

On the contrary such inputs are necessary, such decisions are called for in the case of a technical innovation which can be made operational only by setting up an important and costly apparatus, and which becomes of social importance only by multiplication of similar apparatus. The theme of the inventor unable to find the financier thanks to whom the idea shall be all fact has often been treated in the 19th century as a personal tragedy: thus Balzac draws a parallel between the unrecognized poet, Lucien, and the unrecognized inventor, David.[7] In our day the lack for financial

4. Cf. my article of *Preuves*, April 1965.
5. "Meaningful" is the title of Denis Papin's treatise on steam power (1690): "A New Method to Elicit Very Powerful Forces at a Low Cost."
6. Note that architecture forms an exception of great moment, being far the most important of arts, and requiring vast investments, but I must bypass this great subject.
7. This is in the series *Les Illusions Perdues*, where "les souffrances du Poète" and "les souffrances de l'inventeur" are discrete parts.

support for the putting into operation of a proposed innovation is dealt with from another angle not the loss to the balked inventor but the loss to society from the lack of this innovation or the lag in its introduction. Thus Charles Wilson writes: "The most striking contrast between Britain and France at this period (first half of the 19th century) is the higher rate at which, in Britain, inventions were adopted, developed, and passed into application. No nation in the world showed more vivid inventive genius than the French, but a high proportion of their inventive talent proved abortive or was put to profitable use elsewhere—notably in England and Scotland."[8] The important point here is that new techniques matter socially by "passing into application."

Wilson rightly calls attention to the "rate" of their passing into application, but there is another consideration of moment to us: the selection of those which do pass into application. It will prove a help to clarity if we broach these questions from the angle of an "underdeveloped economy." However loosely used, the term of "underdevelopment" has a concrete and precise meaning: a country is so called in proportion to the lack of application therein of techniques which are current elsewhere. Such was Japan before the Meiji era: it now ranks among the advanced economies, thanks to the great effort which was made to put into application techniques already available.[9] It implies no underestimation of the inventive genius of the Japanese—whereof there is abundant proof—to state that the exceptional pace of their economic progress has been due essentially to the vigorous putting into application of techniques proven elsewhere.

If we now turn to countries which were dubbed "underdeveloped" when Truman formulated (in 1949) his famous "Point Four," we find that they stood in relation to the complex of techniques current in the "advanced" countries in a relation differing by an order of magnitude from that which characterized the Japanese situation in the 1860's. The techniques prevailing in advanced countries and therefore potentially applicable in an "underdeveloped" economy, can be thought of as a backlog of available techniques. The will to put them into application is constrained by the volume of resources which can in total be allocated to that purpose: it follows that a selection must be made, no matter by what complex of decision-processes; and the larger the backlog the smaller the share thereof which can efficiently be transferred within a given period of time. Now in so far as the social pattern and the modes of life depend upon techniques, their evolution shall take a different course in the case of different selections.

8. Holmyard, Singer and Hall: *A History of Technology* (Oxford, 1958), vol. V, ch. 33, p. 800.
9. Japan should be ranked much higher in terms of techniques than it is according to the criterion of per capita income, the critique of which is outside of my present subject.

I am not certain that the true variety of courses available to an under-developed economy is adequately recognized. The general idea which at first inspired development policies was that which had been formulated by Marx: i.e., that the most advanced country today offers to the less advanced the image· of their future. If one resorts to the widely used (and very questionable) criterion of national product or income per capita, one is tempted to say that Japan has caught up with what Britain was when Marx wrote: but surely the Japan of today bears no resemblance to Victorian England. To press the point further, Spain has almost the same per capita income as Japan, but there is very little likeness.

Will you explain the enormous differences between Victorian England, present-day Japan, and present-day Spain wholly by differences in social values and attitudes? If so you entirely abandon the notion that "as Technology goes, so goes Society." For my part I do not jettison it: I seek to put it in its place. It is true that the course of technological change has an enormous impact upon society: but it is no less true that social values are reflected in the course of technological change. If Japan has more general education not only than Victorian England and modern Spain, but more, as I believe, than any Western European country today, this is not an outcome of superior wealth (it is not superior) generated by technology: it is an outcome of deeply imbedded value prior to espousal of industrial civilization, values presumably acquired from China many centuries ago. I cannot resist quoting from a textbook used in the primary schools of China long before the impact of the West.[10] It incites children to study not only by stating that "the man who has not studied is ignorant of justice and social duties," but by offering them picturesque examples: Tche-yin who so loved study that as his poverty forced him to work all day and did not allow him to use a lamp by night, he collected glow-worms to read by their light; Tchou mai-Tchin, who lived by collecting wood, and, as he carried it back from the forest, tied a manuscript to the longest perch so that he could read as he walked. Li-mi, who, while leading cattle, rode a buffalo and read from a book tied to the animal's horns!

To cut short what might become a digression, and to summarize: the techniques current in an advanced country constitute for an under-developed country a backlog of potential change from which a selection has to be made, which has social consequences and which is inspired by social values prevailing in the adopting country.

I have just stressed that, in the case of an underdeveloped economy,

10. The work referred to is the San-tseu king with the commentary of Wang-Tcin-Ching, as translated and edited by G. Pauthier under the title *Le Livre Classique des Trois Caractères* (Paris, 1873).

there must be a choosing, within a backlog of available techniques of those that shall be put into operation. I want to suggest that the same situation obtains, *mutatis mutandis*, in the case of the most advanced economy. In the case of the United States itself, there is a backlog of available techniques, out of which some have to be selected for their prior putting into operation. The difference lies in that for the underdeveloped country the backlog is made up of techniques which are in practice in more advanced countries while for the US, the backlog consists in techniques which are being worked out in its own laboratories.

At the present moment in the US there are innovations which are operational only in a single or a very few pioneering instances: such an innovation shall not become a concrete factor in social life until it has become widespread; and this requires much operational investment. Other innovations have not yet been put into application anywhere but have reached such a stage of technical development that they need only an adequate allotment of investment to bring them into local and limited operational existence. Still other innovations are at earlier stages of development, the provision of more funds can precipitate their maturation. We may thus work up through the applied research stage up to the novelties which are clearly conceivable.

From the moment when a novelty is clearly conceived (I understand this to be called the Hahn-Strassmann point)[11] to the time of its being in such widespread practice that it can be said to be "socialized," its progress at various stages requires successive inputs of resources, which we may think of as successive "generations" of investments. It is our custom to draw a dividing line between the expenditures required to make the innovation operational (investments in the traditional sense of the word) and those required to bring the innovation to the point when it can be brought into operation (Research and Development expenditures, for short R&D). This custom is grounded in history: in the 19th century, investments to put into application were heavy and recorded expenditures (as they have remained), while expenditures to work out an idea to the point of feasibility were light and unrecorded expenditures (a momentous change has occurred here).

During the last twenty-five years a prodigious rise has occurred in R&D expenditures; as their estimates are highly subject to methods of classification, let us be content with the conservative estimate that the volume of such expenditures has multiplied at least twenty times. Therefrom of course an enormous operation of vistas and stimulus to our imagina-

11. I am indebted for this expression to an as yet unpublished essay by Robert W. Prehoda on
*The Future and Technological Forecasting*.

tion. We find ourselves thereby incited to picture American society in the future as one where everything which is now conceivable shall have been socialized. The picture we can thus draw is surely erroneous: it must be erroneous in terms of a near future, because it is not feasible to make all this socially operational in a short time, in view of the amount of resources it would require. It is probably erroneous in terms of the distant future because other inventions shall have intervened and other interests shall have gained vigor. Therefore if we deduced the American society of the future from what seems feasible or likely in American laboratories today, we would be committing a mistake no less than that of deducing the Indian society of the future from the techniques used today in the United States.

But also, and this is far the more important point, this whole realm of the feasible must perforce play in American decision making the role of a backlog out of which the techniques assumed to be the more valuable are in fact selected. Further it seems to me that this backlog is increasing, and that, as a consequence, the selection has to be sharpened and that the future offers a greater variety of possibilities, as the range of the feasible from which choices have to make gains in extension.

That the backlog is increasing is admittedly a hypothesis. It seems to me highly plausible. Let me say how it is based. As I said it is customary to divide investment expenditures from R&D expenditures. Great and legitimate attention has been paid to the multiplication of the latter. Very little—indeed none that I know of—has been paid to the changing ratio between the two. Investment expenditures have not kept pace with the growth of R&D expenditures, indeed that could not conceivably have done so as such pace-keeping would have implied their absorbing more than the whole National Product! Therefrom a presumption that however much the capacity to implement has grown in absolute terms, it has dwindled relatively to the swelling of potential innovations. In other words, as much more becomes technically feasible, much less of the technically feasible can be *embodied* in socially operational plant and equipment. The likelihood of its being so (and I repeat it is not given as a fact) is not impaired by the reliable evidence which can be adduced showing that some innovations become operational in our day much faster than other innovations in the 19th century: that is entirely compatible with nonactivation of other potential innovations.

While changes in classification would no doubt affect the ratio between the variables R&D and Investment, they surely would not do so to the extent of changing the general picture. To doubt then that there occurs a relative decline in the capacity to embody and an increasing backlog, one would have to give more weight than seems reasonable to two suppositions which are mere "intuitions." Possibly the communication of external benefits tends to cheapen the implementation of innovations; possibly the delivery of potential innovations by R&D does not keep pace with the input of resources therein. In these propositions figure terms too indefinite to allow any checking. Let us then say that there may be "something in them"; which would then tend to reduce the imbalance between what is offered as achievable by R&D and what can be undertaken through investments, and thus to slacken the increase of the backlog. The relations hypothesized are perhaps toned down but not substantially altered.

They can perhaps be represented by thinking of an "R&D country," whose population is engaged in digging, refining and fashioning goods which reach the "land of Society" only in so far as they have been picked up and transported by "ships." These ships stand for the operational investments. There being an imbalance between the output of the R&D population and the capacity of the fleet, there must be a selection of what shall be picked up. The decisions taken thereupon influence the character of change occurring in the land of Society but also they exert an influence on the labors of the "R&D land" which shift from what is least picked up to what is most picked up.

As one perceives the determining importance of such decisions, therefore one is led to ask: by whom are these decisions made, and on what grounds?

The traditional answer would be: business executives make these decisions, on grounds of market expectations. Let us develop this answer. Never mind that these decisions are made by a few, senior executives of important firms, they are and have to be taken into consideration of the value judgments of the great many on whose buying the fortunes of firms depend. The great merit of Business lies in its being fundamentally a servant, while Government is fundamentally a master. Government comes at the front door and makes demands, Business comes at the tradesman's door and makes offers. These must be palatable. If the innovation takes the form of a new process cheapening a commodity or service already in wide use, businessmen know that such cheapening shall be welcomed. If the innovation takes the form of a new good or new service, business executives will try to make sure that consumers are ready to welcome it. In short the very idea of profit-making is to use resources (inputs) in the manner deemed apt to elicit maximal response, that is on the criterion of maximizing the expectation of response; and as the use of resources is ceaselessly reallocated through the feedback of actual responses, it can be claimed that the system tends to produce the best possible selection of techniques.

The validity of this answer is limited, firstly by the simple observation that the industries living from discrete sales to individuals are not by a long way the chief seats of innovations. It is well known that the bunching of innovations occurs in industries closely tied to Government, Government supported or having the Government as their main customer. To this point I shall return later.

The second restriction called for is that the market allows only a limited, and, as it turned out, a biased expression of consumer preferences. The individual buyer by the very act of buying manifests his positive appreciation of the product sold to him; he has no symmetrical means of manifesting his negative appreciation of the nuisances attending the operational process or the use of the new product. By the power of his own purse he can acquire a "good," by the same power he can not dismiss a "bad." Thus the operations of the market do nothing to stem the flow of nuisances, which remains unrecorded in National Accounting itself, based as this is solely on the sales and purchase transactions of a market economy. To stem the flow of nuisances, it may be necessary to substitute for technique $A$, a technique $B$ which is not superior (and may be inferior) in terms of the individual goods it allows individual buyers to acquire, but whose merit lies in its being less productive of diffuse nuisances. Such a shift can not occur as a consequence of discrete actions by individual buyers, it requires Government intervention either prohibiting technique $A$ or putting upon it so heavy a money charge as to make it market-wise less advantageous than technique $B$.

The authorities will find it relatively easy to produce such a shift when the nuisances arise from the use of a process by large firms. By their very dimension these offer easy targets to public opinion and public action. And because of their ample means they are well able to achieve the shifts called for. Unfortunately the bulk of the nuisances attending modern society flow from consumer behavior rather than from that of large firms. This is not often said because the statement violates what a politician once told me some thirty years ago "The First Law of Politics": In the case of any evil you wish to denounce, said he, put the blame on the smallest possible number of people in order to attract the largest possible number of votes.

Instinctive adherence to this "law" leads to underestimation of the part played by homemade nuisances in the global flow. As more goods enter the home, more refuse flows out, ranging from the dumping of cans to the dumping of motor cars. Homemade nuisances pose a major strategic problem: how far can they be remedied by changing the physiochemical nature of entries into the home (so that as they go out they dissolve more easily: paper containers instead of metal or glass containers etc.); how far must it be remedied by vast public endeavors of removal (a magnified sewage system embracing as well as liquids, solids, fumes, and if feasible, noises)?

Whether we are concerned to improve producer behavior or consumer behavior or to repair their side-effects by public undertakings, we run up against the human propensity to act in view of discrete and immediate satisfactions with little regard for more general and distant states of affairs. There is no doubt that the large car powered by an internal combustion engine is a major nuisance in towns, which would become far better places if people moved about in small cars powered by electricity: but manufacturers are well aware that consumers enjoy the large car and the childish sense of power afforded by the internal combustion engine. The cluttering of the valleys of Kentucky by the massive fall-out produced by strip mining of the hillsides is a scene of vandalism: but what buyers require from mining corporations is the cheapest possible coal.

It is all too easy to place the blame upon producers: ultimately it lies in the vigor of our individual concern for immediate maximum getting, combined with the weakness of our collective concern for generating an optimal longterm state of affairs.

This is not, as some say, a trait of our industrial age, though our greater power has sharpened its nefarious effectiveness. Asia Minor formed a most prosperous part of the Roman Empire: in the intervening centuries improvident private and public use of its resources stripped it of woods, starved it of water, made it a land of poverty.

At no time in history have the public authorities exerted as powerful an influence as they do presently upon the daily lives of the subjects.[12] This influence is made possible by the operational development of the techniques of transport and communications. This influence can be exerted, and in part is exerted, to improve the setting of human lives. In so far as future changes in ways of living depend upon the progress of techniques, Government exerts thereby a major influence. This influence is exerted by two chief channels: firstly investments which have an innovational character, which are made for the putting into application of new techniques, now occur with far greater density, in firms tied to the Government than in firms working for a multitude of individual buyers. By firms tied to the government, I mean those establishments, whatever their legal character, whose services depend upon public decisions. Paradoxically enough State owned firms whose services are addressed to the large public are often

12. The use of the term "subjects" is entirely proper relatively to what is being discussed. As Rousseau put it "in a legitimate form of government, the associated are collectively called *the people*, and are severally called *citizens* as participants to the sovereign authority, and *subjects* as subject to the laws of the State," *Social Contract*, Bk. I, ch. 6.

less tied to Government decisions than are private firms who have the Government as their main customer.[13] When the Government passes orders which require innovational investments the cost of which is perforce taken into account in the costing of the product or service provided, it exercises upon the nature of innovational investments an influence no less powerful than by the alternative means of their direct subsidization.

But however important the part played by Government in causing the implementation of feasible innovations,[14] it plays a far greater role at the earlier stages of innovation, that is in R&D. It is well known that the major part of R&D expenditures are financed by the Government. This means that Government is implicitly the selector of the kinds and lines of research to be encouraged.

We fail to grasp the importance of this because we are still haunted by the images of the scientist or artisan who pottering in a shed, come out respectively with major scientific findings or seminal investments. Pasteur used no great means nor did the Belgian waiter Lenoir who built the first motor car. Things are not done this way in our time; and indeed one wonders whether, if a breakthrough happened to be achieved in this artisan manner, it would command any attention. A century or more after the supersession of the artisan by the factory in the realm of production, the same phenomenon has occurred not only in the realm of development, which stands nearest to production, but also in the higher realms of applied research and even fundamental research.[15] Much hardware is called for, and however necessary to findings, its use also adds prestige to their announcement. Just as large establishments have come to dominate the field of industry, so it is in the field of research itself; the material quality of the plant and equipment, the talents of the associates, contribute to the intrinsic worth of the output, and the label to its reception.

This being the state of affairs, the allocation of funds becomes a determining influence. A promising scientist naturally wishes to work with the best instruments, in the best company; these are to be found in the sectors which are most favored by the allocators of funds. Therefrom a cumulative process whereby the lines of research which attract the most money in consequence are magnets to talents, which further justifies their being favored.

13. See Murrey L. Wiedenbaum "Les entreprises privées à destination publique," in *Analyse et Prévision*, vol. 2 (1966), pp. 493–498. An earlier if shorter English version has appeared in *Challenge*.
14. In order to quantify the role of Government in the *innovational* investments one would need to separate such investments from that large part of the investments currently made in society which have no innovational character. I made no such distinction in my earlier confrontation of R & D expenditures with investments in general, deeming it unnecessary to what is but a suggestive approach.
15. Cf. Norman Kaplan, ed., *Science and Society* (Chicago, Rand McNally, 1965).

As the progress of research leads development, which leads the implementation of new techniques, and as the introduction of these in the social
field influence the pattern of social arrangements and individual lives, the
guidance exercised upon R&D in general and more especially upon Research, by the power of the purse, is a determining influence of our social
future. The process of allocation might be called the "Ministry of the
Future."

Indeed this Ministry of the Future exerts not only a powerful concrete influence on what the future shall be but also it exercises even today
a notable influence on our views of the future, which are of course shaped by
what we hear of research in progress.

Let me take a concrete instance. Our civilization is characterized by
increasing expenditure of power. We have acquired this energy from the
burning of stores: ours is an incendiary civilization. I find it a most striking
thought that if we relied upon the burning of wood for the present-day
expenditure of energy, we would burn up all the forests of the world in
three years.[16] This does not mean that we are in any danger of lacking
materials for burning: while estimated reserves of oil, including that which
can be retrieved from shales and bituminous sands would cover only some
sixty years of consumption at the present level, coal represents no less
than 600 years of present consumption, while beyond that we can, as it
has been dramatically expressed "burn the rocks" to produce atomic
energy.[17]

However, there exists an alternative to the burning of our dwelling-
place. As against the stores we can burn there are flows we can utilize. The
yearly flow of solar energy into upper atmosphere is equivalent to fifty
thousand times our yearly consumption of energy; considering only that
part of solar energy which hits bare ground it alone represents a yearly
supply equivalent to five hundred times our yearly consumption.

It is not necessary to worry about the false problem of the exhaustion
of energy stores to appreciate the importance of shifting gradually our
procurement of energy from burning to the utilization of continuing
flows. This would be an enormous improvement of our collective manners
which are those of drunken soldiers, using anything they can lay hands
upon to make a fire. Such a shift would have great social and moral implications. I do not find them contemplated in pictures of the future: the
reason lies in there being so little research in that direction.

A field which is not so neglected but which is very parsimoniously

16. All figures quoted from a study made for OECD by E. Jantsch.
17. W. R. Derrick Sewell: "Humanity and the Weather," *Scientific American*, spring, 1966.
    The author is editor of *Human Dimensions of Weather Control* (Chicago, University of
    Chicago Press, 1966).

endowed is weather control: this obtains, I gather, seven million dollars per year.[18] And yet if we understood the movements which occur in the atmosphere, we might dispell hurricanes in the making. It appears from Lloyd's account that hurricane Betsy cost this organization some twenty million pounds sterling and another ten to other insurers.[19] This should stir the imagination to consider the damage wrought by similar hurricanes in the poorer countries of the world which are not in a position to make good the losses suffered. Here we have a type of research of enormous importance to the underdeveloped countries.

And this instance raises a major moral question. The rich countries of the world alone have the human and material resources required for important research. While this great advantage has been at least fairly earned, it does not follow that it should be used for the exclusive advantage of the nations which have earned it. On the contrary, because research resources are concentrated in the advanced countries, therefrom follows a moral obligation to use them in the best interests of mankind generally. Impeding the formation of hurricanes would be a boon to the countries most affected, which are also the least able to repair the damages. The imagination may go beyond this and picture an improvement of the regime of rains in India: what a boon that would be.

Surely it is right that those who lead in research should address efforts to objects of moment to large parts of mankind. But it is hardly surprising that Government support for R&D in advanced countries should give little weight to the welfare of other nations: it does not give very much to the welfare of our own people.

In the United States four fifths or more of Government financed R&D expenditures are for purposes of international power politics and national prestige. The Department of Defense absorbed 62.3 percent, NASA, 17.2 percent, which add to nearly 80 percent; while the largest part of the 10.1 percent devoted to the Atomic Energy Commission was also destined to military ends. The author from whom I take these figures (referring to fiscal 1963) comments: "Of course products and processes which increase productivity or demand in other sectors of the economy may arise from military and prestige oriented programs. But these benefits—commonly referred to as 'spillover'—are strictly incident to the main purpose; there is also some reason to believe that the spillover from military

18. Their figures were given in the *Financial Times*.
19. If I stress this point, however obvious, it is because of the utterly silly statements one often encounters, about a minority of the world's population "enjoying" the major part of "world income," as if world income were a given fact available for distribution, instead of being a mere fanciful aggregation of the very different products of very different activities in different countries.

and space programs has been quite modest in recent years."[20] I pretend to no expertise on this great subject. The fact of importance here is that most of this R&D is not meant at all to enhance the amenities of life for the multitude.

As it would be impolite to press my critique of what is done in the United States, I turn to the instance of the supersonic transatlantic plane. I have never felt happy about this: it is of course an achievement, nor can its usefulness be denied. But usefulness in the case of resource applications is comparative: is this the best that could be done for people with that amount of endowment?

This raises the question of speed. Many people find it extremely exciting that the speed of transatlantic travel should increase by ever greater leaps. The speed will be more than doubled when the supersonic plane goes into service, possibly in 1969, but the speed may be again multiplied perhaps five times by 1984, when the hypersonic plane could be in service, provided the required resources are applied to the stages of research, development and production. New York would then be within forty minutes flight from London.[21]

How wonderful! In the 1820's such a journey took twenty-five days. In 1838, the *Great Western* achieved the crossing from Liverpool in the breath-taking time of fifteen days. What gains have we not achieved in speed, and how much greater they become in successive periods! Yes, but there is another way of looking at the same phenomenon. The economy of travel time achieved by the *Great Western* was ten days, the economy expected of the supersonic plane is more than three hours, and the economy which might conceivably be obtained from the hypersonic plane would be less than three hours. If on a time graph from 1820 to 1984 you plot successive gains attained or hoped for, the shape of the curve shall be very different according to your choosing as ordinate either the speeds achieved, or the economies of travel time: in the first case the curve rises by ever large leaps, in the second case by ever smaller fractions.

This exemplifies a general proposition dear to my friend Ely Devons, i.e., that graphic representation of phenomena depends upon basic value judgments. If the value which inspires me is pride in human achievements, I shall naturally use the speed curve and no other view of the phenomenon shall be of interest to me; if on the other hand the value which inspires me is the improvement in human lives, then I shall use the second curve. This

20. Frederic M. Scherer "Government Research and Development Programs" in Robert Dorfman ed. *Measuring Benefits of Government Investments* (Washington, The Brookings Institution, 1965).
21. My authority here is C. L. Boltz, scientific editor of the *Financial Times*, in the August 3, 1966 issue.

shall then lead me to estimate the benefits accruing from the successively faster planes in terms of savings of travel time for increasing numbers of travelers. However important the figures obtained for such savings of time per year, if we place them in a balance, with on the other side the man-hours of travel time which can be saved on the "journey to work" by equal expenditures, then the gain from greater transatlantic speed must seem very much the lighter one.

By this comparison I find that the social benefits of speeding up transatlantic flight are well below the opportunity cost: that is the social benefits which might be conferred by an alternative use of equivalent resources. Of course my presentation is very rough. It is meant merely to illustrate an attitude, i.e., that public support for technical innovation is justified by the relevance of the innovation to the improvement in the ways and quality of life, and that its contribution in that respect is to be weighed against the contributions of alternative uses of resources.

I doubt whether anyone would dispute the principle; but it does tend to be forgotten in the climate of understandable excitement generated by a fast succession of "feats." A feat in any sector of technical endeavor rightly attracts praise and moral credit, and this moral credit lends force to demands for further and larger support. Thus public funds get channeled toward what is most exciting and impressive rather than toward the more service-able in terms of people's daily lives. As more talent gets involved in that direction, more political weight is acquired in the elite circles where the process of distribution takes place.

The enormous contribution which the laboratories made to the war effort stands at the source of their great leap forward in material and social status: the association of a great deal of research and development with power requirements has persisted or has been renewed. It is then perhaps not surprising that the model of the War Machine should however un-consciously color the thinking of many researchers, and that many advances, however unrelated to military purposes, should work toward imparting to Society some characters of the War Machine.

It may well be a dual play of unconscious associations which generates in so many of our contemporaries an anxiety about "the Society which Technology fosters." There is, to my mind, some absurdity in the exhorta-tions we hear to adjust to a Technological Society. Why should we? Is it not more reasonable to harness the processes of innovation to procure a life rich in amenities and conducive to the flowering of human personalities. No generation has been more free to lay the foundations of the good life. But we shall not be free if we do not become aware of our freedom.

# THE POWER OF VALUES II

# Economic attitudes in Latin America and the United States

*John P. Powelson*

## Introduction

In the decline of liberalism, Latin America has moved farther and faster than the United States. In those Latin American countries accounting for the preponderance of both population and economic growth (such as Mexico, Venezuela, Brazil, and Argentina), State control over all manner of economic activity, either actual or projected, is more pervasive than in the traditionally liberal United States. This is not to deny that free enterprise is flourishing or to propose that free decision has been eclipsed. Rather, central planning, State ownership of large enterprises, licenses and price controls to allocate resources, all are increasingly used.

But the fact of control is a minor part of this paper. Rather, its thesis invades the reason and philosophy and their implications for United States foreign policy. It is widely accepted that an increased measure of government intervention is necessary in less developed countries simply to "catch up." It is my belief, however, that the basis of control in Latin America is more deeply ingrained than that. Out of a revulsion to the libertine freedom of the nineteenth century, the philosophy has evolved that unrestricted private initiative and the sanctity of private property do not lead to the most efficient use of resources, the selection of appropriate final products, just prices, and a fair distribution of income. This philosophy, rather than the urgency of economic growth, may underlie the tendency toward control.

The distinction between philosophies held in the United States and Latin America requires first some definitions. We call a "productionist ideology" one belonging to those individuals who believe that, in general, wealth has historically been the reward for invention, saving, sacrifice, and production, and poverty the punishment for idleness and waste of resources. I associate it also (for reasons shown below) with a belief that

233

market prices are the most rational means of allocating economic resources and distributing titles to product, and that private property should not be expropriated without full and immediate compensation. An "appropriationist ideology," on the other hand, belongs to those individuals who believe, in general, that the present owners of wealth are not those who themselves created it or inherited it from ancestors who did; rather, they or their ancestors gained it by conquest and appropriation. I associate this ideology (also for reasons shown below) with belief in the justice of counterpoised controls, a rejection of market prices as allocators of resources, and a willingness to appropriate private property under certain conditions. Needless to say, although the ideologies are competing and one is the opposite of the other, nevertheless the same individual may hold both in different degrees.

The investigation leads me to believe that the productionist ideology is part of the dominant thinking in the United States and that this thinking demonstrates a high degree of consensus. Latin America, on the other hand, is divided between those who hold productionist and those who hold appropriationist ideologies.

The homogeneity of United States economic philosophy and the heterogeneity of that of Latin America make foreign economic policy a multitensioned affair. In many cases the United States has yielded to the leading Latin American pressures, as in the coffee agreement and certain elements of foreign-aid policy. Basically, however, the United States government views the Alliance for Progress as a projection of our own image for imitation by Latin America, with all the elements of the productionist ideology. Where this has been modified over time within the United States, especially in the three decades since the great depression, such modifications—and no more—are incorporated in our proposals for Latin American development.

These limitations to the Alliance will give rise to future tensions in all fields of economic policy, such as commodity prices, tariffs, foreign aid, and private investment. In particular, United States policy treats wealth as if it were monolithic in origin. Our productionist ideology is so firmly held that we make no distinction between property earned primarily by saving and sacrifice and that gained by conquest. This failure to distinguish may redound to the disadvantage of United States investors abroad if the appropriationist school in Latin America achieves political power and if it, too, commits the sin of supposing that the origin of all wealth is monolithic.

In addition to a study of existing literature and the laws and practices of sample countries, the present study has relied on a questionnaire circulated to approximately 2,000 businessmen, students, and government officials in the United States and eighteen Latin American Republics (all but Cuba and Haiti), with 563 returns from Latin America and 285 from the United States. The questionnaire is reproduced in the appendix.

## The market mechanism

For all the exceptions taken to it in practice, the economic philosophy is still dominant in the United States that prices arrived at by free bargaining between buyer and seller provide the most efficient mechanism to determine what goods will be produced and to allocate factors of production and inter-mediate products among them.

Inherent in this philosophy is the belief that profit-seeking tends to maximize values. In Schumpeterian terms, there is no profit in equilibrium, the condition where general knowledge and practice has caught up with all inventors and entrepreneurs so that no producer has an advantage over others. At this theoretical point, competition has driven market prices of output to a point just sufficient to cover prices of all inputs, including capital. (What is popularly called "profit" is often, to Schumpeter, simply a return on capital, or interest.) Schumpeterian profit occurs only when a new invention (call it product $A$) or new technique gives a temporary advantage to some entrepreneur, so that he may sell his output at a market price greater than the cost of inputs. On the assumption of full employment, he attracts factors of production away from the old products (call them $B$, which may alternatively be the same product produced with old techniques). But the value of $A$ (measured by its market price) is equal to the cost of inputs (all obtained from $B$) *plus profit*, while the sacrifice in value of $B$ is equal only to the market cost of inputs lost to $A$ (since there is no profit in $B$). Hence $A$ contributes greater value to gross national product than has been lost by diminished output of $B$, and profit-seeking has maximized values. Nevertheless this conclusion depends on the appropriateness (in some deeper, philosophical sense) of market prices as measures of the value of both $A$ and $B$ and of the factors of production transferred.

Of course, there are many exceptions to the universality of the market mystique in the United States. Transport and utility rates are regulated, prices of agricultural products are supported, minimum wages are specified, and from time to time the government influences the price of steel. Many of the same exceptions apply in Latin America, and at first blush the underlying philosophy would appear similar.

But there is a fundamental difference. Exceptions to the market mystique in the United States are either considered temporary, or they are quantitatively insignificant, or they are intended to recreate the effects of price competition in instances where monopoly alone is practical. The first case—temporary—applies to agriculture, despite the fact that support prices have existed for over three decades. The fact that farm income per capita is less than average for the country and that the agricultural population is declining, both relatively and absolutely, indicates that supports are not high enough to reverse the "natural" impact of the technological revolution in agriculture but only to soften its blows.

Minimum wages are "temporary" in another sense. Like union pressure, minimum wages are likely to drive the cost of labor to a point higher than its productivity. But the viability of United States enterprise, with its capacity for technological advance and its high degree of substitutability of factors of production, soon remedies this. So long as effective demand is high (and this is the problem for United States policy), labor displaced by the initial productivity-cost disproportion is soon brought into production again, at a higher market price that compares with the minimum wage. The absence of chronological unemployment (even though it was feared in the late fifties and early sixties) testifies to the long run equivalence of minimum wages to the market price of unskilled labor in the United States, in contrast to Latin America where it is not uncommon for high minimum wages and 20 percent unemployment to exist side by side over long periods.

The second case—quantitatively insignificant—applies where particular political circumstances or economic goals, usually local, override the market mystique, as in subsidized subway rates in New York. (In most cities, transportation rates are intended to cover costs.) The third case—recreation of the effects of competition—apply to railroads and utilities. The telling fact is that, with few exceptions (such as New York subways), any tampering in the market prices in the United States does not violate the principle that returns should cover cost, a precept frequently ignored in Latin America.

The same areas of exception thus take a different character in Latin America. Here the market mystique is consistently violated, both in the name of economic growth and to force redistribution of income. The regulation of railroad and utility rates transcends the necessity to reverse the impact of monopoly. There is no Smyth vs. Ames rule of fair return on fair value. Rather, transport and utilities are basic commodities (*artículos de primera necesidad*) whose "just" price is not one that covers cost but one that puts them within the grasp of all, rich and poor alike.

The same holds true for agricultural prices, which are often controlled not to soften the blow of technological change upon farmers, but because free market prices would be too high for poorer consumers to pay. Price supports whose main purpose is to protect producers are confined primarily to exports (coffee, sugar, beef, cotton, and the like), where consumers are foreign. In articles for domestic consumption, there is a greater tendency to hold prices lower than the market would yield, and to subsidize farmers to the extent that their political power demands it or in case the supported foods would not otherwise be produced. In Mexico, the *Compañía Nacional de Subsistencias Populares* (CONASUPO) sets prices of corn, wheat, and beans (*frijoles*); it buys and sells these products with government subsidies. In Argentina, the *ley de abastecimiento* fixes the prices of basic commodities, mostly agricultural. In many countries (such as Chile and Brazil), controls have fluctuated with the necessities of inflation.

Finally, the area of price control outside of basic services and agriculture is far wider in Latin America than in the United States. In Mexico the prices of automobiles and textiles are controlled through the Ministry of Industry and Commerce. In Colombia, the constitutional provision that the State has broad power "to intervene in the exploitation of public and private business" has been interpreted by Congress to include general price control.

The belief that business enterprise need not—in many cases should not—earn a return that covers its costs, transcends the fields of agriculture and utilities. The idea is growing that business enterprise should perform social services apart from earning a profit (and often in contrast to earning a profit). Such a philosophy, of course, is tantamount to agreement that prices freely bargained are not socially acceptable. A few miles outside Mexico City, a new industrial complex known as Ciudad Sahagún consists of a scrap-iron recovery mill, a company producing railroad cars, and an automobile assembly plant (Renault and Dina buses). All require continuing State subsidies, justified on the ground that a new city has been created and that the industries themselves have provided schools, housing, employment, and social services.

The difference in price philosophy has caused inter-American controversy not only among foreign investors in utilities and transport, but also in the field of foreign aid. From 1956 until 1962, the government of the United States subsidized the Bolivian government budget in connection with the latter's monetary stabilization program. In order to diminish its costs and to "put the Bolivians on their own feet," the United States insisted that the budget-draining losses of the nationalized petroleum company (*Yacimientos Petrolíferos Fiscales Bolivianos*) and mining company (*Compañía Minera Boliviana*) should be decreased and eventually wiped away. To do so would require an increase in the price of gasoline and of foods sold by the commissary of the mining company to its workers. The reply of the Bolivian government stressed not only the political difficulties, but also the fact that these were "social corporations," designed not to earn profits but to employ people and provide them with the basic necessities of life. Gasoline, they said, was the life blood of truck transport (which carried most of the food to market), and only if it were subsidized would it be possible both to provide food for the poor at "reasonable" prices and to permit adequate return to truckers.

In passing, it is interesting to comment on the differences between "direct" subsidy of the poor, as in the United States, and the "indirect" subsidies of many Latin American countries. In the United States, those unable to pay their own way (as measured by market prices) are provided for by unemployment insurance, relief, or other charities. Socially, it is a disgrace to belong to one of these groups, and there are pressures to remove oneself as rapidly as possible. Economically, their subsidization does not tamper with the market mechanism or interfere with normal processes except for the direct budgetary drain. Even where charity is dispensed in kind (foodstuffs), care is taken that it should be "surplus" and already removed from the market.

Where "indirect" subsidies are granted through price control of basic commodities, on the other hand, there is no shame in being poor. In fact, poor people are often dignified in Latin America by being called "humble" (*gente humilde*) rather than "poor" (*pobres*). But relief through the price mechanism would not be considered efficient by North Americans, since such subsidies become available to rich and poor alike. First-class bus rides are four cents (U.S. equivalent) in Mexico City for everyone, and corn-flour *tortillas* are just as cheap for the wealthy as for the humble.

## Market vs. controlled prices—a statistical appraisal

In the questionnaire circulated in connection with the present study, respondents were asked to check their emotional reaction (positive, negative, or neutral) to a list of fifty words and phrases, among which was "government-controlled prices." On this one, the replies were as follows:

| | UNITED STATES | | | | LATIN AMERICA | | | |
| --- | --- | --- | --- | --- | --- | --- | --- | --- |
| | *Pos.* | *Neg.* | *Neut.* | % *Pos.* | *Pos.* | *Neg.* | *Neut.* | % *Pos.* |
| Students and teachers | 25 | 72 | 39 | 18 | 75 | 19 | 19 | 66 |
| Businessmen | 4 | 49 | 4 | 7 | 84 | 39 | 18 | 60 |
| Government employees | 6 | 37 | 17 | 10 | 120 | 101 | 49 | 44 |
| Employees of international organizations (UN, IMF, etc.) | 0 | 8 | 3 | 0 | 9 | 13 | 4 | 35 |
| Other | 2 | 2 | 0 | 50 | 2 | 8 | 2 | 17 |
| Totals | 37 | 168 | 63 | 14 | 290 | 180 | 92 | 52 |

In addition, respondents were asked the following questions, with answers given directly below each question:

Consider the following five US corporations: Aluminum Company of America, Gulf Oil Company, General Motors, General Electric, and Sears Roebuck, and Company.

(a) Do you believe it is in the national interest of Latin American governments to fix maximum prices for goods sold by subsidiaries of these companies in Latin America for local consumption?

| | UNITED STATES | | | LATIN AMERICA | | |
|---|---|---|---|---|---|---|
| | *Yes* | *No* | *% Yes* | *Yes* | *No* | *% Yes* |
| Students and teachers | 67 | 62 | 52 | 95 | 42 | 69 |
| Businessmen | 8 | 49 | 14 | 72 | 64 | 53 |
| Government employees | 14 | 46 | 23 | 182 | 86 | 68 |
| Employees of international organizations | 2 | 9 | 18 | 12 | 14 | 46 |
| Other | 4 | 1 | 80 | 4 | 8 | 33 |
| Totals | 95 | 167 | 36 | 365 | 214 | 63 |

(b) Suppose you were (or are) a citizen of the United States, with a right to vote there. Would you vote for a candidate favoring US government price ceilings on all goods offered for sale (at home and abroad) by these and other large companies?

| | UNITED STATES | | | LATIN AMERICA | | |
|---|---|---|---|---|---|---|
| | *Yes* | *No* | *% Yes* | *Yes* | *No* | *% Yes* |
| Students and teachers | 19 | 111 | 15 | 71 | 65 | 52 |
| Businessmen | 2 | 55 | 4 | 55 | 79 | 41 |
| Government employees | 1 | 59 | 2 | 137 | 126 | 52 |
| Employees of international organizations | 0 | 11 | 0 | 9 | 17 | 35 |
| Other | 2 | 3 | 40 | 6 | 6 | 50 |
| Totals | 24 | 239 | 9 | 278 | 293 | 49 |

This question does NOT refer to the five companies listed above. Do you believe it is in the national interest of Latin American governments to fix maximum prices for goods sold locally by locally-owned large private corporations?

| | UNITED STATES | | | LATIN AMERICA | | |
|---|---|---|---|---|---|---|
| | *Yes* | *No* | *% Yes* | *Yes* | *No* | *% Yes* |
| Students and teachers | 51 | 79 | 39 | 88 | 48 | 65 |
| Businessmen | 6 | 51 | 11 | 60 | 73 | 45 |
| Government employees | 15 | 45 | 25 | 156 | 110 | 59 |
| Employees of international organizations | 3 | 8 | 27 | 13 | 13 | 50 |
| Other | 5 | 0 | 100 | 2 | 9 | 17 |
| Totals | 80 | 183 | 30 | 319 | 253 | 56 |

With few exceptions, the answers to all questions show Latin American respondents favoring price controls and North American respondents rejecting them. Among students and teachers, businessmen, and government employees, the emotional reaction to the phrase "government-controlled prices" was overwhelmingly negative among the United States respondents, but it was positive among Latin American, although not overwhelming in the case of government employees. It is curious to note that even Latin American businessmen responded positively by a vote of 84 to 39.

In response to the other questions, both Latin American and North American respondents distinguished between large corporations in the United States and those (domestic or foreign) operating in Latin America. In a close vote, North American students and teachers (primarily students) were willing to favor price controls in Latin America (applied to both United States and local corporations), but they did not want them at home. All other United States groups were overwhelmingly opposed to price controls in any of the three cases (except for the statistically-insignificant "other"), but the margin opposed was greater when the controls would be applied within the United States.

Latin American respondents were more divided. They voted against price controls within the United States, but by a very slim margin (293 to 278) swung by businessmen and employees of international organizations, other groups being slightly in favor. But within Latin America, they were heavily in favor of price controls on large enterprise, both foreign and domestic. Predictably, the businessmen voted in favor of controlling foreign companies but not their own. The slim margin on the latter (73 to 60), however, will surprise some.

Curiously enough, when asked their emotional reaction to the term "market prices," more Latin American respondents voted positively than negatively, as did North Americans also.

| | UNITED STATES | | | | LATIN AMERICA | | | |
| --- | --- | --- | --- | --- | --- | --- | --- | --- |
| | Pos. | Neg. | Neut. | %<br>Pos. | Pos. | Neg. | Neut. | %<br>Pos. |
| Students and teachers | 71 | 8 | 57 | 52 | 42 | 20 | 51 | 37 |
| Businessmen | 38 | 2 | 17 | 41 | 70 | 15 | 56 | 50 |
| Government employees | 31 | 3 | 26 | 29 | 127 | 43 | 101 | 47 |
| Employees of international organizations | 8 | 1 | 2 | 43 | 16 | 2 | 8 | 62 |
| Other | 2 | 0 | 2 | 50 | 6 | 1 | 5 | 42 |
| Totals | 150 | 14 | 104 | 56 | 261 | 81 | 221 | 46 |

When the same people (Latin American respondents) react positively to government-controlled prices, vote in favor of price controls on large enterprises, and then react positively to the concept of market prices, one must conclude either that the term "market prices" means little to them (and the large number of neutral responses would support this) or that their definition of market prices includes those controlled by government.

Certain other words in the questionnaire also give clues as to the relative willingness of Latin American and North American respondents to accept controls. Latin American respondents voted heavily positive for government ownership and North American respondents heavily negative. North American respondents were negative to revolution in all groups, Latin American respondents divided (although negative in total).

GOVERNMENT OWNERSHIP

| | UNITED STATES | | | | LATIN AMERICA | | | |
| | *Pos.* | *Neg.* | *Neut.* | %<br>*Pos.* | *Pos.* | *Neg.* | *Neut.* | %<br>*Pos.* |
|---|---|---|---|---|---|---|---|---|
| Students and teachers | 30 | 57 | 49 | 22 | 74 | 11 | 28 | 65 |
| Businessmen | 1 | 40 | 16 | 2 | 88 | 27 | 26 | 62 |
| Government employees | 9 | 26 | 25 | 15 | 132 | 66 | 72 | 49 |
| Employees of international organizations | 1 | 6 | 4 | 9 | 18 | 1 | 7 | 69 |
| Other | 1 | 3 | 0 | 25 | 6 | 3 | 3 | 50 |
| Totals | 42 | 132 | 94 | 16 | 318 | 108 | 136 | 57 |

REVOLUTION

| | UNITED STATES | | | | LATIN AMERICA | | | |
| | *Pos.* | *Neg.* | *Neut.* | %<br>*Pos.* | *Pos.* | *Neg.* | *Neut.* | %<br>*Pos.* |
|---|---|---|---|---|---|---|---|---|
| Students and teachers | 38 | 62 | 36 | 27 | 66 | 22 | 25 | 58 |
| Businessmen | 8 | 35 | 14 | 14 | 31 | 96 | 14 | 22 |
| Government employees | 13 | 23 | 24 | 21 | 98 | 126 | 47 | 36 |
| Employees of international organizations | 1 | 7 | 3 | 9 | 14 | 10 | 2 | 54 |
| Other | 1 | 3 | 0 | 25 | 4 | 5 | 3 | 33 |
| Totals | 61 | 130 | 77 | 22 | 213 | 259 | 91 | 38 |

The results of this questionnaire with respect to Latin America are consistent both with that area's literature emanating from there and with studies done by others. In article after article in the professional journals (it would be an undertaking in itself to cite them all), the necessity of control is pleaded. To take just one example, when Raúl Prebisch wrote of the application in Latin America of technology developed in the United States and hence not necessarily applicable in the former, he argued that "it is necessary to apply capital rationally in such a way that labor-saving investments are used in an appropriate mix with labor-intensive and those that must be continuously added to take care of population increase. *This is certainly not something that can be resolved entirely by the free play of economic forces in countries in development.*"[1]

Another example comes from the *Manual on Development Projects*, written by the Economic Commission for Latin America of the United Nations (based in Santiago, Chile, and staffed principally by Latin Americans). Here profitability is listed as the most important criterion for selecting development projects, but far from the only one. Rather, consideration should also be given to questions of employment, foreign exchange, geographic location, and the like, any one of which might cause a discrepancy with market-price criteria.[2] Antonio García of Mexico has made a similar list of criteria, which depart even more widely from market considerations.[3]

Studies by others also reflect a Latin American tendency to bypass the market mechanism and depend on economic controls, including prices. In a sample of opinions of union leaders conducted by the *Centro de Estudios del Desarrollo* of the *Universidad Central de Venezuela*, the following questions were asked that touch on State controls, with results as indicated (in percentages):[4]

|  | *Agreed* | *Indifferent* | *Opposed* | *Don't Know* | *No Reply* |
|---|---|---|---|---|---|
| The State should not regulate rents | 15.9 | 1.4 | 81.8 | 0.9 | — |
| The State should control the price of land and the value of housing | 93.0 | 0.9 | 4.2 | 1.4 | 0.5 |

In addition, respondents were asked to check the statement below that best expressed their opinion concerning the role of the State in the economy (with results in percentages):[5]

| | |
|---|---|
| The economy should develop without any State intervention | 1.4 |
| The State ought to intervene in the economic sector solely to orient private enterprise | 15.9 |
| The State ought to control only basic industries (e.g., electricity, petrochemicals, iron and steel) | 53.7 |
| The State ought to assume total control of the economy | 26.6 |
| Don't know, or didn't answer | 2.3 |
| Total | 99.9 |

1. Raúl Prebisch, "La repuesta de América Latina a una nueva política de cooperación económica internacional," *Trimestre Económico*, No. 112 (October–December, 1961), p. 679. Italics in original.
2. United Nations, New York, 1958.
3. Antonio García, "La estructura social y el desarrollo latinoamericano," *Trimestre Económico*, No. 129 (January–March, 1966), pp. 3–41.
4. *Estudio de Conflictos y Consenso*, Serie de Resultados Parciales 1 (Caracus, Central University of Venezuela, 1965), p. 30.
5. *Ibid.*, p. 71.

In an investigation of public opinion in Colombia, Nehnevajsa and Scafati questioned a sample of 1,000 Colombians (stratified by area) concerning their opinions on the "most expected," "most desired," and "least desired" pattern of many aspects of Colombian economic and political life in 1970. Among their questions was the following (with answers in percentages, nationwide only):[6]

ORIENTATIONS TO ECONOMIC PLANNING:

|  | *Most expected futures* | *Most desired futures* | *Least desired futures* |
|---|---|---|---|
| No planning | n.a. | n.a. | 70.0 |
| Total planning | n.a. | 42.9 | 11.1 |
| Key sectors | 26.0 | 29.7 | n.a. |
| Key industries | 30.7 | 19.9 | n.a. |

Although the question does not include price controls as such, nevertheless it is hard to conceive of "total planning" (most desired pattern by 42.9 percent of respondents) that would not interfere with free operation of the market mechanism.

## Appropriationist vs. productionist attitudes toward wealth and poverty

Control mechanisms in less-developed countries are widely supported on the ground that they are essential to promote rapid economic growth. Growth might occur, some argue, in a haphazard way without interference by the government, forming its own pattern at a leisurely pace, much as it did in the more developed countries of Europe and North America. But this is not enough. Now there is the demonstration effect, which didn't exist during the industrial revolution. Nations want to skip centuries, and government interference is the only way. Theories of the big push (e.g., Liebenstein), plus Gerschenkron's contention that the more backward a country, the more rapidly it will modernize, support this position.

But this is not all. There is a related school of thought, with influence widely felt in Latin America, holding that the uncontrolled market mechanism will not only widen the gap between more and less developed countries, but actually retard the growth of the latter. Raúl Prebisch and the so-called "ECLA group" (U.N. Economic Commission for Latin America) have been the principal exponents of this school in Latin America.

6. Jiri Nehnevajsa and Aldo C. Scafati, *Images of Colombia, 1970 Project Futures*, Department of Sociology, University of Pittsburgh (unpublished), April, 1965.

From the more developed countries, it is found in the writings of Gunnar Myrdal, Hans Singer, and Robert Theobold.

These "backwash theories" are widely known and merit only brief summary here. Whatever the historical reasons may be, they propose, the mere fact that when one group of countries lags behind the most advanced means it will be pushed farther back. Centers of literacy, education, and knowledge of the more developed areas will skim off whatever skilled people the less developed may slowly create; industries tend to locate where industries already are (because of external economies, such as skilled labor availability, infra-structure, etc.) and where mass markets have formed. The market mechanism leads to richer rich and poorer poor.

When this theory is coupled with preoccupation over the initial causes of poverty (why is it, historically, that some nations have achieved and others have not?), and when these initial causes are linked with conquest, colonialism, and other forms of injustice, the market mechanism becomes only one more weapon to be treated alongside of armed intervention and slavery.

Let me submit the following thesis to test (by questionnaire). It is proposed that acceptance or rejection of the market mechanism is correlated with another element of the national value system—a productionist or appropriationist ideology toward wealth and poverty. In the productionist ideology wealth is valued not only for its intrinsic worth but for the success that it symbolizes: the wealthy person is admired for his achievements. Likewise, this ideology associates poverty with failure, and the poor man, though sympathized with, is disdained for lack of achievement. The appropriationist ideology, on the other hand, applies to those who associate wealth more with piracy and plunder than achievement. The wealthy man is not admired, but scorned for his commitment of immoral acts. Likewise, poverty derives from oppression by the wealthy. The poor are not slothful but victims.

In view of the relationship between poverty and economic under-development, the question asked earlier—whether Latin American countries apply controls to promote economic growth or to protect the poor—melts into insignificance. In the long run, Latin American economists tend to believe, protection of the poor implies economic growth, and controls expedite both.

Yet, from this fusion, another question arises—whether economic planning should be concentrated on maximization of the gross national product, let the fruits fall where they may, or whether it should pay attention to an "equitable" distribution even where the latter implies sacrifice of the former. The Latin American Free Trade Area and the Central

American Common Market are cases in point. In each, Latin Americans have decided to pay special attention to the distribution of new industries among countries, granting special privileges to those (such as Paraguay) that an undiluted market mechanism might bypass, even though such preference may interfere with a maximization of product for Latin America as a whole. Such decisions—which have been criticized in the United States—are indicative of both an appropriationist ideology toward wealth and poverty and of an acceptance of the backwash theories of economic underdevelopment.

The appropriationist ideology is the opposite of the productionist and there is a continuum of variant attitudes between them. To test whether attitudes of Latin American respondents are skewed toward the appropriationist end and North American toward the productionist end, they were asked to check adjectives they considered applicable to specific wealthy persons. The question read as follows:

> Think of someone you consider to be wealthy—either someone you know personally, or else a famous person of the nineteenth or twentieth century. *Do not mention his name.* (Though your answers should relate to a specific person, please try to select someone you consider more or less typical of wealthy people.) Check all words in the following list that apply to this person. (The list is found in the Appendix on pp. 261-262).

Some respondents criticized the question, arguing that they would check one set of adjectives if they thought of one person and another if they thought of another, and they did not consider wealthy people a "type." The criticism is well taken, but for the purpose of this study, there are two replies. One is that each respondent had a free choice among the wealthy people he knew of, and it is reasonable to suppose that many chose the one they felt most strongly about. The other is that even though no one person may consider "wealthy" to be a type, nevertheless the answers of a large number of respondents in a given group will somehow reflect the attitude of the group toward wealth in general.

Sixty adjectives were selected and listed in random order in the questionnaire. In the compilation, however, they were divided into the following groups[7]

1. *Productive* (presumably deserves wealth because he created it): eager, leader, imaginative, creative, innovating
2. *High-order positive qualities* (economically beneficial to others): helpful, just, honest, trustworthy, benevolent

---

7. Six words were not put into any group.

3. *Low-order positive qualities* (attractive, but not necessarily beneficial to others): virtuous, kind, friendly, honorable, courteous, respectful, humble
4. *Luck* (either with or without risk): lucky, fortunate, winner, speculative, venturesome
5. *Skill* (can be used either in production or appropriation): intelligent, shrewd, genius, wise, discerning, skilful, intellectual, cunning
6. *Low-order negative qualities* (unattractive, but not necessarily harmful to others): covetous, pompous, vain, hypocritical, ostentatious, arrogant, odious
7. *High-order negative qualities* (economically harmful to others): bad, conqueror, bloodsucking, criminal, murderer, deceptive, oppressive, unjust, offensive, pitiless, vengeful, inhuman
8. *Elitist:* powerful, military, oligarchic, aristocratic, intellectual

Questionnaires were scored in the following way. The number of checks after all words in a group was counted separately for Latin American and North American respondents. Each group total was then divided by the number of words in the group and again by the number of respondents (563 for Latin America and 285 for the United States). The result was a score, ranging from zero to 100, applicable to each group.

In view of the large number of words in the list (60) and the tendency of respondents to check only a certain number (some checked as few as four or five, very few more than twenty), a score above 40 is high for a group.

The scores, by North American and Latin American respondents, appear below:

|  | United States | Latin America |
|---|---|---|
| Productive | 55 | 38 |
| High-order positive qualities | 41 | 27 |
| Low-order positive qualities | 38 | 29 |
| Luck | 48 | 38 |
| Skill | 49 | 42 |
| Low-order negative qualities | 10 | 30 |
| High-order negative qualities | 6 | 14 |
| Elitist | 3 | 3 |

From this compilation, the picture one gathers is roughly the following. To North American respondents, the dominant characteristic of wealthy men is that they have been productive. Their wealth is coupled with a high degree of luck and skill. They have also served in benefit to others, and they are personally attractive as well. They are not thought of as oligarchic or elitist, and they have few negative qualities.

To Latin American respondents, skill, luck, and productiveness were about equal in importance, with skill leading slightly over the others. Some felt that wealthy men have been economically beneficial to others, but many others did not. A smaller number (but large compared to North American respondents) felt that wealthy men have acted in ways harmful to others. Wealthy men divide about evenly between those with attractive and those with unattractive personal characteristics. Surprisingly enough (at least to me), few Latin American respondents thought of wealthy men as oligarchic or aristocratic.

A few observations must be made about the aggregations, which suffer from the characteristics of any attempt to force individual variables into group moulds. The "skill" group, for example, includes those who may be skilful in attaining their wealth in either positive or negative ways. The word "wise" may be thought of as positive, but "cunning" as negative and "shrewd" perhaps as neutral. Latin Americans rated "cunning" only 11, compared to North Americans 22; the two groups rated "shrewd" almost equally (and very high), 71 for Latin Americans and 69 for North Americans. Latin Americans rated "wise" 43 to 44 for North Americans.

In the "luck" group, one may distinguish between blind luck and luck that gives returns to calculated risk. The word "venturesome," for example, implies that some value has been put on the line, and the wealthy man has taken positive risks. North American respondents rated that word very high (49) compared to Latin American respondents (17).

Do the results of this questionnaire demonstrate that a productionist ideology is dominant in the United States and an appropriationist ideology in Latin America? If the sample is representative (and it may be challenged on this ground, as explained in the appendix), I believe the answer is positive for the United States, but mixed for Latin America. If one speaks in relative terms, and again assuming the sample to be representative, it probably shows that the productionist ideology is more widespread in the United States than in Latin America, with the obvious converse that the appropriationist ideology is more widespread in Latin America than in the United States.

Perhaps the most outstanding result is that North American respondents appear to be a fairly homogeneous group, while those from Latin America are divided. Again assuming that the sample is representative, one may conjecture whether the inability of Latin Americans to form a firm ideology, either productionist or appropriationist, may contribute to the lack of consensus characteristic of many of their economic and political endeavors.

## Nonmarket prices and the appropriationist ideology— some theoretical elements

Earlier sections of this paper have demonstrated that Latin American respondents showed a greater inclination to accept government-controlled prices for the products of large-scale enterprise than did North American respondents. Citations from the literature, the practical experiences of planning, and studies by others confirm the tendency in Latin America to substitute government control for the market mechanism. I have also shown that Latin American respondents reflect a greater degree of the appropriationist ideology than do North American, even though the Latin American answers reflected considerable diversity. We are now led to ask whether there is a connection between the two—is one phenomenon caused by the other?

There is nothing in either the present questionnaire, or the documented experience of others, that I know of, that would supply an answer. We must therefore resort to induction, advancing some tentative hypotheses.

Let us start by suggesting possible explanations for the greater extent of the appropriationist ideology in Latin America than in the United States. One may be that the present owners of wealth or their ancestors *have* gained it more by appropriation than by production in Latin America, but that the reverse is so in the United States, and that the peoples of each area tend to polarize on what has been their greater experience. Latin Americans often point out that the Spaniards came to find gold, plunder, and monopolize trade, whereas the English landed in North America to settle and raise families. Feudalism in agriculture, the association of prestige with land ownership and the assignment of menial work to Indians, became the Latin American social order. The monopolist psychology of businessmen, the status gained by birth, bribery, or political influence rather than by inventiveness, the stress on high-unit-profit, low-volume output, all induce appropriationist ideology. By contrast, the United States is often presented as the country of the protestant ethic, genius, innovation, low-cost output at high volume, and political and economic restraints on the power of large groups.

But the historical explanation is not entirely satisfactory, for the exceptions are many. We of the twentieth century frequently forget the nineteenth, with its Southern plantation system and slavery, free-wheeling industrial barons, corruption and scandals, and wealth by high-pricing monopolies.

Let us therefore look for a second explanation, in the degree of success of the economic system. By all reasonable measures (such as gross national product per capita or equitability in income distribution), the United States has been more successful than Latin America.

It is only natural for those who have been successful to ascribe their accomplishment to their virtues and the failures of others to their faults. Only the productionist ideology is consistent with this position, for the successful—rewarded by wealth—cannot view their gains in any other way. Likewise, the poor "deserve" to be poor, for the market system smiles impersonally on all men.

Those who have failed, on the other hand, tend more to ascribe their failure to conditions imposed upon them and over which they have no control. The importance of capital in economic growth weighs heavily in the theories of appropriationists (like Marx), whereas personal genius is emphasized by productionists (like Schumpeter). ECLA economists have blamed Latin American backwardness on lack of capital, which in turn has been caused by the price system. According to them, the high price of manufactures and low prices of raw materials have strengthened profit margins in the United States and lowered them in Latin America, thus facilitating the accumulation of capital in the former and making it impossible in the latter.

Finally, the rejection of the market mechanism must also be related to the distribution of income. Let us revert to the proposition, outlined in the first section of this paper, that profit-seeking tends to maximize values. Here it was pointed out that this belief depends on the appropriateness of market prices as measures of the value of both product $A$ and product $B$, as well as of the factors of production transferred.

In Latin America, where incomes are probably more highly skewed than in the United States,[8] many believe that market prices not only transfer income to the wealthy, but also cause goods demanded by the wealthy to be produced at the expense of those needed by the poor. Demand is composed of two elements: utility and income. If many are poor and few are wealthy, then market criteria will lead to the production of gold doorknobs for the few while the many go without houses.

This position has been articulated by Neale as follows:

> They (economists in less developed countries) reject advice (to allow prices in self-regulating markets to direct the use of resources) for two reasons: first, because they have been convinced by their experience that they are

8. Four studies that reveal the disproportion are: Roberto Jadüe, *Distribución probable del ingreso de las personas en Chile, período 1950–1960* (Economic Commission for Latin America); Banco Central del Ecuador, *Memoria del gerente general, ejercicio 1958* (Quito, 1959); Ifigenia M. de Navarrete, *La distribución del ingreso y el desarrollo económico de México* (Mexico, D.F., 1960); and Carl S. Shoup and others, *Informe sobre el sistema fiscal de Venezuela*, in Ministry of Finance, *Estimación de la distribución del ingreso personal* (Caracas, 1960). Comparative data from all these studies are combined in a single table in Vito Tanzi, "Personal income taxation in Latin America: obstacles and possibilities," *National Tax Journal*, June 1966, page 159.

often in a better position (because of their greater knowledge) to use resources effectively than are less well-informed and less-skilled persons operating in a self-regulating market; and second, because the prices generated in such a market, while they may reflect the relative importance of goals within the limits of traditional values, can make the attainment of new value orientations even more difficult. For instance, distribution of cement and corrugated iron to those most willing and able to pay in India is likely to reinforce the value of "conspicuous housing" at the expense of the new productive value embodied in "masonry wells with iron persian wheel lifts." There is an argument for pricing corrugated iron (needed for the buckets of persian wheels) with a high "turnover tax" included in the price if the shortage and high black market price reflect farmer demand for persian wheels; but when, as is often the case, the high price includes a large element of "conspicuous roofing demand" and there are farmers who could be induced to buy persian wheels at "cost plus a little" but not at "equilibrating" prices, "reliance on prices" can frustrate the extension of modern irrigation technology.[9]

In summary, many Latin American economists look upon the price system as another arm of colonialism and appropriation. Given the skewed distribution of income, which they see both within their countries and in the world at large, they suppose the rich (through monopoly, political power, or other influence) to be in a better bargaining position than the poor. Finally, the same uneven income distribution (often attributed to appropriation) leads to the production of luxury goods for the wealthy, while resource allocation to basic economic instruments as well as the needs of the poor are sacrificed.

## Attitudes toward business and capitalism—a digression

One result surprising to me, and possibly to United States readers as well, is that while Latin American and North American respondents were divided on government ownership and price controls, nevertheless both

| | UNITED STATES | | | | LATIN AMERICA | | | |
| | Pos. | Neg. | Neut. | %<br>Pos. | Pos. | Neg. | Neut. | %<br>Pos. |
|---|---|---|---|---|---|---|---|---|
| Big Business | 135 | 41 | 92 | 50 | 409 | 62 | 92 | 73 |
| Capitalists | 156 | 26 | 86 | 58 | 213 | 156 | 76 | 48 |
| Businessman | 207 | 16 | 45 | 77 | 425 | 35 | 103 | 76 |
| Stockholder | 207 | 6 | 55 | 77 | 426 | 27 | 110 | 76 |

9. Walter C. Neale, "The Economy and Public Administration in Developing Countries," CAG Occasional Papers, mimeographed by Comparative Administration Group, American Society for Public Administration, University of Maryland, April, 1966, pp. 7–8.

groups reacted positively toward the words big business, capitalist, business-man, and stockholder, as indicated above. (To conserve space, subgroups are not shown separately.)

The surprise resulted from the fact that—for reasons shown above—I had come to associate rejection of the market mechanism with an appropriationist attitude toward wealth, and *to me* wealth is associated with business, capitalism, and stockholders. (Most of the wealthy men *I* know of gained their wealth through business.) Upon reflection, however, it occurred to me that the positive reactions of Latin American respondents may not be inconsistent with their other responses. Those of the productionist ideology would be expected to react positively to business, etc. Those of the appropriationist ideology, on the other hand, may associate wealth more with conquest and landowning than with business. In short, they might dignify business without dignifying wealth, and they may consider government ownership and price control consistent with the legitimate rights of the respected private sector. These remarks are purely conjectural, however. (Had I thought of this relationship earlier, I might have designed the questionnaire so as to investigate it.)

## "Social justice" and "legal justice"—another digression

The term *justicia social* is frequently heard in Latin America. It was a watchword for Perón in Argentina, and it has been widely included in political platforms in other countries. What does social justice mean, and how does it differ from legal justice? Many Latin Americans believe that, just as the market mechanism does not necessarily lead to just prices, so also the dispensation of "justice" by the courts is not necessarily "fair." It is felt by some that legal justice depends on an adequate economic and social position, education, and ability to defend oneself in a court, which are not qualities attainable by, say, peons on an *hacienda*.

Is it not fair to argue that those who feel social justice is different from legal justice probably belong more to the appropriationist ideology, supposing that the courts (like market prices) are one more weapon for transferring wealth from the poor to the rich, in undeserved fashion? By the same token, those who believe that legal justice and social justice are the same might be associated with the productionist ideology.

Note the following results in the emotional reaction to the two terms. United States respondents registered an almost identical vote for the two concepts, whereas Latin American respondents—while voting positively for both—nevertheless registered a significantly higher positive vote for social than legal justice, and a higher negative vote for legal than social justice.

Furthermore, Latin American respondents were less enthusiastic percentagewise about legal justice than North Americans (voting 80 percent positive as opposed to 90 percent), students being the least positive (71 percent). When it came to social justice, however, Latin American respondents were 91 percent positive, as opposed to 86 percent among United States respondents.

LEGAL JUSTICE

| | UNITED STATES | | | | LATIN AMERICA | | | |
| --- | --- | --- | --- | --- | --- | --- | --- | --- |
| | Pos. | Neg. | Neut. | %<br>Pos. | Pos. | Neg. | Neut. | %<br>Pos. |
| Students and teachers | 120 | 4 | 12 | 88 | 80 | 8 | 25 | 71 |
| Businessmen | 51 | 1 | 5 | 89 | 116 | 8 | 17 | 82 |
| Government employees | 56 | 1 | 3 | 93 | 223 | 16 | 31 | 83 |
| Employees of international organizations | 10 | 0 | 1 | 91 | 21 | 1 | 4 | 81 |
| Other | 3 | 0 | 1 | 75 | 11 | 0 | 1 | 91 |
| Totals | 240 | 6 | 22 | 90 | 451 | 33 | 78 | 80 |

SOCIAL JUSTICE

| | UNITED STATES | | | | LATIN AMERICA | | | |
| --- | --- | --- | --- | --- | --- | --- | --- | --- |
| | Pos. | Neg. | Neut. | %<br>Pos. | Pos. | Neg. | Neut. | %<br>Pos. |
| Students and teachers | 119 | 6 | 11 | 88 | 103 | 2 | 8 | 91 |
| Businessmen | 47 | 1 | 9 | 82 | 121 | 8 | 12 | 86 |
| Government employees | 53 | 2 | 5 | 88 | 254 | 6 | 11 | 94 |
| Employees of international organizations | 10 | 0 | 1 | 91 | 25 | 0 | 1 | 96 |
| Other | 2 | 0 | 2 | 50 | 11 | 1 | 0 | 91 |
| Totals | 231 | 9 | 28 | 86 | 514 | 17 | 32 | 91 |

## Policy implications

We have represented the United States as a country of high degree of unity in its productionist ideology, and Latin America as a group of countries with divergent ideologies but stronger emphasis on the appropriationist than is found in the United States. We turn now to the implications of this finding on United States foreign policy.

Economic policy is carried out through various instruments, such as tariffs, import arrangements, loans, participation in commodity agreements and study groups, and the Alliance for Progress. In recent years policy has responded to several pressures put on the United States by Latin American governments. They have sought special privileges in trade, such as unilateral tariff concessions (which have been denied); they have urged United States membership in the coffee agreement (which was granted); they have pressured the Agency for International Development to shift loan emphasis from a "project" to "program" basis, with loans predicated on the existence of an over-all development plan rather than the profitability of particular projects (which was done). From time to time there have been threats to expropriate United States investments (which have been resisted).

The tensions arising out of negotiations in all these lines may be either related to differences in ideology toward market prices and wealth or explained simply as the bargaining of two groups, each trying to obtain advantages (both political and economic) for itself. The direction in which past tensions have been resolved may give some clue as to which of these explanations predominates, as well as some prediction on future tensions.

From the point of view of US foreign policy, the Alliance for Progress is an effort to influence Latin America in favor of the productionist ideology. Not our productionist ideology of 1929, but that of today, for significant changes have occurred in the meantime. A whole armament of policy instruments has been forged internally, which have become a model for foreign policy and the fashioning of others in our image.

The great depression struck at the heart of the productionist ideology, for it demonstrated that poor people (e.g., unemployed) were not necessarily responsible for their poverty. Those who still believed that to be the case were labeled "conservatives," but the dominant force (dubbed "liberal") consisted of those who initiated a movement of government policy to strengthen the bargaining power of the weak. This movement has gone through successive stages of public works to promote employment, price supports for agriculture, formal organization for labor, and now civil rights. In all cases, it has been directed toward changing the politico-economic structure, either to provide government with more powerful weapons to promote employment and prosperity or to equalize bargaining power among groups that had been disadvantaged over time, such as labor with the advent of big business or farmers with the technological revolution in agriculture. The goal is a system of countervailing power, in which government is one of many forces, rather than one in which government takes the leading role in policing the others. Agricultural price supports are still thought of (I believe) as something to diminish over time, and it is hoped that market processes will be preserved as relative bargaining positions are redrawn.

This is the image that United States diplomats want to project upon Latin America through the Alliance for Progress and other instruments of economic policy. As officially interpreted by the United States, the Alliance contains only elements that have already been incorporated into our domestic structure. We have never espoused confiscation in connection with agrarian reform, as have Latin American appropriationists. Rather, reform is conceived more in terms of opening new lands and of applying technical assistance, just as in our own history.

In all other cases, prototypes for the Alliance are found in elements of our own social revolution in the thirties and forties. That for national development plans (Title II, Chapter II) is surely the Full Employment Act of 1946, in which for the first time the United States officially embraced targets for the economic system. The Alliance calls for self-help through a series of measures (Title II, Chapter II), that can be directly traced to the New Deal, such as improvement of human resources, promotion of research, more efficient use of natural resources, technical assistance to agriculture, adequate remuneration of labor, promotion of unions, and improved systems of distribution and sales. Among these also is more rational taxation, by which we mean greater reliance on income taxes and property taxes designed to induce efficient use of land, just as we have in the United States. Government intervention in the construction of low-income housing (Title I, paragraph 9) and national policies for economic stability (Title I, paragraph 10) are nothing more than we have already experimented with at home.

Latin Americans are more divided than we are on the goals of the Alliance for Progress. Although united in favor of foreign aid as a general principle they do not envisage the Alliance as a projection of the image of the United States. On the other hand, they are not unified on the politico-economic system they would like to see evolve. Consequently, diplomacy becomes a multi-tensioned affair, with a uniform and reasonably well defined thrust from the United States pulling against a variety of Latin American forces.

In many cases, the United States has succumbed to the leading pressure from Latin America. We have joined the coffee agreement. Nevertheless, we dislike the role of policeman and look upon it as a temporary arrangement (like our own agricultural supports?) to be abolished once coffee supply is brought into line with demand. While many Latin Americans hold the same view, others suppose the coffee agreement to be the prelude to a wider range of international manipulation of the prices of primary products in general.

The movement from project to program loans in the Alliance is another accommodation to pressure from Latin America. Latin American governments have long complained about tying aid to projects and the necessity to "prove" their profitability through accounting forecasts, when to them profitability was not the most essential criterion. Their resistance took form in the fact that they simply did not come up with enough projects adequately analyzed to the satisfaction of United States negotiators, and the Alliance would have bogged down had not another form of loan been conceived.

In trade policy other than the coffee agreement, the United States has not yielded to Latin American pressures for unilateral reduction of duties and for continental preferences because opposing forces at home and in policy toward Europe have been too strong.

In another area of tension—inflation—the United States has been committed to a policy of monetary stabilization while many Latin American governments have openly espoused government deficits as means of promoting economic growth. Monetary stability is a corollary to the productionist ideology, for the market mechanism works efficiently only when there is a *numeraire* with stable value. In this connection, it is interesting to note the emotional reactions registered by North American and Latin American respondents to the word "stability." Once again the North Americans show a high degree of homogeneity, while Latin Americans —to many of whom stability means stagnation—reflect some diversity.

| | UNITED STATES | | | | LATIN AMERICA | | | |
|---|---|---|---|---|---|---|---|---|
| | *Pos.* | *Neg.* | *Neut.* | %<br>*Pos.* | *Pos.* | *Neg.* | *Neut.* | %<br>*Pos.* |
| Students and teachers | 110 | 3 | 21 | 82 | 92 | 14 | 7 | 81 |
| Businessmen | 50 | 1 | 6 | 88 | 69 | 64 | 7 | 49 |
| Government employees | 54 | 0 | 6 | 90 | 210 | 44 | 16 | 78 |
| Employees of international organizations | 9 | 0 | 2 | 82 | 9 | 11 | 6 | 35 |
| Other | 3 | 0 | 1 | 75 | 12 | 0 | 0 | 100 |
| Totals | 226 | 4 | 36 | 85 | 392 | 133 | 36 | 70 |

In all the above areas, the prospect for the near future is continuing tensions, cropping up periodically and being resolved by compromises in which the United States will not substantially alter its ideology or its pressure for the adoption of the same ideology in Latin America. So long as Latin Americans remain divided, one may expect that the United States will continue its support for those of their politicians who favor "productionist" solutions.

There is one area of tension, however, in which the productionist and appropriationist ideologies may clash head on—that of agrarian reform. Opposition to land expropriation without compensation is a corollary of the productionist ideology and the axiom that merited wealth should not be taken away. It is thus firmly embedded in United States law and must be accepted by other countries, at least with respect to United States property, as a condition of foreign aid.

Note the following differences in emotional reaction to the word "confiscation." Though both groups voted negative on balance, once again the replies of North American respondents show far greater uniformity than those of Latin Americans.

|  | UNITED STATES | | | | LATIN AMERICA | | | |
|---|---|---|---|---|---|---|---|---|
|  | Pos. | Neg. | Neut. | %<br>Pos. | Pos. | Neg. | Neut. | %<br>Pos. |
| Students and teachers | 7 | 109 | 20 | 5 | 28 | 49 | 36 | 25 |
| Businessmen | 1 | 54 | 2 | 2 | 52 | 61 | 28 | 37 |
| Government employees | 3 | 50 | 7 | 5 | 50 | 166 | 55 | 19 |
| Employees of international organizations | 0 | 11 | 0 | 0 | 8 | 10 | 8 | 31 |
| Other | 0 | 3 | 1 | 0 | 2 | 9 | 1 | 17 |
| Totals | 11 | 227 | 30 | 4 | 140 | 295 | 128 | 25 |

Fortunately for United States policy, the property most ripe for confiscation is not that of North American businesses but the holdings of Latin American feudal landowners. It is here, in fact, that the appropriationist ideology is most strongly felt, as evidenced in speeches by left-wing (and not so left-wing) presidents and in the proposed agrarian laws of some countries. Prominent Latin American economists argue in favor of confiscatory agrarian reform on the ground that the abolition of feudalism is essential to production incentives and increased output.

In emotional reaction to the word, "landowner," United States respondents were heavily positive and Latin Americans heavily negative. (Landowners were not, however, a group to which the questionnaire was circulated, although some landowners may coincidentally have belonged to other groups.)

|  | UNITED STATES | | | | LATIN AMERICA | | | |
|---|---|---|---|---|---|---|---|---|
|  | Pos. | Neg. | Neut. | %<br>Pos. | Pos. | Neg. | Neut. | %<br>Pos. |
| Students and teachers | 64 | 25 | 47 | 47 | 23 | 73 | 17 | 20 |
| Businessmen | 75 | 3 | 9 | 86 | 47 | 51 | 43 | 33 |
| Government employees | 31 | 8 | 21 | 52 | 45 | 151 | 75 | 17 |
| Employees of international organizations | 4 | 1 | 6 | 36 | 7 | 12 | 7 | 27 |
| Other | 3 | 0 | 1 | 75 | 3 | 2 | 7 | 25 |
| Totals | 147 | 37 | 84 | 60 | 125 | 289 | 149 | 22 |

United States policy, however, has not clearly distinguished between the private property of feudal landlords and that of United States businesses.

True, the suspension of foreign aid applies only to confiscation of the latter, but this limitation stems from the fact that Congress does not consider it has the mandate to protect property of foreigners. In all other respects—including subtle influence in the shaping of agrarian reform laws—our diplomacy has accepted that confiscation of *any* property constitutes a threat to United States property.

Over the long pull, this is probably a strategic error. The *universal* sanctity of private property confirms the view that wealth is monolithic in origin; it *all* arises from production and *all* is deserved. So long as Latin Americans also accept that the origin of wealth is monolithic, with many belonging to the appropriation school, they will make no distinction among properties to be confiscated. Rather than stress universality, United States foreign service officers and businessmen alike should attempt to persuade Latin Americans of the peculiar attributes of private property *of North American ownership*—its origin in industry, sacrifice, and saving—and specifically dissociate themselves from Latin American landowners unable to claim the same virtues. Such a policy would free the United States government to take a stronger position on agrarian reform, and it might also save North American investments from winding up on the losing side.

I am indebted to Susan Gurin and Constatine Soumelis, students at the Graduate School of Public and International Affairs of the University of Pittsburgh, for their assistance in research and tabulation. Georgia Mihalik, who prepared the punch cards and did the sorting, also deserves a vote of thanks as does the Computing Center of the University of Pittsburgh.

I also owe thanks to the Carnegie-IBM grant to the Department of Philosophy of the University of Pittsburgh for the project on technology and values, of which the paper is a part, and from which funds were made available to finance the questionnaire. Additional funds came from the Ford Foundation grant to the University of Pittsburgh in its international dimensions program.

It is impossible to list all persons who helped in the distribution of the questionnaires, since many took three or four copies informally to give to their friends. Students at the Management for Development Projects Seminar at Pittsburgh sent some to colleagues in their home countries. Students and former students of the *Centro de Estudios Monetarios Latinoamericanes* also filled them out and found others to do so.

The following people in the following countries distributed questionnaires to their colleagues or students and returned the completed forms to me:

*Argentina:* Alberto Fracchia; *Brazil:* Raimundo Fernandez Carvalho, Roberto Procopio Note; *Bolivia:* Jorge Arteaga, Jose Epstein, Martha Luna, Carlos Vargas; *Colombia:* Jesús Tello; *Costa Rica:* Alvaro Sancho; *Chile:* Daniel Bitrán; *Ecuador:* Luís Torres; *El Salvador:* Victor Manuel Moreno; *Guatemala:* Mario Asturias; *Honduras:* Salvador Gomez; *Mexico:* Barbara Gómez, Ernesto Herrera, B. A. Tidics; *Panama:* Josefina Revilla; *Peru:* Javier Otero, Teresa Pareja; *Dominican Republic:* Delio Canela, Luis Guerrero; *United States:* Carl Cloe, John Delaplaine, John Dreier, Dwight Brothers, John Finan, Edward Frierson, Richard Gookin, Howard Lippincott, Ragaei El Mallakh, J. C. McKeen, A. J. Merphy, Raymond Mikesell, Patrick Morris, James Nettles, Alden Pendleton, Mark Perlman, Keith Pouder, Stephen V. N. Powelson, Raymond Richman, David Smith, John L. Stone; *Uruguay:* Alfredo Castelli, Edgardo Noya; *Venezuela:* Bernardo Ferrán, Enrique Landaeta, Domingo Maza Zafala.

## APPENDIX

Approximately 2,000 questionnaires were printed, about half in Spanish and half in English, in addition to the 400 of the National Research of Colombia. It is impossible to tell how many of these were distributed, however. Several batches were lost in the mail, substitutes sent, and sometimes the original batches later turned up and were used in whole or in part. Several respondents duplicated the questionnaire themselves and passed their own copies among their friends. All control over distribution was thus lost at an early stage, and it has only been possible to count the returns.

Since I did not have adequate funds to finance more than one random sample through a professional polling institution, I used my friends and colleagues for distribution. This in itself destroys the random nature of the sample, but the bias is perhaps reduced by the fact that they in turn distributed the questionnaires to others. The one exception was some 4000 questionnaires distributed among a list of Colombian businessmen and government employees by the National Research of Colombia.

The difference in language led to certain problems. In many cases it was hard to find a single word in each of Spanish and English that were equivalents of each other apart from context. Some words I had initially planned to use were rejected because there was no exact equivalent in the other language. Some may argue with my choices of translation, but this was made in consultation with Latin Americans and decisions often reached only after considerable discussion.

Question 1 includes several dummy words, such as corruption, chaos, love, and Princess Grace, whose purpose was to emphasize that an immediate emotional reaction was wanted, not a well-conceived and deeply reasoned intellectual response. Another reason for dummy words was to avoid revealing to the respondent the kind of study that was to be done from the questionnaire, so as not to prejudice his replies.

Even so, upon receiving the returns from the questionnaire, I decided that fewer words in question 1 were actually useful to the study than I had contemplated when the questionnaire was circulated. Like motherhood, "everyone" is in favor of income tax, invention, worker, private initiative, profit, election, economic integration, literacy, competition, etc., and against monopoly communism, and colonialism. By hindsight, I feel it would have been well to include "expropriation" as well as "confiscation" and "socialism" instead of "communism."

The inclusion of dummy words in question 1 had its adverse effects. Several Mexican students took a look at question 1 and decided to go no further, since the questionnaire was "silly" and the professor must be "loco." Students in Bolivia and Argentina refused to fill it out because of their belief (totally erroneous) that it was either C.I.A. or Pentagon supported and a follow-up of Project Camelot.

Two words were included in question 1 in English (agrarian reform and inflation), but through a misprint were omitted from the Spanish questionnaire. They were struck out of the final tabulation.

A total of 563 replies was received from Latin America and 285 from the United States. Returns by Latin American countries were as follows:

| | |
|---|---:|
| Argentina | 25 |
| Bolivia | 55 |
| Brazil | 20 |
| Chile | 7 |
| Colombia | 145 |
| Costa Rica | 8 |
| Dominican Republic | 26 |
| Ecuador | 32 |
| El Salvador | 26 |
| Guatemala | 17 |
| Honduras | 13 |
| Mexico | 63 |
| Nicaragua | 1 |
| Panama | 12 |
| Paraguay | 5 |
| Peru | 36 |
| Uruguay | 16 |
| Venezuela | 47 |
| Not indicated | 9 |
| Total | 563 |

The questionnaire itself follows (in both English and Spanish):

# QUESTIONNAIRE

## (Spanish)

### CUESTIONARIO SOBRE IDEAS FILOSÓFICAS HACIA LA RIQUEZA, LA POBREZA, GRANDES EMPRESAS, ETC.

El cuestionario adjunto tiene el propósito de acumular información para un estudio del impacto del crecimiento económico en los valores humanos (en el sentido de ideas filosóficas). El estudio es parte de una serie auspiciada por la Facultad de Filosofía de la Universidad de Pittsburgh.

Esta investigación es de puro interés intelectual. No tiene nada que ver con ningún gobierno y no depende de apoyo gubernamental.

A fin de mantener completa anonímidad, rogamos no firme el cuestionario. A los efectos de la codificación de las contestaciones, por favor llene la siguiente información:

Nacionalidad .........................................

Es Usted:
Alumno? ..............................................
Maestro? ............................................
Hombre de negocios?..........................
Funcionario del gobierno?....................
Funcionario de una
    organización internacional? ..............
Otro (indique cual) .............................

POR FAVOR, TRATE DE LLENAR EL CUESTIONARIO EN QUINCE MINUTOS. La primera opinión es más útil que ideas bien pensadas.

### PRIMERA PREGUNTA

Indíquese si su reacción emocional a cada una de las palabras o expresiones siguientes es positiva (buena), negativa (mala), o neutral (no hay reacción en general). La reacción emocional no depende de un análisis intelectual, sino de la emoción que usted siente cuando lee la palabra. Si no está seguro, indique neutral.

|  | Positiva | Negative | Neutral |
|---|---|---|---|
| corrupción | .............. | .............. | .............. |
| cáos | .............. | .............. | .............. |
| amor | .............. | .............. | .............. |
| democracia | .............. | .............. | .............. |
| sociedad moderna | .............. | .............. | .............. |
| impuesto sobre la renta | .............. | .............. | .............. |
| terrateniente | .............. | .............. | .............. |
| revolución | .............. | .............. | .............. |
| hotel de lujo | .............. | .............. | .............. |
| justicia social | .............. | .............. | .............. |
| justicia legal | .............. | .............. | .............. |
| televisión | .............. | .............. | .............. |
| grandes empresas | .............. | .............. | .............. |
| inversión extranjera | .............. | .............. | .............. |
| la Princesa Grace | .............. | .............. | .............. |
| precios de mercado | .............. | .............. | .............. |
| capitalista | .............. | .............. | .............. |
| comunismo | .............. | .............. | .............. |
| propaganda | .............. | .............. | .............. |
| confiscación | .............. | .............. | .............. |
| invención | .............. | .............. | .............. |
| obroro | .............. | .............. | .............. |
| accionista | .............. | .............. | .............. |
| nuevo | .............. | .............. | .............. |
| iniciativa privada | .............. | .............. | .............. |
| utilidad (ganancia) | .............. | .............. | .............. |
| elección | .............. | .............. | .............. |
| nacionalización | .............. | .............. | .............. |
| militar | .............. | .............. | .............. |
| integración económica | .............. | .............. | .............. |

## (English)

## QUESTIONNAIRE ON PHILOSOPHICAL IDEAS TOWARD WEALTH, POVERTY, BIG BUSINESS, ETC.

The attached questionnaire is intended to gather material for a study on the impact of economic growth on human values (in the sense of philosophical ideas). The study is part of a series being sponsored by the Philosophy Department of the University of Pittsburgh.

This research is purely of intellectual interest. It is conducted independently of any government interest or support.

In order to maintain complete anonymity, do not sign your name. However, to help correlate the answers, please fill in the following information:

Your nationality .........................................

Are you:
Student...............................................
Teacher ............................................
Businessman .......................................
Government employee...........................
Employee of an
International organization ..................
Other (indicate) ....................................

PLEASE TRY TO COMPLETE THE QUESTIONNAIRE IN FIFTEEN MINUTES. First impressions are more useful than well-thought-out answers.

### FIRST QUESTION

Indicate whether your *emotional* reaction to each of the following words and phrases is positive (good), negative (bad), or neutral (no general reaction). Emotional reaction does not depend on intellectual analysis, but on the kind of feeling that passes through you as you read the word. If you do not know what your feeling is, check neutral.

|  | *Positive* | *Negative* | *Neutral* |
|---|---|---|---|
| corruption | ............... | ............... | ............... |
| chaos | ............... | ............... | ............... |
| love | ............... | ............... | ............... |
| democracy | ............... | ............... | ............... |
| modern society | ............... | ............... | ............... |
| income tax | ............... | ............... | ............... |
| landowner | ............... | ............... | ............... |
| revolution | ............... | ............... | ............... |
| luxury hotel | ............... | ............... | ............... |
| social justice | ............... | ............... | ............... |
| legal justice | ............... | ............... | ............... |
| television | ............... | ............... | ............... |
| big business | ............... | ............... | ............... |
| foreign investment | ............... | ............... | ............... |
| Princess Grace | ............... | ............... | ............... |
| market prices | ............... | ............... | ............... |
| capitalist | ............... | ............... | ............... |
| communism | ............... | ............... | ............... |
| inflation | ............... | ............... | ............... |
| advertising | ............... | ............... | ............... |
| confiscation | ............... | ............... | ............... |
| invention | ............... | ............... | ............... |
| worker | ............... | ............... | ............... |
| stockholder | ............... | ............... | ............... |
| new | ............... | ............... | ............... |
| private initiative | ............... | ............... | ............... |
| profit | ............... | ............... | ............... |
| election | ............... | ............... | ............... |
| government ownership | ............... | ............... | ............... |

|                                  | Positive | Negative | Neutral |
|----------------------------------|----------|----------|---------|
| alfabetismo                      | ............. | ............. | ............. |
| colonialismo                     | ............. | ............. | ............. |
| productos primarios              | ............. | ............. | ............. |
| imperialismo                     | ............. | ............. | ............. |
| independencia                    | ............. | ............. | ............. |
| intervención                     | ............. | ............. | ............. |
| sindicato                        | ............. | ............. | ............. |
| tasa de interés                  | ............. | ............. | ............. |
| campesino                        | ............. | ............. | ............. |
| ayuda exterior                   | ............. | ............. | ............. |
| planificación gubernamental      | ............. | ............. | ............. |
| exportación de materias primas   | ............. | ............. | ............. |
| precios controlados por el gobierno | ............. | ............. | ............. |
| ingualdad racial                 | ............. | ............. | ............. |
| hombre de negocios               | ............. | ............. | ............. |
| dictador                         | ............. | ............. | ............. |
| internacionalismo                | ............. | ............. | ............. |
| estabilidad                      | ............. | ............. | ............. |

## SEGUNDA PREGUNTA

Teniendo en cuenta las cinco empresas siguientes:

Aluminum Company of America (Cia. do Aluminio de EE.UU.)
Gulf Oil Company (petroleo)
General Motors (automóviles Chevrolet, Buick, Cadillac)
General Electric (refrigeradores, radios, etc.)
Sears, Roebuck y Compañía.

Por favor conteste las siguientes preguntas marcando (—) en los espacios que corresponden a su respuesta:

1. Cree usted que está dentro del interes nacional de los gobiernos latinoamericanos fijar precios máximos para los productos vendidos por subsidiarios latinoamericanos de estas empresas para el consumo nacional?

Sí................ No................

2. Supongase que fuera ciudadano de EE. UU. con derecho de votar. Votaría usted por un candidato que favorieciera precios máximos fijados por el gobierno norteamericano sobre los productos ofrecidos por éstas y otras grandes empresas para ventas locales y exportaciones?

Sí................ No................

3. Supóngase que un gobierno socialista en los EE. UU., elegido popularmente, nacionalizara las cinco empresas. Cree usted que dentro de de un período de dos años, los precios de la mayor parte de los productos que venden serían:

Mayores.............. Menores.............. Iguales.............. Ninguna opinión..............

4. Si una aplicación rigurosa de las leyes anti-monopólicas de los EE. UU. dividiera con éxito estas empresas en unidades pequeñas y competidoras, cree usted que después de dos años, los precios de la mayor parte de los productos que venden serían:

Mayores.............. Menores.............. Iguales.............. Ninguna opinión ............

5. Esta pregunta NO se refiere a las cinco empresas arriba mencionadas. Cree usted que está dentro del interés nacional de los gobiernos latinoamericanos fijar precios máximos para productos vendidos localmente por grandes empresas privadas de propiedad nacional?

Sí................ No................

|                           | Positive | Negative | Neutral |
|---------------------------|----------|----------|---------|
| military                  | ........ | ........ | ........ |
| economic integration      | ........ | ........ | ........ |
| literacy                  | ........ | ........ | ........ |
| colonialism               | ........ | ........ | ........ |
| primary products          | ........ | ........ | ........ |
| imperialism               | ........ | ........ | ........ |
| independence              | ........ | ........ | ........ |
| intervention              | ........ | ........ | ........ |
| labor union               | ........ | ........ | ........ |
| interest rate             | ........ | ........ | ........ |
| peasant farmer            | ........ | ........ | ........ |
| monopoly                  | ........ | ........ | ........ |
| competition               | ........ | ........ | ........ |
| foreign aid               | ........ | ........ | ........ |
| government planning       | ........ | ........ | ........ |
| raw materials exports     | ........ | ........ | ........ |
| government-controlled prices | ........ | ........ | ........ |
| racial equality           | ........ | ........ | ........ |
| land reform               | ........ | ........ | ........ |
| businessman               | ........ | ........ | ........ |
| dictator                  | ........ | ........ | ........ |
| internationalism          | ........ | ........ | ........ |
| stability                 | ........ | ........ | ........ |

## SECOND QUESTION

Consider the following five U.S. corporations:

> Aluminum Company of America
> Gulf Oil Company
> General Motors
> General Electric
> Sears, Roebuck and Co.

Please answer the following questions by appropriate check marks:

1. Do you believe it is in the national interest of Latin American governments to fix maximum prices for goods sold by subsidiaries of these companies in Latin America for local consumption?
Yes.................    No.................

2. Suppose you were (or are) a citizen of the United States with a right to vote there. Would you vote for a candidate favoring U.S. government-fixed price ceilings on all goods offered for sale (at home and abroad) by these and other large companies?
Yes.................    No.................

3. Suppose a popularly-elected, socialist government in the United States should nationalize all five companies. Do you believe that two years later the prices of most goods they sell would be:
Higher.................    Lower.................    Same.................    No opinion.................

4. If a rigorous enforcement of anti-trust laws should successfully divide these companies into small, competitive units, do you believe that two years later the prices of goods they sell would be:
Higher.................    Lower.................    Same.................    No opinion.................

5. This question does NOT refer to the five companies listed above. Do you believe it is in the national interest of Latin American governments to fix maximum prices for goods sold locally by locally-owned large private corporations?
Yes.................    No.................

Marque todas las palabras en la siguiente lista que considera adecuadas para describir a esta persona:

| | | |
|---|---|---|
| bueno | ganador | jactancioso |
| victorioso | innovador | arrogante |
| aristocrático | malo | especulador |
| inteligente | virtuoso | amigable |
| astuto | criminal | cortés |
| reaccionario | asesino | odioso |
| vencedor | engañoso | ofensivo |
| genio | líder | innócuo |
| sensato | materialista | benévolo |
| con suerte | imaginativo | despiadado |
| juicioso | opresivo | vengativo |
| hábil | justo | dominante |
| codicioso | afortunado | respetuoso |
| intelectual | creativo | honrado |
| afanoso | amable | honorable |
| servicial | poderoso | aventuroso |
| chupa-sangre | injusto | valiente |
| humilde | militar | digno de confianza |
| taimado | vanidoso | oligarca |
| pomposo | hipócrita | inhumano |

## TERCERA PREGUNTA

Piense en alguien que usted considera rico (adinerado)—ya sea alguien que conozca personalmente o una persona famosa del siglo 19 o 20. *No escriba el nombre de esta persona.* (Aunque sus contestaciones deben corresponder a una persona específica, rogamos trate de relacionar alguien que usted considere posee las caracteristicas típicas de las personas ricas.)

Check all words in the following list that apply to this person.

| | | |
|---|---|---|
| good | winner | ostentatious |
| victorious | innovating | arrogant |
| aristocratic | bad | speculative |
| intelligent | virtuous | friendly |
| shrewd | criminal | courteous |
| reactionary | murderer | odious |
| conqueror | deceptive | offensive |
| genius | leader | innocuous |
| wise | materialistic | benevolent |
| lucky | imaginative | pitiless |
| discerning | oppressive | vengeful |
| skillful | just | dominant |
| covetous | fortunate | respectful |
| intellectual | creative | honest |
| eager | kind | honorable |
| helpful | powerful | venturesome |
| bloodsucking | unjust | brave |
| humble | military | trustworthy |
| cunning | vain | oligarchic |
| pompous | hypocritical | inhuman |

## THIRD QUESTION

Think of someone you consider to be wealthy—either someone you know personally, or else a famous person of the nineteenth or twentieth century. *Do not mention his name.* (Though your answers should relate to a specific person, please try to select someone you consider more or less typical of wealthy people).

# THE POWER OF VALUES III

# The professional commitment
# of educated women

## Sonia S. Gold

### Central issues

This paper is concerned with tracing some of the links between the professional commitment of educated women and the goals and values of society as well as the technological conditions involved in their realization. Analysis of this kind seems necessary if rational and culturally-relevant decision-criteria are to replace prevailing tradition-bound conceptions in evaluating the desired role of women in contemporary society and in guiding the search for new life style paradigms. Such explorations will also open broader perspectives bearing on life styles for men as well, on the re-allocation of resources among the professions and on some of the processes underlying behavioral responses to shifting values and technological potentials.

Attention will be focussed first on the frequently undefined alternative work models which underlie statistical estimates of the future need for women in professional occupations as well as proposals for changing normative social goals in this area. After examining the implications of such models for women's life styles, the discussion will turn to the antiworld of leisure models and their contrasting implications for life styles in general as well as the altered patterns suggested for women.

Scholarly studies and public discussion emphasize that a growing number of women are searching for new life styles, thus giving witness to dissatisfaction with those actually experienced, to rejection of the view that current life styles are immutably fixed, and to a belief that cultural innovation in this realm is desirable and possible.[1] Search has already terminated for some not only in advocacy of professional commitment as a core element

---

1. Referring to organizational behavior, March and Simon, have offered the observation that "If the environment is perceived as malevolent and/or barren, search behavior will not necessarily follow from a decrease in satisfaction."[35, p. 50] This proposition is also relevant to individual search behavior.

in life style design, but in actual participation. This group is now concerned with fostering social adaptations and influence processes in support of this position. But the search has also ended for some in a continued adherence to a nonprofessional, nonwork way of life and they are concerned with warding off the threatening social pressures generated by the first group. The search is still actively underway for the third, and probably largest group, which has still to achieve sufficient clarification of needs, objectives and means either to permit choice between the foregoing positions or to develop intermediate or new options.[2] These groupings cannot be considered as stable, however. Reevaluation is likely to occur with the experience of personal choice, with exposure to continued ideological debate and conflicting influence efforts, with changes in the cognitive bases for decision, and as a result of the changing pressures of successive stages of the life cycle.

Over the past two decades, a large number of educated women have "slipped" into the professions with implied social consent, but without the facilitating conditions and general social sanction which has been the goal of much of the suasion exerted over the last five years. Nevertheless, the professionally committed woman who is continuously involved over much of her lifetime is still in the minority. Forecasts can attempt no more than the extrapolation of recent patterns with "adjustments" based either on assumed value structures in the culture at large (or for given subdivisions in the population) or on professional personnel requirements derived from an assumed set of social goals and technological conditions. In looking ahead, such assumptions are impossible to avoid and difficult to make. Professional participation by women is likely increasingly to be a matter of choice among the options available to the individual woman not only within a stable framework of social goals and values, but also within a changing framework of values in which life style decisions of men as well as women are involved.

Estimating exercises of this sort, however defensible technically, cannot effectively define "real targets" for which social policies can be formulated. Because they presume only the continuation of present values,

2. Reliable empirical confirmation of this statement is very much needed. Without such data, we can only conjecture about how a very large group of individuals view their life styles. College alumni surveys, of which there are many, sometimes provide clues to this question. In this connection, mention may be made of a study conducted at an undergraduate college in which students were asked to evaluate the position of women in Western society. Results disclosed that a majority of senior women (but not senior men) perceived the position of Western women as less than "ideal." However, the majority were not able to offer constructive suggestions about how her position could be improved, although they were able to do so when evaluating the position of women in another (Islamic) society. Few mentioned professional partipation as a vital lack, which, if widely sanctioned would alter their evaluation. (Unpublished study by the author, Margaret Morrison Carnegie College, 1965.)

behavior and policies, they may seriously misrepresent future social requirements of changing individual preferences and, therefore, the social policies
which shifts in social orientation toward work and leisure values may entail.
On the other hand, influence efforts in behalf of professional commitment
which assume that society will require all educated women to become
professionally committed, or that all educated women will exercise a preference for professional commitment, may likewise contribute to serious
discrepancies between requirements and preferences necessitating remedial
social action. While neither arbitrary nor vague definitions of target aspirations with respect to professional commitment can serve as effective policy
guides, it is not certain that a stable social consensus exists around which an
array of specific targets can be fashioned.

It seems useful, therefore, to analyze more fully the implications
of the existing dissensus on work and leisure values and of future technological developments for women's choices with respect to professional
commitment. If the view is taken that ideological debate involving pre-
commitment to a given life style for women is not likely to be in aid of
rational choice; that strengthening of the factual and analytic base, though
desirable, will not yield a scientifically determined "correct" role, given the
plasticity of biocultural behavior and the range of social adaptations which
has been observed; and that the technological and cultural future is "open";
then the search for life style paradigms would seem to require intensive
exploration of both the choice process and the role of values.

## Work and leisure models

Conflicts among prevailing guides to women's decisions about professional commitment seem to rest on contrasting conceptions of work and
leisure as central values in future society. Advocates of leisure models employ
premises about the external world, including its technological future, and
about individual psychological needs and behavior which are almost totally
at odds with those used by work-model advocates. Establishing the relative
probabilities attached to these alternative views is conceivable in respect
to the factual premises. But work and leisure models incorporate value
premises as well and no resort to facts can reconcile such differences. The
simple typology of work and leisure models which follows reveals the
fundamental divergencies in their factual and value premises.

1975 and 1980 have become target dates for predictions about the
future. Ironically, whereas 1975 has frequently been chosen as the target
year for required manpower projections, implicitly extending the imperatives of the work culture into the next decade, 1980 is frequently chosen as

the year to symbolize the crossing of the frontier into a leisure culture. The two sets of projections have disparate origins, of course, for no one presumes that a five year turnaround from the work to the leisure culture would suffice to prepare the institutions and adaptations required in such a fundamental transformation of life conditions.

## A. Work models

Work models relate to the familiar world: The institutions, behavior and goals of this world can be observed; nor is great imaginative strain involved in apprehending its values. Such models are of two basic types. One views the external world as requiring disciplined, organized effort in a work context in order to achieve desired social ends, including material welfare. The other focuses primarily on the nature of man and regards commitment to purposive goals carried out under the discipline of external constraints and stimulus as a necessary condition for maintaining individual psychological and social equilibrium.

1. BASIC ELEMENTS OF THE SCARCITY MODEL[3]

a. Scarcity is still the basic datum of human existence; significant unmet needs of a nontrivial nature exist both in our society and in the world; there is no foreseeable future in which such will not be the case; technological innovation may alleviate but will not terminate this situation; technological advances may also create new needs and hence contribute to further resource stringencies.

b. Increases in the material well-being of the disadvantaged, and fuller responses to previously neglected needs of the entire society will require prodigious productive effort demanding the participation of educated women as well as men for a long time to come.

c. No real choice as between work and leisure values exists, since it

3. Leland Hazard contended that American goals as formulated by the President's Commission on National Goals in 1960 exceeded our resources by a substantial margin thus coercing the development of priorities for their achievement. [23] Subsequently, Leonard Lecht confirmed the judgment that a scale of priorities was necessary because "costs projected for full realization of all the goals are estimated to exceed the gross national product anticipated in 1975 by approximately $150 billion or 15 percent of G.N.P. [32] Using a world, rather than a national frame of reference, Chamberlain affirms the continued relevance of scarcity: "The one-time expectation of a leisured society which would be free to indulge itself expansively in the arts or in pastimes would long since have evaporated as a mirage! . . . To a far greater extent than is the case today, Americans would be working for others . . . because it was required of them under the existing international order." [9] Although widely interpreted as declaring economic scarcity to have been abolished, Galbraith's thesis really affirms its continued relevance insofar as he sees society confronted with choices among competing ends and argues for a reallocation of resources presently absorbed in the satisfaction of some wants which he deems sated and inferior to others which he regards as starved and superior. [18]

is not likely (or would not be moral) that Western society will live on its own plateau of material achievement without helping the severely disadvantaged elsewhere in the world.


2.   BASIC ELEMENTS OF THE PSYCHOLOGICAL MODEL[4]

a. Work is a token of man's seriousness about himself and his world; human beings require goals and goal-directed activity for full development and to avoid suffering from ennui, melancholy and meaninglessness.

b. The need to know, to understand and to act are basic human needs; thwarting of these needs in harmful to the development of personality; adequate fulfillment of these needs in our society is possible only through participation in the work culture.

c. The highest levels of creative achievement in most fields of endeavor require continuous commitment; the complexity of the universe demands a professional, disciplined effort in man's effort to increase his understanding of his own potentialities and the nature of his possible environments; the dilettante will not help to win the riddle contest with the Universe, nor will he contribute to or sustain high culture.

## B. *Work models and women's life styles*

The question of professional commitment now looms as a "decision" for the educated woman because society appears to offer her an option, whereas it does not do so for men. It is recognized, of course, that it is not a perfectly free option and that many barriers to unconstrained choice exist. If work values should continue dominant in the culture for reasons such as those just presented, the decisions of women concerning professional commitment would have an obvious bearing on feasible social goals. Assuming also, the persistence of the "peculiar" feature of our society—which ties success in the professional and managerial ranks to increasing workloads along with increasing rewards, status and power[5]—such decisions by women would have a bearing on the sharing of central cultural values and on the consequent life styles of men and women.

4. Thus, Murphy asserts " . . . the curiosity impulse is one of the most powerful, one of the most difficult to assuage, that man possesses . . . it is the nature of man to lean hard upon the external structure—giving aspects of reality. He *needs* contact with reality even more than he needs escape from it . . . the mind as a whole is molded by that with which it makes contact . . . such curiosity is highly contagious and civilization has been built largely by socially transmitted demands for specific kinds of understanding."[42] For other sources which ascribe importance to such needs as "need to know," "need to understand," "need to create," see [30] and [37]. In reference to the view that intelligence is developed by "struggle and conflict," see [13].
5. See [24] and [63] for discussion of problems connected with the uneven distribution of leisure in comtemporary society

1.   SOME IMPLICATIONS OF THE SCARCITY MODEL

It has been claimed that a significant degree of national consensus has been achieved on a broad array of economic, social and cultural goals.[6] If true, this consensus must have developed in advance of estimates of the real cost of the goals. If the goals offered by President Eisenhower's Commission on National Goals are assumed to approximate the true content of the goal consensus, we can discover from a recent study that aspiration goals exceed available resources by a wide enough margin to compel national concern with goal priorities and choice as well as with means of augmenting the resource base. Although estimates of the real resource cost of the goals, including the human requirements, have still not become available, it seems probable that studies now under way will disclose a serious gap between required and available professional personnel. Hence, the men and women who helped to shape the consensus on goals as well as attendant estimates of probable participation rates will be compelled to reconsider and reorder their goal choices.

Alternatives for dealing with severe shortages in the entire professional corps, if they should occur include: (1) narrowing the array of goals; (2) reducing standards for all or some subset of goals; (3) voluntarily or coercively increasing the workloads of those already in the professional corps; (4) expanding the professional corps through the addition of hitherto underutilized resources, including educated women, in order to help meet the demands of accepted goals or to reduce the work loads for over-worked men; and (5) major programs may be initiated to develop and adopt manpower reducing technological innovations. Which of these adjustment paths would be preferred by those who have shaped the goal consensus is not known. But it seems probable that choices among the unattractive alternatives of shrinking back social welfare targets or increasing work burdens or expanding work opportunities for women are not likely to be considered seriously so long as technological innovation continues to be regarded as a magic wand for overcoming resource shortages relative to goal requirements.

It is obviously difficult to predict the course and effects of technological innovation and hence make proper allowances for it in the goals-resources appraisal. Technological progress offers potentials for advancement in various possible directions depending on the objectives of those who generate and those who adopt innovations. Hence, manpower requirements in given professional sectors may be reduced through mechanization and through the

6.  Colm states that "goals research becomes feasible because some consensus is evolving about goals which are desired. Goals research becomes required because choices need to be made about priorities and combinations of goals and the manner in which to pursue them. Here the need for scientific guidance arises. It is the phase which we have now entered."[12]

development of supporting subprofessional occupations. But technological advances may also lead to creation of new wants and more complex ways of satisfying established wants, thereby increasing professional manpower requirements. Indeed, all of our experience during the past 75 years and more suggests that while both kinds of developments occur, the latter has consistently outweighed the former to generate continuously expanding needs. In view of the absence of authoritative bases for anticipating significant reductions in professional manpower requirements via technological innovations, rejection of the desirability of sharply increased work loads for present practitioners means that increased professional participation by educated women *is a necessary condition for goal achievement*. Willingness to consider the latter will accordingly contribute to support of the consensus on present goal aspirations; but unwillingness will force the consensus to regroup around reduced aspirations or to accept other discomforting adjustments.[7]

Efforts to encourage increased professional participation have been impeded to some extent because it is not known how many *more* professional women will be needed over the next decade beyond the numbers of men and women likely to be available without additional programs to influence the outcome. Influence efforts have also been even more seriously hampered by gaps in our knowledge of the factors involved in decisions to participate or not. Whereas studies of the psychological and social correlates of this decision are increasing, little attention is being given to the extent of *awareness*, *approval*, and *understanding* of social goals among various age and social groups and what such goals are presumed to entail in the way of professional resources. This may be attributed in part to pessimistic assessment of the efficacy of cognitive factors and of the adult socialization processes in prevailing psychology theory.[8] If such hypotheses are regarded as irrefutable, however, the implication should be clearly recognized that influence efforts directed to present high school and college women students and graduates who are not professionally oriented—the reservoir from which increased professional womanpower over the next decade must be drawn—are not likely to elicit much response. Instead, such hypotheses suggest that influence efforts involving basic values can only bear fruit over a generational span if altered normative conceptions of feminine

7. Failure to array goals, manpower requirements and expected availabilities may lead to recurrent fears that women will be competing with men in a manpower surplus context. Obviously, increases in the number of available professional women implies some possible competition for specific positions. The projected demand-supply relationship to 1975 suggests that *all* professional men and women likely to become available throughout this period are needed. Hence, women need not be burdened with this fear that they are displacing men. [7]
8. To illustrate this point of view, see [6] and [39]. For a dissenting view, see [66].

behavior are transmitted and internalized in the early years. But changing the environment and experiential content of the early years would still require a prior value revolution among those who shape childhood development.

As over against the foregoing, it may be argued that influence efforts *can* succeed if the need to achieve and the inclination to professional participation have been thwarted in outlet by inadequate or obsolete professional preparation, by prejudice and by other barriers limiting opportunity, perception of opportunity, or preparation for opportunity. Thus, the elimination of barriers, improvements in the climate of acceptance, the dissemination of information about professional opportunities and the creation of other facilitating services may well increase the numbers of educated women who would actively seek professional engagement through activating those with latent but underdeveloped professional potentials. As yet, however no reliable data are available about what proportion of the professionally unengaged actually possess latent professional potentials, nor about what proportion are animated by a positive set of values which precludes professional commitment.

It is, of course, possible that many have joined in a consensus on social goals which make demands on manpower resources beyond available and expected reserves and, at the same time, individually expect to pursue a set of private goals which are at variance with the concurred-in social goals. Agreement with the general view that improved and increased medical care is desirable, combined with an assumption that *somebody else* will be interested in providing the service and with a failure to anticipate the personal impacts of deteriorating standards because of manpower stringencies may illustrate a widespread phenomenon. Thus, the observation that increasing income and increasing education exert contrary influences on the decision to work calls attention to the real possibility that, in a growing affluent society, social goal aspiration may expand while the availability and interest of educated women in professional participation actually declines. Since both income and education levels are expected to rise over the next decade, the outcome for professional participation by women may depend on the relative rates of increase in these two variables—unless a fundamental value shift in favor of professional commitment should occur or be induced.[9] (See [22] and [41].)

The reinforcement of our newly formulated social goals would accord-

9. Thus, statistics on the participation rate among women 35 years old and over reveal "a downturn among those with some college education."[27] There is no warrant for ascribing this pattern entirely to "income effect." Moreover, income effect may be a summary way of stating the possibility that rising income levels generate the acquisition and pursuit of new interests and values which preclude professional involvement. The *positive motivations* of the nonworking educated group need to be probed.

ingly seem to urge reevaluation of the accumulated evidence as well as the collection of new evidence bearing on the efficacy of cognitive factors in value change. Further probing of this question seems especially desirable as the population becomes more highly educated. In particular, studies are needed to determine whether the effects of cognitive inputs differ according to the environments entered, the means used, the issues or values dealt with, and the population groups involved. The frequency of religious and literary reports on value crises in adulthood emphasizes the possibility that not all childhood commitments in this area are irrevocable. Otherwise, the conception of an educated man *capable* of autonomous, rational choice behavior based in part on relevant cognitive information is to be judged as entirely chimerical. And the ineluctable fate of every generation will have been decreed in early years, with the entire overlay of subsequent experience and education to no avail.[10]

2. SOME ADDITIONAL ASPECTS OF GOAL ACHIEVEMENT

a. *The organizational environment:* The expectation is pervasive that social goal achievement will necessarily take place in an organizational setting, involving professionalization and specialization of function, requiring high levels of educational attainment, with standards of performance controlled by a system of inducements and coercions, and with status, reward, influence and power linked to achievement and hierarchical positions which have to be earned and are subject to termination. But organizational life obviously encompasses much diversity and the possibility of such variations is relevant to the suitability of given organizational environments for women and vice versa.

Some of the viewpoints which express hostility to increased professional commitment by women may be associated with opposition to the social goals which are operative (as will be discussed later). But some opposition to professional commitment by women exists because of the required organizational setting and the conditions it imposes. In essence, however, what is being questioned is the optimality of organizational life for men as well as women—given the strains and fear of failure which impersonal judgment about performance and competence entails, the inevitable interpersonal rivalries in competitive settings, the loss of autonomy, and the energy

10. Until additional empirical evidence becomes available, there seems to be little basis for choosing between the point of view that (1) "everyday human valuation is largely unconscious, and thus never more than an approximation of a rational intellectual game," and the view that (2) " . . . as in the case of interest, so, in the case of personality, it is necessary to recognize the pervasive factor of cognition. At a certain stage of complexity, underconditioning of reflexes is superseded by meanings and judgments . . . " [47, p. 62].

demands of work and achievement which therefore shrink other interests, capacities and responses. [15] More positive appraisals of the potentials of organizational life have also been offered, of course.[11] At any rate, the issue of professional commitment which was seen earlier to require consideration of a larger issue (i.e., social goals) is also found to necessitate inquiry into a broader issue: The impact of the organizational environment on the well-being of its members.

The concept of a "suitable" profession for women as found in the literature on the subject is far from clear, but it seems to contain two elements which are relevant here. One concerns the social purpose of the activity, which may be described as nurturant or nonnurturant. The other concerns the set of conditions under which the activity is carried on, thus involving the individual's criteria of attractiveness. Use of either or both criteria as guides for the deployment of women throughout the professions has also engendered disagreement. Thus, women have been urged to concentrate on the nurturant goals of society as well as on pioneering in work environments which accommodate a larger range of human values than purely task-oriented organizations are likely to arrange.[12] It is not entirely clear whether proponents of this view regard women as somewhat superior beings in whom nurturant impulses are dominant; or whether, given a deficiency of nurturant activities in society, women ought to be exhorted to compensate for this lack as a social contribution; or whether feminine nature would suffer blight if caught in a nonnurturant environment. Historical evidence would seem to indicate that both men and women have concurred and participated in the nonnurturant behavior of society and have also carried out specialized nurturant functions. And both men and women have functioned in environments which were malign and harmful to the participants as well as the reverse—the long arduous day of the nurse prior to 1920 may not have been more suitable for her than the long day of a male steel worker, for example.

Obviously, there is a choice to be made. It will have to be made in part by considering the goals aimed at by the entire society, the priorities

11. If is, of course, much easier to draw up a bill of particulars containing only debit or credit items in appraising organizational life, than to arrive at a balance between them. Simon discusses this tendency in [57]. For one attempt to strike a balance, see [13]. The fact that " . . . success is a term not applied very often to women"[40] is not disturbing to those who do not endorse the goals pursued or the organizational context in which they must be pursued. On the contrary, the opportunity cost of "success" in terms of values given up is assessed as too high, even if successful persons "conceive of themselves as being happy only when they are working hard." (*Ibid.*) It must also be noted that, like "success," failure is a term not often applied to women.

12. Thus, Erik Erikson has expressed the hope that "revolutionary reappraisal of women's life styles may even lead to the insight that jobs now called masculine force men, too, to inhuman adjustments." [16]

accorded various activities, and the locus of personnel shortages, as well as the developing preferences of men and women. The sharp division of the society into nurturant and nonnurturant activities and environments, with sex role differentiation sharply maintained on this basis, is really a matter of ideologic preference. Within the context of goals and goal achievement, it cannot be claimed that the diffusion of women throughout the professions is required, unless it can be shown that personnel shortages are evenly distributed among all employments. Similarly, it cannot be claimed that concentration in nurturant activities or environments will not serve goal needs, unless it can be shown that more severe personnel shortages will obtain in nonnurturant pursuits. Even so, by entering the professional corps, women make a contribution by alleviating stringencies wherever they exist or by replacing or releasing men to do so.

b. *Patterns of continuity and discontinuity:* From the point of view of satisfying personnel requirements, full-time professional engagement represents the preferred pattern. This preference is based on the assumption that higher social returns will accrue from the social investment in individual competence: quantitatively, because professional skills are exercised over the entire period of a working life; and qualitatively, because maturation of skills and maximum achievement is cumulative in most professional fields and requires unbroken years of absorption.

Obviously, in order to provide the required number of professional work hours, the greater the number continuously engaged, the lower the total number of women needed over the next decade. Nonetheless, the modal pattern of work involvement by women has been one of discontinuity: a brief work interlude; withdrawal during early marriage and child dependency; and a return thereafter. Post-hoc, this pattern has been accepted, even approved, as the one which minimizes conflict and strain, which accommodates nonwork as well as work values and, hence, as the best compromise despite the fact that both society and the individual woman must settle for less than maximum achievement. Moreover, it is widely assumed to be the pattern most likely to persist.

Factors contributing to the instability as well as the stability of this pattern should be examined, however, in assessing its future. For one, prevailing child-rearing practices are being critically examined. If practices should shift in the direction of increased emphasis on independence training, and if supportive institutions such as earlier schooling should develop, shifts in the career strategies of women away from this three-stage pattern, can be anticipated. [53] The stability of this three-stage pattern may also depend on whether it is the result of a planned program and whether the experience of withdrawal from and return to the world of work satisfies the expectations and aspirations of the individuals involved. There is a danger that a planned programmatic character has been imputed to what has been for some the outcome of: A failure to develop awareness by early adulthood of the need to combine work and nonwork values as well as a strategy for doing so; a failure to guess the psychic and other costs of withdrawal and return; and a yielding to the immediate pressures and pleasures of child rearing with only meager plans for return. Under these conditions, the return may be accompanied by a sense of permanent loss of professional momentum and awareness that discontinuity entails limited options which fall short of expected intellectual stimulus and satisfaction. But there is no reason to assume that each generation of women must repeat this experience.

In attempting to predict the persistence of the three-stage pattern, it seems necessary to discover how returnees evaluate the choices they have made, or the patterns they fell into, because they are now (and presumably have been) in the process of transmitting their evaluations to their own maturing progeny. The latter constitute the reservoir of professional potential for the next decade. They also constitute one of the important groups through whom seed influences inducing a shift in values in the direction of unbroken professional commitment would be likely to take place.

If the three-stage pattern persists over the next decade, the professional losses both to society and the individual could be minimized by reducing the average number of years involved in withdrawal and by encouraging continuing educational growth—during this period—i.e., by which converting an unplanned into a planned experience. Thus, instead of permitting professional knowledge and skills to erode during the period of withdrawal, these could actually be enhanced in accordance with the modern view that continuing education has become necessary to professional development because of the rapidity with which knowledge and skills become obsolete. Indeed, a more recently trained returnee may have a greater immediate potential in some professional situations than someone whose skills have been continuously exercised but not updated.

Viewed more broadly, the return phase offers an excellent opportunity not only to test the learning potential of the middle years, but to pioneer the development of new mid-life careers, thus opening up the possibility of career transfers to men as well. In a work-oriented culture with individual life spans long enough to make two twenty year careers possible, such a development may come to be regarded as one of the most prized luxuries of an affluent society, opening up possibilities of hitherto unforeseen variety and stimulus. [8] Successful demonstration that a genuine, albeit late, career is possible might even serve to reinforce the three-stage pattern as feedback communication from returnees to others within their influence orbit emphasizes the positive aspects of the experience. The three-stage pattern would tend to persist in any event to the extent that the return phase is motivated by factors other than intellectual, professional and career objectives—such as the desire for additional income, or the stimulus of institutional associations.

To some extent, part time but continuous professional engagement, avoiding prolonged withdrawal during the child-rearing period, may be even more advantageous than the three-stage pattern. That it has not been developed as a serious option so far may be attributable largely to the inflexible attitudes of hiring institutions reflecting their limited needs thus far. If severe personnel stringencies develop over the coming decade, increased exploration of this alternative may be expected.

Continued neglect of the withdrawal period may also be responsible for the short period, but recurrent, discontinuities traceable to some returnees' unclear objectives, or unrealistic expectations, or maladaption in the situations encountered. Unplanned returns may also be accompanied by attenuated intellectual discipline and limited capacity for self-sustaining, impersonal absorption in the substance of work undertaken. Disenchantment then follows on assumption of work responsibilities, as the burdens seem to outweigh the rewards. Such cycles of flight from leisure to work and back again to leisure may be repeated several times. It is difficult to assess the costs and returns of such a pattern, but it is unlikely that either the social or individual net gain is satisfactory.

There has been a continuing need, of course, for empirical testing of the hypothesis that only positive career and intellectual motivations will provide a stable nucleus of women professionals all other motivations providing but weak defenses against winds of discontent and contributing to instability. But this need is becoming increasingly critical as average family income rises and rival interests which absorb large blocks of time appear.[13]

3.   SOME IMPLICATIONS OF THE PSYCHOLOGICAL VARIANT

The psychological variant of the work model implies that educated women will, or should, seek professional involvement because very few who avoid work can escape symptoms of malaise, since sufficiently absorbing and enduring rival pursuits of a nonwork nature do not seem to exist in our society. The concept of an "open" society ought therefore to include appro-

13. For importance of intrinsic values in women's career strategies, see [60]. Although other intrinsic values may be sought, the view taken in this paper stresses the work itself as the basis for stability of professional involvement.

priate professional opportunities for women as well as men, even if this requires a resetting of goals and modification in social practices to accommodate this need.

The foregoing assumes that women recognize this need and are prepared to enter the world of work as soon as opportunity is offered. Paradoxically, however, many women who are assumed to be victims of a painfully empty leisure condition, accept and even endorse it. Pejorative references are frequently made to work-aversive attitudes to inertial mental habits, to trivial pursuits, to intellectual and social and economic dependency, and to disenfranchisement from the world of responsibility and power as the inevitable outcome of a nonwork way of life and as evidence of malaise, whether recognized by the women themselves or not. Even if all of the foregoing were true, however, what possible justification is there for seeking to stir this group (and the generation presently in their keeping) into dissatisfaction, in the hope of precipitating search activity which will culminate in the choice of work involvement as the best alternative to present life style? Social goals which are enjoined by survival pressures, or simply enjoy consensus, may provide one form of acknowledged justification. Alternatively, some have posited a moral obligation to develop innate intellectual capacities to their fullest. But ethical justification for the latter in the absence of compelling social need has been questioned.[14] This social need may be expressed in a concrete set of immediate social goals, or in the general injunction that driving élan is essential to cultural survival.[15] However, since all educated women have not participated in the professional tasks of society in the past, it is hard to explain why it has become more compelling for them to do so in the future as a general moral obligation to sustain cultural momentum. On the contrary, an "open" society might be defined as one in which available options are open to all, but in which no option, including a preference for leisure pursuits, is censured in the absence of compelling social reasons for preferring one mode to another.

The psychological model may involve two different areas of adjustments. One calls for social-institutional adjustments when the number of women who prefer work exceeds opportunities to do so. The other involves

14. Thus, Baier concludes that outside of social context there is no morality which can underwrite a "duty to develop one's talents." [2]

15. For this point of view, see *Walden Two*, in which the founder of the community declares: "Happiness is our first goal, but an alert and active drive toward the future is our second. We'll settle for the degree of happiness which has been achieved in other communities or cultures, but we'll be satisfied with nothing short of the most alert and active group—intelligence yet to appear on the face of the earth. . . . It is characteristic [of man] to discover and to control, and the world doesn't long remain the same once he sets to work. Look at what he has done in spite of the political and economic chaos in which he has always lived. And that characteristic will survive in a successful community. It must survive or less efficient cultures will somehow come out on top." [58]

changes in individual values and life style choices when social objectives require participation at levels beyond those spontaneously chosen by women. In the latter case, assault on selfperpetuating aspects of nonwork preferences, including drastic steps to change the aims of early conditioning, may have to be considered.

The first possibility could occur if work attraction and leisure-aversive factors now discernible as significant in the choices of some professional women were diffused throughout the larger body of uninvolved women. Positive response to work-attraction stimuli has been described as rooted in high "need achievement" and high energy levels which were channeled into intellectual activity at an early age under the influence of parental or other authority figures and which crystallized at an early age in a self-concept requiring achievement as a basis for self-esteem. Where these are present, the opportunity cost in terms of other values which have to be foregone if work is chosen as a central value—barriers in the form of social prejudice, hostility of male colleagues, deviancy from normative conceptions of desirable as well as actual modal feminine life style, limited opportunities and enhanced possibilities of rejection and failure—are not discouraging to professional commitment. [54] and [55] The foregoing may describe the process of professional commitment for the few exemplars of the highest achievement. Hence, one need not expect, on this analysis, any serious imbalances between the numbers of women seeking professional engagement and the opportunities available. But most educated women will not fit the portrait sketched.

In considering the lower orders of achievement which are the destiny and potential of most professionals, male and female, it is possible to anticipate a growing response to work-attraction stimuli as the educational experience sharpens intellectual appetites, as social norms change and as barriers come down, as they have been, however slowly. The hypothesis here offered is that social-psychological correlates of the highest orders of professional commitment and achievement in a general social milieu which is not encouraging to this choice—the setting from which current empirical findings are derived—need not be the same for lower orders of achievement in an approving milieu. Predictions of possible future responses by women to work attraction stimuli which do not take account of this possibility are almost bound to be misleading.[16]

The possibility that large numbers of women will seek professional commitment because of leisure-aversive attitudes, must also be considered.

16. For emphasis on persistent psychological and social correlates of scientific achievement, see [54]. For a warning on the need to supplement such data before offering definitive judgments about aptitudes and interests and before formulating policy proposals, see [8].

Such attitudes may develop during withdrawal years in several ways. For example the period of withdrawal, involving heavy within-the-home work loads during early child-rearing years and too-light demands in later years, may also entail general social isolation and stimulus deprivation not overcome by ad hoc voluntary associations with religious, recreational or other purposes. Also, nonprofessional life may come to be perceived as one of general disenfranchisement in a society where status, responsibility and power are largely determined by work roles and work competence, although enclaves of specialized functions for women may exist in the arena of public affairs. In addition, the severe demarcation in knowledge and interests, which is the outgrowth of differentiation in life-long activity, combined with the heavy time demands which a work life requires of men may be viewed as limiting the amount of shared time which is possible for men and women.

The educational experience itself, as well as predisposing psychological-social attributes, may contribute to the development of these attitudes as it creates needs and interests which might otherwise remain dormant. On the other hand, innovative development of nonwork associations and institutions now in their incipiency may provide greater intellectual-social stimulus in the future. To the extent that such activities are shared by men, as their work loads are reduced, discomfort with the polarities created by work and nonwork roles for men and women may be mitigated.[17] On balance, therefore, it is difficult to predict whether leisure aversive attitudes will increase, thus contributing to an increase in the proportion of educated women seeking a professional way of life. Unresolved differences in ideologic and scientific judgments about the polarities and identities in sex role which are inevitable and therefore accepted, desirable and therefore cultivated, objectionable and therefore attacked, contribute to uncertainty about future trends.[18]

Finally, despite the force of work-attractive and leisure-aversive experiences, large numbers of women may not be activated into seeking professional life if rival values and satisfying pursuits outside of a work

17. It is a peculiar feature of contemporary society, in the United States, at least, that non-work time is shared, the occupational realm remaining as the major "redoubt" of sex role differentiation. [44]
18. For illustrations of each point of view in turn, see [44], [16] and [53]. In the future, normative recommendations with respect to women's life styles will have to take account of recent research which offers "evidence that prolonged subjection to an inordinately monotonous or unstimulating environment is detrimental to a variety of psychological functions." [4] Because the experience of the nonprofessional educated woman involves stimulus withdrawal, it may be even more injurious than deprivation of stimulus never savored. Educated women are first exposed to organized stimuli during school years in an environment largely shared with men. These stimuli are then withdrawn during the early child-rearing years and only weak substitutes are available because of the relative poverty of stimulus organization outside of the work culture.

context are discovered. The following section, which shifts attention to the positive case for leisure, explores this possibility.

### C. Leisure models

The foregoing discussion of the implications of work models for women's life styles loses relevance to the extent that a leisure culture is the imminent, inevitable or preferred model of the future. Saturated as modern Western man is with the values of a work culture, the leisure models thrust him into an uncharted world, sometimes assumed to more nearly resemble a void than a social landscape in which he might find himself at home. Nonetheless, an anti-work credo has been burgeoning. Before exploring the implications of this development for women's life styles, central propositions of several variants of leisure models are summarized.

Three leisure models can be differentiated by their distinctive views of contemporary malaise, of social need, of economic-technologic possibilities, of individual developmental requirements and of value preferences and consequences. While all involve diminished emphasis on the centrality of work, these models may be distinguished according to: whether they assume the inevitability of leisure as an imminent and pervasive social condition for which cultural preparation is needed in order to create leisure competence and to ensure "high culture"; or whether they emphasize the leisure model as a moral imperative, without regarding a leisure society as inevitable unless its values are understood, preferred and assisted into cultural life. Further differentiation may also be made according to whether the model adopts an attitude of moral neutrality toward the spectrum of activities which will qualify as leisure pursuits, regarding all activities as of equal cultural acceptability; while a shift to "higher order" activities is the philosophic ground of other models, with even work to be preferred to trivialized leisure. These divergent perceptions of reality and the ends of individual and social action are emphasized in the material which follows.

1.   THE INEVITABLE-TEMPORAL MODEL[19]

This model rests on a core of propositions such as:

a.  A mass leisure society will inevitably emerge in the West. Although, we are on the very threshold of such a society, we have been closing the door

19.  For references to an end of the scarcity era, see [50]. It is interesting to note that Utopian thought has either assumed that economic scarcity has been eliminated, given any definition of imaginable human wants, or that scarcity can be eliminated through socially conditioned limitation of wants. Both themes are repeated throughout the issue of *Daedalus* devoted to an analysis of Utopian thinking. Thus, Frye asserts, "man obviously needs far less for the best life than he thinks he needs."[17] See also [28]. Similarly, Bettelheim declares that, "It was the efficiency of modern technology that made us rich. But now that we are rich we need not sacrifice to this god any more."[5] For a point of

on it. This resistance represents a cultural lag which needs to be overcome, otherwise we will be confronted with a crisis in leisure competence. Scarcity is no longer a fundamental fact of existence; Western society is living far beyond any desirable optimum of consumption; it is irrational to tie men to goals of consumption in order to maintain productive activity for employment and income.

b. Effort must be shifted into leisure pursuits without test of traditional market criteria for their encouragement and survival; new social modes to give expression to these activities must be designed outside the framework of the market.

c. Leisure and high civilization are correlates: a leisure tradition can be created without destroying moral and social equilibrium. The educated individual can find meaningful purpose and satisfying social relations in leisure pursuits if cultural values provide sanction and the social structure provides outlet and support.

d. Education is the major instrument for effecting a transition to the leisure society and for sustaining it once it has been achieved. It is the central institution displacing the importance of productive organizations characteristic of work-oriented cultures. It must itself be transformed to fulfill this social mission.

2. THE "ULTIMATE" LEISURE MODEL[20]

This model, so named because a concern for spiritual ultimates is its central focus, rests on the following cluster of propositions, which are largely of a value rather than a factual nature:

a. Work has become "totalitarian," encroaching on previously

view linking leisure and civilization, see [3] and [26]. Even the knowledge required and developed by the leisure society will be affected, as is indicated in the following statement by Maslow, " . . . science in general and psychology in particular is not exempt from these cultural climate and atmosphere effects. American psychology . . . is over pragmatic, over Puritan, and over purposeful. This is evident not only in its effects and avowed purposes but also in its gaps, in what it neglects. No textbooks have chapters on fun and gaiety, on leisure meditation, on loafing and puttering, on aimless, useless, and purposeless activity, on aesthetic creation or experience or on unmotivated activity. That is to say, American psychology is busily occupying itself with only half of life to the neglect of the other . . . and perhaps more important—half." [37] For a report of recent research calling attention to the importance of nonpurposive behavior in motivation theory despite its long neglect, see [4].

20. For references illustrative of this point of view, see [14] and [48]. For a discussion of the nature of interpersonal relations in the work world of a complex industrial society, see [39] and [40]. For discussion of the uneven distribution in modern society, see [63]. Also see Riesman's view that " . . . those who are privileged in being able to choose their own work are becoming increasingly under privileged with respect to leisure and perhaps also with respect to the pace at which . . . they must respond to the demands upon them. A polarization is occurring between the toiling classes and the leisure masses." [51]

protected enclaves, shutting out other values and engulfing the entire culture. A leisure society is not inevitable; it will have to be "valued" and created. Unabating productive effort to satisfy unlimited material wants is destructive of true culture, spirit, and the human personality. A man completely bound to "tasks" of whatever kind is barred the way to his deepest self, communion with the larger universe; is doomed to an existence which is, in fact, anti-God. Work is almost wholly devoted to profane ends; only leisure can be supportive of sacred ends.

b. Work has become an opiate covering up the experience of spiritual pain and poverty; the harm already accomplished by the dominant work ethic is already severe; repair of this damage requires a fundamental change in inner vision about the purpose and measures of existence; only concentration on spiritual ultimates can provide the counterforce to the not-yet exhausted power of the work ethic. The contemplative constitutes the highest order of human activity; life should be lived as a Noble Game which has its own disciplines and rewards.

c. Even intellectual activity is increasingly carried on in a factory atmosphere, involving fragmentation of tasks, loss of autonomy and diminution of positive and morally satisfying affect relations. The whole man can only be restored by freeing him to discover integration in higher order leisure pursuits.

d. The uneven distribution of leisure in our society, in inverse relation to competence to deal with it, represents social irrationality and a drag on high culture. The heavy work commitments borne by managerial, intellectual and professional groups will have to be reduced in order to allow them to realize other values, even if much of this commitment to work now seems to be self-imposed.

3. THE "CIVIC" MODEL[21]

This model stipulates leisure as a necessary condition for enriched civic-cultural life. Proponents of such a model advance propositions such as the following:

a. Participation in a high culture community requires leisure for adequate individual performance. The work-bound can only be part-time citizens.

b. The maintenance of a true sense of community depends on voluntarism for imaginative and fresh approaches to problems of the human community.

21. For illustrative advocacy, see DeGrazia's view that, "For the makers of the country, the good life was the life of leisure. They believed in it, and they themselves led such a life as long as they could. . . . Creativeness in politics, if it is to come, will come from leisure."[14]

c. The volunteer role needs to be enlarged and enriched, through creation of intermediate social forms between the individually private and the collectively public. Leisure is an absolute requisite for this path of development.

d. Related to the former, but emphasizing the need for benevolent dispositions in society, educated and leisured citizens ought to use their leisure to perform a healing mission for the world and to sustain these important values which cannot find expression in work.

## D. *Implications of leisure models for women's life styles*

Inasmuch as leisure-based societies, like work-based societies, can develop different institutional-behavioral responses to the choice dilemmas which confront every society—as the temporal, ultimate and civic variants within the set of leisure models imply—it seems pointless to assess the implications of any one arbitrary conception of a leisure society for women's life styles.

One of the problematic aspects of a leisure society concerns the degree of differentiation in social role to be fostered or tolerated, whether on the basis of sex or some other principle. Another concerns the selection of acitvities and institutions through which preferences for cultural sharing or differentiation will be expressed. Answers to questions of desired social polarities and identities are fundamental to the organization of the leisure society.

There is no *a priori* reason for presuming that differentiation on the basis of sex will persist or that it will disappear in a leisure society; either event is possible.[22] Differentiation in social role on the basis of sex may be freely cultivated for the sake of variety and stimulus. Where this occurs, no special social penalties or rewards will be attached to activities which emerge as predominantly male or female. But differentiation may be constrained by social rules which link status, power and reward with activities not open to women. In the latter case, women would have to decide, as they now have to in our own society, whether to reject differentiation in social role on egalitarian grounds, or to attempt sharing in male activities when they appear to be intrinsically worthwhile and to cultivate differentiation where they do not (when judged in the light of some "higher" social value than sex equality).

This case illustrates the philosophic dilemma of finding acceptable criteria of social choice and of establishing priorities among them in all societies. In our own society, for example, equal diffusion of men and women

22. Thus, it is interesting to note the exclusion of women from the leisure community devoted to Noble Games in *Magister Ludi*. [25]

among professions classified as both nurturant and nonnurturant has been advocated partly as a policy required by social necessity, but also as an article of egalitarian ideology. [5] But viewing the problem from another vantage point entirely, the judgment has been offered that nurturant activities and institutions are so undermanned and undervalued in contemporary society that women looking for a constructive social purpose ought to consider this in seeking to maximize contributions to beneficent social activities. In a male head-hunting society, an enlightened choice might imply that segregation from male culture was preferable to sharing in it.[23]

Wherever women have a "free" choice, finding acceptable criteria for choosing may represent the real moral burden. Other strategic choices in a leisure society, as in any other, involving conflicting value criteria for both men and women might include: (1) the extent of organized activity versus scope for individual action; (2) the dominance of any single value— intellectual, artistic or religious—versus attempted accommodation of several on an equal footing; (3) encouragement of public versus private pursuits; and (4) encouraging competitive versus cooperative social relations. Sex equality with respect to any of the above may appear to be a relevant criterion, if it should happen that male and female modalities fell along the lines of division posed above. But sex equality could not be the sole criterion, nor necessarily the one always accorded the highest priority. Where separate modalities were not already in force on such issues, women as well as men would have to search for acceptable criteria for social choice.[24]

Clearly, much of present debates about the place of professional

23. Erik Erikson has expressed the hope that "there is something in women's specific creativity which has waited only for a clarification of her relationship to masculinity (including her own) in order to assume her share of leadership in those fateful human affairs which so far have been left entirely in the hands of gifted and driven men, and often of men whose genius of leadership eventually has yielded to ruthless self-aggrandizement. Mankind now obviously depends on new kinds of social inventions, and on restitutions which guard and cultivate that which nurses and nourishes, cares and tolerates, includes and preserves." [16] It is relevant to this discussion to note that when confronted with a similar hope not quite thirty years ago, Virginia Woolf produced her bitter and provocative answer to the effect that women lacking power and access to power, influence, self and social esteem, money, appropriate education and experience simply could not perform this mission. [65]

24. Thus, the community in *Magister Ludi* [25] represented a highly organized competitive society in which intellectual values were predominant. Quite different societies are obviously conceivable as literary exercises and in reality. Thus, there is no certainty, because there is no demonstrable necessity, that any given value will predominate, such as has been claimed, for example, for the dominance of esthetic values in the leisure society of the future by Aschenbrenner. [1] Moreover, although a leisure society is often depicted as benign, malign potentials may be heightened as destructive energies are no longer absorbed in economic pursuits.

commitment in the lives of educated women must be regarded as culturally irrelevant to a society passing through the "shock front" from a work to a leisure ethos. [49] Rather, women's efforts to cope constructively with present dilemmas of leisure—the uniquely burdensome gift of modern technological culture to the middle class educated woman—might be used to transform speculative Utopian exercises in thinking about a leisure society into "laboratory trials" on behalf of the emergent society in which leisure will be Everyman's lot. Study of the leisure life modes which have actually been experienced could be used to provide helpful clues to what otherwise must be a completely conjectural effort to deal with future behavioral possibilities,[25] even though some aspects of present leisure experience (embedded as they are in a work-dominated culture) may not be germane to, and may even be misleading for, a leisure society. The presence of educated women who can be reached individually and through voluntary, organized groups provides rich experimental opportunities for the study of leisure. Negative experiences, if studied may provide the data for recommending critical changes for transforming leisure into a more positive experience, thus pioneering some of the conditions necessary to mass adjustment to a leisure society. For example, the claim has been made that significant intellectual activity can be carried on outside of an organizational setting in a leisure society and that contributions to knowledge can be made on this basis in virtually all fields. [49] Positive demonstration would be more helpful than speculative claims in this area, especially since some recent studies of autonomy and creativity suggest that some externally imposed constraints may be more conducive to optimum performance than total freedom.[26] [45] Successful efforts to enhance the intellectual and cultural life of educated women who are not now professionally engaged, through serious experimental trial of various kinds of organizations, stimuli and

25. Many conjectural attempts have been made. The following almost elegiac listing of behavioral qualities which will be shut out in the leisure society, leaves the positive content of behavior a continuing mystery. "Given these assumptions, certain ways of life, certain kinds of character and sensibility, certain varieties of experience are obviously ruled out. Most forms of heroism and endurance, many kinds of resourcefulness and ingenuity, many hallowed attainments and disciplines, and a host of traditional consolations and inducements are incompatible with assured material ease. What then is left? If leisure and abundance foreclose these possibilities, surely they must open the way for others." [28] For a positive statement of behavior and values in a leisure society, see [49].
26. The outlook for intellectual achievement in a leisure society may appear bleak for those who believe that "if a man is given absolutely free choice, he prefers pleasure to achievement, but if a situation urgently calls for achievement he can quickly adapt to the situation." [46] Apart from the difficulty of defining "absolute free choice," the meanings of "pleasure" and "urgency" may acquire different content in different societies. Thus, pleasure can be linked to achievement in a leisure society, if the intellectual task is approached in the spirit of a game. Or pleasure may be derived from the social relations and esteem of valued friends sharing similar interests. The latter may even acquire some urgency, if acceptance in a private social circle depends on intellectual competence.

other relevant conditions would offer significant social gains.[27] Experimental approaches could also test the conditions for maximizing values other than achievement, with special attention to compatible and incompatible value combinations.[28] In this connection, experimental study of the range of possible styles in interpersonal relations in a variety of leisure pursuits would be useful, since such relationships may be one of the most satisfying and luxurious of values cultivated in a leisure society.

## Values, technology and professional commitment

The analytical structure underlying much of the preceding discussion can be summarized by means of the schematic diagram which follows:

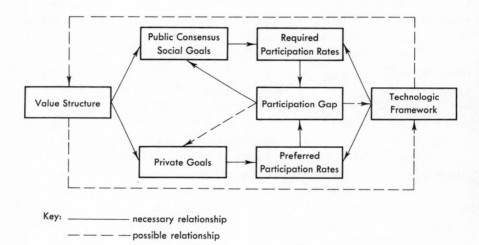

Key: ———————— necessary relationship
     — — — — —possible relationship

Viewed within such a framework, values and technology, which jointly determine actual professional participation rates, both transmit their impacts along two pathways. One pathway traces the demand for professional women to the combined effects of values on social goals and of a given technologic order on the resources required for satisfying those goals. The other pathway traces the supply of professional women to the combined

27. A study of the leisure competence of men has produced some melancholy results bearing on the quality of cultural life even among professional and intellectual groups, the supposed custodians of high culture. [31]. A parallel study of women has not been undertaken. Although often referred to as "culture-bearers" in our society, it is not really certain that evidence would support this flattering view.
28. Gellner declares " . . . the virtues of achievement and the virtues of enjoyment are not identical and, indeed, they are probably incompatible."[20, p. 142.] Other points of view have been expressed, of course. Empirical evidence on compatibilities and incompatibilities could be more useful than intuitions, however.

effect of values on private goals and of the work-attraction qualities of the technologic order on preferred participation rates.

In the short run, defined as a period in which values and technology are fixed, three kinds of imbalance may lead to a participation gap: (1) a given value structure may engender incompatible social and private goals; (2) a given technologic order may have contrary effects on required and preferred participation rates; and (3) a given value structure and a given technologic order may not be fully congruent in their effects. Where this occurs, only limited adjustment options are available in the short run. If imbalances should eventuate in required participation rates being unsatisfied, curtailment of social goals will be coerced and need not involve any value shift. If imbalances should result in preferred participation rates in excess of requirements, unsuccessful search for professional employment may occasion some alteration in private goals, without any supporting value shift (e.g., temporary withdrawal from the search for professional engagement).

Over an intermediate period, defined as one in which some changes in values and technology can occur, the participation gap can be narrowed by resort to modest, readily adopted adjustments in the technologic order and by marginal value shifts. Where the imbalances involve unsatisfied demand, the adjustments might involve determining the size of the "latent" professional group, developing cognitive bases for positive decisions on professional participation and altering the organizational environment along known and promising lines which do not involve fundamental transformations as, for example, recent experimentation with less than full time medical residencies. Where the imbalance involves excess supply, the intermediate period does not offer ready options unless social goals have been previously curtailed by assumed personnel shortages and if value sanction for goal expansion has formed previously.

Over the long run, the participation gap can be closed by fundamental changes in either values or technology or both. When the imbalance is in the nature of a supply deficit, fundamental value shifts conducive to an increase in preferred participation rates and to limitation of additional social goals can reduce the gap or technologic innovations can lower participation requirements. If the imbalance takes the form of excess supply, fundamental changes in values supportive of social goal expansion or of new private goals which entail withdrawal of interest in professional commitment, may be necessary unless offset by technologic development of new wants for which value support already exists. For example, recent bio-engineering developments which have expanded medical goals make heavy demands on professional skills and are in part a response to the high value placed on longevity in our society.

Any congruence between required and preferred participation rates can be disturbed, of course, by subsequent autonomous changes in values or technology or both. Where this occurs, a period of adjustment would be required before generating a new level of professional participation resting on a different values-technology base. Thus, for example, a growing preference for leisure over goods—a value change directly affecting private and social goals and therefore, both required and preferred participation rates— would engender search for technologic innovations which promised reductions in personnel requirements and the neglect of innovations which could serve only to expand wants. On the other hand, if technology uncovered an economic cornucopia which provided for present wants without serious effort, the value structure would have to carry the strain of adjustment by developing moral sanctions for leisure and hence modifying social and private goals.

The foregoing conceptual framework appears helpful in identifying some determinants of professional participation, in tracing the sequential linkages among them, in selecting adjustment paths among alternative options if a participation gap results, and finally, in anticipating the consequences of any given shift in the mesh of relationships.

This framework may also serve as a reminder that decisions focussed directly on the question of professional commitment are tied to other decisions, which ramify out through a large social domain. Hence, any recasting of normative positions with respect to the place of professional commitment in the lives of educated women calls for decision on a much larger array of issues. For example, the tissue of professional commitment is sometimes appraised by means of a single criterion, namely, equality. But without reference to assumed social goals, technologic conditions and male modal patterns, it would not be possible to specify whether equality entails more or less work involvement.

Equality would obviously be represented by quite different conditions in a work centered and a leisure centered society. In the context of our own society, an ideological position in favor of professional commitment is not a single decision, but a network of decisions involving value, judgmental and factual premises about: the enduring hold of work culture on the lives of men; the importance of some degree of purposive activity expressed through intellectual, artistic, civic or cultural efforts for individual well-being and development;[29] the necessity of fostering this development within

29. In this connection, it is interesting to ponder Simon's view that the intellectual experience as such, despite increasing specialization in focus, "provides common ground" as important as "loving, hating, eating and shivering provide common ground." Should one then regard isolation from this basic life experience as a divisive force in society and as serious a deprivation to the individual as blindness in a "seeing" culture? [57, pp. 263–264.] The view that man never "becomes as free as he can be until he really acquires and uses his mind. That mind of his is not a gift. It is achieved,"—this view also seems relevant to this issue.

the disciplines and rewards of work institutions, even if this should require an expansion of social goals; the consequences of denial of access to (or rejection of) such work experience; the assessment of the opportunity cost of professional commitment; and the desired direction of further technological development. Since equality is a term with ambiguous content, the value justification for professional commitment requires a more specific set of premises embracing an array of interconnected social and individual values and a concrete set of technological conditions.

Because the historic evidence indicates that technology can be developed under the spur of values so as to serve many value ends—for example— to reinforce work values or support leisure values; to increase differentiation in the life styles of men and women, or to reduce it—technology cannot itself provide the ultimate ground for defining normative positions on the question of professional commitment and thus simplify the moral task of deciding what is desirable and possible. Recent sociological and psychological approaches to the question of life style, have muted the significance of real choice at crucial stages in the life cycle. Increasing attention to the choice process, including empirical verification of the value and factual premises which function as criteria of choice in the selection of social and individual goals, seems likely to develop partly as a result of the critical scrutiny of previous approaches.[30] Further study of the choice process becomes essential if the future is regarded in any sense as "open" with respect to the issues raised in this discussion, and if this openness presages value conflict because one lifetime and one society cannot embody all qualities or all objectives which may be deemed desirable.[31]

30. Thus, Simon has declared, "The difficulties in role theory drop away if we adopt the viewpoint that social influence upon decision premises. A role is a specification of some, but not all, of the premises that enter into an individual's decisions. Many other premises also enter into the same decisions, including informational premises and idiosyncratic premises that are expressive of personality. . . . Unless the premise is taken as unit, role theory stands in danger of committing an error that is just the opposite of the one committed by economic theory—of not leaving any room for rationality in behavior. If a role is a pattern of behavior, the role may be functional, from a social standpoint, but the performer of the role cannot be a rational actor—he simply acts his part. On the other hand, if a role consists in the specification of certain value and factual premises, then the enactor of the role will ordinarily have to exercise rationality in order to attain these values. A role defined in terms of premises leaves room for rational calculation in behavior."[56]

31. For additional references critical of role theory, see [33] and [36]. For emphasis on value conflict as inevitably part of the human situation, see [34], [47], [52] and [10]. The difficulties in achieving consensus on criteria of choice may be illustrated by Geiger's resort to a technological criterion [19] and its condemnation by Ellul[15]. But it is only by means of critical review of explicit criteria that knowledgeable choice can be fostered, whether by organizations or individuals [56, p. 89]. It may be one means of escaping the loss of freedom implied by "conditioning," whether early or late.

## REFERENCES

[1] Karl Aschenbrenner, "The Coming Supremacy of the Aesthetic," *Diogenes*, Spring 1966, pp. 13–24.

[2] Kurt Baier, *The Moral Point of View*, (Ithaca: Cornell University Press, 1958), pp. 214–230.

[3] Clive Bell, "How to Make a Civilization," in [31, pp. 33–43].

[4] D. E. Berlyne, "Curiosity and Exploration," *Science*, July 1, 1966, p. 26.

[5] Bruno Bettelheim, "The Commitment Required of a Woman Entering a Profession in Present-Day Society," in [38, p. 16].

[6] Orville G. Brim, Jr., "Socialization Through the Life Cycle," *Items*, Social Science Research Council, Vol. 18, No. 1, p. 5.

[7] Wallace R. Brode, "Approaching Ceilings in the Supply of Scientific Manpower," *Science*, January 24, 1964, pp. 313–324.

[8] Mary I. Bunting, "The Commitment Required of a Woman Entering a Scientific Profession," in [38, p. 22].

[9] Neil W. Chamberlain, *The West in a World Without War*, (New York: McGraw-Hill, 1963), p. 47.

[10] C. West Churchman, "Review (of Abraham Kaplan, *The Conduct of Inquiry*)," *Science*, January 17, 1965, pp. 283–284.

[11] Harlan Cleveland, "Dinosaurs and Personal Freedom," in *Saturday Review*, February 29, 1959, pp. 12–14.

[12] Gerhard Colm, "Introduction," in [32, pp. 4–5].

[13] C. R. DeCarlo, "Perspectives on Technology," in [21, pp. 8–37].

[14] Sebastian DeGrazia, *Of Time, Work and Leisure*, (New York: Twentieth Century Fund, 1962).

[15] Jacques Ellul, *The Technological Society*, (New York: Alfred Knopf, 1965).

[16] Erik Erikson, "Reflections on Womanhood," *Daedalus: The Woman in America*, Spring 1964, pp. 604–605.

[17] George Frye, "Varieties of Literary Utopia," *Daedalus*, Spring 1965, p. 345.

[18] John K. Galbraith, *The Affluent Society*, (Boston: Houghton, Mifflin, and Co., 1958).

[19] G. R. Geiger, "Values and Inquiry" in Roy Lepley (ed.), *Values: A Cooperative Inquiry*, (New York: Columbia University Press, 1949), p. 106.

[20] Ernest Gellner, *Thought and Change*, (Chicago: University of Chicago Press, 1965).

[21] Eli Ginzburg (ed.), *Technology and Social Change*, (New York: Columbia University Press, 1964).

[22] Seymour Harris (ed.), *Education: Public Policy*, (Berkeley, California: McCutcheon Publishing Corporation, 1964), pp. 322–333.

[23] Leland Hazard, "Can We Afford Our National Goals," *Harvard Business Review*, May–June 1962, pp. 174–178.

[24] August Heckscher, "Reflections on the Manpower Revolution," *The American Scholar*, Autumn 1964, p. 572.

[25] Herman Hesse, *Magister Ludi*, (New York: Henry Holt and Co., 1949).

[26] Johan Huizinga, *Homo Ludens*, (London: Routledge & Kegan Paul, 1949).

[27] Denis F. Johnston and Harvey R. Hamel, "Educational Attainment of Workers in March 1965," *Monthly Labor Review*, March 1966, p. 257.

[28] George Kateb, "Utopia and the Good Life," *Daedalus*, Spring 1965, p. 454.

[29] John Maynard Keynes, *Essays in Persuasion*, (New York: Harcourt Brace and Co., 1932).

[30] Clyde Kluckholn, Henry Murray and David Schneider, *Personality in Nature, Society and Culture*, (New York: Knopf and Co., 1956), pp. 15–16.

[31] Eric Larabee and R. Meyersohn (eds.), *Mass Leisure*, (New York: The Free Press, 1958).

[32] Leonard Lecht, *Goals, Priorities and Dollars*, (New York: The Free Press, 1966), pp. 18–19.

[33] D. J. Levinson, "Role, Personality and Social Structure in the Organizational Setting," in [59, p. 428].

[34] Karl Mannheim, "Roots of the Crisis in Evaluation," in W. C. Bennis, K. D. Benne and R. Chin (eds.), *The Planning of Change*, (New York: Holt, Rinehart and Winston, 1961), pp. 99–101.

[35] James G. March and Herbert A. Simon, *Organizations*, (New York: John Wiley and Sons Inc., 1959), p. 50.

[36] Don Martindale, "Limits of and Alternatives to Functionalism in Sociology," in Don Martindale (ed.), *Functionalism in the Social Sciences*, (Philadelphia: The American Academy of Political and Social Science, Monograph 5, 1965), pp. 144–162.

[37] Abraham Maslow, *Motivation and Personality*, (New York: Harper and Row, 1954), pp. 94–97.

[38] J. Mattfeld and C. Van Aken (eds.), *Women in Science and Engineering*, (Cambridge: M.I.T. Press, 1965).

[39] David McClelland, *The Achieving Society*, (New York: Van Nostrand and Co., 1961), p. 415.

[40] ——, *Talent and Society*, (New York: Van Nostrand and Co., 1958), p. 140.

[41] James A. Morgan et al., *Income and Welfare in the United States*, (New York: McGraw Hill, 1962), pp. 113, 122.

[42] Gardner Murphy, *Human Potentialities*, (New York: Basic Books, 1958), pp. 123–125.

[43] Russell Nye and W. Lois Hoffman, *The Employed Mother*, (Chicago: Rand McNally, 1963).

[44] Talcott Parsons, *Essays in Sociological Theory*, (New York: The Free Press, Rev. Ed. 1959), p. 91.

[45] D. Pelz and F. M. Andrews, "Autonomy, Coordination and Stimulation in Relation to Scientific Achievement," *Behavioral Science*, March 1966, pp. 89–97.

[46] Stephen Pepper, *The Sources of Value*, (Berkeley, California: University of California Press, 1958), p. 366.

[47] Ralph B. Perry, *Realms of Value*, (Cambridge: Harvard University Press, 1954).

[48] Josef Pieper, *Leisure*, (New York: Pantheon Books, 1964).

[49] John R. Platt, "The Step to Man," *Science*, August 6, 1965, pp. 610–611.

[50] David Riesman, *Abundance for What?*, (New York: Doubleday and Co., 1964).

[51] ——, "Leisure and Work in Post-Industrial Society," in [31, p. 375].

[52] Walter R. Reitman, "Personality as a Problem-Solving Coalition" in Tompkins and Messick (eds.), *Computer Simulation of Personality*, (New York: John Wiley and Sons Inc., 1963), pp. 83–84.

[53] Alice S. Rossi, "Equality Between the Sexes," *Daedalus*, Spring 1964, pp. 628–634.

[54] ——, "Women in Science: Why so Few?", *Science*, May 28, 1965, pp. 1200–1201.

[55] ——, "Barriers to Career Choice of Engineering, Medicine or Science Among American Women" in [35a, p. 85].

[56] Herbert A. Simon, *Administrative Behavior*, (New York: The Macmillan Company, Rev. Ed. 1961), pp. 30–31.

[57] Herbert A. Simon, "A Computer for Everyman," *The American Scholar*, Spring 1966, p. 258.

[58] B. F. Skinner, *Walden Two*, (New York: The Macmillan Company, 1948), p. 209.

[59] Neil Smelser and W. T. Smelser (eds.), *Personality and Social Systems*, (New York: John Wiley and Sons Inc., 1963).

[60] H. Turner, "Some Aspects of Women's Ambition," *American Journal of Sociology*, November 1964, pp. 271–285.

[61] Otto Von Mering, *A Grammar of Values*, (Pittsburgh: University of Pittsburgh Press, 1961), p. 89.

[62] Paul Weiss, *Nature and Man*, (New York: Henry Holt and Co., 1947), p. 200.

[63] Harold L. Wilensky, "The Distribution of Leisure" in Edward Smigel (ed.), *Work and Leisure*, (New Haven: College and University Press, 1963), pp. 107–145.

[64] ——, "Mass Media and Mass Culture," *American Journal of Sociology*, April 1964, pp. 173–197.

[65] Virginia Woolf, *Three Guineas*, (New York: Harcourt, Brace and Co., 1938).

[66] Dennis Wrong, "The Oversocialized Conception of Man in Modern Society," in [59, pp. 183–193].

# THE POWER OF VALUES IV

# New urban structures

## David Lewis

I do not suppose that any of us can be in any doubt about the scale and complexity of the challenge confronting the world's major cities. As a designer and as one involved also in the education of designers, I want to put forward some ideas concerning the changes in urban structure which are occurring as a result of this challenge. Ancient as city living is, the new urban structures I am going to discuss, the new physical forms of cities, are without historical precedent.

The most obvious component of urban crisis is population growth. The total number of people alive in the world today can be calculated only approximately; nevertheless there can be no doubt about the critical acceleration of world populations. From the dawn of history to the time of the Mayflower the total population of our globe had grown to half a billion people. By 1830 the world's population was one billion people; by 1930, just a century later, it had grown to two billion; by 1960, only a generation later, it had reached three billion. At present rates of growth, only fifteen more years will be needed to add the fourth billion. By the year 2000 it is estimated that there will be seven billion people on this planet.[1]

It is hardly surprising that, in sheer size alone, a sharp distinction must be made between the finite and physically comprehensible cities of the past and the vast, sprawling metropolitan regions which are building up in every country today. In the post-Renaissance pre-Industrial past, the ratio of agriculture-oriented populations to city dwellers was usually more than four to one. Already in highly industrialized countries this ratio has been more than reversed during the last half century. Britain is a country where at the beginning of the nineteenth century the rural population still outnumbered by ten to one those living in cities of 100,000 people or more. Today 90 percent of a dramatically increased population now lives and

---

1. World Population Growth, by Harold F. Dorn, in *The Population Dilemma*, ed. by Philip M. Hauser, (New York: Prentice-Hall, 1963), pp. 7–29; papers from the Twenty-third Assembly, 1963.

earns in huge metropolitan industrial regions. A broadly similar process is occurring in the United States. Already 70 percent of the population lives and earns in urbans areas, and it may be expected with some confidence that the figure will be over 90 percent within twenty-five years—during which period the present population is expected to increase by two-thirds its

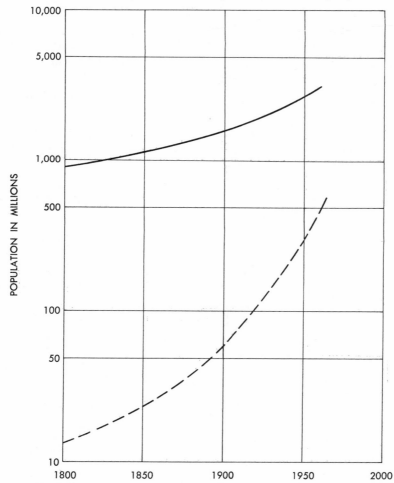

This graph, previously published in *Scientific American*, shows how rapidly the world's gross population (black line) is urbanizing: the dotted line traces the growth of cities with populations of 100,000 or more.

present size, or double. Such increases in urban population are affecting the structure of every major city in the world.

Ironically the impact is greatest on the cities of the less developed countries, and these are, of course, the cities least able to cope with the problem. In a recent book, *Man's Struggle for Shelter in an Urbanizing*

*World*, Charles Abrams' forecast that in Africa, the present urban population of 58 million people will grow to 294 millions by the year 2000; in the same period of thirty-five years urban populations will grow from 144 million people to 650 million in Latin America, and in Asia the present urban population of 559 million people will grow to 3,444 millions.[2] Major cities in most underdeveloped countries are already surrounded by huge squatter settlements, composed of self-constructed shelters built of junk materials, rolled out kerosene tins, strips of linoleum, burlap, and even paper. Today millions of people are living in peripheral slums of this kind, without latrines, sewage, garbage disposal, or even piped water, and certainly without education, health facilities, or nominal political rights. Peru, for example, has a squatter history of only twenty-five to thirty years; yet the number of people living in squatter settlements—or "barriadas" on the fringes of the major cities already amounts to some 40 percent of the country's total urban population.[3]

In some respects the development of these squatter settlements is parallel to the urbanization, during the nineteenth and early twentieth centuries, of the more highly industrialized countries. The basic similarity is one of migration from country to city. Many of us, now firmly established in our highly industrialized urban societies, forget how close to us our rural origins are. In the United States, for example, the migration of agricultural populations to cities has amounted to 28 million between 1920 and 1960. The process is still continuing. In 1929, the proportion of those employed in agriculture was 25 percent; by 1950 it as 15.3 percent; by 1960 it was 8.7 percent; by 1965 it was 6.4 percent; by 1975 it is expected to be less than 4 percent.[4] Perhaps our suburbia of ranch houses on one acre lots

2. *Man's Struggle for Shelter in an Urbanizing World*, by Charles Abrams (Boston: M.I.T. Press, 1964), p. 294; estimates by Homer Hoyt, Study of International Housing, United States Senate, 88th Congress, First Session, March 1963, p. 17.

3. The growth of many of these slums is extremely rapid. The Carrabella group of barriadas outside Lima was first settled in 1957; today it has a squatter population of over 100,000. The city of Amman, in Jordan, had a population in 1958 of 12,000 people; three years later the population was 247,000. On the hillaides above Rio de Janeiro there is already a squatter population of 800,000; in Ankara, Turkey, the number of squatters is nearly 50 percent of that city's population; at present rates of growth, the peripheral slums of Manilla in the Philippines will have over a million squatters 25 years from now. Squatter settlements of this kind occur in and around most of the major cities in the underdeveloped countries of the world. Sources: "Dwelling Resources in South America," by John C. Turner, William Mangin, Patrick Crooke and Catherine S. Turner, special issue of *Architectural Design* (London), August 1963; "The Urbanization of the Human Population," by Kingsley Davis, *Scientific American*, vol. 213, No. 3 (September 1965), p. 52; "The use of Land in Cities," by Charles Abrams, *Scientific American*, vol. 213, No. 3 (September 1965), p. 152.

4. Sources: "The New Society," by Oscar Handlin, *Proceedings of the Urban Design Conference*, Harvard University, April/May 1965; "The New Technology is Shaping a New Labor Force," by Charles C. Killingsworth, in *The Computer and Society, Six Viewpoints: The New York Times*, April 1966.

where so many of us, in distinct income brackets, enjoy being half in, half out of the city, may be indicative of this transition. Certainly the tangled urban and county tax and legal structures of this country reflect its proximity to rural institutions.

There are, however, crucial differences between the urban crises in underdeveloped countries, and the challenges with which cities are faced in the industrially developed nations. In the industrialized countries of Europe and Northern America, migration is more a question of a changing ratio of population distribution: agriculture-oriented communities decline, or remain static, as the huge urban agglomerations grow larger and larger. But in several underdeveloped countries the total population increases are such that the growth or rural populations is outstripping migration to cities in spite of large-scale migration. In India the rate of population growth is 2.5 percent per annum. In Brazil it is 3.2 percent per annum. The general population increase in South America as a whole is such that only some 20 percent of the growth of cities is due to migration. The rapid expansion of cities is thus due proportionately more to population growth in their traditional slums than to migration. In Venezuela, in spite of migration to Caracas and other cities, farm population increased in the decade 1951–1961 by 11 percent. Yet by 1961 the number of squatters in Caracas represented 35 percent of the city's total population, and in Maracaibo, Venezuela's second largest city, they totalled over 50 percent.[5] Compounding population growth in the underdeveloped countries therefore results in an apparently insoluble situation in which under productive agricultural communities are gaining population while, simultaneously, the cities are being surrounded by rapidly growing slums.

Faced with the poverty of these slums—the flies and stagnant water, the uncollected garbage, the absence of sewage, the lack of education, the high unemployment figures, magnified by rapid population growth, as well as by the fact that in most instances the land on which the slums have so rapidly developed was in the first place illegally seized—the question still remains whether it is fundamentally good policy to reach for one's bulldozer as a primary weapon. Two points, I think, should be made. The first is that the magnitude of these slums, in virtually every underdeveloped country of the world, at the present moment and irrespective of their compounding growth, is already far beyond the capacities for reconstruction of national or international organizations. The second point is that, if one looks at the problem the other way round, from the point of view of the

5. Sources: Kingsley Davis, *op. cit.*; *Squatter Settlements, the Problem and the Opportunity*, by Charles Abrams, Department of Housing and Urban Development, Washington, D.C., 1966.

inhabitants themselves and what they have achieved with virtually zero resources, an heroic social dynamic becomes suddenly evident in a number of squatter settlements in various parts of the world. John Turner shows how the establishment of many barriadas in Peru is preceded by months of secret, careful surveys, on the basis of which streets and lots are laid out in geometric form with 2,500 square feet for each family. Settlements, which began only a few years ago as squalid shacks of matting attached to poles, or corrugated iron nailed to a framework of packing-case slats, are now evolving into a regular street system of permanent or semi-permanent housing, patiently built up—a few bricks or rafters at a time as individual families manage to save up for them—by internally coordinated cooperatives of mutual aid and the exchange of labor and skills among neighbors. In many barrios democratically elected committees attempt to maintain order; and in the absence of official recognition these committees struggle against considerable odds to raise funds among the slum dwellers themselves for schools, electricity, sewers and piped water.[6] Not only in Peru but in Turkey, Pakistan, and several other Latin American countries, barrios are gradually evolving into ordered and permanent sectors of the city. Experiments (such as, for instance, localized projects undertaken by the Peace Corps in North Africa or Latin America) in providing architectural services somewhat in the manner of health clinics, though thus far limited in scale compared with the size of need, have been extraordinarily successful in encouraging house building with proper foundations, roof and wall structures, staircases, and ventilation.[7] And the pride of achievement and community identity which develops shows very clearly that the official and prestigious projects, which involve rows of neat and antiseptic high-rise slabs—those respectable tear sheets from the glossy magazines of modern architecture—are thoroughly misplaced in these circumstances, for they are at once a drain on already overextended national budgets, and they deprive the barrio dweller of his urge to participate in making a city environment for himself and his children. What is perhaps needed, then, is not a posse of police armed with eviction notices, revolvers and nightsticks, but categorically different policies aimed at generating and harnessing a developing social dynamism.

Under such policies there would be land concessions and a system of loans for building materials; there would be government provision of basic

6. John C. Turner, William Mangin, Patrick Crooke, and Catherine S. Turner; *op. cit.*
7. "In Adana, Turkey, 44 percent of the houses are made of brick; 17 percent of concrete block, and 38 percent of wood and brick; 60 percent have electricity and 13 percent have water; in Erzincan, half are made of wood and half of adobe; in Erzerum, 90 percent are of masonry construction and 10 percent of adobe." Charles Abrams, *Squatter Settlements, the Problem and the Opportunity*, *op. cit.* For first-hand account of architectural advisory services to barriada dwellers in Peru, see Margaret Grenfell on "Squatter Settlements in Peru" in *The Pedestrian in the City*, ed. by David Lewis, (Princeton: Van Nostrand, 1966).

large-scale utilities such as sewers, water, electricity and paved roads, as urgently needed services and as generators of local employment; there would be trained personnel to operate schools and health centers to be built by the communities themselves. And implicit is official acceptance of the fact that one of the principal ways by which modern cities grow is by peripheral addition (parallel, for example, is the extending suburbia of the industrialized countries). In the rapidly urbanizing cells of the barrio-type in particular, community identity and creative social dynamism are crucial.

The reasons for the compounding urbanization of the present century are many and complex. Population growth is, of course, only one of them. From 1800 to 1950 the proportion of world population living in cities of 200,000 people or more rose from 2.4 percent to 21 percent. As the graph on p. 295 shows, the aggregate growth of cities is not only much more rapid than world population growth, but is accelerating. In the United States alone it is estimated that 160 million people will be added to the population during the next generation, of whom well over 90 percent will be urban. Cities have been called man's greatest and most intricate artifact. Concentrations of political power and religion, art and learning, industry and opportunity, cities are categorically different from rural settlements and have by long tradition attracted the vigorous, the ambitious, the adventurous, the articulate. But the process by which our old and highly differentiated cities have aggregated over the centuries, continually made and remade in handwrought fragments by innumerable generations of people, some famous in the history of their art, the majority nameless, providing their inhabitants with an astonishing range of place and association, and each unified by its own distinct culture, cannot be repeated in the twentieth century.

In both the highly industrialized countries and the underdeveloped countries, the vast new urban populations of the world are involved in the creation of a global urban culture entirely new in the history of cities. The gravitational pull in the lives of these new people is towards the twentieth century technological city. During the short lifetime of each of us several ancient and living cultures in Africa and Asia have either totally disappeared or are in the process of doing so. The Western mode of life is emerging dominant, not due to any moral superiority but due to modern technics, in particular the technologies of communications, and consumer production and distribution. From Lagos to Singapore, from Manila to Zanzibar, the image of the modern city to ordinary people is the glittering curtain-wall tower, reflecting the timeless movements of sky and clouds in its glass. The empty-bellied migrant from the land moves to the city in search of employment for himself, but for his children he is in search of education, the fulfillment of his twentieth century city dream, in which each of his sons will be an urban professional, a lawyer, a doctor, an engineer, a politician, or a university professor.

In the United States the effects of this process are clearly visible, Small country towns and cities are losing population and are beginning to decay with little chance of attracting new investment. In each of these towns and cities, decay takes root first in the central areas, the fulcrum of the community's life. It is tragic to see the decline of historic commercial main streets, with their broad tree-lined pavements and colonial architecture, built with simple precision and humanist scale. And the crucial population which these cities are losing—apart from the low income poor who are the first to be hit by the recession—is the talented young, who leave home for college and university education, and never return, thus depriving rural cities of their future community leadership.

One reason for the decay of country towns and cities in the United States is, then, the phenomenal growth of the nation's major metropoli, which are acting as population magnets on an enormous scale. Another is that rural cities are becoming less and less centers for the agricultural communities that surround them, with the result that their main economic base is decaying. We have already noted the continuing decline in the United States population earning its living directly from the land, resulting in a drop in agricultural employment from 8.2 million in 1945 to 4.8 million in 1964—or 42 percent—in spite of productivity gains.[8] This has been due of course to technological changes in agriculture which are currently transforming, not simply the scale, but the whole character of the production, processing and marketing of food. These technological changes cover the full range from machinery for seed planting and harvesting, fertilizers and insecticides sprayed from aeroplanes and helicopters, and the developing microclimatology of animal husbandry, to the technologies of food storage, deep freezing, preservation of grain supplies, canning, dehydration and so forth, directly related to market economies planned as an equitable and continuous process of distribution, and terminating in our wheeled supermarket baskets in which we do our weekly harvesting. Yet should it not astonish us to know that—although we live in a generation in which we enjoy, in the United States as in most European countries, for the first time in the whole history of man, an uninterrupted supply of fresh produce, in season and out—agriculture and food processing are still among the most backward of modern technologies? Within the known technologies of microclimatology, photosynthesis, soil control, and automated food processing it is already possible to realize increases in production potential sufficient

8. Charles C. Killingsworth, *op. cit.*

to support 15,000 people per square mile of flat land. The impact which such technologies will have when applied to a world where, according to U.N. Food and Agriculture Organization estimates, 35 to 50 percent of the world's people are undernourished or starving, or where, in India alone, some 50 million children are destined to die during the next ten years of malnutrition,[9] are only today being tentatively calculated. But one thing is certain. In the various countries of Africa and Asia, where over 70 percent of the population gains its livelihood directly from the soil, often by primitive methods unaffected by modern technology, the main impact will be felt in the cities.

As a result of such general trends, the cities of the United States are gaining new population at a rate of 100,000 people a week. In a message to the Senate and to Congress on March 1, 1965, President Johnson put it dramatically when he said, "During the next fifteen years, 30 million people will be added to our cities—equivalent to the combined populations of New York, Chicago, Los Angeles, Philadelphia, Detroit, and Baltimore."[10] Perhaps it would be as well to add that at present rates of growth this estimate is somewhat conservative. However, the President's choice of cities is suggestive; for the gravitational pull to urban areas in the United States, as in every country of the world, is not equal to all cities, but overwhelmingly to a few major cities. The main population concentrations today are on the eastern seaboard, around the Great Lakes and in California. Already some 38 million people live on the coastal strip from New Hampshire to northern Virginia, representing 2 percent of the total United States population concentrated into 1.8 percent of its area. At present rates of growth, it is estimated that by the year 2000 the population of the same area will have reached some 100–120 million people.

When we face predictions of this kind it would be as well to ask what changes in urban form as we know it today will result from such population pressures. It is a common fault to think that tomorrow's cities will retain their present form—and gradually strangle themselves in a combined density of automobiles and people. This is complete nonsense. Modern mobility and communications systems, among several other technological factors of far-reaching significance, have set the major cities of today on paths of evolution which make them categorically different from the cities

9. During the World Food Congress, June 1963, it was stated: "Every day of this week some 10,000 will die of malnutrition or starvation. In India alone, 50 million children will die of malnutrition in the next ten years. More than half of the world's 3 billion live in perpetual hunger." *World Design Science Decade, 1965–1975*, Document 4, by John McHale (Carbondale: Southern Illinois University, 1965).
10. President Lyndon B. Johnson, "Message on Cities" to the US Senate and Congress, *Congrssional Record*, vol. 111, no. 39 (March 2, 1965), pp. 2312–2316.

of the past. Traditionally, for the last five thousand years, since the Sumerian civilization, when Mesopotamian man first began to live in urban settlements, cities have been concentrations of great insularity, intricate, teeming and compact, in powerful juxtaposition to the countryside surrounding them. They were closed-form cities—autonomous, mononuclear and culturally insular. To some extent the great cities of the United States eastern seaboard—Boston, New York, Philadelphia, Baltimore and Washington—still function in this traditional way. Each has a metropolitan center which acts as a generator and concentrator of complex vibrant activity, to which men and women in their hundreds of thousands commute daily from dormitory areas. In fact the optimum size of a metropolis is often given, not in mileage or even population, but in maximum commuter time, say fifty minutes, from the edge of the city to its core. Thus although suburbia may represent for us our connection with an immediate rural past, the extent of suburbia, and hence of the metropolis itself, is controlled somewhat ironically by distance in travel time from the traditional core of the city. And here lies one critical factor in the evolution of urban form. Improving mobility systems (the construction of more in-city rapid transit systems, airports with larger passenger capacities, more controlled-access parkways with high speed limits) means continued suburban expansion without increases in commuter time. And continued expansion, in population, commerce, traffic, and so forth, increases the congestion of the mononuclear city—decimating it with more and more distribution lanes, and threatening to bring about its ultimate strangulation.

But cities in our age of unprecedented dynamism are no longer autonomous and self-sufficient. This implicitly inward-looking, insular form of the single-center city is in conflict with the dynamism of modern mobility and communication systems. The United States as a whole has become a complex network of communications and services; and every major city, and thus every citizen, is a component of this intricate network—connected by telephones and television, power grids and consumer production, airways and highways, and in the not too distant future by systems of interstate rapid transit at projected speeds of up to 1,000 m.p.h. We will soon reach the point where there will be one automobile on our highways to every adult of the national population. In some states this figure has already been surpassed, the product of some 500 billion dollars in automotive industrial investment. Indeed within ten years it is expected that some 225 million people will use 80 million automobiles in this country's urban areas.[11] The immediately visible and undigested effects are, of course, the huge throughways and interchanges which ram through the metropolitan fabric, the

11. Charles Abrams, *The City is the Frontier* (New York: Harper & Row, 1965), p. 14.

disproportionate percentages of valuable land absorbed by parking lots in central areas, and the city streets whose flow capacities are frequently more than halved by parked cars. But the revolution in urban structure is profound and absolute. For the speed of travel and of other communication networks have so altered the time/space demensions of geographic distance— both national and international—that they have undermined, and will ultimately destroy, the fixed, closed forms of our single-center cities.

As our major cities get larger, their traditional autonomy and self-sufficiency decrease, for urban autonomy and self-sufficiency are contradictory to the complex and rapidly developing networks of communications,

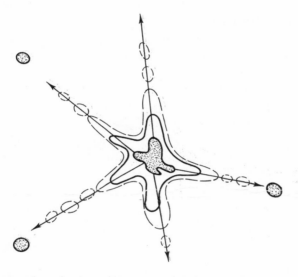

Typical radial expansion of metropolitan areas along transportation routes, towards and ultimately absorbing traditionally independent satellite towns and cities as well as new suburban estates in a species of urban form peculiar to our age, the open-form, multinuclear and multidirectional city, infinitely additive and variable in its capacity for growth and change.

services, and distribution of specialist products on which they increasingly depend, and to which they themselves contribute. The closed urban form, the finite and mononuclear city of tradition, gives way to a new species of urban form in which the basic factor is mobility; an open-form, multinuclear, multidirectional city—a city which is infinitely additive and infinitely variable in its capacity for growth and change.

Although the new form has not yet been achieved, its main characteristics are already everywhere apparent. An optimum commuting time may be fifty minutes; but the more fluent and faster a city's multidirectional highway and rapid transit systems, the greater will its geographic as well as its population expansion become. In every major city, corporations, department stores, small shops, industries, and high-rise apartments are decentralizing. One reason is the difficulty and deteriorating economics of circulation in the central areas. It was estimated in 1962 that some five billion dollars is lost every year in rush hour traffic jams.[12] Another is the high cost of land and of increasing taxation in the center city, compared with cheaper easily available land and special tax inducements or hidden subsidies, offered by the metropolitan counties. Yet a further reason is the decentralization of middle and upper middle income groups to suburban housing estates, from which much employment in light and research industry and management are drawn. In the decade 1950–1960 three-quarters of all metropolitan growth occurred outside the 'center city, and nine out of eleven of the largest cities declined in population to their metropolitan suburban areas,[13] as the demand of two-automobile families for split-levels, on half-acre lots, within easy reach of a super highway, remains undiminished. Most of this decentralization is at the moment wasteful and haphazard. Suburban estates each have their drive-in shopping center, to which you cruise along your six-lane highway. Once a suburban drive-in has been located, it becomes the focus for the almost arbitrary development of gas stations, motels, restaurants, light industries, decentralized office structures and so forth, with discordant architecture and graphics, to say nothing of resultant traffic and service entanglement. Yet it does not take a feat of imagination to visualize these facilities put together, in one project area, in properly considered and fluent relation to the economics of distribution, servicing, mobility, and land values. If one thinks of an assortment of facilities such as, for example, education, government offices, department stores, shops, motels, and high density housing, to name but a few, and if one thinks of the things they share rather than their points of difference, one will see straight away that underlying their dissimilarity there is a whole series of things they have in common—for example, the circulation and distribution of people, the circulation and storage of vehicles, the distribution of freight, their lines of water, power, communications and so forth. And it is then possible to go one stage further, and conceive of an engineering structure being designed which would house all of these common factors—a common linking structure (or "infrastructure") into which each building with its particularized use can then be hooked.

In some cities, structures of this kind are already being built. In the central areas of Philadelphia, passenger concourses serving mass transit

---

12. *Report, on H.R.* 11158, House Committee on Banking and Currency, 87th Congress, Second Session, July 3, 1962, cited by Charles Abrams, *ibid.*, p. 11.
13. Charles Abrams, *The City is the Frontier, op. cit.*, p. 8.

lines, and multi-deck parking structures, form the common structure on which multiple shopping and office structures are based. A recent announcement from New York indicates that new education complexes of considerable size will be based on parking structures below them, whilst air rights above will be leased or sold for offices and high density housing. New plans for

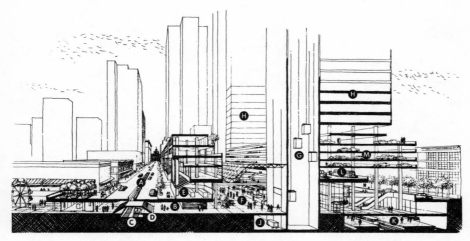

The San Francisco office of Skidmore, Owings & Merrill made an intensive one-year study of Market Street, Philadelphia, in 1965/6. This sectional perspective shows Market Street as a wide shopping artery with a multilevel spine on its northern side. The street is a vehicular platform (A) over a main level of pedestrian activity (B) and subway tracks (C). At this concourse level bridges (D) lead to shops and spaces on the south side of Market. The new buildings on the north side (E) contain shops and offices, and a wide glass-roofed pedestrian mall (F). Office towers (H) are served by freight elevator shafts (G) which rise from service bays (J) which, like the commuter railroad lines and concourses (K), are at subsurface levels. Parking decks and bus terminals are in structures above the passenger concourses (L) and (M). (Courtesy: Architectural Forum).

education centers in Pittsburgh intend to integrate cultural and commercial facilities, housing and government offices, in structures based on transit. In the new city of Cumbernauld, Scotland, the central areas are virtually a single multi-deck structure, nearly a half mile in length, which includes most of the multiple functions of a true urban core—civic administration, law courts, corporation and professional offices, hotels, shops and markets, a central library, auditoria and cinemas, and high-density housing, in a complex interplay of spaces. Built astride a highway and parking decks, on the principle of the complete separation of pedestrians from traffic, it is a structure conceived specifically as a rational, intricate, vibrant and dense place of human exchange.

The first large suburban drive-ins came into operation just over a decade ago. By 1963 they were doing more than a third of the nation's

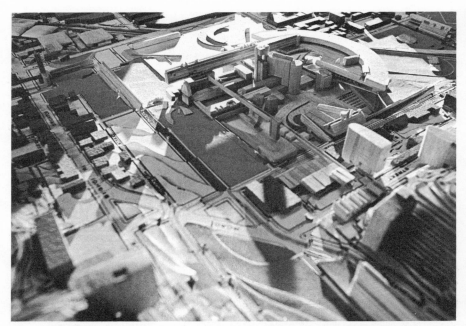

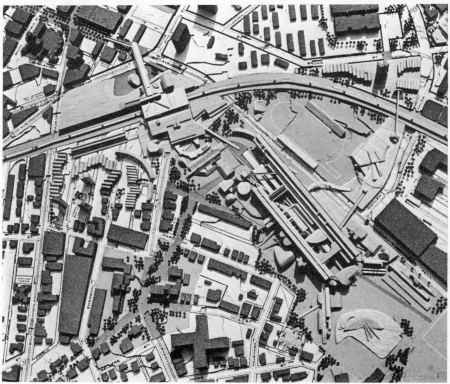

retail business. At first, because wide acres of farmland outside dense cities were transformed suddenly into choice available land for development by the construction of limited access highways with great cloverleaf intersections, the economics of the first drive-ins dictated a pedestrian shopping island, square or L-shaped in configuration, with a sea of asphalt surrounding it for parking and service. But, as we have already pointed out, once a suburban shopping center has been located, it becomes the focus for other development. Northland, outside Detroit, to cite as an example one of the best

The first phases of the central areas of the new city, Cumbernauld, in Scotland, are shown here under construction. This multideck structure, built to use the air rights over traffic routes and parking decks, will be nearly half a mile in length when complete and will contain most of the multiple functions of a true urban core. Designer: Geoffrey Copcutt.

## CAPTION TO PHOTOGRAPHS OPPOSITE

The plans for new education centers in Pittsburgh include five Great High Schools, with 5,000 students in each. These education centers are each conceived as a new and integrated cultural/commercial sub-core of the inner city and designed to serve a residential urban population of 120,000. Illustrated here are the urban designs for Northside (A) and East Liberty (B) in Pittsburgh; using air rights over traffic routes and parking decks, each includes housing, commercial areas, and cultural facilities such as theaters, galleries and auditoria in addition to its large-scale education facilities. (Designers: Geoffrey Copcutt, David Lewis and James N. Porter of Urban Design Associates.)

designed[14] of the earlier large shopping centers, has become the focus of suburban housing estates, decentralizing corporations—Reynolds Aluminum, for example, is there, with a spectacular building by Minoru Yamasaki shining brightly in the sun—motels, gas stations and the rest. As a result,

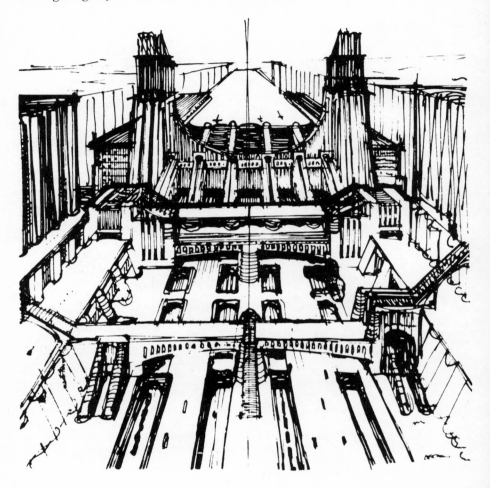

Antonio Sant' Elia. Stazioni Aeroplani, 1912, a drawing from the Citta Nuova series showing tall buildings linked by pedestrian decks and bridges, rising above several traffic and railroad levels, with an airport in the background.

land prices, responding immediately to this situation, are beginning to force into design and construction in the United States the first compact and integrated multilevel park-and-shop structures in suburban situations. And developers in turn, responding to the tendency towards multioperational

14. Northland, Detroit, was designed by Victor Gruen Associates.

cluster, are beginning to offer total centers as a combined package, in which
not just shopping but offices, motels and so forth are built into a multideck
air-conditioned structure, which is based on integrated traffic access,
parking decks, service bays, and utilities, as a single design. It now takes
only one further step for us to recognize the decentralized urban cores of
the future in these multilevel centers, with their air-conditioned pedestrian
decks, and landscaped plazas, segregated from the traffic ramps, parking
decks, and rapid transit concourses below; and that the mononuclear metro-

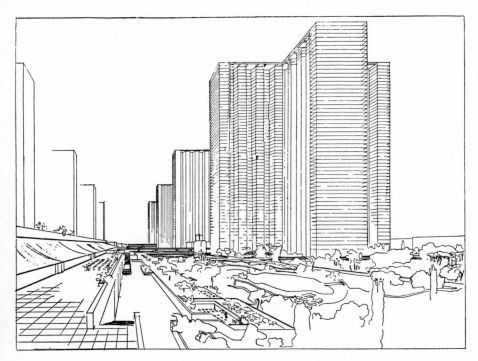

Le Corbusier. Ville Radieuse, 1924/5. This drawing shows tall blocks rising from parkland
and pedestrian squares and bridges which, by using air rights over fast traffic ways, continue
unbroken the residential/pedestrian texture of the city. The pedestrian squares and bridges
have restaurants, entertainments, and shopping precincts, and are landscaped.

poli of recent tradition are currently dissolving into new multinuclear forms.

Historians of architecture will quickly recognize the irony of how
close to the classic, early modern movement theories of Sant' Elia and Le
Corbusier this idea essentially is. Sant' Elia's series of drawings for the
Citta Nuova, from 1912–1914, show a city core conceived in several pedes-
train decks. Skyscraper blocks rise through these decks, and below there are
elevated railroads and automobile highways. His designs even include an
airport, a remarkably early premonition of the dynamic role of air travel

in the evolution of urban form. The influence of Sant' Elia, who was killed in the First World War, on Le Corbusier's Ville Radieuse is well known. In the early 1920's Le Corbusier was working in a strictly axial classicism, and pioneering the clear sharp architectural forms which reflected the machine tooling and production of the 1920–1940 period. In his 1924 Ville Radieuse drawings, traffic flows freely and swiftly along divided highways beneath pedestrian bridges and plazas at various levels. These bridges and plazas, conceived on the principle of complete traffic/pedestrian segregation, are really the urban squares of the old city, translated into modern usage, with restaurants and cafes, shops and theaters, and land-

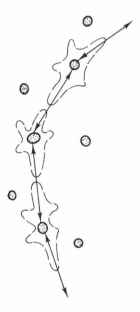

A federation of previously separate metropoli form a megalopolitan corridor, with satellites and new cities in conserved countryside as part of the linear megalopolitan system.

scaping. And above these plazas—on columns so that the pedestrian city is not impeded—rise gigantic glass-walled towers. And like Sant' Elia, Le Corbusier includes an airport.

The major metropolitan form we can see clearly emerging, then, has not one center but several. These centers are linked to each other by highway and rapid transit networks, and by other forms of communication such as shortwave radio and telephones and closed circuit television. Gradually a federation of interdependent cores, linked by fluent communications and fast distribution systems, is replacing the mononuclear form of the past. And as urbanization proceeds and the population of the metropolis grows, further cores will be added to the system, most probably in the form of new cities or satellites, designed to optimum sizes, and surrounded by countryside conserved for leisure. This is somewhat the process which Jean Gottman described when he coined the word "megalopolis,"[15] applied to the currently developing urban form of the United States east coast. As we have already remarked, today's population of some 38 million living on the coastal strip from New Hampshire to northern Virginia, representing 21 percent of the total United States population, is expected to increase to 100–120 million by the year 2000. The traditional mononuclear form of Washington and Baltimore, Newark and New York, is dissolving as these cities expand. In this particular case their form of expansion tends to be linear—because their most powerful communication links are in a north-south coastal strip rather than radial, and their centers are interconnected with fast traffic corridors such as highways, air corridors and the new North East Corridor rail rapid transit system. As a result, these cities are rapidly growing towards each other. A new urban form is evolving which might be expected to mature within a generation, in which these once separate metropoli are being merged into one super-city. The once independent cores such as Manhattan or downtown Philadelphia are becoming interdependent cores in the new megalopolitan urban structure. The tendency is thus toward a gigantic urban form, radial or linear, based on an attenuated network of communication systems, with high-density nodes at the interstices. And the current form of the metropolis, in which a commuter, living on its suburban edge, might spend 40 or 45 minutes in travel time to reach the city center, now gives way to a new concept in which that same commuter, living between two, or more, city cores, might spend a maximum of 40 or 45 minutes in travel time to reach a central area in any two or more alternative directions. Already in our current technology we have mastered the major problem of providing a continuous and unbroken microclimate, constantly agreeable summer and winter, across the entire city. From our thermostatically controlled, air-conditioned, centrally heated and equably humidified colonial farmhouses in the city, we may bowl along limited access highways in our private air-conditioned maximum visibility bubbles at 60 m.p.h., accompanied by a full orchestra, and arrive in the parking decks of our multideck air-conditioned, pedestrian/traffic segregated urban centers, for work, education, shopping or culture, without even venturing into the open air!

The importance of this open, multidirectional urban form is that it promises to be much more efficient, and adaptable to change, than the

15. *Megalopolis. The Urbanized Northeastern Seaboard of the United States,* by Jean Gottman (Boston: M.I.T. Press, 1961).

mononuclear form which it is replacing. For no longer is metropolitan size controlled (or restricted) in its growth by the capacity of its central areas. The increasing loads implied by growth and change are distributed within the infinitely additive metropolitan network of cores. And not only are the cores themselves interconnected by rapid and fluent transportation, but so, too, are the residential sectors they serve. Aristotle thought that the ideal city should be limited to 5,000 inhabitants, so that everyone would know everyone else, and the adult male population could have a direct voice in government and policy. Some of the most perfectly planned cities of Greek antiquity, such as Priene on the Greek mainland and Miletus in Asia Minor, were small like this, in which every relationship, from small domestic rooms and colonnaded courts to the civic areas of the temple and the agora, formed a sophisticated sequence and implicit unity of space and scale. In our own time, cities of five to ten million inhabitants have become commonplace.[16] But accompanying the sheer geographic size of cities comes the phenomenon of mobility and speed, providing wholly new space/time dimensions, with their profound impacts not only on the physical forms of cities but on social and kinship patterns as well.

A generation ago the average American travelled locally, hardly ever internationally. Today the gross number of passenger air-miles travelled grows in hundreds of millions annually. Since 1961 commercial US airlines have shown an average continental increase of 13 percent per year, an intercontinental increase of 20 percent per year, and an increase of 26 percent per year on local feeder lines. In the current year commerical airlines will make some seven million scheduled flights from 600 airfields. And then there are 120,000 private planes on 5,000 additional airfields, owned by corporations, engineers, farmers, salesmen and sportsmen.[17] Within a generation, space travel may be more common than supersonic travel is today. For we have only to recall that Lindbergh's classic flight across the Atlantic occurred less than forty years ago at speeds averaging less than 100 m.p.h.; and that the first commercial use of jets occurred only eight years ago, bringing flight speeds up to 600–700 m.p.h., even on short-haul runs, with 200 passengers seated in soft air-conditioned comfort munching snacks and watching movies. Multidirectional options are a fact of today's life, in leisure as in work, over short distances and long. Theaters like Stratford, Ontario, play nightly to international audiences. In winter hundreds of thousands of leisure seekers exercise the option of skiing in

16. The vast increases in human population notwithstanding, "from 1800 to 1950, the proportion of people living in cities of more than 20,000 leaped from 2.4 percent to 21 percent." Charles Abrams, *The City is the Frontier*, op. cit., p. 3.

17. "Will Air Transportation Improve?", H. Guyford Stever, Carnegie Conference, Pittsburgh, June 4, 1966.

Vermont or skindiving in the Caribbean. As Hans Blumenfeld has pointed out, one of the radical changes which mobility has brought about in urban living is that the city is no longer the only focus for sport, entertainment and culture.[18] This is not only true of the city's relation to the country, but also of the country's relation to cities. For as agriculture becomes increasingly mechanized and operated on industrial-corporate principles and as low-income agricultural populations decrease, the pastoral focus is no longer the local market town, but a choice of cities, within reach by highway and air. The dichotomy of country and city is dissolving as urban form begins to enclose vast tracts of countryside in its mobility web, and as urban management methods envelope man's earliest and most traditional industry. And in the cities themselves job mobility and transience, particularly at management levels, are already so much the order of our day that in seventy major United States cities, including New York, average residence is less than four years.

The structural effect is a lattice of communication on a national scale;[19] a macrocosm of the metropolitan network which I have attempted to describe. At the interstices of the lattice are major cities, just as there are cores and sub-cores at the interstices of the lattice in the metropolitan scale. Physically, urban man may belong to a neighborhood focussed on its own urban core. But his professional, kinship and friendship patterns are maintained over thousands of miles. Aristotle's notion of an acquaintance-ship of 5,000 is probably still maintained in everyman's experience—not within the geographic boundaries of a single community, but across the city, the nation and even intercontinentally. Communications and mobility extend urban man's vocabulary of options. These options will continue to compound. The nearest urban core may be the one in which he shops for food; but he may shop for clothes in another, for books in yet another; and his favorite restaurants may be dispersed throughout the city or be located fifty miles away in the countryside. Unfortunately, the social and urban forms corresponding to these characteristics are basically different from the contemporary conceptions of most urban designers and planners. The need

18. "The Modern Metropolis," by Hans Blumenfeld, *Scientific American*, vol. 213, no. 3 (September 1965), p. 64 ff.
19. "In a traditional society, if we ask a man to name his best friends and then ask each of these in turn to name their best friends, they will all name each other so that they form a closed group. A village is made of a number of separate closed groups of this kind. But today's social structure is utterly different. If we ask a man to name his friends and then ask them in turn to name their friends, they will all name different people, very likely unknown to the first person; these people would again name others, and so on outwards. There are virtually no closed groups of people in modern society. The reality of today's social structure is thick with overlap—the systems of friends and acquaintances form a semi-lattice, not a tree." "A City is Not a Tree," by Christopher Alexander, *Design*, no. 206 (1966), p. 51; also *Architectural Forum*, April and May 1965.

for the construction of new cities, for example, is now widely recognized.[20] Reston, the new city outside Washington, has caught most of the news as the first planned settlement in the United States for 350 years. Others, such as Columbia in Maryland, and various new city projects in Arizona and California, are on the way. Although these new cities are each located as part of a metropolitan constellation, they are conceived as self-sufficient. Yet the larger physical, economic and cultural realities of today all point in the opposite direction. Cities are no longer autonomous in this way. Estimates show that passenger air travel, inside the United States alone, will double in ten years, and gross freight distribution by air will double in seven years. And these estimates are likely to be conservative. STOL (Short Takeoff and Landing) and VTOL (Vertical Takeoff and Landing) aircraft will soon be in commercial use for short runs and long. VTOL particularly—an aircraft capable like helicopters of landing in restricted areas but, once in flight, of performing with the speeds and capacities of the usual turboprop and smaller jets—will certainly even further promote the direct interrelation of new cities and satellites with major cities, and major cities with each other.[21] At airports and terminals themselves three-dimensional radar, and computer-aided techniques for landing aircraft and getting them in the air, computerization of passenger and freight handling, and the increasingly automated solution of interface problems, will all step up the speed and efficiency of getting from plane to destination with telling effects on volumes and time/distance ratios. Meanwhile, within our present technological capability, fully automated and air-conditioned rapid transit cars, running silently on elevated guideways and with headways controlled by computers, can make all intra-city and corridor nodal links at high speeds and rush hour volumes; while related technologies applied to automobiles and to highway engineering are just round the corner. The effect is a fundamentally new space/time dynamic, open-ended and continuous, peculiar to our period,

20. "The Case for Building 350 New Towns," by Wolf von Eckhardt, *Harpers Magazine*, December 1965, pp. 85 ff.

21. "Straight helicopters, compound helicopters, as well as lift engine, fan-in-wing, tilt engine and tilt wing VTOL and STOL aircraft are being tried for important roles in the military battlefield and near battlefield transportation. Most of the technical points which are important for future civil aviation are being developed for these military projects. As successes of certain models become apparent, civil aviation will be able to use them, or reasonable modifications—helicopters for intra-city and short-range intercity transportation, and more advanced VTOL aircraft for longer-range feeder lines. It is my opinion that this area is not being neglected in the development of aircraft. I do believe that as the VTOL aircraft are developed, the air traffic control system must be prepared to incorporate them in its total transportation picture. And I also think that Congress should study ways to encourage airline operators, or entirely new entrepreneurs, possibly by subsidies, possibly by changes in regulations, to try some experiments in actual VTOL transport companies. This could easily be an important part of the Northeast Corridor—Boston/New York/Washington high speed transport experiment." H. Guyford Stever, *op. cit.*

with ramifications at profound social and cultural levels as well as in our personal lives, replacing the old conception of life (and urban form) as discontinuous, self-sufficient and contained.

This acceleration of development in the technologies of mobility and communications is, of course, matched by similar accelerations in several other technologies. As John McHale says, the integration "of scientific discovery into engineered application has progressively shortened as industrialization has developed its momentum—the steam engine took about 100 years to full application; electricity less than 50 years; the internal combustion engine under 30 years; the vacuum tube only 15 years; and present developments in electronics, plastics, etc., are integrated within less than a year."[22] But not only is the integration of scientific knowledge into industrial production accelerating; acceleration in the processes and marketing of industrial output compound the impact of new knowledge and new formalities of interrelationship in swift progressions, the ramifications of which we can only vaguely guess. "Consider, for example, what is happening in certain fields, as typified, say, by the high-energy accelerators of modern physics. . . . In the late 1920's, atomic particles could be accelerated to roughly 500 thousand electron-volts of energy. Successive inventions raised the limit to about 20 million volts in the 1930's; to 500 million by about 1950; and to 30 billion by the 1960's. Today one machine under construction is designed for 50 billion volts."[23] It is now twenty years since the first electronic computer went into operation. Today there are 30,000 in the United States alone, the fastest of which can compute a million times more quickly than a skilled arithmetician. "Compared with the computers of a decade ago, today's machines are about a hundred times faster, their electronic portions a hundred times smaller, and most important, the cost of carrying out a given information-processing task is as much as 1,000 times less expensive. These advances will probably be matched in the next decade. . . ." thus providing today a thousand times as much computing power as existed ten years ago, and forecasting a million times as much ten years from now.[24] One of the most hopeful factors in the world today is the implicit internationalism of scientific knowledge. The impact of these dynamic or exponential progressions on the cultures of the world— bringing them rapidly, if at the present time unequally, into a single cultural family—is ensured by the speed of development in our communications and mobility systems. It seems incredible that today when astronauts circle the earth at almost 20,000 m.p.h. there are many men alive who saw,

22. John McHale, *op. cit.*
23. *The Step to Man*, by John R. Platt, Professor of Biophysics and Physics, University of Chicago, quoted by John McHale, *op. cit.*
24. Paul Armer, "What will the Computer do Next?" in *The Computer and Society, op. cit.*

and even flew, the earliest flying machines. Men and materials are but a few hours distant from the farthest points on our globe; and spoken and visual communications are capable of instantaneous transmission throughout the world via Telstar satellites. But the profounder impact is that of the tools themselves, the machinery and its products which acknowledge no national boundaries and which transform natural resources into a growing international language of physical production and consumption from the largest to the smallest scale. And the importance of these progressions is that many of them imply an intricate and systematic chain-coordination of men and minds in, as Buckminster Fuller has said, not local but "universal patterns or networks."[25]

The opportunities are obvious. But the hurdles are also formidable. It is as well to bear in mind that the differentials in man's development have at no time in history been so vast. At this moment, there are Stone Age societies extant to whom the wheel and the raw beginnings of agriculture are unknown. Yet this is not the most important differential. Far more important is the fact that the low-income populations who are flooding into cities are aware of how the affluent and socially privileged live, and aware of the universality of the technological culture now being created; yet they are faced with conditions which thwart their cultural transition and integration, bringing nearer and nearer the social and political disaster which must surely spring from the widening gap between the "haves" and the multitudinous rapidly procreating "have-nots" of the world. As recent race riots in major metropolitan centers in the United States testify, the underdeveloped countries have no monopoly of this circumstance. In contrast to the major cities of the underdeveloped countries and their peripheral slums of appalling poverty, cities in the United States are surrounded by suburban ranch houses gleaming brightly in the sun. But in virtually every large city in the United States, as in Europe, the central areas are encircled or perforated with slums. Low-income Negro populations, a high percentage of whom is rural in origin, have moved into the decaying but once expensive townhouse/residential streets of fifty years ago, which have been vacated by middle- and higher-income groups who have moved perpetually outward with suburban extension. Today large tracts of would-be prime real estate in the centers of cities are devastated by slums. According to the 1960 Census of Housing there were 58 million units in the nation as a whole, of which 15.7 million were substandard, mostly in cities and affecting some 47 million people. These central city slums, most of which

25. John McHale, *op. cit.*; see also "The Design Initiative" by Buckminster Fuller, *World Design Science Decade 1965–1975*, Document 2 (Carbondale: Southern Illinois University Press, 1963).

are tenements controlled by absentee landlords, are expanding racial ghettos in which the geographic or man-made configurations of traditional urban neighborhoods—valleys, parks railways, or highways—become boundaries reinforced by the innumerable permutations of social circumscription. Migration from the south due to agricultural lay-off and racial pressures has been such that Negro populations in the north have more than doubled since 1940. "By 1960 the central cities of the twelve largest metropolitan areas accounted for 24 percent of all United States Negroes. The migration saw Negroes become 29 percent of Detroit's and Cleveland's population, 35 percent of Baltimore's, a quarter of Philadelphia's, 34 percent of Newark's, and 55 percent of Washington, D.C.'s. New York City's Negro population held to 15 percent of total in 1960, largely because of the in-migration of Puerto Ricans, who began pouring in after 1940 and competed with the Negro for the available jobs. Some 10.3 million or more than half the (total) nonwhite population lived in the central cities in 1960; this represented a gain of 63 percent in a decade."[26] But simultaneously with this in-migration of Negroes, whites were moving to the suburbs. According to the 1960 Census of Housing less than a third of the nation's urban whites were living in the central areas. The effects are clearly shown in public school enrollments. During the past twenty-five years the number of Negro children in public schools in Chicago has risen from 9 percent to 51 percent; in New York City from 8 percent to 47 percent; and in Pittsburgh from 14 percent to 37 percent. In Washington, D.C., the ratio of Negro children to white in public schools has already reached almost 9 to 1. With more and more whites sending their children to private schools or migrating to suburban areas, the segregation process is gradually overtaking education. In Pittsburgh, for example, the number of *de facto* segregated schools has risen from eight to nineteen in the last fifteen years. A series of chain reactions is set up. One of these is the difficulty of obtaining competent and dedicated teachers in these declining environments, and under culturally destructive social pressures. In 1960, 47 percent of all United States Negroes over twenty-five years of age had less than an 8th-grade education. It is hardly surprising that while 47 percent of all employed whites were in white collar jobs, only 17 percent of all employed Negroes earned their living comparably. Thus the median income for Negro families in 1963 stood at $3,465 per annum, compared with $6,548 for white families, and the unemployment rate for Negroes was double that of whites.[27] Today, in our major cities, 80–95 percent of Negroes are residentially segregated, in conditions of obsolescence, circumscription, and hopelessness.

26. Charles Abrams, *The City is the Frontier, op. cit.*, pp. 54, 55.
27. Charles Abrams, *ibid.*, pp. 56, 57.

It is difficult to see how the problem of the vast urban populations currently living without adequate shelter or in conditions of large-scale urban obsolescence can possibly be dealt with unless heavy increases in gross output, and more rapid advances in the technical fields of materials, and tooling for industrialized component production and mechanized construction, are made on national and international scales.[28] However, to equate technical solutions with total solutions is a dangerous and inhuman oversimplification. What industry and science are able to put into our hands are tools—but not the ability to create urban forms or through these to express our value judgments. There can hardly be any doubt, for example, that mobility renders circumscription in the city obsolete. Mobility and communications presuppose urban forms in which man is brought in relation to man in a complementary and ever closer network of inter-dependence that has much to say in the fields of human social relationship. The modern civil rights movement is forcing open housing and job opportunities.

Several cities are moving towards more enlightened education policies. The Pittsburgh plan illustrated in these pages involves the construction of five Great High Schools, each of 5 to 6,000 students, to be placed in "neutral" areas between white and Negro ghettos and with service areas so large that integration is inevitable, based on mobility systems. And these education centers will contain not simply schools, but shops, offices, museums and art galleries, theaters and sports facilities, and public open spaces, based on highways, rapid transit concourses and parking decks, a new and integrated focus for hitherto segregated communities. In the words of President Johnson: "Tomorrow's school will be a school without walls—a school built of doors which open to the entire community. To-morrow's school will reach out to the places that enrich the human spirit—to the museums, the theaters, the art galleries, to the parks, rivers and mountains. It will ally itself with the city, its busy streets and factories, its assembly lines and laboratories—so that the world of work does not seem

28. "According to the 1960 Census of Housing, about 6.3 million households with incomes under $4,000, and an additional 2.2 million households with incomes over $4,000, lived in units needing complete replacement. There are approximately 1.5 million new housing units built each year, but population growth, demolition of old structures, migration to other sectors of the country, and other losses account for almost all of this construction. Even if we were to increase production by over 30 percent, a majority of the 8.5 million substandard units would still be standing by 1970. If the housing needs of moderate income families are to be met and a high volume of housing production is to be sustained, then what is needed now is a direct attack on reducing housing costs through exploration of advanced technological potential. Recent years have seen many improvements in building materials, but few in building techniques. . . . It is clear that we cannot adequately rehouse America by existing methods. This can be done only if advanced production techniques are introduced." From *Report of the National Commission on Technology, Automation, and Economic Progress*, February, 1966.

an alien place for the student. Tomorrow's school will be the center of community life, for grownups as well as children—a shopping center of human services."[29] Facilities of this kind, large nodes linked across the city by mobility networks, are in fact the fundamental restructuring devices which are central to the mainstream of the modern developing city. And urban design then becomes the art of creating, from these complex strands of evolutionary development—some of them physical, in the form of large-scale engineering infrastructures, some of them economic and statistical, some of them institutional in the form of government and administration, some of them spiritual in the form of social aspiration—the detailed three-dimensional shape of our evolving cities.

There is not a city in the world whose form can be prejudged. Every city is a living organism, with its own past and its own peculiar evolution. Our widespread recognition of the need for urban design is recognition of the need for men able to comprehend the complex process of cities in rapid change, and to give shape to their evolution. The role of the urban designer is a patient and dual process of research, and the wholly fresh discovery of appropriate form. Technology, mobility, communications, indicative of the intricate twentieth century language of the developing global family of mankind, have put our cities on paths of evolution categorically different from the cities of the past. The problems from which the designer must create the new urban form of the world's cities are immeasurably larger than any previous constructional problems in history, but programmatically they are highly particularized, and are more than matched by our technological capacity. Yet no matter how large these problems are, the urban form itself must still be the product of the most careful and detailed three-dimensional design. For on this depends the very quality of urban life itself.

29. Address by Lyndon Baines Johnson to the American Association of School Administrators, Atlantic City, February 16, 1966.

# THE POWER OF TECHNOLOGY

# Challenges for urban policy

## *Leland Hazard*

The discussion in this article occurs within the general frame of a theme: The Impact on American Values of the Current Revolution in Science and Technology. The project is guided by philosophers, something new in a century in which philosophy has been relegated to a discipline other than economics, social or political science, psychology, and anthropology—if any such *other* can be—in an age of fragmented learning.

The key phrase in the general theme is "current revolution," since that phrase implies that there is some aspect or characteristic of present science and technology which has an impact of unique significance for our American complex of values. Rapid transportation, in the air, on water, and on land; television, in which I include global, instantaneous transmission of mass messages as well as video telephone for private communications; the computer, by which I mean a closed system of electronic controls, managing mechanisms without human intervention, to produce goods, retrieve information, make decisions and judgments for the direction of society; and contraceptives, those suitable for mass employment by females (without the exercise of repetitive volitions), such as the coil or a comparable one-time technique—certainly these technologies are having an impact on American values. That is truism. But is the impact unique in our time in comparison with the impact of technology in other times?

Whether these four current technologies which I shall discuss—and there are obviously others of major significance—are impacting upon values in America today in a more revolutionary way than earlier new technologies and climates of life impacted upon the then values, that is a question on which we may well pause. I assume that technology has always been and will ever be a prime factor in the conceptualization of individuated or named values.[1] Technology is a way of living, of being, perhaps of becoming. Technology is the tactic of living, to borrow Spengler's phrase. And William

1. This assumption will be sharply disputed. See LaPierre's arguments against technological determinism in *Social Change* (New York: McGraw-Hill, 1965), pp. 253 *et. seq.*; and McClelland's "Achievement as a Prime Factor in Economic Growth" in *The Achieving Society* (Princeton: D. Van Nostrand Company, Inc., 1961). [*Continued on p. 321*

James would agree—a value is a name for what works, what has utility.

If these propositions are of less than universal application in all terrestrial time and space, then, without prejudice to the general application, I confine them in this discussion to the Western World since the 16th century, in and following which Copernicus put the earth and man in diminished scale; Darwin (Wallace, too) described the conditions for quality of life; and Freud set limits to man's ability as an agent to employ resources to modify the course of events so as to attain his ends.

Western man, Faustian man, when he meets new technology, uses it—and from the ensuing benefits, rewards, and penalties constructs schemes of values, which, in turn, changing technology will rearrange on the scale, downgrading some, upgrading others. If there are values beyond the impact of changing technology, i.e., values which have arisen independently of the tactics of living, then we may leave them aside, because the object of this project is to identify the American values upon which the current revolution in science and technology is having, or may have by the year 2000, a downgrading or an upgrading impact.

Agriculture and the tool were revolutionary technological changes and prime movers in changing the climate and quality of life. It we take 600,000 years as the period in which true men have existed (if the period is longer, the argument remains the same), then the nomadic method of life occupied almost all of that time—all but the last 10,000 or 11,000 years. Agriculture was new technology. Whoever first saved the seeds, planted them, and then gathered the fruits of the plants began the change upon which all civilization, for better or for worse, is based. Mrs. Peachum put it well in "The Threepenny Opera":

> "Whatever you may do, wherever you aspire.
> First feed the face, and then talk right and wrong
> For even the saintliest folk may act like sinners
> Unless they've had their customary dinners. . . ."[2]

LaPierre says, " . . . it is only when and where, for whatever reasons, new beliefs, values, and ideas emerge and gain some currency that change in technology is likely to occur." *Op. cit.*, p. 271. He does give printing and the subsequent new media of communication credit for facilitating new technologies.

McLuhan, on the other hand, credits the new printing technology of the 16th century with creating individualism and nationalism. *Understanding Media: The Extension of Man* (New York, 1964: McGraw-Hill, Paperback Edition, 1965), pp. 19, 20.

Whether social changes, and hence changes in value magnitudes, occur when changes in ideology and organization come first and technology comes after as a consequence, or vice versa, as Ogburn would have it (see LaPierre's treatment of Ogburn in *op. cit.*, p. 31), may be forever a chicken and egg question. The same data are employed to reach opposing conclusions.

---

2. Kurt Weill, "The Threepenny Opera," English adaptation of lyrics by Marc Blitzstein; music by Kurt Weill, original lyrics by Bert (Bertolt) Brecht; as recorded by MGM from Production at Theatre de Lys, New York City.

The murder of Abel by Cain (*Genesis*, 4) could be part of the lore reflecting the primitive conflict between two technologies: The nomadic herding of domesticated animals (Abel) and the cultivation of domesticated plants (Cain). The account has it that the Lord had "respect" for Abel's offering of the "firstlings of the flock" but disrespect for Cain's offering of "the fruit of the ground." And so Cain in his frustration over reacted. The commentators have been so preoccupied with Cain's un-Christian question, "Am I my brother's keeper?" (probably a thoughtless question blurted out under pressure), that the deeper meaning of the myth—conflict of technologies—has not been sufficiently noticed. The drama of competing technologies, walking man versus riding man, would be re-enacted at any central city intersection today, if looks and curses could kill.

Whatever the impact of technology in today's complex societies, its original role, that is, the role of the tool, in the creation of man is emerging as speculatively crucial. It now appears that man-apes, able to run, but not to walk, on two legs, and with brains no larger than those of apes now living, had learned to use tools—sharp-edged stones found in nature—for digging or killing.[3] A contemporary anthropologist has observed chimpanzees picking up dried sticks and poking them into termite nests, then withdrawing them to lick off the clinging insects. If no sticks were available, the chimps have been seen to pull off a live twig, strip it of leaves (make a tool), and carry it as far as a half-mile before finding a termite nest.[4]

Pre-man suffered the dilemma of incompatibility of the hand tool and quadrupedalism. Induced by the advantages of the tool, he practiced slow motion (essential for hunting) on hind legs, tool in a forepaw (hand), until the long, straight pelvis of the ape, which provides support for quadrupedal locomotion, become the short, broad pelvis of man, which curves backward, carrying spine and torso in bipedal position. Washburn says that the fossil record substantiates the suggestion, first made by Charles Darwin, "that tool use is both the cause and effect of bipedal locomotion. . . . in the man-apes the beginnings of the human way of life depended on both inherited locomotor capacity and on the learned skills of tool using."[5]

My introduction, now nearing completion, might have been compressed to an assertion and a question: Since technology (tools) made man, could or can any technology ever have had or ever have a greater impact than that original prime intervention of technology to produce a new species

3. Sherwood L. Washburn, "Tools and Human Evolution," *Scientific American*, Vol. 203, No. 3 (September 1960), p. 63.
4. Jane Goodall, "My Life Among the Chimpanzees," *National Geographic Magazine*, Vol. 124 (August, 1963), pp. 272, 308.
5. Washburn, *op. cit.*, in footnote 3, pp. 67, 69.

of life? It may be that the concern underlying the theme of this project is that the "Current Revolution in Science and Technology" is *unmaking* man. But such a concern would assume that man is something apart from his techniques. His origin belies that assumption. Man is in and of his technology as his technology is in and of him.

This is not to say that men will stampede from old values individuated in the climate of life generated by some older technology and rush to new values deemed appropriate to some new technology. Quite the reverse. The value assessments appropriate to the new technology are not immediately obvious; and, in any case, there will be Ogburn's well-known cultural lag. "The ideology of a society, its body of symbolic constructs, is often more resistant to change than is its technology or organization. . . ."[6] But change will occur (new values for old or new orders of relative magnitudes of values) because "in the more economically successful countries, people have been trained to pay more attention to what other people are saying through mass media"[7]—an obvious consequence of technological change in means of communication.

Toynbee, relying heavily on Bergson, described society as a " 'field of action' but the source of all action is in the inidividuals composing it." The "creative personality," of whom there are but a tiny minority in any time, must "transfigure his fellow men into fellow creators by recreating them in his own image."[8]

The impact of technology is a critical, if not a prime, aspect of social change in the modern Western World. But society clings to old norms (values individuated in an earlier climate of life made largely by an earlier technology or absence of technology). New technologies demand changes in placement of old values on a new scale of value assessments. This will be accomplished by creative personalities—Carlyl's heroes, who, since urbanism is the dominant form of social organization in the contemporary world, must be found among city fathers rather than at the plow, under the tree, in the desert, or within monastery walls. Let us proceed, then, to the question: What new types of urban leaders will arise and what will (or should) they do creatively to guide the four new technologies which I shall discuss to a new climate of life and to that end, what types of values will be rearranged on the scale of value magnitudes?

For the purpose of discussing rapid transit and its antithesis, the private automobile, I take megalopolis to be a given. Whether the unit is New York-to-Washington, Boston-to-Norfolk, the five counties of Western

6. LaPierre, *op. cit.*, in footnote 1, p. 98.    7. McClelland, *op. cit.*, in footnote 1, p. 192.
8. Alfred J. Toynbee, *A Study of History*, Abridgment of Volumes I–VI by D. C. Somerwell (New York: Oxford University Press, 1947), p. 211 *et seq.*

Pennsylvania (with some of eastern Ohio included and Pittsburgh being the core), or any of such complexes anywhere—mobility is the essential. David Lewis in his contribution to this volume ably documents the new, open-ended urban form which can result from recent technological advances in urban planning. I agree with him that mobility is the *sine qua non* of the new urbanism. I might assign a lesser role to highways and to the meandering automobile and bus and a greater role to the rapid transit vehicle moving almost ubiquitously upon fixed rights-of-way. But I need not add to his excellent statement of why megalopolis is new in the world's history and why it is the prime challenge of the 20th century.

The automobile is the *bete noire* of mobility. It requires ten to fifteen times the space needed by any other means of ground lòcomotion, from human legs to any mass transit vehicle, per foot-person movement. By definition space is scarce in urbanism. Yet the automobile is as accepted in the American culture as apple pie and deodorants. Why?

Let us look at the values clustered about the automobile. Most of them will seem good enough until I detail the values which the automobile has downgraded. The values upgraded by the automobile are: one's own pleasure; economic security; convenience in style of life; self-fulfillment; self-reliance; power; freedom from interference (liberty); privacy; novelty; human dignity. The values downgraded by the automobile are: love and affection; friendship; reasonableness and rationality; prudence; devotion to family; conscientiousness; law and order; freedom from interference (liberty); service to others; natural beauty; culture; reverence for life.

Producers of automobiles, producers of concrete, highway departments, producers of gasoline, owners of automobile graveyards, filling stations, and motels will cheer the upgraded values and proclaim them as the eternal conditions of the good life. They will all disagree that any values *are* downgraded or will argue that the downgraded values are no longer values. In any case, they will argue that, even if in an automobile society some values are lost or are downgraded, the price is nevertheless not too high to pay for the gained or upgraded values. Proponents of mass-rapid transit to replace the private automobile in congested urban areas will be equally biased in favor of the second category of values.

It will be noted that I have included the "value of freedom from interference" in both the upgraded and the downgraded categories of values. This is intentional. The same technology may exert opposite effects upon the same value depending upon how the technical instrumentality is employed, or by whom, or whether it is available to all members of the society. This is true of the automobile to a special and easily demonstrated extent.

In a democratic world it is a proverb that liberty is not license. To quote Edmund Burke, "Liberty, too, must be limited in order to be possessed"; or J. S. Mill, "All that makes existence valuable to anyone depends upon the enforcement of restraints upon the action of other people." These are vaunted truisms about liberty, but the automobile has given its owner more liberty than his pedestrian fellow citizens. When man meets automobile, the machine prevails.

Even among automobile owners the manner of use determines whose liberty prevails. Drive your car along any important street of any city. The street was paved and is maintained at great expense to you and to all citizens so that automobiles may pass that way. Yet any single person with his 125 square feet of closed space and his 3,000 pounds of weight (contemporary man's fortress) may immobilize that street in whole or in substantial part, and does it time and time again. If you ever walk, pass along one of those streets at a rush hour and observe the expression on the faces of the automobilists dismounting to pick up a packet of pins, or a potted petunia, or a copy of *Naked Lunch*, immobilizing sometimes blocks of other motorists. The dismounted motorist's face will exhibit utter social unconcern. He has parked his castle, and other motorists cannot attack him without intolerable damage to their own castles.

Suppose you stopped the dismounted motorists and quoted William Hazlitt, "The love of liberty is the love of others; the love of power is the love of ourselves." The response would probably not be a question, "Who is Hazlitt?" No, your accosted automobilist would not ask about Hazlitt, being in no need of information beyond that which he already possesses, as Ortegay Gasset has pointed out.[9] He would, however, express the opinion that cities, streets, and stores should be so designed that he could drive his car right up to and alongside the pin counter. It does not matter whether the common man preceded the automobile or vice versa. For our purposes, which was cause and which effect we may disregard. The fact is that the automobile has so vastly enlarged the common man's capacity to implement his personal liberty that that value is either sharply upgraded or sharply downgraded, depending upon whether the instrumentality is possessed or not, and upon how it is used.

Presently, the American society has decided in favor of the values upgraded by the automobile unlimited, however the automobile may be used and whatever values are downgraded. The nonenforcement of parking regulations; the preemption of public streets for private, overnight parking; the failure to curb highway billboards, heavily used for automobile adver-

9. Jose Ortega y Gasset, *The Revolt of the Masses* (New York: W. W. Norton & Co., Inc., 1932), p. 97.

tising, or roadside automobile junkyards; the assumption that 50,000 automobile deaths per year are all caused by bad driving, never by unsafe cars; the fiction that because the states and federal government employ the taxing power to expropriate the gasoline tax to build highways, the users of automobiles are paying their own way (the gasoline tax does not pay for policing streets and highways, running traffic bureaus and traffic courts, providing morgues, hospital and ambulance services for the dead and injured)—the evidence is overwhelming that in the mid-twentieth century the American society is opiated by the automobile and that this folk addiction has been supported by whatever rationalization comes to hand. But the automobile unlimited is a recent aspect of American society. Actually, the automobile probably represents a self defeating technology and one which is so out of keeping with burgeoning urbanism that it will pass as a socially dominating factor as surely as the Beatles will pass.

The automobile will pass because it takes up too much space for what it does. It may not be possible to determine how many angels can dance on the point of a pin. That question may constitute as good a concept of infinity as any other exposition of that subject. But there is no uncertainty about how many motorized camels can pass through the eye of a municipal needle. For example, if all the people who enter Pittsburgh's Golden Triangle came by automobile at the national average of 1.5 persons per car, all of the space in the Triangle's approximately 374 acres, except a mere 16 acres, would be consumed by horizontal parking. If 700 car-parking stations were erected to provide vertical parking, so much space would be preempted that there would still be insufficient room for the institutions which bring people to the Triangle and, therefore, no point in coming.

The automobile has emphasized convenience in style of life. Its early impact was to create what is now becoming a delusion: that it is possible to go everywhere and anywhere sitting down. Incongruously, it will be new technologies of mass-rapid transit which will more nearly achieve the ideal of ubiquitous urban mobility than the self-canceling automobile technology. Our society has been so intensively preoccupied with what John Keats has called our insolent chariots that there has been literally almost no research in new means of mobility for urban areas. But there are signs on the horizon.

Steel wheels on steel rails carrying heavy cars up to 80,000 pounds in weight have been and are the technology for moving masses of people. For what that technology does is far more efficient than the automobile. An eight-lane freeway has a person-trip capacity of 9,000 at a capital cost of $1,600 per person. An express or local train has a person-trip capacity of 50,000 at a capital cost of $440 per person—five times the work at one-fourth the cost. But even so, the conventional mass-rapid technology does not do enough. Its weight, size, and noise confine it to more or less straight-line corridors, force it underground in the heart of urban centers, and preclude its negotiating the grades and curves necessary to an ubiquitous system. The conventional mass-rapid transit technology still requires the automobile or bus at the collection point in the urban periphery and underground installations at the discharge points at the urban heart.

A new transit technology is well advanced in theory and partially demonstrated in the Pittsburgh-Allegheny County area. The wheels are pneumatically rubber-tired and run on lightweight, concrete tracks. The cars, carrying thirty passengers (the cars could be smaller, carry fewer persons, and weigh less), now weigh only a fourth of the weight of conventional transit cars. Grades up to three times those possible for steel wheels on steel rails and curves far sharper than in a conventional system are feasible. The noise level is so low that in the existing demonstration the recording devices have not even registered. So this system can be integrated into office, apartment, hotel, and institutional buildings on the one hand and into residential areas on the other—at last truly ubiquitous facilities for urban mobility.

The essentials of the system are multiplicity of cars, operating on a network of exclusive rights-of-way, covering the urban area in spider-web form; continuous operations with spacing of cars or trains of cars in seconds or minutes; and the whole system computer controlled—no motorman, who, given electronic technology, is an anachronism from the days of the coach and four.

It is feasible to conceive computer procedures by which, as riders enter the system, they push destination buttons, which signal the central computer. If points of congestion show up at the computer, it orders more cars or orders slight detours of moving cars within the spider web, so that all cars keep moving; no one sits in frustrating immobility on an expressway or on a main line, and all arrive on schedule. It is feasible to conceive that there would be no such thing as missing the train. The computer receives your signal instantly, knows how soon a car or train will reach you, and will send for you specially, if necessary, within the time limits. If the program is that no passenger ever waits at any time of day, at any place, for more than two minutes, then the computer will keep that promise as no man could.

What impact on American values would ensue from such an innovation in urban transit technology? Upgraded would be: physical well-being and comfort (the experience of uninterrupted forward motion); for the same reason, convenience in style of life and self-respect; love and affection; friendship; reasonableness and rationality; conscientiousness; service to others; equality and civil rights; democracy; social justice; peace; and reverence for life—all would be upgraded because they are values which ensue from human contact and human awareness of humanity. Prudence and law and order would be emphasized because of the discipline symbolized by an ubiquitous system as obvious as street signs and street lights and as regular in movement as the stars. Also emphasized would be the values of natural beauty and aesthetic beauty in architecture, the rider being able to use his eyes for such amenities rather than to avoid death; also culture, the rider being able to read en route; also personal beauty (good grooming), since the quiet dignity of movement in a total urban system would be more conducive to personal dignity than the undisciplined disarray of movement by automobile.

The values downgraded by mass-rapid transit of the' type I postulate would be: one's own pleasure; self-reliance; prowess and ability; power; privacy; novelty. There may be a question whether "power," as a value, would be downgraded, since an ubiquitous transit system working automatically, regularly, invariably for the urban citizen might give him that vicarious sense of power which comes, for example, to the citizen of a strong nation.

In conclusion about mass-rapid transit and the automobile as competing technologies with differing impacts upon values, one caveat should be noted. Even so powerful a technology as the automobile does not utterly abolish a value. The automobile has had its most powerful downgrading impact upon the values of love and affection, friendship, reasonableness and rationality, conscientiousness, law and order (discipline and self-restraint), and voluntary service to others. Yet in the power blackout in New York, even without sight, except from automobile headlights, and without communication, except for transistor radios, order existed (I use the word "existed" rather than the phrase "was maintained"); and there was evidence of acute realization by the citizenry of utter interdependence. The automobile has downgraded the values which relate to human interdependence, but in the New York blackout case those values became temporarily dominant under a special circumstance. Failure of technology may upgrade values which are normally downgraded when the technology works.[10]

I move to television and the computer without actually leaving ubiquitous mass-rapid transit for the reason that both are involved in the new concept of comprehensive urban mobility. We have been preoccupied with the concern that television is the vehicle of bloody westerns and Gleasonian nonsense and that the computer will produce mass unemployment.[11] But television is doing much more than to serve advertisers.

10. *Daedalus*, Summer 1966, pp. 805, 808.
11. Herbert A. Simon, *The Shape of Automation* (New York: Harper & Row Publishers, Inc., 1965), Chapters 1 and 3 to the contrary.

It is watching for bank robbers, thus enhancing law and order; surveying and reporting the moon's surface, thus advancing scientific knowledge; not to mention television's instantaneous reports to the whole globe of any event anywhere, thus contributing to the sense among all peoples of *one world*. There are presently two tests to determine a community's cultural progress: (1) how much chemical fertilizer is used to promote agricultural productivity and (2) how much, if any, steel production measures the community's industrial potential. A third test will soon be added: what are the community's facilities for receiving, and transmitting for widespread popular reception, the messages from television satellites? Just as the alphabet and Arabic numerals were great leaps forward toward global culture, so television pictures, increasingly abstracted into symbols, will be one of the next important world ordering technologies.

We have seen that the computer is a benign factor in mass-rapid urban transit. When we visualize a fixed transit complex, serving megalopoli of ten, twenty, thirty millions of people, in a form as complex as that of the spider web with vehicles responding singly or in mass to the innumerable variables in demand within that complex, we welcome a superhuman intelligence to order the behavior of such a system. By superhuman intelligence I speak not in mystical terms but only of electronically manipulated mechanisms in which may be stored unlimited information and which can recall, organize, compare, and orient that information for a given needed action in an instant of time—all more comprehensively and immediately than any man or group of men *could*. We need not bother ourselves with the stock questions or jokes, such as whether a computer can compose a poem, ask a question, appreciate a sunset, or make love. It can provide mobility for concentrations of humanity of such density or of such contiguous extent as to make a difference in kind, rather than in degree, in the human way of life. The computer, therefore, takes its place with fire and the wheel as new technology in the development of man's cultures.

In addition to Simon's careful analysis of the really slow pace at which the computer will replace men,[12] there is the creative, affirmative factor that mobility far beyond any prior experience of mankind will enable the individual to probe, explore, experiment in multiple choices of meaningful activity far beyond any possibilities he has ever before enjoyed. At long last, because of the computer and related electronic controls, our bucolic heritage will loosen its grip and we shall become truly urbane. In an agrarian society it is a virtue (value) not to move beyond the confines of the husbanded land. That land and its crops and its animals must be tended—protected against predators, the elements, and the strokes of outrageous fortune. So as more

12. Simon, *ibid.*, pp. 94, 95.

productive agrarian technology has sent men from the land into cities, the old value of immobility (prudence) clings in a cultural lag to make it seem that mobility by technology is a luxury and, therefore, not a prime community responsibility. This bucolic tyranny will pass. Men now living will see urban mobility as much a community service, without special charge for each use of the service, as street lighting, policing, and sewage disposal. The computer will be at the heart of the service.

Television too will play a benign role in communications within urbanism. When we realize that comprehensive mobility in vast urban areas will be accomplished by a system of horizontal elevators, automatically maneuvered according to need, over an intricate system of interlocked and always exclusive rights-of-way, we naturally ask what about accidents, failures of equipment, human mischief, and other untoward developments? Television can and will maintain constant surveillance, car by car, route by route. Television can and will alert human central monitors, in the end perhaps only the computer itself, so that skills far in excess of those of a human motorman can be brought at once to bear upon the troubled spot.

By another token television will diminish the need for mobility in urban areas. The video-telephone will facilitate much communication which presently seems to require face to face meeting or face to face assembly of conferees and decision makers. It is a folkway of many executives that they must bring the pressure of physiognomy and manual gesture to the negotiation or must observe the eyes and facial expressions of a conferee: as my own cliché for this predilection, employed over many years, puts it, "to watch the other fellow's ears wiggle." A new generation of executives, of whom there will be more and more at the creative level, as the computer performs more and more routine functions, will replace the time-honored conference with the video-telephone.

I will now briefly, and again out of personal, professional experience, this time in the law, speak about the role of the computer and television in retrieval of information. Since the English Lord Coke in the early 17th century firmly established the practice of recording and rationalizing judicial decisions, Anglo-American proceedings in law have involved the case-by-case, reasoning-by-analogy procedure. This process means that judges and lawyers must know what were the facts in earlier cases; how the cases were decided; and why. The process is said to be the genius by which our law is kept organic and our society dynamic.

However, we have four centuries of recorded English decisions, including now for our American law the multiplicity of decisions from the courts of fifty states and from our federal judical system. Although these decisions are well indexed, and although we have Alexander Pope's *dictum* that index hunting ne'er turned student pale, yet the task of finding out what is the law, which concerns judges and lawyers much more than the spectacular criminal cases which preoccupy our news media, *is* Herculean. The day will come—not at once, because the task and its cost will be stupendous—when the millions of cases in Anglo-American law will be indexed to a computer and the search for the relevant precedents will be automatic and the essentials of the relevant cases will come up on television before the searcher. Will such automation eliminate lawyers? Far from it! But lawyers, especially the younger lawyers, will speedily become more creative, their energies released for constructive thought rather than exhausted in exhaustive manual searching.

Before speaking of the contraceptive technologies, I will make an intermediate summary of the impact of the computer and of television upon American values. The context within which I appraise that impact in urbanism, the way of life which will soon be that of 90 percent of all Americans and of all the peoples of the Western industrialized world, indeed in the foreseeable future for most of the globe. (Tokyo is now the largest city in the world.)

Downgraded by the computer and television will be: self-reliance, prowess and ability, freedom from interference, privacy, prudence, patriotism, and human dignity. Upgraded will be: physical well-being and comfort, economic security, friendship, intelligence, reasonableness and rationality, law and order, culture, novelty, equality and civil rights, social justice, peace, and internationalism.

I have included the contraceptive among the four technologies selected for discussion of technological impact upon American values because, as in the case of the other three, it is urbanism which is the new and inevitable mode in the human way of life. It is in urbanism that population unlimited is becoming unsupportable.

It is not enough to contemplate open-ended urbanism, important as is David Lewis' contribution to this project. There will be an end to open-endedness. The ultimate constraint is global space, which at present rates of population growth will reduce men to standing room only in 600–800 years. (Of course, they will kill each other off long before that time just to get room in which to move and breathe.)

But there is another constraint, equally important with that of limited global space. There is but a limited supply of the accumulation of the products of man's spirit. There are only so many Titians; so many Picassos, although he has been prolific; so many Michaelangelos or Henry Moores (imagine a Henry Moore in every shopping center); so many rare books, cathedrals, Richardson Court Houses, old trees; only so much of the rare man-made graces in the limited store which has survived from the ages. If the numbers of man, despite new urban mobility, preclude feasible access to the limited accumulation of the products of man's spirit, then men may evoke some form of ant-like learned techniques for survival but men will be alienated from their heritage—will become lost souls in any spiritual sense.

Population increase may be the only change in all time which makes mere numbers a difference in kind rather than of degree. For all of pre-history and for much of history the human female has had to reproduce somewhere near her physiological limit for the social unit to survive. At the beginning of the Christian era the world population was perhaps 200–300 million. By 1650 the number was only 500 million, and in another 200 years (1850) the world population was only a billion. Then Jenner discovered smallpox inoculation and, later, dietitians discovered spinach—just to pick two of many cases—and by the year 2000 the 1850 population, in only 150 years, will have increased sevenfold to seven billion.[13] The technologies of medicine and of hygiene have deferred death and so have made the population explosion. The technology of the coil (or its equivalent) is, and will be increasingly, a counteracting technology. Indeed, the two technologies are, and will be, as competitive as those of Cain and Abel. It may be said here that reverence for life *may* be a value which preexists, and is quite independent of, any and all technology—an exception to the general proposition that technology makes and changes values. Reverence for life, or conduct implying such reverence, is subhuman as well as human. The contest between the artificial heart and the coil will be long and bitter, but the coil will prevail. Technology will curb population.

There are numbers of men beyond which the quality of life will so deteriorate that leaders will successfully call for a reduction in numbers. Critics will call this assertion unsupported. They will mumble about new sources of food and, confronted with space limitations, will propose measures such as multilevel housing warrens on earth, or space platforms, or coloniza-tion of other planets. But man has not yet lost the common sense which helped him make society. Some things he knows.

Society itself is a consequence of constraints. Sahlins says, "In selective adaptation to the perils of the Stone Age, human society overcame or subordinated such primate propensities as selfishness, indiscriminate sexuality, dominance, and brute competition. It substituted kinship and cooperation for conflict, placed solidarity over sex, morality over might. In its earliest days it accomplished the greatest reform in history, the over-throw of human primate nature, and thereby secured the evolutionary

13. *Population Bulletins*, Population Reference Bureau, Inc.,Washington, D.C., February, 1962, Vol. XVIII, No. 1 and October 1965, Vol. XXI, No. 4.

feature of the species."[14] All this man did without any controlled experiments. One of the most striking proofs of man's common sense if the almost universal prohibition against incest, despite the absence of any invariable genetic reason for the taboo, as the case of Cleopatra, herself a product of generations of incest, proved. Man *made* society *above the family* out of his common sense by barring incest.[15]

I repeat the proposition that when new technology emerges men (women in this case) will use it. The perfect technology for contraception is not yet invented, barring abortion—not really a contraceptive technology. In any case, the technology of contraception is rapidly developing, and men and women have an increasing number of choices—ranging from the ancient sheath, through abortion, sterilization (male or female), the pill, and the foams, to the coil or loop. I take the coil only as a symbol of relatively effective (80 percent) technology and as psychologically certain, because only one act of volition is required—the female submission to an insertion which, while it must be done properly, is scarcely as technical as the most minor of surgery.

What will be the impact of effective contraceptive technology on some of the values we have considered? One's own pleasure is a value which will be upgraded. The fear of the unwanted child either in marital or extra-marital sex relations is a factor which inhibits mature, physiological and psychological, gratification. From this more mature gratification will ensue the upgrading of physical well-being and comfort, self-respect, self-ful-fillment, love and affection, devotion to family, personal beauty and good grooming, human dignity, reverence for life.

The value, reverence for life, will be also downgraded by effective contraceptive technology, depending upon cultural and religious habits of thought. Whether such technology will upgrade or downgrade reverence for life will depend upon the ideological, religiously induced or otherwise,

14. Marshall D. Sahlins, "The Origin of Society," *Scientific American*, Vol. 203, No. 3 (September, 1960), p. 86.

15. Leslie A. White, *The Science of Culture* (New York: Grove Press, 1949), pp. 303, 305, 327, 328. How *did* the prohibition against incest come about? Tylor suggests that "Again and again in the world's history, savage tribes must have had plainly before their minds the simple practical alternative between marrying-out and being killed out. . . . " "The evidence, both clinical and ethnographic," says Leslie A. White in *The Science of Culture*, "indicates that the desire to form sexual unions with an intimate associate is both powerful and widespread. Indeed, Freud opines that 'the prohibition against incestuous object-choice [was] perhaps the most maiming wound every inflicted . . . on the erotic life of man.' Psychology discloses an 'incestuous wish' therefore, not a motive for its prevention. The problem yields very readily, however, to culturological interpretation. Man, as an animal species, lives in groups we well as individually. Relationships between individuals in the human species are determined by the culture of the group—that is, by the ideas, sentiments, tools, techniques, and behavior patterns, that are dependent upon the use of symbols and which are handed down from one generation to another by means of this same faculty."

set of the individual. If, as seems obvious, numbers of men adversely affect the quality of life, then reverence for life *which is* will prevail over reverence for life (in the abstract) *to be*. But this problem of ideology (closely related to the Western World concept of sexual unions for procreation only) is fast yielding to contraceptive technologies. Apart from the impediment of a religious or cultural nature, it is difficult—as it was not difficult in the cases of the other technologies—to identify values which will be downgraded by the technology of contraceptives.

It will be urged that the value of devotion to family may be downgraded by the freedom for promiscuity provided to the female by a technology such as the coil. But the family in its origins is based upon division of labor and function, and not upon love. If the sanctions of division of labor and function are weakening because of modern industrial society, including job opportunities and new technologies of housing and housekeeping, in urban and industrial communities, the process will continue without regard to the efficacy of contraceptives.

Urbanism on a vast scale—masses of people living in high densities—is new in the life of man, as new as agriculture and settled abode were new when the nomadic way of life was superseded: The herder replaced by the cultivator. Technology both forces and sustains the new urban way of life. Leaders able to cope with the new form of mass-community must understand, employ, and promote the technologies appropriate to megalopolistic community.

For a cross section, then, of the impact of the current revolution in science and technology on American values I conclude by appraising the impact of urbanism, one of man's supreme technological achievements, on certain significant American values. Upgraded by urbanism will be: physical well-being and comfort; economic security; convenience in style of life; self-fulfillment; love and affection (if population is controlled); leisure; friendship; intelligence; reasonableness and rationality; law and order (if population is controlled by new available techniques, mobility is provided, and technology such as television is employed for more or less comprehensive surveillance by authorities to detect early public activities suggesting disorder); aesthetic beauty; equality and civil rights (if adequate mobility and adequate technical surveillance are provided); peace, as urbanism over the globe, reported and interpreted by global television, erases senses of difference; human dignity; reverence for life *which is*.

Downgraded by urbanism will be: one's own (indisciplined) pleasure-antisocial license, self-reliance, wealth, prowess and ability, success, power (except for the vicarious sense of power), freedom from interference, privacy, devotion to family, idealism (a concept too imprecise for the technics necessary to urbanism), patriotism (urbanism will outmode the national state), and democracy. (This last item needs to be qualified: the technical management of urbanism will call for technicians whose selection cannot be safely left to balloting, but democracy in the sense of civil rights as distinguished from its political sense need not be downgraded.)

Will all this change the behavior of man? Yes! Technology has changed his behavior and his values since some primate first learned and remembered the advantages of the tool. As for optimism or pessimism—those words are not sufficiently discriminating for the purposes of this paper. I adhere nevertheless to the faith that urbanism is a new game for man and quite worth the candle.

# THE INTERPLAY OF TECHNOLOGY AND VALUES

# The emerging superculture

## *Kenneth E. Boulding*

It has been pointed out by B. L. Whorf and a number of writers that one of the problems of those who are trained to think in Indo-European languages is that nouns tend to be substituted for verbs. There seems to be something about the subject-predicate-object structure of the sentence in these languages which inhibits us from talking about activity as such, and which leads us into reification, that is, talking about processes as if they were things. Both the words "technology" and "values" are examples of this peculiar linguistic difficulty. Whether there is any such "thing" as a value it is hard to know in the absence of any secure knowledge about the physical or physiological substructure of the valuation and choice processes of the human nervous system. For all I know, love may be coded into one chemical and hate into another; but up to now at any rate we have not been able to identify these structural forms. What we observe is not values but valuation, that is, an activity which may be inferred from the study of behavior, guided by introspection on the choice process.

Similarly, technology is not a thing. It is also a process, a complex set of ways of doing things with both human and material instruments. Again, perhaps, as a thing it may be represented by some as yet quite unknown structure in somebody's head in terms of knowledge. Up to now at any rate, this carrier cannot be observed directly, and what we observe in technology is people applying means to secure ends.

Among social scientists, economists have probably paid the most attention to the problems involved both in the choice process and in the processes of technology. Oddly enough, the problems are formally rather similar. In his attempt to describe the process of choice, the economist has postulated a utility or welfare function according to which every relevant state of the field or social system is given an ordinal number which indicates an order of preference, first, second, third, and so on. In what is called a strong ordering, each state of the field is given a unique ordinal number; in a weak ordering, different states of the field may have the same ordinal number, in much the way that students may be bracketed in a class list. As the economist sees it, then, the problem of valuation is that of ordering a field of choice and then selecting the first on the order of preference. This is the famous principle of maximizing behavior, as it is called, which is simply a mathematical elaboration of the rather obvious principle that people always do what seems to them best at the time. It has always surprised me, as I have remarked elsewhere, that such a seemingly empty principle should be capable of such enormous mathematical elaboration. It can only be given content, of course, if there are some information processes by which the preference field can be spelled out and the preference function described. Where the field which is to be ordered consists of a set of possible exchanges under a given system of exchange opportunities or prices, certain broad properties of the preference function, at least, can be deduced from the observation of differences in behavior in response to different price systems. This is what is called the "theory of revealed preference." Theoretically, we suppose that we can deduce the preference function of an individual from the differences of his observed behavior under different price structures. In practice, of course, because of the sheer difficulty of observing the behavior of the same individual under different price structures, what we observe is some kind of aggregate behavior of the behavior of different individuals under different price structures, and we deduce from this some kind of aggregate or average preference function. If the preference functions of different individuals are not widely dissimilar, there is some justification for this procedure.

Just as preferences, or the valuation process, is described by economists as a utility function, so technology is defined by a production function. The forms of these two functions, in fact, are highly similar, in fact virtually identical. A production function relates physical inputs of some kind to physical outputs of some kind. In this case, the field consists of all possible or relevant combinations of inputs and the function describes the quantities of outputs which are associated with each combination of inputs. It tells us, for instance, that with quantity $x$ of labor and $y$ of land we will get $z$ of potatoes. In the case of the production function, we can frequently assume not merely ordinal numbering of the product but cardinal numbering. In the case of the utility function, all we know is that of two combinations of inputs, one gives more utility than the other if it is preferred. In the case of the production function, we can usually measure the product directly so that we know not only that one combination of inputs gives more potatoes than another, but we know how much more, and we know, indeed, how great a quantity of potatoes is given in each combination of inputs. Oddly enough for the purposes of price theory, this richness of information about the production function is unnecessary, and all we really need to know to determine the equilibrium price structure is whether any given combination of inputs gives us more, less, or an equal amount of product than another.

Figure 1, which is very familiar to economists, illustrates the two concepts. Here we suppose two variables, say inputs in the state of the system, measured along $OA$ and $OB$. We then postulate a function in the third dimension, of which the curves $C_1$, $C_2$, etc. are contours. These are called isoquants in the case of the production function, in which, shall we

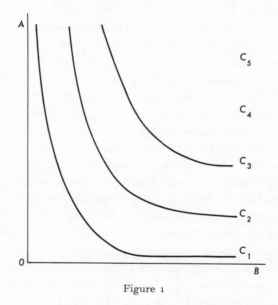

Figure 1

say, $OA$ measures the quantity of labor, $OB$ the quantity of land, and all combinations on one of the isoquants represents a given quantity of product. In the case of the preference function these are called indifference curves, and represent all combinations of two inputs to which the decision maker is indifferent, that is, which have the same utility. Utility can be thought of as the product of the decision making process, much as potatoes are the product of a production function; and the form of the two functions is likely to be very similar. In the case of the utility function, however, the indifference curves are given merely ordinal numbers so that we know which of any two indifference curves represents the higher utility and is the more preferred. In the case of the production function, the isoquants can be given a cardinal number representing the actual quantity of product.

In elementary economic theory it is generally assumed that both the utility or preference functions on the one hand, and the production functions on the other, are given factors in the social situation. As a first step in the process of analysis, this is quite legitimate, for it is important to deduce the consequences of any given set of preferences and technologies. The moment we try to make the system dynamic, however, it becomes very clear that neither the preferences nor the technologies are given, for they are both derived from a learning process which itself is dependent on the very dynamics of society which we are investigating. This proposition that both values, that is, preference functions, and technologies or production functions are learned is the key to any dynamic theory of society, though unfortunately we know far too little about the learning processes involved. Values and technologies, preference functions and production functions, interact to produce a price system, a system of exchange opportunities, not only in the narrow sense of a system of commodities with which economics usually concerns itself, but in the large sense of the whole social system of terms of trade, that is, the totality of what we give up for what we get. The concept can even be broadened to include what I have elsewhere called the grants economy and the integrative system, by which we give and receive unilateral transfers; for these, too, depend on preference functions and identifications which must be learned.

Because of the greater richness of information which seems to be available at the level of the production functions, the learning process can perhaps be perceived more easily there. Even if we look at a technology as relatively simple as that of peasant agriculture, it is clear that the whole process by which inputs are transformed into outputs is one that must exist in the mind of the producer before any production process will be set in motion. We will not plant seeds unless we have some image in our mind of a process of production by which certain activities of plowing, planting, weeding, fertilizing, and so on will eventually produce a harvest. Men lived on top of rich soil long before they ever thought of devoting it to agriculture, and unless there is an image of a whole productive process in their minds, the sequence of steps required for the process will not be carried out. The same simple principle is true of the most complex industrial process. An automobile, for instance, originates in the mind of the engineers and designer; it develops as a set of detailed blueprints and information which organizes an assembly line, and its production requires an enormous amount of communication of specialized knowledge. All human artifacts, indeed all capital, can be regarded as human knowledge imposed on the material world. All processes of production originate in the minds of men and have to be maintained in the minds of men if these processes themselves are to continue. Even the perpetuation of the simplest productive process requires the transmission of an elaborate body of knowledge from one generation to the next, for all human knowledge is lost every generation by the sheer processes of death. Learning is not something which can be done once and for all; it is something which must be repeated to the last detail in every generation, if existing processes are even to continue.

Production functions are not merely transmitted from one generation to the next in an educational process, for what might be described as a net learning process goes on which actually improves them in a developing society. What we call economic development, indeed, is largely a learning process by which improved production processes are learned. Two rather distinct processes are involved here: first, the innovative process by which a new image of a production process is created in the mind of someone which existed in no other mind previously; and second, the educative process by which the image of a production process in one mind is transmitted to another. Both of these are necessary if there is to be development. If there are no innovative processes and education is successful, the knowledge of each generation will be transmitted unimpaired to the next. We should not overlook the possibility of degenerative processes, in which the knowledge of one generation is impaired in transmission to the next, and in which there-fore technology declines and productive processes become less productive. The rate of technological development depends almost entirely on the amount of resources which a society devotes to the innovative process and to the educative process. Of these, the innovative process is the most mysterious. We do not really understand the sources of human creativity. Many societies have existed and continue to exist in which all attention is concentrated on the process of transmitting unimpaired the images of one generation into its successor. A good example of this would be the traditional Indian village, or shall we say the Amish society of the United States. The object of the educative process here is to produce children who are exact replicas, in their images, of the parents. We can be pretty sure that in-novation will not be carried on unless it is rewarded, and in traditional societies, where the innovator is looked upon with suspicion or even horror as one who violates the ancient dignities and destroys the sacred patterns of the society, innovation is not likely to be successful.

It is a proposition for which there is a good deal of historical evidence that the innovator is likely to be one who is in some sense a "refugee," that is, who is in a degree an alien in the society and yet who has a role and a status that can be accepted. The refugee in the literal sense, that is, one who has been driven out of his previous home and who has sought refuge in another society, is no longer bound by the traditional ways of doing things because his traditional environment is no longer around him. On the other hand, because he is an alien in the society to which he goes, peculiarities of behavior are tolerated in a way that the native does not enjoy. It is not surprising, therefore, that in India and Pakistan it is the refugees who have been vigorous entrepreneurs. It is not surprising also to see the important innovative role that groups like the Jews or the Parsees, the Syrian and Lebanese traders, the Chinese outside China, and other displaced peoples have played in the whole process for world development. There may also be "internal refugees" as well as external ones, the noncomformists like the Quakers and Methodists in England, who played a disproportionate role in the first Industrial Revolution of the eighteenth century, the Samurai, especially the Ronin or masterless Samurai in nineteenth century Japan, the Calvinists in Europe, and so on. These are people who might be described as internal aliens, who are in some sense alienated from the established patterns of the societies in which they live, but who nevertheless have a recognized status as nonconformists and dissenters, which gives them, as it were, license to innovate.

Innovation, of course, is useless unless it is supplemented with a fairly large investment in the educative process. There is no point in having innovations unless they can be imitated. This educative process, of course, is by no means confined to formal education, although as technologies become more complex the role of formal education in transmitting them becomes more important. Even in complex societies like the United States, however, a great deal of the educative process by which innovations are transmitted through the population is quite informal. Transmission takes place by word of mouth or simple observation, through advertising and commerical propaganda, in face to face groups, and so on. The rate of transmission throughout a society of successful innovations depends, of course, to a considerable extent on the value system in the society, and particularly its willingness to innovate. A society which regards all old things as good and new things as bad will be unlikely to innovate in the first place and even if there are innovations, they will take a long time to establish themselves. A society which has the reverse value system, in which new things are regarded as good simply because they are new and old things as bad just because they are old, will put a high value on innovation and innovations will spread rapidly.

The last observation illustrates a principle of the utmost importance, that values and technologies constantly interact on each other in the dynamic processes of society because both are created and transmitted by a common learning process. The learning of values, that is, of preference functions, is less obvious, perhaps, than the learning of technologies;

nevertheless, all societies devote a noticeable amount of resources to the process of the transmission of preference functions from one generation to the next, and societies differ enormously in their tolerance of innovation in preference functions. It is clear that there is a certain genetic base for preference functions, but in the case of man, this represents a very small proportion of the total. In the insects and even the birds, the preference functions seem to be generated almost wholly by genetic processes, that is, the genes or genetic structure contains an information code which builds certain preferences into the phenotype which it creates. An oriole has a strong *preference* for building oriole nests, but this preference is not learned from its parents, it is built into the bird by its genes. The same seems to be true of insects, although in the highest insects like the bees there does seem to be a certain process of communication and education. For the most part, however, even the bee does not have to learn how to be a bee it simply *knows* how to be a bee. As we move towards the mammals and still more towards the primates, the proportion of the value structure which is learned increases. A kitten learns in part how to be a cat from its mother, not from its genes. Monkeys, it would seem, have to learn even such things as sexual behavior from their parents. As we move to man, instincts, that is, the value system which is built in by the genetic system, shrink to a very small proportion of the total. We do seem to have a genetic value system at birth which includes such things as high preference for milk, warmth, and stimulation and low preferences for loud noises, falling, and hunger; but on this slim genetic base we finally achieve preferences for transubstantiation or atheism, surplus value or free private enterprise, oysters, raw fish, olives, alcohol, chastity, and self-immolation. Genetics provides only the vaguest of drives. It seems fair to say today that there are no instincts in man in any detailed sense of the term, and that practically the whole of his value structure is learned from parents, from teachers, from his peers, from the mass media, and from information inputs of all kinds which pour into him both from outside and from within and continue perhaps even in sleep. From the moment of birth, we are the recipients of enormous inputs of information, out of which we gradually build our image of the world in regard to space, time, causality, the future, and values. Our preference functions are not innate; they are a product of our total information input, operating, perhaps, within certain guidelines laid down by our genetic inheritance. The old problem of the relation between heredity and environment has never been solved, it has simply been laid aside because we do not know how to answer it at present. That genetics imposes certain predispositions is very plausible, but it is clear also that in the mass, whatever individual peculiarities may be due to individual differences in genetic structure tend to cancel themselves out, and that the value systems of a culture are transmitted in the processes of that culture by the information inputs which the culture generates. There is nothing, for instance, in the genetic composition of a Japanese American that prevents him from becoming 100 percent American in culture. If he is only 99 percent American, it is because certain physical difference affect a little the way he is treated and the information inputs which he receives. Apart from this slight difference, however, the Nisei will learn to like coffee and eggs and bacon for breakfast as over against the rice, raw egg, and soup of his Japanese cousin, who may be genetically identical.

At this point I believe I can detect a subterranean rumble from the moral philosophers, who are likely to object to what seems to be my identification of values with valuation, and of valuation with preference and choice. Surely, some of them will argue, the choice between good and evil, right and wrong, is qualitatively different from the choice between bacon or sausage for breakfast; and still more, they may argue, concepts of utility or preference functions cannot account for problems of freedom, justice, and still less for mercy, pity, peace, and love. I am not altogether unsympathetic to their indignation against what must seem like economics' imperialism, that is, the attempt on the part of economics to take over not only all the other social sciences but moral philosophy as well. Nevertheless, I am prepared to defend my identification of the problem of values with the problem of preference, though I will gladly concede to the moral philosopher that this can operate on a number of different levels. Thus, while economics tends to assume a preference function, the moral philosopher raises the question of the choice among preference functions themselves. What I think this means in terms of the dynamic process of society is that the learning processes by which we learn our preference functions are not simply arbitrary, nor are they purely relative and culture-bound, but that there are certain selective processes which are in a real sense universal. It seems to be a plain fact of observation that cultural and moral relativism of a pure sort tends to break down when it is pressed too far. It is all very well for the relativist to observe that it is very interesting that some people eat their grandmothers and some do not, but that no one should pass any moral judgment on this interesting difference of behavior. When, however, somebody proposes to eat *him*, there is some tendency for relativism to break down. What we have to recognize here is that in the processes by which we learn our preferences, there are certain information inputs and certain sources of information which are peculiarly salient and effective in the formation of preferences. Preferences are always learned from a reference group, as the social psychologists call it. This may be, in the first instance, the family group with which the individual identifies early, even though the identification, as psychoanalysts have pointed out, is often ambiguous. All societies have produced religious and educational institutions which also are salient in establishing preferences, but these preferences are subject to innovation just as the production function is subject to innovation. The Aztecs had strong preferences for human sacrifice and rather messy religious rituals. Under the joint challenge of the Conquistadores and the Jesuits, Spanish baroque churches celebrating a symbolic sacrifice were substituted in the preference system for the human victims. The relative role of the Conquistadores and the Jesuits in this is almost as difficult to estimate as the role of heredity and environment. We can be pretty sure, however, that one without the other would not have been very effective. In other words, it was a complex mutation-selection process by which old values are challenged by new values, old technologies by new technologies, and indeed these two processes are not very different. The images in the minds of the living, both of preference functions and of production functions, have to be transmitted from generation to generation. In the course of transmission the images are changed, and they both may be changed by innovation or mutations, some of which prosper and spread through the minds of the living, and some which do not.

The problem of the complex interaction between our preferences and the technologies is rendered particularly acute in the present epoch by the fact that we have been going through enormous changes in both technology and values, that is, in our images of what inputs produce what outputs on the one hand and our images also of what states of the system are preferable to others on the other hand. The Great Transition, as I have called it elsewhere, which began with the rise of modern science around the end of the sixteenth century and which continues with ever accelerating change up to today, is a change in the state of man as great, if not greater, as in the change from the neolithic village to urban civilization; and I have described as the change from civilization to post-civilization, civilization being the state of man typified, shall we say, by the Roman Empire or by the poor countries such as Indonesia today. (Certainly if the Roman Empire were around today we would regard it as an extremely poor country and would be giving it aid on a large scale.) This great transition was preceded by a long period of accelerating folk science and folk technology, a period also of slow but continuous change in values and preferences. In the West we can date this preparatory period roughly from the fall of Rome and the rise of the great monastic orders; in China it can be dated from a little earlier, perhaps the beginning of the Han Empire. The so-called Industrial Revolution of the eighteenth century in England and Western Europe represented essentially the culmination of this process of folk technology. It owed very little to science, even though science, as it were, was developing underneath it. The steam engine and the spinning jenny are not in essence very different from the printing press and the clock. The theory of the steam engine, for instance, which is thermodynamics, did not develop until the early nineteenth century, and the steam engine itself clearly owed nothing to it. In the latter half of the nineteenth century, however, the science-based industries began, which could not have developed at all without the previous development of a certain branch of science. Of these, the chemical industry was the first, the electrical industry the second, the biological industry the third, and the nuclear industry the somewhat premature fourth. Today in the developed countries, more than half the economy is producing products and using methods which would have been virtually inconceivable a hundred years ago. Never in the whole course of human history has there been a change as rapid at that which has taken place in the last hundred years.

In this great transition there has been a constant interplay between changing technologies and changing values, both of these being an integral part of the larger process of change in what Teilhard de Chardin calls the "noosphere" or the totality of images of the world in the minds of the living. The interaction between values and technologies is so complex that it is quite impossible to say which precedes the other. It is a hen and egg problem in $n$ dimensions. It seems fairly certain, for instance, that there were changes in values, that is, preference systems, which were a necessary prerequisite for the rise of science, in the direction of introducing higher preferences for change, for the authority of nature rather than the authority of sacred books and ancient writers. These changes in values, however, were not unconnected with certain preceding changes in technologies, for instance the rise of the money economy, development of accounting, and the subsequent opportunities for more rational behavior in the light of better information. A strong case can be made out, indeed, that in the origins of science it was the machine that preceded the scientific or mechanical image of the world. The clock, for instance, preceded the Copernican-Newtonian image of the solar system as the great clock; the water pump preceded the discovery of the circulation of the blood, just as the steam engine preceded thermodynamics. The development of the more elaborate folk technology imperceptibly changes the values of the society which used it, and by giving man a little power over the material world perhaps increased his desire for knowledge about it.

On the other hand, there are also changes which occur fairly spontaneously within the system of values and preferences. The Max Weber thesis of the impact of the Reformation and especially of Calvinism on economic activity and technology is well known. Once the authority of the Pope had been challenged and a high value has been placed in the Protestant countries on successful dissent, the legitimation of dissent in general is a fairly easy step. The legitimation of dissent, as we have seen, is an essential element in the innovative process; therefore innovation must be legitimated if it is to be rapid. It is not surprising, therefore, that Luther's initial break with Rome was accompanied by the more radical Anabaptists and followed by Calvin, George Fox, John Wesley, and the more radical religious reformers. It is not surprising either that it was out of this radical nonconformity that the great changes in economic institutions and technology of the seventeenth and eighteenth century largely developed. In this case, the development of a religious value system which stressed the immediacy of personal experience as over against the authority of a pope or even a king, which stressed veracity as a high virtue and which also stressed simplicity of life and thriftiness and the sacredness of the material world, should provide the groundwork for enormous changes in knowledge and technology.

These considerations perhaps throw some light on the puzzling question of why the breakthrough into science and the technology that is related to it and based upon it took place in Europe rather than in China. The great work of Joseph Needham on Chinese technology has opened our minds in the West to the fact that at least up to 1600, the folk technology of China was considerably ahead of that in the West, and that indeed many of the essential developments in the western part of the old world were not only anticipated in China, sometimes by hundreds of years, but in many cases actually derived from China. This seems to be true, for instance, of such things as the stirrup, on which so much of the medieval aristocratic culture was based, which reached Europe from China or Tibet by about the eighth century. Such essential technologies as that of clockwork and printing were likewise discovered in China long before they were discovered in Europe, although here the actual connection is more obscure and the European discoveries may be independent. The exact relation of innovation to imitation remains one of the mysteries of human history.

In spite of the fact, however, that China had been the superior of the West for so long and unquestionably was still the superior of the West, shall we say in 1600—from 1600 on Europe takes an enormous spurt forward under the impact of the rise of modern science, whereas China proceeds in the old slow pace of folk technology. It may be indeed that China was too successful (one very fundamental principle of social science is that nothing fails like success). Perhaps the very disjointed and disintegrated structure of Europe, with its many centers of power, its religious and national divisions, its separation of ecclesiastical from political power, and at the same time its active network of trade and communication (the result partly of its long coastline and waterborne traffic), made that fraction of difference which carried Europe over the watershed into science. China, at any rate did not make this transition. This fact has dominated the history of the last 300 years.

As we compare Europe with China, the subtle and constant interaction between values and technology again becomes apparent. In the fifteenth and sixteenth centuries, for instance, as the Ming voyages, indicate, China clearly had the technology to explore the world and to expand its culture, and the fact that it did not do so is almost certainly due to the value systems of its rulers, which favored withdrawal, stability, and staying at home. By contrast, the Spanish and the Portuguese, in what might be described as the last great burst of the Crusades, discovered and colonized America to the West, and Eastward as far as the Philippines and Japan. This was indeed the moment of globalization, the moment in human history at which the earth ceased to be a great plain and became a sphere. All this, indeed, was before the rise of science, but the high values and rewards given to adventure, exploration, and discovery from, say, 1450 to 1600 in the West, unquestionably helped to create the value system which later gave rise to Galileo and his successors. The hens of value produced the eggs of technology; the eggs of technology the hens of value, in an ever-increasing, ever-expanding process of increasing complexity.

By way of conclusion, or perhaps an epilogue, let us take a brief, speculative glance at the implication for future values and perhaps even for future technology of the great transition through which we are now going. Its most obvious and immediate impact is the separation out in the world of two cultural systems, the superculture on the one hand and traditional cultures on the other. It is hardly too much to say that all the major problems of the world today revolve around the tension between these two cultural systems. The superculture is the culture of airports, throughways, sky-scrapers, hybrid corn and artificial fertilizers, birth control, and universities. It is worldwide in its scope; in a very real sense all airports are the same airport, all universities the same university. It even has a world language, technical English, and a common ideology, science.

Side by side with the superculture, and interpenetrating it at many points, are the various folk cultures, national, religious, ethnic, linguistic, and so on. The tensions between the superculture and traditional cultures are felt at a great many points. We see it, for instance, in the international system, where the superculture has given the traditional cultures of the national states appalling powers of destruction which are threatening the whole future of man. We see it in race relations, where the superculture moves towards uniformity, the absence of discrimination, and differentiation by roles rather than by race or class or other ascribed category. We see it in education, where formal education tends increasingly to become the agent of transmission of the superculture, leaving the transmission of folk culture to the family, the peer group, and more informal organizations. We see it in religion, where the superculture tends towards the secular and traditional culture preserves the sacred.

At a great many points, these tensions between the superculture and traditional cultures produce challenges to traditional values and even disintegration of these values. Family loyalties are replaced by loyalties to larger and more abstract entities; national loyalties are eroded by inconsistencies between the national state and the world order which the supercultural requires; religious loyalties are eroded by new views of man and the universe; political loyalties are eroded by new images of the social system arising out of social sciences.

The picture, however, is not merely one of constant retreat and erosion of traditional values in the fact of the superculture. There is also the transformation and regeneration of traditional values under the impact of the superculture. A strong case can be made, indeed, for the proposition that the superculture itself does not generate the values and preferences which will support it, perhaps because of the very fact that it has to be transmitted through channels of formal education of a more or less authoritarian kind. Traditional culture, on the other hand, is transmitted through the family, the peer group, and intimate relations which are capable of creating much more intense value commitments and stronger preferences than the more abstract and cold-blooded relationships of the superculture. We do not feel towards the airport or the chemistry textbook the degree of emotional involvement that we have with the family, the nation, or the little brown church in the wildwood.

As an integrative system, the superculture is really very weak. Fellow scientists kill each other in national wars almost as enthusiastically as co-religionists. Scientists have not raised money very much to help other scientists, and while they have a certain sense of occupational community, this does not usually go much beyond the rather tenuous bond of the professional association. People die for their countries, even for their faith, but very few people have died for biochemistry. Up to now at any rate, therefore, the ethical values of mankind on the whole have arisen out of the traditional cultures rather than out of the superculture. There is something to be said for the proposition, indeed, that it is only countries which have strong traditional cultures and as a result strong ethical systems which are able to create or adapt to the superculture, and that where the traditional culture is weak, the society will have great difficulty in making adjustments to the superculture. Japan is perhaps one of the best examples of a society in which the traditional culture is very strong and in which it generates principles of ethical judgment and behavior which are friendly to the superculture and which permit it to develop at an enormous rate. In a greater or lesser degree, this is true of all the successfully developing countries. It is by contrast those countries in which the traditional culture cannot adapt itself and produces values which are unfriendly to the superculture that development is most difficult. The contrast between Japan and India in this respect is most instructive. In some cases the traditional culture has proved so incapable of adaptation to the impinging superculture that it has been virtually destroyed. This seems to be the case in China, and to a smaller extent in the other socialist countries.

From the point of view of this paper, communism is a curious phenomenon which represents on the one hand a vehicle for bringing traditional societies into the superculture and which expresses many of the values of the superculture, such as education, equality of status for women, the abolition of castes, and so on. On the other hand, ideologically it represents what is really a prescientific view of society, and its results in a curious fixation of the socialist countries on the attitudes and ideologies of the nineteenth century. Ideologically it is a kind of folk science lying somewhere between an unsophisticated folk image of society on the one hand and empirically based scientific concepts on the other. At certain points, therefore, it may assist, and at other points it may hinder the transition and adaptation of a society to the superculture.

The inability of the superculture to produce adequate values of its own and the adaptability of certain aspects of traditional culture is reflected strongly in the continuing strength of the religious institution in the developed societies. This is nowhere more striking than in the United States, which is at the same time perhaps the furthest advanced towards the superculture and yet is also a society whose history has been characterized by the rise of the numerical strength and power of the churches. What we seem to face in the future, therefore, is a very complex set of mutual adjustments, in which an adapted traditional culture transmitted in the family, the peer group, and the church will create ethical values and preferences which are consistent with the world superculture. If the superculture simply destroys the traditional culture in which it is embedded, it may easily destroy itself. On the other hand, if the traditional culture does not adapt to the superculture, it too may destroy itself. This is a precarious balance, and not all societies may achieve it. The costs of a failure to achieve it, however, are very high, and there is great need, therefore, for widespread self-consciousness about the nature of the problem, and a willingness to put resources into solving it.

# PART III CONTROL

# THE SHIFT OF POWER

# Technology, planning, and organization

## *John Kenneth Galbraith*

1

   In accordance with well-regarded academic custom I should like to begin by going a decent distance back of my subject. It is my intention to examine the effect of modern technology, the planning that it occasions and the organization that it requires on the location of power in the modern economy. But I propose to begin with a brief reference to the oldest of economic problems, that of the relation between what economists have anciently called the factors of production.

   Few matters have been more faithfully explored by our profession. Until recently, the problem of efficiency in production was envisaged, almost entirely, as one of winning the best combination between capital, labor, land and the entrepreneurial talent which brought them together and which managed their employment. The elucidation of these arcane matters, by means of diagrams, remains one of the prime pedagogical rites of economics. Changing technology, it is conceded, is more important than proportioning in determining what can be obtained from any given stock of the factors of production. But there is no way by which intelligence on the role of science, technology and productivity can be adnumbrated at length in a textbook. So economic theory after conceding the important continues to deal at length with the matter on which doctrine is available.

   Economists have been equally concerned with the way in which factor prices—rents, wages, interest and profits—are determined. Indeed, in the classical tradition, the subject of economics was thought of as falling in two parts: The problem of value having to do with the determination of the prices of goods and the problem of distribution having to do with how the income resulting from the sale of products and services was divided between landlords, workers, capitalists and those who, as entrepreneurs, united access to capital with the ability to bring it into organized combination with labor and land or other natural resources.

A further aspect of the relationships between the productive factors has, however, been of less interest in conventional economic analysis. That is how power comes to be associated with one or the other of the factors in the firm or the economy at large. This is a puzzling omission. Power is an interesting subject. On first coming on any form of organized activity— a church, platoon, government bureau, political machine, mob, or house of casual pleasure—our instinct is to inquire who is in charge. Then we inquire as to the qualifications or credentials which accord such command. Organization, in other words, almost invariably invites the question: How did he (or she) get control?

## 2

One reason this question was slighted in economics was that for a long time, in classical economic inquiry, no worthwhile exercise of power in economic affairs was recognized. In the classical tradition—that of Adam Smith, David Ricardo, J. S. Mill, and Alfred Marshall—and increasingly as concepts were better defined—the business enterprise (like that of the farmer today) was assumed to be small in relation to the market that it served. The price that the entrepreneur received was impersonally and competitively determined by the market. So were the prices he paid to his suppliers. So were the wages he paid. So was the interest he paid on borrowed funds. Profits reduced themselves to a competitive level. The ideal volume of production for the firm was externally established by the relation of costs to the market price at various levels of output. Such was the situation under conditions of competition—what, with later refinement, came to be called the model of pure competition. If the man in charge has no power to influence his prices, costs, wages, interest, if even his ideal output is externally determined and his profits subject to the leavening of competition, one can be rightly unconcerned about his power. He has none. This absence of power explains the libertarian appeal of the market system to many men.

This unconcern continued in the classical tradition until well into this century. Having been excluded in the beginning, it has had a hard time winning a foothold. But in other currents of thought it has achieved more prominence.

In particular there was Marx. In the middle of the last century he brought the subject of power energetically and passionately into economic discussion. The notion of a system of competitive—and hence passive and powerless—enterprises he dismissed as an exercise in vulgar apologetics. Production in modern industrial society is dominated not by those who supply land or natural resources, not yet by those who supply labor but by those who supply or control the supply of capital. Authority in economic life rests with a "constantly diminishing number of the magnates of capital . . . (who) usurp and monopolise" the advantages of industrial production.[1] And their power extends on to the state. It becomes an executive committee serving the will and convenience of the capitalist class.

Economics in the central or classical tradition has come to accept certain of the basic features of the Marxian view. The notion of the competitive market, to which numerous producers were passively subject, disappeared even from the textbooks. Those in charge of the business enterprise were routinely accorded the power over prices and output that is associated with monopoly, small numbers or oligopoly, or some unique feature of their product. Now only propagandists, hired professionally to make the case for modern business, argue for the existence of pure competition, this being the one test that, most signally, it would not pass. This is market power. It is agreed as Professor Kaysen suggests that the "Market power which large absolute and relative size gives to the giant corporation is the basis not only of economic power but also of considerable political and social power . . . "[2] But the further ramifications of political and social power are not much pursued.

And one important fact is assumed. If there is power; it is supposed that naturally and inevitably it belongs to capital. This is true within the firm and outside. Power is the natural prerogative of ownership. The claims of the other factors of production are inherently surbordinate. In the assumption that power belongs as a matter of course to capital, all economists are Marxians. Let me pursue this point.

In the last three decades, evidence has been accumulating of a shift of power from owners to managers within the modern large corporation. The power of the stockholders has seemed increasingly tenuous. A few stockholders assemble in an annual meeting, and a much larger number return proxies, ratifying the decisions of the management including its choices for the Board of Directors to speak for stockholders. So long, at least, as it makes profits—in 1964 none of the largest 100 industrial corporations and only seven of the largest 500 lost money—the position of a management is impregnable. The stockholders are literally powerless. To most economists, as to most lawyers, this whole tendency has seemed of questionable legitimacy. Some, in accordance with the established reaction to seemingly

1. Karl Marx, *Capital* (New York: Modern Library), Chapter XXXII, p. 836.
2. Carl Kaysen, *The Corporation in Modern Society* (forthcoming).

inconvenient truth, have sought to maintain the myth of stockholder power. Others, including all Marxians, have argued that the change is superficial, that capital retains a deeper and more functional control. Some have conceded the change but have deferred judgment as to its significance.[3] Yet others have seen a possibly dangerous usurpation of the legitimate power of capital.[4] No one (of whom I am aware) has questioned the credentials of capital, where power is concerned, or suggested that it might be *durably* in eclipse. If there is power, it was meant to have it.

## 3

Yet, over a longer range of time, power over the productive enterprise —and by derivation in the society at large—has shifted radically as between factors of production. The eminence of capital is a relatively recent matter; until about two centuries ago no qualified observer would have doubted that the decisive factor of production was land. The wealth, military power and the sanguinary authority over life and liberty of others that went with land ownership assured its possessor of a position of eminence in his community and of power in the state. These perquisites of land ownership also gave a strong and even controlling direction to history. For the great span of 250 years, until about a hundred years before the discovery of America, it helped inspire the recurrent military campaigns to the East which are called the Crusades. Succor for Byzantium, which was beset by the infidels and redemption of Jerusalem, which had been lost to them, served, without doubt, as a stimulant to religious ardor. But the younger sons of the Frankish nobility badly needed land. Beneath the mantled cross beat hearts soundly attuned to the value of real estate. Baldwin, younger brother of Godfrey of Bouillon, found himself faced on the way to the Holy City with the taxing decision as to whether to continue with the redeeming armies or take up an attractive piece of property at Edessa. He unhesitatingly opted for the latter and, only on the death of his brother, did he leave his fief to become the first King of Jerusalem.

For four centuries following the discovery of America, appreciation of the strategic role of land gave it an even greater role in history. The Americas were populated—as also the Steppes and the habitable parts of the Antipodes. Once again religion went hand in hand with real property

3. Cf. Edward S. Mason, "The Apologetics of Managerialism," *Journal of Business* (University of Chicago) January, 1958. And "Comment" in *A Survey of Contemporary Economics*, pp. 221-222.
4. Cf. Adolf A. Berle, Jr., *Power Without Property* (New York: Harcourt, Brace and Company, 1959), pp. 98 *et seq.*

conveyancing, somewhat disguising the role of the latter. Spaniards considered themselves commissioned by God to win the souls of Indians; Puritans believed themselves primarily under obligation to look after their own. For Catholics and Cavaliers the Lord was believed to favor rather large acreages with the opportunity these accorded for custody of (and useful labor by) the aborigines and, as these gave out, of Africans. For Puritans, and Protestants generally, merit lay with the homestead and family farm. But these were details. In the New World, as in the Old, it was assumed that power and responsibility belonged, as right, to men who owned land. Democracy, in its modern meaning, began as a system which gave the suffrage to each and every person who owned land—and to no others.

4

The economic foundations of this eminence of land, and the incentive to its acquisition, were exceedingly firm. Until comparatively modern times, agricultural production—the provision of food and fiber—accounted for a large share of all production as it still accounts for 70–80 percent of output in countries such as India today. Subject to such rights as law and custom accorded to subordinate tenure, power to engage in agricultural production rested with land ownership. This, *pro tanto*, was power over a very large share of all economic activity.

The other factors of production were not of decisive importance. Agricultural technology was stable and made small use of mechanical power or other capital equipment. Thus a sparse supply of capital was matched, an important but sometimes neglected point, until a couple of hundred years ago by an equally meager opportunity for its use. If implements, work, stock or seed were lost this was not decisive; the modest requirements could be replaced.

The same was true of labor. Its historical tendency had been to keep itself in a condition of comparative abundance. David Ricardo, having regard for experience to that time, could hold in 1817 that "no point is better established than that the supply of labourers will always ultimately be in proportion to the means of supporting them."[5] This was to say that all that might be required would be forthcoming at, or about, the subsistence wage. The labor supply could be easily increased or replaced. But to get more land was difficult, and lost land was, as likely as not, irreplaceable. So

5. David Ricardo, "On the Principles of Political Economy and Taxation," *The Works and Correspondence of David Ricardo*, ed. by Piero Sraffa (Cambridge, 1951), p. 292.

land was strategic and not even the philosophers whose ideas ushered in the Industrial Revolution—Smith, and especially Ricardo and Malthus—could envisage a society where this was otherwise.

5

Then in the last century, in what we all agree to call the advanced countries, land was dethroned. The search for land, set in motion by its strategic role, uncovered a munificent supply. The Americas, Russia, South Africa and Australia were all discovered to have a large, unused and usable supply.

Meanwhile, mechanical inventions and the growth of metallurgical and engineering knowledge were prodigiously expanding opportunities for the employment of capital. From this greater use of capital came greater production and from that production came greater income and savings. It is not clear that in the last century the demand for capital grew more rapidly than the supply. In the new countries, including the United States, capital was generally scarce and the cost was high. In England, however, over most of the century, interest rates were low. But a diminishing proportion of the expanding production was of agricultural products and hence dependent on land. Iron and steel, ships, locomotives, textile machinery, buildings and bridges increasingly dominated the national product. For producing these, comand of capital, not land, was what counted. Labor continued to be abundant in most places. Accordingly, the man who owned or supplied the capital now had the strategically important factor of production. Authority over the enterprise, as a result, now passed to him.

So did prestige in the community and political power. At the beginning of the nineteenth century the British Parliament was still dominated by the landed great; by the end of the century its premier figure was the Birmingham industralist and pioneer screw manufacturer Joseph Chamberlain. At the beginning of the century, the United States government was dominated by the Virginia gentlemen; by the end of the century it was profoundly influenced by—depending on one's point of view—the men of enterprise or the malefactors of great wealth. The Senate was called a rich man's club.

This change, a point of much importance for what I am about to say, did not seem natural. George Washington, Thomas Jefferson, and James Madison seemed appropriate to the positions of public power. Public influence exercised by Jay Gould, Collis P. Huntington, J. P. Morgan, Elbert H. Gary, and Andrew Mellon seemed more suspect. The landowners were credited with capacity for action apart from their own interests and action in their own interest—the defense, for example, of slavery—seemed somehow legitimate. The capitalists were not credited with action apart from interest and their interest seemed less legitimate. This contrasting impression has not yet been exorcised from public attitudes or the elementary history books. We may lay it down as a rule that the older the exercise of any power the more benign it will appear and the more recent its assumption the more dangerous it will seem.

### 6

While capital in the last century was not scarce, at least in the great industrial centers, it was not in surplus. But in the present day economy, capital is, under most circumstances, abundant. The central task of modern economic policy, as it is most commonly defined, is to insure that all intended savings, at a high level of output, are offset by investment. This is what we have come to call Keynesian economic policy. Failure to invest all savings means unemployment—an excess of labor. So capital and labor have a conjoined tendency to abundance.

Back of this tendency of savings to surplus is a society which, increasingly, emphasizes not the need for frugality but the need for consumption. Saving, so far from being painful, reflects a failure in efforts by industry and the state to promote adequate consumption. Saving is also the product of a strategy by which the industrial enterprise seeks to insure full control of its sources of capital supply and thus to make its use a matter of internal decision. It is an effort which enjoys great success. Nearly three-quarters of capital investment last year was derived from the internal savings of corporations.

Capital, like land before it, owed its power over the enterprise to the difficulty of replacement or addition at the margin. What happens to that power when supply is not only abundant but excessive, when it is a central aim of social policy to offset savings and promote consumption and when it is a basic and successful purpose of business enterprises to exercise the control over the supply of capital that was once the foundation of its authority?

The plausible answer is that it will lose its power to a more strategic factor—one with greater bargaining power at the margin—if there is one. And there is.

Power has passed to what anyone in search of novelty might be forgiven for characterizing as a new factor of production. This is the structure of organization which combines and includes the technical knowledge, talent and experience that modern industrial technology and planning require. This structure is the creature of the modern industrial system and of its technology and planning. It embraces engineers, scientists, sales and advertising specialists, other technical and specialized talent—as well as the conventional leadership of the industrial enterprise. It is on the effectiveness of this structure, as indeed most business doctrine now implicitly agrees, that the success of the business enterprise now depends. It can be created or enlarged only with difficulty. In keeping with past experience, the problem of supply at the margin accords *it* power.

## 7

The new recipients of power, it will be clear, are not individuals; the new locus of power is collegial or corporate. This fact encounters almost instinctive resistance. The individual has far more standing in our formal culture than the group. An individual has a presumption of accomplishment; a committee has a presumption of inaction. Individuals have souls; corporations are notably soulless. The entrepreneur—individualistic, restless, equipped with vision, guile, and courage—has been the economists' only hero. The great business organization arouses no similar affection. Admission to the economists heaven is individually and by families; it is not clear that the top management even of an enterprise with an excellent corporate image can yet enter as a group. To be required, in pursuit of truth, to assert the superiority of the group over the individual for important social tasks is a taxing prospect.

Yet it is a necessary task. Modern economic society can only be understood as an effort, notably successful, to synthesize, by organization, a personality far superior for its purposes to a natural person and with the added advantage of immortality.

The need for such synthetic personality begins *first* with the fact that in modern industry a large number of decisions, and *all* that are important, require information possessed by more than one man. All important decisions draw on the specialized scientific and technical knowledge; on the accumulated information or experience; and on the artistic or intuitive reaction of several or many persons. The final decision will be informed only as it draws on all whose information is relevant. And there is the further important requirement that this information must be properly weighed to assess its relevance and its reliability. There must be, in other words, a mechanism for drawing on the information of numerous individuals and for measuring the importance and testing the reliability of what each has to offer.

The need to draw on the information of numerous individuals derives first from the *technological* requirements of modern industry. These are not always inordinately sophisticated; a man of moderate genius could, quite conceivably, provide himself with the knowledge of the various branches of metallurgy and chemistry, and of engineering, procurement, production management, quality control, labor relations, styling and merchandising which are involved in the development of a modern automobile. But even moderate genius is in unpredictable supply; and to keep abreast of all the relevant branches of science, engineering, and art would be time consuming. The answer, which allows of the use of far more common talent and with greater predictability of result, is to have men who are appropriately qualified or experienced in each limited area of specialized knowledge or art. Their information is then combined for the design and production of the vehicle. It is the common public impression, greatly encouraged by scientists, engineers and industrialists, that modern scientific, engineering and industrial achievements are the work of a new and quite remarkable race of men. This is pure vanity. The real accomplishment is in taking ordinary men, informing them narrowly but deeply and then devising an organization which combines their knowledge with that of other similarly specialized but equally ordinary men for a highly predictable performance.

The *second* factor requiring the combination of specialized talent derives from large-scale employment of capital in combination with sophisticated technology. This makes imperative planning and accompanying control of environment. The market is, in remarkable degree, an intellectually undemanding institution. The Wisconsin farmer need not anticipate his requirements for fertilizers, pesticides or even machine parts; the market stocks and supplies them. The cost is the same for the farmer of intelligence and the neighbor who under medical examination shows daylight in either ear. There need be no sales strategy; the market takes all his milk at the ruling price. Much of the appeal of the market, to economists at least, has been the way it seems to simplify life.

The extensive use of capital, with advanced technology, greatly reduced the power of the market. Planning, with attendant complexity of task, takes its place. Thus the manufacturer of missiles, space vehicles or modern aircraft must foresee and insure his requirements for specialized plant, specialized talent, arcane materials and intricate components. These the market cannot be counted upon to supply. And there is no open market where these products can be sold. Everything depends on the care with

which contracts are sought and nurtured, in Washington. The same complexities hold in only lesser degree for the maker of automobiles, processed
foods and detergents. This firm too must foresee requirements and manage the
markets for its products. All such planning is dealt with only by highly-
qualified men—men who can foresee need and insure the supply of production requirements, relate costs to an appropriate price strategy, see that
customers are suitably persuaded to buy what is made available and, at yet
higher levels of technology and complexity, see that the state is persuaded.

Technology and planning thus require the extensive combination and
testing of information. Much of this is accomplished, in practice, by men
talking with each other—by meeting in committee. One can do worse than
think of a business organization as a complex of committees. Management
consists in recruiting and assigning talent to the right committee, in intervening on occasion to force a decision, and in either announcing the decision
or carrying it, as a datum, for a yet larger decision by the next committee.

It must not be supposed that this is an inefficient device. A committee
allows men to pool information under circumstances that allow also of
immediate probing and discussion to assess the relevance and reliability of
the information offered. Loose or foolish talk, or simple uncertainty, is
revealed as in no other way. There is also no doubt considerable stimulus
to mental effort; men who believe themselves deeply engaged in private
thought are usually doing nothing at all. Committees are condemned by
those who are caught by the *cliché* that individual effort is somehow superior
to group effort; by those whose suspicions are aroused by the fact that for
many people group effort is more congenial and pleasant; by those who do
not see that the process of extracting, and especially of testing, information
has necessarily a somewhat undirected quality—briskly conducted meetings
invariably decide matters that were decided beforehand elsewhere; and by
those who fail to see that highly-paid men, when sitting around a table as a
committee, are not necessarily wasting more time, in the aggregate, than
each would waste all by himself. Forthright men frequently react to belief
in their own superior capacity for decision by abolishing all committees.
They then constitute working parties, task forces, operations centers or
executive groups in order to avoid the truly disastrous consequences of
deciding matters themselves.

8

This group decision-making extends deeply into the enterprise; it
goes far beyond the group commonly designated as the management.

Power, in fact, is *not* closely related to position in the hierarchy of the enterprise. We always carry in our minds an implicit organization chart of the business enterprise. At the top is the Board of Directors and the Board Chairman; next comes the President; next comes the Executive Vice-President; thereafter comes the Department or Divisional Heads—those who preside over the Chevrolet division, large generators, the computer division. Power is presumed to pass down from the pinnacle.

This happens only in organizations with a routine task, such, for example, as the peacetime drill of a platoon. Otherwise the power lies with the individuals who possess the knowledge. If their knowledge is particular and strategic their power becomes very great. Enrico Fermi rode a bicycle to work at Los Alamos. Leslie Groves commanded the whole Manhattan Project. It was Fermi and his colleagues, and not General Groves in his grandeur, who made the decisions of importance.

But it should not be imagined that group decision making is confined to nuclear technology and space mechanics. In our day even simple products are made or packaged or marketed by highly sophisticated methods. For these too power passes into organization. For purposes of pedagogy, I have sometimes illustrated these matters by reference to a technically uncomplicated product, which, unaccountably, neither General Electric nor Westinghouse has yet placed on the market. It is a toaster of standard performance except that it etches on the surface of the toast, in darker carbon, one of a selection of standard messages or designs. For the elegant hostess, monograms would be available, or even a coat of arms; for the devout, there would be at breakfast an appropriate devotional message from the works of Norman Vincent Peale; the patriotic, or worried, would have an aphorism urging vigilance from Mr. J. Edgar Hoover; for modern economists, there would be mathematical design; a restaurant version could sell advertising, or urge the peaceful acceptance of the integration of public eating places.

Conceivably this vision could come from the President of General Electric. But the orderly proliferation of such ideas is the established function of much more lowly men who are charged, specifically, with new product development. At an early stage in the development of the toaster, specialists in style, design and, no doubt, philosophy, art and spelling would have to be accorded a responsible role. No one in a position to authorize the product would do so without a judgment on how the problems of design and inscription were to be solved and the cost. An advance finding would be over-ridden only with caution. All action would be contingent on the work of specialists in market testing and analysis who would determine whether and by what means the toaster could be sold and at what cost for various quantities. They would function as part of a team which would also include merchandising, advertising and dealer relations men. No adverse decision by this group would be over-ruled. Nor, given the notoriety that attaches to missed opportunity, would a favorable decision. It will be evident that nearly all power—initiative, development, rejection or approval— is exercised deep down in the company.

So two great trends have converged. In consequence of advanced technology, highly capitalized production and a capacity through planning to command earnings for the use of the firm, capital has become comparatively abundant. And the imperatives of advanced technology and planning have moved the power of decision from the individual to the group and have moved it deeply into the firm. What have been the consequences? Let me go back again to the corporation and its owners.

9

In the mid nineteen-twenties it became known that Colonel Stewart, the Chairman of the Board of the Standard Oil Company of Indiana had, in concert with some of the men who later won immortality as the architects of the Teapot Dome and Elk Hills transactions, organized a highly specialized enterprise in Canada called the Continental Trading Company. This had the sole function of buying crude oil from one Colonel E. A. Humphreys, owner of a rich Texas field, and reselling it to companies controlled by the same individuals, including the Standard Oil of Indiana, at a mark-up of twenty-five cents a barrel. It was an excellent business. No costs were involved, other than a small percentage to the Canadian lawyer (who served as a figurehead and disappeared when wanted for questioning), and for mailing out the proceeds after they had been converted into Liberty Bonds. (If some of these had not been used, most carelessly, to bribe Secretary of the Interior Albert B. Fall and others to pay the deficit of the Republican National Committee, Continental might have forever remained unknown.) It was Colonel Stewart's later contention that he had always intended to turn over the profit to Standard of Indiana to which it rather obviously belonged. But, absent mindedly, he had allowed the bonds to remain in his own possession for many years. In 1929 Standard of Indiana was only eighteen years distant from the decree which had broken up the Standard Oil empire of John D. Rockefeller of which it had been an important part. The Rockefellers reacted sternly to this outrage; the elder Rockefeller had, on notable occasions, imposed a somewhat similar levy on his competitors, but *never* on his own company. They still owned 14.9 percent of the voting stock in the Indiana Company, and were deemed to have the controlling interest. With the aid of the publicity generated by the Teapot Dome scandal, his own standing in the financial community and a very large expenditure of money, John D. Rockefeller, Jr. was able to oust the Colonel, although only by a narrow margin.[6] In the absence of the scandal and his ample resources, he would have had little hope.

Forty years ago the notion that the owners could not control a corporation was novel and disturbing. As I have noted, we still question its legitimacy—although the divorce of ownership from control in the modern corporation is taken for granted. We see that it is in harmony with the abundance of capital and the fact that this is no longer at the margin the decisive factor of production. And it is in harmony with the tendency for power to pass deeply into organization where it is beyond the reach and beyond the competence not only of owners but of any individual. The decision to establish Continental Trading Corporation was a simple one. Once discovered, there was no problem in comprehending the facts or the motives. Had the problem been an error of equal cost in planning petro-chemical development or marketing strategy, an owner would be nearly helpless in his effort to intervene. Control in the modern corporation is an accommodation to capital abundance and to the group decision making that technology and planning have made imperative.

### 10

One would expect a further and adverse effect on the power of those associated with the supply of capital. This has become abundant; corporations have their internal sources of supply. Accordingly, the banker, whose co-operation, as it was euphemistically called, was once essential for the success of the enterprise, has no longer a strategic role. Similarly the investment banker, insurance company, and professional investor. Though they have grown in size, one would expect that they have declined in importance.

And there can be little doubt that this is what has happened. In the last half of the last century and the early decades of this century the great bankers were part of our folk legend. Their power may have been suspect but the names of Jay Cooke, Jay Gould, the elder Morgan were of enormous majesty. Everyone knew them. It did not seem out of character that, when at odds with the government over the alleged anti-trust violations of the Northern Securities Company, the elder Morgan should tell the first Roosevelt to "send your man to my man and they can fix it up." It would

6. Cf. Berle, *op. cit.* and Means, *op. cit.*

seem out of character today. Today, there is no banker whose name is
known outside the financial community and very few who are known to the
whole financial community. Fame, in the modern financial world, requires
—massive larceny always apart—that one collect modern art, have Japanese
wrestlers perform in the lobby or stage ping pong contests in the street.

The prestige and power of the unions have also, almost certainly,
been declining. Their power too is derived from a factor that is comparatively
abundant and which suffers also from its competition with abundant capital
and sophisticated technology. The relative—and in many recent years
absolute—decline in trade union membership is related to the decline in
numbers of production workers. And this, in turn, is the result of capital
substitution based on capital abundance.

## 11

That engineers, scientists, and technicians within the business
enterprise are already laying claim to eminence and influence that results
from this shift will surely be evident. Increasingly they will move into the
senior posts. The President or Board Chairman, who had as his principal
qualification his close liaison with the financial community, is probably an
anachronism. Capital is no longer that important. He is being replaced by
men whose skills are related to organization, recruitment, information
systems and the other requisites of effective group action. These men are
handicapped, in the political environment, as the older capitalist entrepreneur was not, by their commitment to group behavior. But this handicap
is not total. It does not interefere, for example, with exceedingly intimate
association in Washington with the suppliers of government contracts.
Anyone familiar with Washington will agree that it is this, often highly
technical, influence, not that of bankers, which is decisive in modern business–
government relations.

## 12

Influence under these circumstances accrues also to those who supply
trained and highly qualified manpower. It is silly to suppose that the current
great expansion in educational enrollment and resources is the result of a
new age of enlightenment resulting from mass reading of *The Affluent
Society*. It is the result of pressures generated by the new relationship
between the factors of production and the now strategic role of qualified

men. As the scarcity of capital in Victorian times led men to enlarge on virtues of frugality and saving, so now scarcity of trained talent leads to a similar emphasis on the value of education.

We already see some elementary examples of its effect. Once the tycoon sat on the college board of trustees to keep the impractical academician from making a fool of himself in the world of affairs and to have an eye out for heresy. Now he attends to insure his liaison with his supply of talent. And it is the academic scientist and engineer who puts in a remunerative day or two a week guiding the simple men of affairs through the intricacies of modern science and technology. The pre-Cambrian entrepreneur who once denounced long-haired and radical professors has been warned about hurting the recruitment program.

In both domestic and international affairs one also observes a new note of confidence in the voice of the academic community and, among those who disagree, a new note of regret that it should be heard. Similar was heard from the landlords about the emerging industrial middle class a century and a half ago. We are only a generation distant from the day when the trade unions were urged by right-thinking men to stick to collective bargaining and stay out of politics. I am not completely sanguine as to the way the educational estate will employ its new influences; the faculty meeting is not an utterly encouraging precept. But neither is a trend in influence toward the educated to be wholly deplored.

# VALUES AND MANAGERS

# Private production of public goods

## *David Braybrooke*

The values that technological change may serve remain clear enough until the level of affluence has been reached. Thereafter what needs to be done becomes problematical. New ideals have to be worked out for public policy and for private activity as well, if men are to appreciate the opportunities—and the dangers—opening up before them; and guide technological change in beneficial ways. I shall try to describe how—by pursuing along certain lines values now cherished by them—the managers of private corporations might participate in an important institutional development, which I envisage as a manifold enlargement of the market for what economists call "public goods." This development will eventually transform managers' values to some degree, in a direction which the public may be immediately grateful for. More important, experience with this newly enlarged market will prepare both managers and the public to evaluate further uses of technology in future ways of life. The fact that throughout the development managers would enjoy benefits that motivate them is one reason for thinking the development possible. Furthermore, technological change, by threat if not by pressure, may move managers to seek those benefits in this market rather than in more familiar ones.

## A problem and part of a solution

I shall take as my point of departure a problem extracted—with some elaboration on my part—from J. K. Galbraith. In *The Affluent Society*,[1] Galbraith portrays American society as having emerged from the era of scarcity without having made suitable modifications in conventional economic ideas, or in its attitudes toward production, consumers' preferences, and government expenditures. Formerly the drive for greater output in the private sector of the economy had extra and important backing from the concept of welfare—welfare in the ordinary sense, which has to do with

1. Boston: Houghton Mifflin, 1958.

368

vital needs for food, clothing, shelter, medicine, not with welfare in the neutralized sense to which contemporary welfare economics has reduced it. Output, however one might imagine it distributed, always fell short of supplying everyone's vital personal needs; and the wants or preferences of rational consumers might be assumed to correspond very closely with their efforts to satisfy those needs—except in the case of the rich, which merely presented a problem of redistribution, politically difficult, but (in the light of the ordinary sense of welfare) intellectually straightforward. Now, with the coming of affluence, output suffices in aggregate quantity to take care (in the United States) of everyone's vital needs, indeed of all comforts that would have seemed reasonable to any earlier generation.

Galbraith contends that output has been disproportionately stimulated in the private sector of the economy by deliberate commercial excitation and expansion of wants; meanwhile, long-standing needs in the public sector have gone neglected, needs more and more painfully exposed as the relative concentration of output in the private sector continues. As a result we enjoy (most of us, in the United States and other lucky countries) private affluence, but suffer (even the most comfortable of us) public squalor.

Behind this anomaly, there is to be found the problem of our not being very well prepared intellectually to direct allocations between the private and public sectors. In the private sector, the excitation of wants has generated confusion about needs, which vary with conventions anyway and are all too susceptible to expansion.[2] In spite of fantastic increases in output, people may still be so preoccupied with private needs that they feel unable to afford larger expenditures in the public sector. There are also, of course, ideological reasons disfavoring action in the public sector.

But the problem does not consist merely in being unprepared to give due weight to the public sector in terms of received values. The examples of neglect that Galbraith and other writers have dwelt on have been typically needs already familiar—for good air and water; for recreational space; for well planned cities—that impinge as such upon individual persons and that have gone neglected simply because they require concerted action by consumers—actions not feasible in the market. But suppose these needs are sooner or later taken care of, as (let us hope) the now recognized needs that consumers can take care of privately will have been. Will there not still be resources to allocate, and better or worse ways of allocating them?

They may vanish from conception, however, and hence from sight, if in the private and the public sectors taken together the concept of needs expands in application as fast as output increases. Here is the critical dimension

2. Cf. my companion paper "Needs and Preferences" in *Studies in Moral Philosophy* (Oxford, 1968; *American Philosophical Quarterly* Monograph No. 1).

of the problem of being unprepared to direct allocations; the imaginative freedom with which we might treat the question of allocations, once needs are met, may never be realized if the concept of needs extends its grasp to the limit of our resources. There is a fair chance of this happening; and it may happen as easily in the public sector as in the private.[3] In the past, public policy-making, like private efforts, has been preoccupied with needs and remedies. Extensions in the list of things accepted as requiring public remedy have paralleled the extended applications of "needs" in the private sector.

To obtain full freedom of allocation, we must preserve from the exacting precedence of needs some freedom of maneuver for preferences. We must also preserve, adapt, elaborate, to some degree invent, the conceptual means for making coherent sense out of preferences. Notable among these means are various "molecular" values—organized combinations of "atomic" values—capable of inspiring preferences; dependent on preferences—on free, experimental ventures with preferences—for their development. They include ideals of character; ideals about work and leisure; vocational ideals; career ideals and life-history-ideals.[4]

Since public policy may be called on to create the social environment in which some combination of these ideals can be harmoniously pursued, public discussion of them is required in an instrumental way, to serve ideals once formulated. But public discussion is also required for the generation and formulation of such ideals. The ideals will not become sufficiently distinct and definite for people to attach themselves to, resisting the expansion of needs, if public discussion of ideals and possible environments does not become vigorous and widespread. People have much to learn from each other's experiments in coping with technological change; they cannot dispense with each other's aid and support.

I shall now outline part of a solution to the problem of dealing discriminately with the linked public and private opportunities offered by technological change and rising output.

In this outline, I envisage a development in which the managers of private corporations—the very people now so deeply implicated in the commercial excitation and expansion of private wants—will be led into new lines of activity fertile in occasions for significant public discussion of preferences and ideals.

3. Cf. the companion paper on needs and preferences (mainly concerned with the private sector); and my article, "The Public Interest: The Present and Future of the Concept," in Carl J. Friedrich, ed., *The Public Interest* (*Nomos* V), (New York: Atherton Press, 1962), pp. 129–154.
4. These various types of ideals-types of molecular values—are treated at more length in the paper on needs and preferences, though hardly adequately even there. They demand much more elaborate philosophical investigation than they have had hitherto.

Described shortly, the development would consist in the corporations diversifying their output and sales efforts in the direction of seeking out contracts with various levels of government for the supply of goods for collective consumption—goods that are either clear examples to begin with of what economists call "public goods,"[5] or goods reasonably readily classed with these. Governments—federal, state, and local; perhaps new regional units as well—would simultaneously be active on the other side of the market for these goods. As the private corporations invent and promote public goods on the supply side, governments at various levels would be busy inventing them on the demand side, and seeking out firms capable of producing them.

"Public goods" are defined in the current literature of economics as goods or services the consumption of which by some people leads to no reduction in what remains to be consumed by others.[6] Once they are in existence, the marginal costs of providing their benefits to any additional consumers fall to zero. Any practical system of charging for the benefits would lead some consumers to forego them (at least in part) without making anyone else better off, and hence would obstruct the attainment of maximum welfare (a Pareto optimum). The goods in question are thus candidates for nonprofit administration and for public spending. Standard examples are parks; national defense; open air concerts; police protection; radio beacons. Any species of production that involves large fixed costs and low variable costs, or decreasing costs with increasing scale, invites qualified application of the concept. Goods so produced will be a mixture of public and private goods, candidates at least for public subsidy, without which private firms could not afford to sell them to private consumers at a welfare-maximizing price.[7]

The public goods that would be supplied and demanded in the enlarged market I envisage would in many cases be novel goods. I am supposing that substantial amounts of technological innovation will be directed into this market. Market incentives would join with notions of community (or group) improvement to stimulate the invention of new collective goods.

Some of these novelties may be conjectured:

* packaged systems for community-wide air purification;
* new systems for disposing of trash and garbage;

5. Following Paul A. Samuelson, in "The Pure Theory of Public Expenditure," *Review of Economics and Statistics*, Vol. 36 (1954), pp. 387–389; "Diagrammatic Exposition of a Theory of Public Expenditure," *Review of Economics and Statistics*, Vol. 37 (1955), pp. 350–356; "Aspects of Public Expenditure Theories," *Review of Economics and Statistics*, Vol. 40 (1958), pp. 332–338. Cited by Francis M. Bator, in *The Question of Government Spending* (New York: Harper, 1960), *q.v.*, pp. 88–98; and by Anthony Downs, in *An Economic Theory of Democracy* (New York: Harper, 1957), pp. 170–174.
6. See Bator, *loc. cit.*
7. See Bator, *loc. cit.*; and Samuelson, in the third of the articles cited, at p. 335.

* networks connecting home fire alarm systems with fire department stations;
* systems for "personalizing" everything stealable, including money, so that theft would become pointless;
* the design and installation of small zoos and museums, suitable for towns or neighborhoods with 10,000 people;
* packaging and installing small public parks;
* development of machine and crew techniques for transplanting sizeable shade trees en masse to the naked housing tracts surrounding our cities;
* systems (including central car depots and citizens' band communications) for sharing the use of automobiles;
* versatile neighborhood recreation centers.

These illustrations necessarily give a very limited idea of the field of possible public goods, which largely remain to be invented. They suffice however to illustrate my contention that in this sort of market, the managers of private corporations would have to concern themselves directly with serving concerted public requirements. They would not, I suppose, be merely responding to requirements formulated by governments, but actively contending with one another to formulate attractive suggestions for governments to seize on. The governments, for their part, would in effect be organizing deliberations about opportunities for collective consumption.

On both sides, it must be stressed, the goods would be treated as whole packages—organized systems designed, produced, and installed by the firms supplying them. Under present arrangements, there is of course already a great deal of business done between corporations and the various levels and units of government; but typically it is the government that conceives and designs the public goods. The corporations merely supply parts which the government assembles. In the development envisaged, the corporations would be doing the assembling, and would share the responsibility for the effectiveness of the final package, as it would share the task of initiating designs. The package would, moreover, often embody a custom made application of the organizational resources and techniques of the corporations.

Arbitrarily—but hopefully—I exclude armaments from my vision. I envisage deliberations about public goods of sorts that will shape patterns of peaceful life. Both the managers of the corporations and the representatives of the public would have to consider what sorts of lives—vocations, careers, characters, life-histories—various kinds of public facilities would foster. Lives oriented toward vocations and careers in sports and applied arts— orientations forever safe from technological obsolescence—might demand an enormous proliferation of neighbourhood sports and crafts centers, which could be marketed in large part as packaged installations. Many novelties could be expected in the architecture of such centers and in their equipment.

Some of the novel public goods might well consist, however, not in means of escaping from technology but in means of entering it more fully and gladly. Might there not be packaged systems primarily designed for imaginative education in technology, but leading from educative activity into some sort of effective participation in technological change, with real influence upon technological policies? The whole public might have access to one or another such system—centers something like permanent World's Fair exhibits, but genuinely connected with the networks for political and economic decision making. Among the techniques devised for such centers might be the use of multiple straw-votes, with immediate electronic feedback of arrays of tentative choices; concurrently, exhibition in related arrays of conflicts and consequences; and perhaps as well a standard method of programming value problems for step-by-step expressions of preference. Once these techniques were operating in public decision-making centers, they might well spread throughout the society, being imitated, for example, in the internal organization of private corporations.

I shall expatiate later on the advantages of increased activity by corporations in the enlarged market for public goods. Having outlined the development, I now wish to ask, how feasible is it? How likely is it to happen?

I am very far from having evidence for a conclusive answer, but I can point to some favorable factors, under two headings: first, the values of managers and hence of corporations; second, the threats or pressures of technological change.

## The partial solution compatible with managerial values

If we impute certain values to given people, we imply that the people have favorable attitudes toward some states of affairs and unfavorable attitudes toward others; and that they are disposed to make—and on suitable occasions do make—choices in which these values function as criteria. Sometimes we look to the values for an explanation of the choices—we say that such choices were made because such criteria were used; sometimes we look to the choices for evidence of the values—we hypothesize that such criteria were used because we find such choices being made.[8]

I hold that the managers of private corporations have values that are favorable rather than unfavorable toward enlarging the market for public goods. They use such criteria and make such choices as would conduce to initiating and carrying on their parts in this development; they do not have such criteria and will not make such choices as would obstruct the development.

8. For a general philosophical account of values, which I accept, see Kurt Baier's contribution to this volume.

I impute to these managers certain vocational values, which I suppose function as criteria for them in selecting their occupations, in continuing, in striving for better performance—for successful performance, with success defined by these same values.

Like other salaried employees of large organizations (professors, technologists, scientists) these managers have vocational values that prominently include (1) achievement by innovational contributions (2) the receipt of earnings proportioned to such achievements (3) recognition in the form of earnings so proportioned and in other ways. Corporation managers differ from other kinds of salaried employees, but still resemble managers who work outside industry and commerce, in judging each other and expecting to be judged by innovational achievements specialized in demonstrations of (4) interpersonal competence, exercised in the service of (5) the survival and growth of the corporations that they serve. Their differences from managers elsewhere, for instance in government, which lead them to choose careers in industry for themselves—on the basis of marginal differences in objective facts—concern values placed upon (6) larger incomes and (7) the opportunity to prove their crisis-capacity in what they feel is a harder game, and (8) some readiness to accept chances of more rapid advancement as compensating for increased risks of tenure.

This list sounds so commonplace that an effort is required to see that no part of it goes without saying: every part of the list needs to be founded on evidence; and there are people, including many active in industry, who do not have the individual values mentioned, much less the ensemble (which amounts to a vocational ideal).

The evidence that I have is very mixed in kind and quality, so far as it exists. The firmest evidence supports the imputation of an important value placed on at least marginally larger incomes. Extensive studies of the occupational values of college students have found that those electing a business career tend to place making a lot of money first among their career objectives,[9] and that those who place this first are more likely to choose business.[10]

David C. McClelland, in a very imaginative and wide-ranging study of the drive for achievement, finds that people with a strong drive of this kind are more inclined to believe that pay for accomplishing more and more difficult tasks should increase rapidly. Yet it is not money *per se* that motivates them so much as money as a recognized measure of success.[11]

9. Morris Rosenberg, *Occupations and Values* (Glencoe, Illinois: The Free Press, 1957).

10. James A. Davis, *Undergraduate Career Decisions* (Chicago: Aldine, 1965), (a report by the National Opinion Research Center).

11. David C. McClelland, *The Achieving Society* (Princeton: Van Nostrand, 1961), pp. 235–237.

In imputing the value placed on recognition, I am following what I believe is the prevalent view among psychologists that it is a basic factor in motivation.[12] That higher salaries are a form of recognition is implicit in the very concept of earnings, and can be illustrated in a thousand ways in the literature on business. Other forms of recognition (titles, office accommodations, luncheon arrangements) vary directly with salaries. That the achievements expected of managers—by themselves as well as others—consist in demonstrations of interpersonal competence is something that I infer from current discussions of management and business training.[13] Managers are dedicated to the survival and growth of their firms, partly by the very terms of their employment, partly because of values that are simultaneously vocational for themselves and tests to be applied to the performance of corporations.

The most vulnerable items on the list are the imputed values concerning innovation on the one hand and a harder game with more chances of rapid advancement on the other. These values are very likely much more prevalent among independent entrepreneurs than among the managers working in large corporations.[14] Yet McClelland finds no difference, on psychological tests regarding drive for achievement, between people in business for themselves and managers working in large corporations.[15] Both Rosenberg and Davis have found that students heading for business tend to be singularly uninterested in opportunities to be original and creative; they also include a disproportionate number of students with low academic performance.[16] Yet people with a strong drive for achievement are not necessarily motivated to perform efficiently at school.[17] They are, however, at least in the United States, attracted to business,[18] which in their eyes offers them the kind of work situation that they prefer, namely one "of moderate uncertainty where their efforts or skills can make a difference in the outcome."[19]

Managers seem at least to have the subjective impression that they are

12. See, for example, A. H. Maslow, *Motivation and Personality* (New York: Harper, 1954), Chapter V. McClelland claims at one point the "*achievement satisfaction arises from having initiated the action that is successful*, rather than from public recognition for an individual accomplishment" (*op. cit.*, p. 230), but his evidence is not very compelling, and the claim is not entirely consistent with what he says about money, just cited.
13. Chris Argyris, *Interpersonal Competence and Organizational Effectiveness* (Homewood, Illinois: Irwin, 1962), appears to be a centrally influential work.
14. Lewis A. Dexter (personal communication).
15. McClelland, *op. cit.*, p. 265; *cf.* p. 230.
16. Rosenberg, *op. cit.*, pp. 17, 118; Davis, *op. cit.*, pp. 104–105.
17. McClelland, *op. cit.*, p. 226 ff.
18. *Ibid.*, p. 240 ff.; pp. 259–260. But managers and engineers do not differ significantly in the tests that McClelland cites (p. 267); and the differences between managers and people of similar educational attainment going into other occupations are strangely elusive in McClelland's findings.
19. *Ibid., loc. cit.*, and p. 211.

playing a harder game. They write books about "survival in the executive jungle";[20] and apparently without feeling ridiculous exchange such comments as "Competitive management likes executives who have an instinct for the jugular."[21] Some firms evidently seethe with vicious interpersonal rivalry.[22] Even firms that do not may consider themselves continually beset by competitive emergencies. In spite of steadily growing technological complexity, the telephone companies would seem to be in a rather placid line of business; but one of them at least undertakes to test all junior managers within their first year to see whether they can "stand the fire."[23]

In spite of the mixed evidence, I shall retain the ensemble of imputed values. I wish to argue that the vocational values of the designated managers favor rather than obstruct the incursion by private enterprise into an enlarged market for public goods. What I shall do is argue this point assuming the ensemble as it stands; and also changing the most vulnerable parts of it for their opposites.

It is easy, I think, to establish the point for the ensemble as it stands. The envisaged market would invite innovational achievements in interpersonal competence even more pressingly than familiar markets: Managers active therein would not only have to deal with employees; and also with government officials backed by organized public opinion; they would have to exercise interpersonal competence in novel ways in the very design and construction of the packaged systems for community services that would figure prominently among the public goods to be produced. These systems would have an engineering side; but they would very largely consist in new ways of organizing interpersonal cooperation.

Money would be no obstacle. The managers active in the market would enjoy rewards paid on the scale and according to the principles of the private corporations employing them. They would in this and other ways obtain the forms of recognition at the disposal of the corporations. They would also have a chance, not common in private employment elsewhere, of obtaining public recognition for community services directly in line with their vocations. Yet these same services would, of course, also be services promoting the survival and growth of their corporations.

To managers imbued with the full ensemble of imputed values, bent on

20. The title of a book by Chester Burger (New York: Macmillan, 1961).
21. Elliot Janney, quoted by James M. Black, in *Executive on the Move* (New York: American Management Association, 1964), pp. 66–67.
22. Melville Dalton, *Men Who Manage* (New York: Wiley, 1959); cf. F. L. W. Richardson, Jr., "Rivalry, Revenge and Executive Productivity" and "Managing Man's Animal Nature," in *Pittsburgh Business Review*, Vol. 33, No. 6 (June, 1963), pp. 1–5 and p. 11, and Vol. 34, No. 11 (December, 1964), pp. 1–5 and pp. 11–12.
23. E. D. Maloney of the Pacific Telephone Company, speaking in a symposium at Stanford. *Stanford Graduate School of Business Bulletin*, Winter, 1965, p. 18.

innovation and eager to play a hard game with greater risks but more rapid advancement, the market for public goods would offer some of the excitement of politics as well as the excitement of commercial competition. The many different local projects would offer large responsibilities, while they remain novelties, to the managers in charge. There would be innovation—competition in innovation—to get the business to begin with; and then a variety of chances to experiment and innovate in the course of construction and installation.

But what of the managers whose attachment to values in this part of the ensemble is tenuous or nonexistent? Even they would have congenial roles to play in the market for public goods. Some of the goods might be produced in quantity in routinized ways. Some of the local projects, certainly in time, would become sufficiently familiar and routinized to accommodate managers little interested in original achievement or in risks and excitement. There would also be subordinate roles in novel projects for less enterprising managers; and security in tenure or transfer within the corporate bureaucracy. Thus if we consider managers who depart from the ideal in these respects, we can say that the market for public goods will be broad enough to accommodate their values as well as the values of the managers exemplifying the ideal in every item. I shall not venture to speculate whether the assignments opened up will be nicely proportioned to the numbers of more enterprising and less enterprising managers available.

The values that managers draw from ideology to test not just the attractions of individual vocations, or the performances of individual corporations, but the virtues of whole social systems, also seem to favor activity in the envisaged market.

Undoubtedly, we have to deal with a range of ideologies, not with one uniformly subscribed to by all managers.[24] At one extreme, there are managers who profess doctrines stemming from the laissez-faire exhortations of Bastiat and Spencer or from Locke's chapter on private property. Government should be limited to police functions; businessmen should be able to acquire money without interference and keep it without tax or objection. At the other extreme, there are managers who acknowledge that the theories of competition used to rationalize laissez-faire doctrines do not

---

24. This much can be discovered directly from the public pronouncements made by managers or on their behalf. Cf. Francis X. Sutton, Seymour E. Harris, Carl Kaysen, and James Tobin, *The American Business Creed* (Cambridge, Mass.: Harvard University Press, 1956); and Robert L. Heilbroner, "The View from the Top: Reflections on a Changing Business Ideology," in Earl F. Cheit, ed., *The Business Establishment* (New York: Wiley, 1964), pp. 1–36. A discount also needs to be applied for the difference between public pronouncements and private beliefs: the result of the discount (which I have no means of making), would be to change the distribution of managers within the same range of imputed values. My argument would proceed unchanged.

readily accommodate super corporations. They grant government a large role in protecting the public and accept the necessity of large government expenditures

Some of these managers believe that their corporations have social responsibilities—for example, in sustaining employment, or in controlling pollution—which it is the professional responsibility of managers to see fulfilled.

Even managers of the latter sort may be inclined, more often than not, to discourage government spending in favor of reduced taxes and increased personal spending. But even managers at the other, laissez-faire extreme might digest without much trouble the increased government spending that would occur in the enlarged market for public goods. It is true that the spending will not (as I envisage it) take the directions most acceptable to many conservative businessmen—armaments and warfare. But though Federal contracting and subsidizing would be involved, a good part of the spending would flow through the hands of state and local governments, ideologically more acceptable spenders than the Federal government.

The spending would not take the form of transfer payments—for relief, social work, social security—which raises a spectre in some managerial minds of idle and shiftless people being kept in comfort by wealth that the managers have created and that a corrupted majority rule has forced them to hand over in taxes. The spending will (like a considerable part of armaments expenditures) be directed into the hands of contracting private corporations —on an ideological view, an eminently laudable destination. Corporations— even under conservative management—have not, I think, shown much reluctance in times past or present about accepting government contracts, or even direct subsidies.

In the envisaged market, myriad levels and units of government would bargain with competing private firms for goods and services that under present arrangements tend to be produced by governments themselves if they are produced at all. For *laissez-faire* extremists, having private firms produce them rather than governments would be a step forward. The genuine concern for variety and freedom present in *laissez-faire* beliefs would be substantially met by the variety allowed for in the goods and services bought by different governments. Local governments could aim at different ways of life, and people might shift between localities according to personal tastes.[25]

It would be perfectly possible, furthermore, for personal spending to rise simultaneously with increases in government spending for public goods; the

25. Cf. George J. Stigler, "The Tenable Range of Functions of Local Government," in Edmund S. Phelps, *Private Wants and Public Needs*, (New York: Norton, 1965 Rev. Ed.), pp. 167–176.

two sorts of spending could share the increase in national income. The ideological value attached to a high rate of personal consumption would not have to be repudiated.

The development envisaged thus has a reasonable chance of satisfying the ideological values even of those among the designated managers who have extreme *laissez-faire* views. There is no question about the development being able to satisfy the newer ideology of social responsibility and public service: it would offer multiple concrete examples of ideologically vindicated projects.

## Possible assistance from pressures on management

The enlarged market for public goods is a projection, the prospect of a possible future. It shows how by moves within fairly easy reach an institutional development may occur that would entrain many advantages for the realization of current values and for the emergence of new ones in public discussion. Some of the initial moves are so near at hand that they may occur spontaneously, without a campaign of persuasion, as firms and communities here and there hit upon the possibilities. Some recognizable moves have perhaps occurred already: the contract services of Du Pont, General Electric, and Union Carbide for the Atomic Energy Commission: camp management of Camp Kilmer by Federal Electric for the Job Corps; the participation of insurance companies in medicare; U.S. Gypsum's renovation projects in slum housing; the planned establishment in Arizona and elsewhere of whole new cities by Goodyear, General Electric, and other companies.

Whether the initial moves will be followed up in the quantity and variety envisaged is another matter. I have argued that the values of corporation managers are such as to favor the development; but the favor argued for goes no further than willing acceptance. This acceptance depends, of course, on the market for public goods turning out sooner or later to be attractively profitable. But if it offers the prospect of being profitable, is there anything more to say about its chances of being developed? Cannot the corporations be trusted to discover chances of profit by themselves?

At the outset, however, the development will turn not upon the willingness of corporations to take profits wherever these might be found, but upon their willingness to experiment with new departures in an uncertain situation, where the profits remain to be proved. If the personal values of the managers obstructed such experiments, the risks involved would be that much less likely to be undertaken; so it was of some importance to show that these values are favorable. I can now, with a hypothesis about technology affecting—or threatening to affect—the present jobs of many managers, describe a species of pressure acting upon management that may push favor into activity and multiply experiments in the market for public goods. There are other possible outlets for this pressure; but the pressure, so far as it operates, indicates how technological innovations in the sphere of management itself may push managers and corporations in this direction. Technology helps meet its own problems.[26]

The hypothesis amounts to this: (1) mechanization (substitution of machine processes for physical effort by men) and automation (substitution of machine processes for mental effort) will continue; (2) the tasks now performed in industry by a substantial number of the designated managers will become unnecessary; (3) once these tasks become unnecessary, most of the managers affected will become redundant in their present assignments.

Everyone writing on the subject accepts, I think, the first two parts of the hypothesis. There is some disagreement about how fast mechanization and automation will develop, and some room for conjecture as to how far it will be profitable to carry these processes in different branches of industry.

Leavitt and Whisler, in a famous article,[27] have predicted that as the new information technology comes into widespread use most people in middle management will be demoted. Only a small proportion of the managers whose current assignments become redundant will rise to share the increasingly intricate responsibilities dealt with by committees of top managers. This prognostication lends support to the third part of my hypothesis; but I do not need to go so far. I want, in fact, to treat demotion as just one possibility among others; all that I say in the hypothesis is that a number of designated managers will become redundant in their present assignments, creating an opportunity, perhaps a necessity, of reassigning them.[28]

One may suppose that the redundancy will come about indirectly. Computers will not replace managers one by one; the introduction of computer technology will instead set in motion radical overall reorganizations of management. Some corporations may even now have more managers than they really need for the work to be done; if the work to be done is reorganized, simplified, and in large part handed over to machines, redundancy will

26. A point convincingly, though not whole-heartedly, made by Jacques Ellul, in "The Technological Order," *Technology and Culture*, Vol. 3, No. 4 (Fall, 1962), pp. 394–421 (tr. John Wilkinson); cf. Ellul's book, *La Technique* (Paris, 1962), tr. by Wilkinson under the title *The Technological Society* (New York: Knopf, 1964).

27. Harold J. Leavitt and Thomas L. Whisler, "Management in the 1980's," *Harvard Business Review*, Vol. 36, No. 6 (November/December, 1958), pp. 41–48.

28. Even this prediction is controversial to a degree. Cf. Melvin Anshen, "Managerial Decisions," in John T. Dunlop, ed., *Automation and Technological Change* (Englewood Cliffs, New Jersey: Prentice-Hall, 1962), pp. 66–83.

tend to appear even in corporations hitherto economical in numbers of managers.

What will happen to the managers affected? Some will be eased into retirement. Some of them may be reassigned within their firms to much the same sort of posts as they now hold. If mechanization and automation reduce the quantity of managers needed on the one hand, expanding output, diversifying it, and opening up new sales territories may raise the quantity on the other hand.

In spite of the diversification social output might continue to consist of personal consumers' goods in the same proportion as now. Expansion might be accompanied by intensified frantic efforts to promote private consumption, however frivolous and wasteful it might be. This is one way in which the opportunity for reassignment may be used within American corporations, and perhaps it is the most probable way. Another way, of course, lies in increased armaments and space research expenditures—public goods, but ironically sinister or wasteful ones.

Yet there is surely no guarantee that output expanding along traditional lines will accommodate all the managers to be reassigned, quickly, smoothly, without lay-offs or fears of lay-off. The uncertainties of the situation described by the hypothesis about displacement do in fact confront the designated managers with grounds for considerable alarm. Both those among them who are deciding (in effect) to do away with current managerial assignments and those among them who hold the posts to be done away with—who will be cooperating in making their current assignments redundant—must feel a far-reaching threat to their livelihoods, at least to chances of realizing their values.

One need not suppose that, themselves largely safe, initiating managers will be prepared to do anything very inconvenient or self-sacrificing to help the managers threatened; but one may expect them to assist in various sorts of measures designed to provide new assignments, especially when the assignments contemplated will be profitable to the corporations and satisfactory respecting the shared vocational values. Managers who think themselves liable to be displaced may be expected to be even more receptive. I go beyond expecting receptivity, however: I look for some generous actions, and even more important, a substantial amount of invention and initiative on the part of the managements of some at least of the corporations affected.

I suggest that some of this invention and initiative will find new assignments for managers in the market for public goods. The corporations are under some pressure—at least the pressure of a threat—to find such assignments; and an enlarged market for public goods would be a congenial outlet, though not the only one possible.

## The advantages of the envisaged development

For the reasons canvassed, personal and technological, corporation managers may be much readier to enter into an enlarged market for public goods than some other people traditionally concerned with social progress would be ready to welcome them there. Contemporary left-liberals remain extremely distrustful—for good historic reasons—of private profit-making corporations. Distrust would combine with dislike to make them reluctant to see private corporations making lots of money out of new public projects. Distrust founded in political realism would lead them to fear that the corporations would simultaneously increase their political powers. Many firms are already many times more powerful, economically and politically, than most of the local governments which they would be dealing with; and the authoritarian constitutions of private corporations do not consort well with enlarged powers in a professed democracy.

These misgivings require thorough investigation, before the development envisaged can be categorically recommended. Some of them, however, are answered by the very nature of the development. The authoritarian powers of the corporations would be checked, partly by competition among themselves, partly by the powers exercised by multiple levels and units of government on the other side of the market. Defending themselves against exploitation, these governments would simultaneously be defending their public powers against encroachment. To exercise them would be to defend them.

The institutional arrangements that would emerge from the development would look very different from the arrangements classically expected by the socialist Left. But the Left has not sufficiently exercised its imagination about the future of private corporations. The corporations—in America, certainly—are not going to fade away; and they are not going to ripen to the point of socialization, then undergo expropriation. It is to be imagined that social progress can be carried on ignoring them? To do so, if it were feasible at all, would flagrantly waste human and organizational resources.

A crucial feature of the envisaged development is that it does not leave everything for the government to plan and organize in the public sector; it would make private corporations engines of progressive public policy. There are manifold advantages to be gained from the development. Both in the stages of invention and of first application, new ventures into the market for public goods would offer managers exciting opportunities for realizing their vocational values. (Many of them would also offer congenial employment for workers, too—who might well be happier working, for instance, with trees and flowers on park projects than they were working on their now obsolete assembly line.) There would be lots of organizing to do; lots of things to go wrong; all sorts of people to be managed. Success is likely to be visible, a known public credit to the firm, a matter for recognition within the firm credited, reinforced by some recognition from the community served—or even from the public at large, if the deeds done in this community can be held out as examples to others.

I believe that in the case of many of these collective goods, there would remain interesting opportunities for management (and for nonmanagerial work) even after they ceased (as species) to be novelties. For many of them would require installations custom-designed to some degree, and requiring custom installation: tree planting, for example, in suburbs to any extent irregular in terrain. Others would invite such installation even if they did not require it. One might, for example, imagine smalltown museums being made up largely of combinations of standard components; but the communities concerned might be encouraged by their own leaders to decide upon various distinctive features to be added to the basic combination.

No doubt the values of the reassigned managers would change over time. Discrepancies between the grounds for recognition within the firm and the grounds for official recognition of service to the public would tend to disappear. As a result, the managers affected might become habituated more than they are now, to perfect consistency between these grounds; then concerned that company policies maintain this consistency. The achievements, to some degree unique projects of special organization and installation, would also be more memorable individually. The suggestive association between increasing quantities of output—a typical achievement of the designated managers in their present assignments, but just the sort of achievement most easily taken over by the automatic factory—and proportionately increased earnings would no longer operate so prominently. It would thus be easier, if the public should call for it, to reduce discrepancies between corporation salaries paid in public connections and the salaries of government officials.

To speak technically for a moment,[29] we could expect the values of the designated managers to be redeployed from one sphere of application to another, from the production of other goods to the production of public ones; simultaneously retargeted, so that the typical object of effort becomes an adequate public good, perhaps a unique one, conceived and produced as a whole; and restandardized, with the honors of public service, for example, to some extent displacing monetary rewards as means of recognizing achievement.

We could also expect rescaling—for example, managers might give more

29. Drawing on the technical terminology of Nicholas Rescher's contribution to this volume.

attention to making sure their fellow citizens had interesting lives and less to increasing production or sales regardless of this assurance. This and other changes mentioned would involve redistributing a number of values associated with social progress, extending their support more widely through the managerial class, both among the participating managers and (through discussions within the corporations) to their colleagues.

All the manifold advantages of developing an enlarged market for public goods would be increased by the redirected efforts that the changed values would encourage. In its initial stages, however, the development does not presuppose the changes. The development accords with the values that the designated managers would begin with, and requires them to behave only as they are now ready to behave.

The same reassignments to organizing and installing collective goods demanded by various units of government, state and local, that would give managers new scope for exercising discretion and crisis-capacity represent, on an overall social view, an effective policy of *decentralizing decision-making*. On the corporation side, the policy would offset the encouragement that information technology is currently giving to renewed centralization in the corporations' normal industrial and commercial operations. On the government side, the invention and bargaining called for from small units of government would renew the vitality of these units, evoking more active participation by citizens, and offering a more engaging field for political leadership.

Diversification of corporation profit-making activities in the direction of producing public goods and other goods for collective consumption would build up *within* each corporation *new interests coincident with the public interest*. How different the political picture would be regarding our enormous automobile industry if automobile corporations themselves were as much engaged in traffic-control projects, air-pollution projects, and safety projects, as in selling automobiles! Consider the effect of diversifying the activities of tobacco companies so that they were heavily involved in public health projects. There would, in these cases and similar ones, be voices within the corporations themselves, voices seeking to protect a valuable part of the corporations' own interests, which would moderate the opposition of the corporations to various social policies attractive to the public-spirited. One does not have to imagine that these voices would always be heeded to argue that their presence would do some good.

A similar effect would be brought about by the *circulation* of managers. A lot of managers, one might expect, would occupy for a time posts in the normal industrial and commercial branches of the corporations and then posts in the new branches producing public goods; but then they might be transferred again. Extrapolating present trends, one might expect this circulation to be beneficially complicated by circulation between private employment and government employment and between employment by business and employment in the universities. As a result, the various levels of corporation management would be largely populated with managers of diversified experience, less committed to narrow commercial views.

In the enlarged market for public goods it would become an important part of the corporations' business to look out for such opportunities of public service; to invent them and publicize them (though we are, let it be recalled, contemplating a two-way process, with inventive activity by state and local governments on the demand side). The corporations would, as a predictable consequence, be carried farther into the questionable enterprise of attempting to create tastes through advertising (an enterprise much deplored by Galbraith and others)—but unexpectedly, this time on behalf of public goods, *redressing the imbalance of propaganda* and harmonizing so far at least with Galbraith's own exhortations.

Meanwhile, the most concrete benefits of all would multiply *the public goods* themselves, remedying the backlog of problems, seizing the backlog of opportunities inherited from past economic activity. The problems and opportunities created by current activity would be also dealt with in a more energetic and timely way than heretofore. The third-party costs—for example, of air and water pollution—that have been typical among the problems created by technological change would be remedied by collective solutions. New opportunities of providing public goods hitherto unknown—for example, by centralizing and computerizing diagnostic services; or by modifying local climates—would be quickly taken.

The envisaged development would also make some headway with other types of problems and opportunities. Some of the projects to be organized and installed would be projects of conservation, intended to forestall or offset problems about the depletion of resources. Since so many of them would be locally bargained for and locally oriented the projects would be shaped to match local needs and in many cases (one might expect) they would be designed to remedy adverse shifts of advantage respecting particular regions. The projects would employ workers as well as managers and might compensate as need be for technological unemployment. The projects would easily be assimilated to countercyclical measures and might be varied in quantity to suit national fiscal policy. Finally, there would be some effect in the way of redistribution; consumption and hence real incomes would tend to be equalized as the proportion of satisfactions gained from public goods rose.

The envisaged development will tend to open up conceptual room for debating policies as matters of preference. No doubt both the managers and the politicians involved will try to advertise numbers of the public goods forthcoming as things not merely to be preferred, but inescapably needed. The goods themselves, however, will even from the beginning include amenities that communities could arguably do without. Parks can be dispensed with; more elaborate recreational facilities, dispensed with even more easily. The concept of need does not therefore grasp parks or recreational facilities so firmly as it grasps roads or sewage systems. So far as it does apply to amenities like recreational facilities, it applies only on condition that it tolerates a wide field for possibly very diverse preferences. It may be claimed, for example, that people need recreation; but because recreation connects so intimately with enjoyments and these with preferences, making the claim simultaneously concedes the importance of preferences. If there are, furthermore, variations in needs respecting recreation, these variations will largely reflect variations in preferences.

If debate about public goods is to be debate about preferences, however, what considerations shall be brought up to modify and reconcile preferences? The preferences to be expressed will cry out for relevant means of orientation and guidance; and if the debate is thorough and intelligent, among these means ideals—molecular values—respecting vocations, careers, characters, and life-histories will figure prominently. So far as they are amenities, public goods will typically leave people free to use them or not. But if these public goods displace others, or use resources that might have been available for private consumption, people will have preferences at stake in choosing or rejecting them.

Public goods like neighborhood sports or crafts centers would help engender particular styles of life. Centers for the performing arts, or for liberal adult education, would sustain other styles. Superversatile recreation centers, offering imaginative and technically advanced facilities, would encourage new mixtures of activities, and with them new opportunities for experimental preferences. Choosing among public goods in these and other cases would amount to choosing between social environments, capable in different ways of meeting the preferences which various molecular values inspire and by which they advance or falter. In full debate, not only the preferences, but also the values inspiring them, would command attention.

The development envisaged does not preclude people from rejecting sports centers and the like, and the styles of life founded upon them, in favor (say) of steadily expanding private consumption. (It is wholly to be desired that private consumption be expanded, for many, perhaps for most people living even in the United States.) The market for private goods may well expand side by side with a flourishing and ever expanding market for public goods. Furthermore, in its initial stages, the development may be taken up with projects like controlling air and water pollution that would improve the environment for personal consumption however guided, by ideals of connoisseurship and gourmandizing, or by no ideals at all.

What seems to me crucial is that people should have occasions to consider what they will do with their lives, given the time and opportunities opened up by technology, and by affluence founded upon technology. They need more than occasions to apply received values to choices of environments. They need occasions, which the envisaged development would give them, for exchanging suggestions about adapting and reformulating old ideals; they need occasions to begin inventing and formulating new ones.

In this generation, masses of people have been freed from drudgery only to find to their bewilderment (continually expressed on all sides, for example, in warnings about "the problem of leisure") that character ideals and life-history ideals received from the past are no longer entirely relevant. The values placed upon work and craftsmanship were important ingredients in past character ideals, for example; but technology has continually undermined them from the beginning of the Industrial Revolution. Even professional skills have to some extent been superseded. The possibility of technology sweeping ahead to make given sorts of accomplishment superfluous overshadows with dramatic irony the achievements called for in life-history ideals.[30] There are compensations in the new occupations created by technology; but often these compensations operate for other people, or for the next generation, or are transitory anyway.[31]

Some starting points for public discussion can be foreseen. The question of installing neighborhood sports centers, for example, might well lead to the discovery that with very little adaptation received ideals could be adapted to a life of sports. The excessive value that Americans have been supposed to place on sports, even the excessive professionalization with which they have carried on sports, may turn out to be part of their salvation in the new age of leisure. For sports already offers vocations and careers acceptable to the public; it has room also for character ideals already familiar, and likewise for attractive life-history ideals. Moreover, in none of these respects, it is reassuring to note, is sports ever going to be superseded by technology. Jet planes and rockets flash overhead; but men have not stopped running foot-races—or stopped watching them; and they will never have to.

Vigorous public discussion and development may draw many people into sports—in various capacities—who would otherwise be idle consumers;

---

30. For further discussion of these points, see the third part of the companion paper on needs and preferences.

31. Within a decade, computer technology has already advanced far enough to threaten computer programmers with obsolescence. Cf. H. A. Simon, *The Shape of Automation for Man and Management* (New York: Harper, 1965), p. 48.

but, of course, one need not contemplate sports swallowing up everybody. Other sorts of activity may be intensified simultaneously, by other lines of development and discussion. There are, for example, other permanent preserves in which human activity can flourish safe from the threat of technology: craftsmanship in applied arts; the performing arts; continuous adult education in the liberal arts. With a suitable distribution of facilities, the whole population will be able to repair (after their labors on tasks not yet overtaken by automation) to preserves that suit their personal preferences.

Yet we may hope that technology will be so invitingly organized outside these preserves that people move in and out of them equally happily. The preserves themselves, sensibly managed, will continue to accept all sorts of ancillary devices from technology, sometimes as the basis for new activities (as airplanes and parachutes are the basis for the new sport of sky-diving). Outside the preserves, we might look for the public decision-making centers mentioned earlier—systems for educating people in technology and also providing them with new techniques for its control. We might expect that following the example of these centers the day-to-day operations of private production would be designed in novel ways, to promote educative participation. Our posterity, supplied with suitable practical means, may find their lives made more meaningful in all the branches of their activity by new character-ideals of versatile participation, and new life-history ideals of becoming ever more widely (or ever more deeply) *au courant* with technological change. They may swim happily in currents that they control, in channels that they have themselves projected.

This paper was written as a contribution to the project studying the impact of technological change upon American values, conducted by the Department of Philosophy at the University of Pittsburgh with the support of the International Business Machines Corporation and the Carnegie Corporation of New York. I have profited from discussions with Kurt Baier, Nicholas Rescher, and J. B. Schneewind during my tenure of a research appointment connected with the project; from comments by James A. Wilson of the Pittsburgh School of Business and J. F. Graham and A. M. Sinclair of the Department of Economics at Dalhousie; from criticisms by Lewis A. Dexter, C. E. Lindblom, and a distinguished civil and military engineer named Walter L. Braybrooke; and from remarks by Herbert A. Simon and other participants in the working conference held at the University of Pittsburgh in September 1965. Netta R. Braybrooke drew my attention to a news item about city-building, which I have made use of. Robert Herrick gave me bibliographical help.

# VALUES AND RESEARCH

# The framework of decision
# for major technological innovation

### Bela Gold

## Introduction

Although technological progress has been a powerful force in reshaping our world during the past 150 years,[1] remarkably little is known about the processes whereby such advances are created and brought into widespread use. This may be traced in part to the long prevailing belief that each major technological advance was essentially unique, being ascribable either to inexplicable genius or to an extraordinarily lucky accident. Oddly enough, however, growing realization of the organized structure of science and increasing success in extending its boundaries have likewise failed to enrich our grasp of how technical advances are effectuated—no longer because these are still regarded as incomprehensible, but because they are now assumed to be quite transparent. Thus, technological gains are widely regarded as the virtually inevitable product of organized research and development, with reasonably regularized yields roughly proportioned to the resources applied and effects centered around the guiding objectives of improved products and lowered costs.[2]

Such superficial conceptions would be of little moment were it not for the increasing necessity of learning how this cornucopia functions. The rapid acceleration in the rate of technological progress, the enormous resources which must be invested in its pursuit, the seeming randomness in the volume and direction of its benefits,[3] and, above all, its omnipresent threats

---

1. Illustrative studies include Abramovitz [1, pp. 5–23] and Solow [125, pp. 312–320].
2. Proponents of this general view include: Schumpeter [118, p. 132], Maclaurin [81, p. 104], Galbraith [31, p. 9], and Machlup [78, p. 153]. Opposing views have been offered by: Jewkes, et al, [58, pp. 28–32, 225–230, and 237], Kuznets [73, pp. 47–48], Heald [49, p. 1,111] and Wiesner [143, p. 214]. For an excellent general review, see Nelson [100].
3. For example, see Jewkes [58, ibid], Kuznets [73, ibid], Nelson [101, pp. 299–301], Markham [89, p. 601], Sanders [114, p. 68], Bush [15, p. 1102] and Wirtz [145, p. 43].

to the competitive position not only of individual firms, but of entire industries and even nations—all emphasize our need to clarify the processes
involved. One root of the following analysis is the proposition that
technological advances not only modify the values and behavior modes
of society, but are themselves shaped by the carryover values and implementing beliefs of those who determine how much resources, if any, should
be allocated for developing various kinds of innovations.[4] Accordingly,
attention will be focused first on some prevailing conceptions of the bases
for such managerial decisions and then on the nature and implications
of alternative guides for directing the major innovational programs of
industry.

Analytical structures for exploring new problem areas tend to become
useful only as successive probings transform initially native speculations
into progressively more sharply delineated variables, relationships, processes and criteria. What follows represents the outcome so far of a series of
studies beginning with a volume developing some basic concepts and followed
by: a statistical study of the effects of technological innovations at the level
of aggregates for an array of manufacturing industries in the US; a more
narrowly focused study of technological effects within the American steel
industries; and a fourth concentrated solely on the genesis, development,
execution and results of one major technological innovation in a large
British steel mill.[5] One reason for slowness in developing an effective framework is that reliance on the traditional ritual of the scientific method—
moving smoothly from hypothesis formulation to data collection to analysis
to conclusions[6]—seems to be less helpful in exploring new territory than in
eventually choosing among alternative means of accounting for whatever
phenomena may have attracted the attention of the hopefully alert and
impressionable explorer. Indeed, it is surprising that endless strictures
to adhere to this idealized procedure are so infrequently coupled with
warnings about the probable wastefulness and aridity of hypotheses
crystallized without even reasonable immersion in the complex ac-

4. To illustrate, Klein, tracing the original notion to Schumpeter, suggests that "the forces
   making for efficiency in the narrower sense are deeply ingrained in our society and stand
   in the way of more rapid progress." [69, p. 497]. Others emphasizing the role in resisting
   innovations of behavior patterns conditioned by long prevailing values concerning what is
   considered proper, safe and sound include Maclaurin [82, pp. 178–189], Williams [144,
   p. 125], Rubenstein [110, pp. 385–393] and the findings of a special study by Arthur
   D. Little, Inc. [77, p. 634].
5. The first two have already been completed [36] and [37], the third, which has been
   supported by Resources for the Future, Inc., is scheduled for completion early in 1967;
   and the fourth, which is a joint study with P. W. S. Andrews and E. Brunner of Nuffield
   College, Oxford, is planned for completion by the end of 1968.
6. For indications of the need for more pluralistic conceptions of scientific method, see
   Kaplan [61, pp. 27–31] and Piore [104, p. 19].

tivities and environments whose characteristics are to be diagnosed and explained.[7]

This discussion begins with the assumption that major technological innovations come to fruition within individual firms (or organizations) and are the result of managerial decisions shaped by interactions between changes in external pressures[8] and adjustments in the firm's internal goals, resources and performance prospects—thus suggesting the possibility of developing initially separate (if eventually overlapping) analytical frameworks for each. And resulting decisions, in turn, will initiate new internal and external pressures. Within the chain of relevant managerial decision-forming and decision-implementing processes, analysis will be concentrated on three early links:

a. The role of major technological innovations in promoting the organization's objectives;
b. The processes involved in establishing the technological foundations for major innovations; and
c. The analytical perspectives used in guiding and appraising innovations.

The discussion has been concentrated on major technological innovations both in order to minimize concern with the ambiguous outer boundaries of most attempts to define "technical" "innovations" and also in order to center attention on adjustments large enough to compel overt managerial consideration.

## Elements of a synoptic model

Although the rapidly expanding literature relating to technological innovations is dominated by narrowly focused studies of particular parts of

---

7. On the general aspects of this problem, see P. W. Bridgman [7, pp. 18, 26]; for common shortcomings of analytical models developed in this way, see Kaplan [61, pp. 275–288], Littauer [76, p. B 27] and Bross [8, p. 1,330]. For an illustration of concern about such models in economics, see Carter and Williams [19, pp. 5, 29, 59–62 and 151–152]. For such illustrative constructs, see Kennedy's "Innovation possibility function," [65, pp. 541–547] and the critique of Hicks and Keynes by Carter and Williams [19, pp. 160–163].

8. One significant environmental pressure consists of changes in available technical knowledge (cf. Nelson [98, p. 13], Peck [102, p. 298], Rubel [109, p. 34] and Freeman [30, pp. 21–39]). A second major environmental pressure takes the form of shifts in product and factor markets (cf. Hicks [52, Chapter 6], Brozen [11, pp. 288–302], Salter [113, pp. 43–44], Fellner [28, pp. 171–194], and Kennedy [*ibid*]). Cross-sectionally, new technical knowledge may be conceived as flowing from one firm to others in the industry, to other domestic industries and abroad, as well as in the reverse directions. (For example, see Mansfield [83, pp. 741–766]; and his [85, pp. 290–309], Rosenberg, [108, pp. 424 *et. seq.*], Strassman [129, pp. 16–22], and Woodruff [146, pp. 479–497].)

this extensive domain, many seem to reflect essentially similar, though unstated, conceptions of the basic system of relationships involved. It may be useful to outline a structure of such implicit hypotheses so as to crystallize views which appear to be widely accepted and to highlight the contrasting hypotheses to be offered later.

One of the four major building blocks of such a synoptic model is the belief that technological innovations are inherently attractive, especially in terms of the economic rewards which are considered to be over-riding in business organizations.[9] In one direction, innovations are expected to reduce production costs through decreasing waste, increasing the "productivity" of inputs, or permitting shifts to cheaper factors of production. Other innovations yielding new or improved products are expected to enhance sales revenue through expanding old markets, opening new markets, or permitting higher product prices. Such impressive potentials are held to explain the special predilection for promoting technological advances which is deemed to characterize management, at least in American Industry.

A second major building block centers around the view that technological innovations in individual firms are generally the product of processes which are planned and accordingly tend to be concentrated in the areas chosen by management.[10] As for the controllability of innovation-generating processes, this is usually taken to bear less on the proportion or speed of successes achieved than on the capacity to choose: between pioneering and following others; between high risk-high reward and low risk-low reward alternatives; and between continuing with a succession of inter-related innovations and stopping such a sequence at any given stage.

Another major building block is the view that major technological

9. For reflections of such business attitudes, see Holland [56, Chapter 2], Larrabee et al. quoted in Silk [123, p. 170] and Keezer et al. [63, pp. 355-369]. Economists expressing similar views include: Schmookler [126, pp. 183-190], Carter and Williams [18, p. 38], Nelson [100, p. 101], Brozen [12, pp. 204-217], Sutherland [130, pp. 118-135], and Minasian [94, pp. 93-141]. Those placing primary emphasis on expanding markets include: Sayers [115, pp. 275-291], Coales [21, pp. 239-242], Brown [9, pp. 406-425], Ulin [133, p. 27] and Peck [102, p. 295]. In this connection, special attention should also be given to Penrose's view that "a kind of 'competition in creativity' has become a dominant motif in the pattern of competitive behavior in many industries" [103, p. 106].

10. For assertions that such control is exercised, see quotes from Kreps and Galbraith in Nelson [100, p. 111], as well as Maclaurin [81, p. 104], and Harrel [48, Chapter 8]. For implied acceptance of this view via assertions that business men only do what seems profitable to them, see Machlup [78, p. 153], Fellner [28, pp. 171-194] and Griliches [45, p. 349]. A rationale for approaching such decisions is suggested by Nelson [101, p. 300]. Choices about the degree of pioneering and risk to be undertaken are suggested by Mansfield [85, pp. 290-311] and by Anthony and Day [3, p. 128]. Such assumptions are also implicit in the wide range of studies which seek to deduce decision processes and rules by working backward from actual results, as though these represented an essentially planned or reasonably probable outcome.

advances are generated through a chain of essentially rational decisions organized with self-improving feedbacks.[11] Specifically, the objectives of such innovational efforts are assumed to derive from the organization's defined goals. In turn, it is assumed that alternative means of promoting such technological objectives are appraised by scientists and engineers in order to estimate prospective benefits, risks and costs on the basis of procedures which are reasonably reliable and likely to become increasingly accurate as the result of cumulative experience. Subsequent managerial decisions are then presumed to supplement the foregoing with objective determinations concerning the availability of needed resources, the attractiveness of estimated returns as compared with attendant burdens, and the most propitious time to initiate approved undertakings. It is also supposed that actual results are compared with earlier expectations, so that significant deviations may be used as bases for improving future evaluations.

One additional building block is the increasingly pervasive belief that research and development programs constitute the most important means of effecting significant technological progress within individual firms and, hence, of enhancing growth and profitability.[12] This view seems to rest on such assumptions as the following: that many, and perhaps most, major products and processes are surrounded by technological frontiers which offer reasonably numerous opportunities for achieving major advances; that the most promising of these can be identified by experts in the relevant technical fields; and that the chances of succeeding in such attempts can be substantially improved by increasing the resources applied to them. An alternative source of encouragement to this heavy emphasis on research and development programs seems to be the increasingly common tendency to trace the outstanding successes of selected prominent firms back to earlier achievements in research and development, often without serious attention to other possible influences.

Taken together, these building blocks yield a model which combines

---

11. For the relationship between management goals and research criteria, see Rubenstein [111, pp. 95–105]. For references to the elements of such evaluative processes, see Hertz [51, p. 212], Siegal [122, pp. 161–177], Mottley and Newton [95, pp. 740–751], Spengler [128, p. 434] and Jones [59, p. 1094].

12. For comments at the level of industries or higher levels of aggregation, see Freeman [30, pp. 21–39], Terleckyj [132, in P. M. Gutmann, p. 143] and Rubel [109, p. 44]. For expectations and empirical findings that research inputs may be expected to rise on the average with increases in research outputs, see Silk [123, p. 170], Ulin [133, p. 27], Mansfield [86, pp. 319–349] and [87, pp. 310–322] and Comanor [23, pp. 182–190] as well as Machlup [78, pp. 152–153], and Griliches [45, pp. 349–350]. For a penetrating study of the limited extent to which even firms famous for their research capabilities have relied for growth on internal discoveries, see Mueller [97, pp. 80–86] and [96, pp. 323–346].

the appeals of simplicity, rationality and seeming relevance both to widespread interpretations of recent business experience and to common conceptions of the decision-making processes of management.

## Weaknesses in the synoptic model

Studies of technological change in recent years have yielded a confusing patchwork of new concepts and empirical results, which may well be characteristic of the exploratory period in new fields before the centripetal pressures of rigorous analysis begin to produce a coherent nucleus shading off into at least vaguely discernible frontiers. Both the difficulties of effectively grasping such a large and chaotic domain and the common assumption of the nonspecialist that whatever is familiar is probably understood have encouraged reliance on relatively simple notions by those who are concerned only with particular bits of the field, or who wish only to use part of it as a foundation for models centered around their own specialties. Serious examination of the relevant literature, however, reveals ample basis for doubt about virtually every major element in the preceding synoptic model.

In presenting the synoptic model, attention was given first to the motivations for undertaking major innovational programs. The claim that such decisions seek to promote the dominant business objective of profitability through increasing markets and reducing costs would seem to be reasonable enough, but too superficial to be helpful. Such guides do not explain how choices are made between allocating resources for new innovational programs as over against production, marketing and other functions presumably serving the same over-riding objectives. Nor do they explain how choices are made among alternative innovational ventures; or even how profit criteria are applied in balancing a low probability of gaining substantial rewards after an extended period of uncertain duration against the certainty of significant and perhaps mounting outlays over an indefinite period. Until a more effective bridge is developed between eventual general objectives and the quite specific choices which managers must make, there is likely to be continuing resort to the meaningless rationalization that: IF managers made a given decision, they must have expected it to be profitable. Moreover, it would seem to be worth exploring the possibility that increasing concern with research and development programs may be engendering new perspectives in managerial definitions of the composition, dimensions and patterns of profit and related desiderata—thus opening the way to new strategies and decision criteria.

Field studies also suggest the need to consider a variety of other direct motivations, some of which may, of course, be traced back to the general goal of profitability.[13] For example, some managers feel that because the future will undoubtedly be different, survival requires participation in the stream of change even if one is not sure of where it is leading and cannot contrive persuasive estimates of attractive returns from individual undertakings; and a rather similar view holds that innovations which are technically sound will eventually pay, although attendant investments usually do not seem justifiable at the time of consideration. What may be regarded as a bootstrap argument holds that innovations are necessary to maintain the quality and morale of development staffs; and some have extended this argument to affect the image of progressivism of the firm and its capacity to attract good personnel. At a seemingly far distant pole from these, Keynes argues that many major business decisions are taken "as a result of animal spirits—of a spontaneous urge to action rather than inaction." And still others see such decisions as traceable to "policy," regarded as an undefined complex of strategies which overshadows whatever quantitative assessments of outlays and returns can be made for individual proposals.

Although almost every empirical contribution is valuable in view of the paucity of information, most studies have almost inevitably been confined to such fragmentary coverage of the surrounding domain as to advise against the generalization of their results. Not only have they tended to encompass only a few outstanding industries and companies instead of anything approaching "representative" coverage, but most have concentrated on successful projects rather than examining cross-sectional samples of all undertakings, and most have also been restricted to recent, as well as relatively short, periods. In addition, the analytical integration of these various undertakings is hampered by the continuing absence of effective bases for classifying different kinds of innovational undertakings [73, p. 30].

At levels beyond the firm, numerous challenges have been offered to the thesis that R & D outlays lead to major innovations which, in turn, engender economic growth. Some note that beneath the average association between aggregates for R & D and for economic output may be found wide variations in such relationships between successive time periods, among different regions, and among industries. Others go on to stress that such statistical relationships may be quite misleading until they can be based on more careful explorations of the nature of research and technological changes and the means whereby these are likely to alter the loci, composition, quality and magnitude of goods and services.[14] At the level of the firm, despite

13. Illustrations of such views include: Hershey [50, p. 263], Sutherland [130, pp. 118–135], Carter and Williams [19, p. 56], Nelson [100, p. 124], Keynes [66, pp. 161–162] and Andrews and Brunner [2, pp. 355–356].
14. For example, see Rubel [109, pp. 30–31], Wiesner [143, p. 214], A. D. Little report [77, p. 642], Gordon [43, p. 274] and Carter and Williams [18, p. 19].

an array of perceptive studies by Mansfield and a few others, there is wide-spread agreement that available evidences of correlation between innovational efforts and profits or growth are still far from convincing.[15] There is also some empirical evidence suggesting that a succession of major innovations failed to lower average total unit costs significantly, even after deflation, in each of a number of large industries [37, pp. 108–118].

One of the most critical elements of the synoptic model concerns whether management can choose or control: the specific areas in which innovations will eventuate; the balance in its innovational portfolio among high, medium and low "payoff-and-risk" projects; and the proportions between undertakings which are far from, and those which are near, fruition. Although almost all students agree that research and major developmental undertakings are subject to great uncertainties, such general warnings are frequently brushed aside in the course of constructing rational models to guide managerial decisions in this area. Unfortunately, the overwhelming evidence from empirical studies so far is that, except for relatively routine improvement projects, unpredictability is pervasive. It seems to be difficult to predict: the kinds of inventions or discoveries likely to occur; the kinds of applications likely to be made of new discoveries; how close to successful fruition given undertakings are; and even how alternative designs or carefully developed theoretical models will turn out.[16]

However compelling the logic of rationally structured and quantitatively scaled models for evaluating innovational proposals as a basis for management decisions, most of the evidence from field studies indicates that these are either not used at all, or play only a minor role. Indeed, the need to account for such seemingly widespread perversity reaches beyond innovations to investment decisions at large. Probing somewhat deeper, empirical studies suggest that, when evaluative models are used, the target or cut-off criteria prove to be either vague or quite flexible in most instances and are further cushioned by a variety of often partially concealed allowances.[17]

---

15. For supporting evidence, see Mansfield [86, pp. 319–340] and [87, pp. 310–322] as well as Minasian [94, pp. 100 et seq.] and Comanor [23, pp. 182–190]; for expressions of continuing doubt, see Griliches [45, pp. 349–350], Hitch [55, p. 193], Sanders [114, p. 64], Mueller [96, p. 344], Hershey [50, p. 263] and Quinn and Cavanaugh [105, p. 118].

16. The widest coverage of these points is provided by Jewkes et al. [58, pp. 150–151, 225–226, 230 and 237] and Nelson [100, pp. 112–113, 118] and also in his [101, pp. 299, 301]. Other useful findings are provided by Kuznets [73, pp. 47–48], Mueller [96, pp. 323–358], Marshall and Meckling [92, p. 463], Klein [68, pp. 478–480; 69, p. 508], Carter and Williams [18, p. 19], Coales [21, pp. 239–242], Rubel [109, pp. 35, 43] and von Braun [141, p. 1080].

17. Relevant findings for innovations are provided by Carter and Williams [19, pp. 59–65, 73–74, 105], Nelson [100, pp. 124–125], Williams [144, pp. 116–118], Andrews and Brunner [2, pp. 355–356] and Sutherland [130, pp. 118–135]. For a recent critique of the state of investment theory, see D. M. Lamberton [74, Chapter 5].

Moreover, post-mortems reveal that actual costs and returns are frequently at considerable variance with expectations,[18] that relationships between innovational inputs and outputs fluctuate over a wide range and that, for all the hope of improvement through feedbacks, there is no evidence of increases in the "productivity" of persons engaged in innovative activities.[19]

## Changing guides in managerial decision-making

In exploring management decisions in respect to major innovations, it seems useful to begin by considering the general guides which condition managerial sifting of information and weighing of alternatives in taking action on individual proposals. Such deep-rooted value orientations are especially influential when issues are not obviously determined by the available evidence alone, i.e., when important elements of the evaluation process are missing or largely indeterminate and hence have to be filled in by judgments for whose consequences executives must accept responsibility. Indeed, such value orientations are even likely to condition conceptions of how much and what kinds of information should be gathered before decisions can be made [19, p. 103]. It is to these foundations that it may be necessary to turn, therefore, both in seeking to account for consistent patterns of decision among an array of individually varied proposals and in seeking to design strategies for altering such patterns [144, p. 125].

Several decades have passed since a foreign visitor characterized American managers as tending to rely on action in place of thought and optimism in place of analysis. Whatever fragments of contemporary truth may have been caught up in this observation, students of the managerial ethos realize that it has been subject to far-reaching transformations under continuing pressures from changes in technological imperatives and potentials as well as from changes in social objectives and political constraints.

The general nature of such reorientations in decision frameworks may be illustrated by the familiar sequence of metamorphoses which led from producing goods for one customer at a time to producing simultaneously for many customers by increasing the number of production units using essentially small scale methods and on to mass production techniques incapable of producing small quantities economically. Distribution progressed similarly, of course, from servicing one customer at a time to servicing many customers

18. Examples are provided by Carter and Williams [19, pp. 89–92], Marshall and Meckling [92, pp. 471–475], Rubel [109, p. 35] and Gold [37, pp. 105–110].
19. See the findings of Enos [27, p. 310], Griliches [45, p. 349], Hitch [55, p. 193], Mueller [96, pp. 342–344], Sanders [114, pp. 64, 68], Markham [89, p. 601] and Worley [147, p. 234], as well as the strong experiential judgments of Quinn and Cavanaugh [105, p. 118], Heald [49, p. 1111] and Bush [15, p. 1102].

simultaneously by multiplying the utilization of small scale methods (more salesmen, more small stores hooked into chains, etc.) and on to mass marketing techniques (e.g., national advertising) not economical for small scale operations. Both in production and in marketing, each of these transformations necessitated extensive changes in the tasks to be performed, skills required, risks involved, organizational adaptations developed and even in the time perspectives for planning and evaluating performance. The resulting necessity for reshaping the values and supporting behavior patterns underlying managerial decisions has always been clearly perceived on the basis of hindsight. But it can hardly occasion any surprise that managers, like other people, tend to face new problems and situations by relying on the knowledge and judgments tested by past experience and hence exhibit behavior which seems inhospitable to major innovations. Thus, production and marketing innovations either had to be cut down into bite-size experimental doses or face long delays. The latter has been illustrated by the even more shocking changes, as viewed in the upper echelons of production-dominated companies, forced by the fact that mass production methods have enhanced reliance on mass marketing for survival—with attendant shifts in budget, organizational power and the influence of ideas which seemed distasteful as well as alien to specialists in manufacturing.

Although analogies are notoriously unreliable, it may be of interest to consider the implications of adjustments in research and development functions similar to those undergone by production and marketing. A shift from a few scientists and engineers working individually to laboratories with large staffs continuing to employ small scale methods has already occurred with some frequency in the US and Western Europe. Even larger scale and more specialized operations may well emerge in increasing numbers, perhaps along lines already reflected by some governmental installations. And the very powers of mass marketing to saturate existing markets more rapidly may tend to encourage the intensification of R & D programs in some industries to create the new products for which their marketing organizations are waiting to stimulate demand—a possibility which has been illustrated during the past twenty years by the pharmaceutical drug industry's sharp increase in research budgets.[20]

Readjustments in the managerial ethos have also been forced by (a) industry's expanding array of highly specialized functions, necessitating efforts to integrate their quite distinctive contributions and to determine changes in the relative need for each; and (b) increasingly comprehensive and sophisticated criteria for evaluating corporate performance, urging the justification of an increasing proportion of decisions on objective grounds.

20. For revelant data on the drug industry, see Comanor [22, pp. 377–382].

Together, these and other major industrial developments, it may be hypothesized, have induced gradual shifts in such general guides within the
decision-making framework of management as the following:

1. Favoring short term profitability over prospective long term gains;
   > But the increasing need for heavy capital facilities and the mount-
   > ing concern of investors and prospective employees with growth
   > potentials have tended to alter the balance between these goals.
2. Favoring direct revenue-producing operations over activities offering
   only indirect benefits;
   > But the increasing problems of coordinating complex organiza-
   > tions has led to a rapid expansion of staff functions, e.g., accounting,
   > finance, budgeting and corporate planning.
3. Favoring continued specialization on established products and processes over trying to invade the established specialties of others;
   > But increasing diversification has been encouraged by demonstra-
   > tions that the disadvantages of less experience with given products
   > and processes may be more than offset by advantages in selling or
   > distribution of servicing facilities, etc.
4. Favoring the benefits of maintaining the prevailing allocation of
   budget and influence among major components of large organizations over the possible gains offered by adjustments likely to disrupt
   such harmony;
   > But the development of new technologies combined with needs
   > which cannot be dealt with adequately within existing organiza-
   > tional units has forced acceptance of quality control, data proces-
   > sing, market research and executive development.
5. Favoring efforts to maximize the efficiency of established operations
   over diverting resources to explore new kinds of undertakings;
   > But new technological potentials and market pressures have led
   > manufacturers to consider backward and forward integration, new
   > distribution arrangements and financing terms for customers as
   > well as the expansion of product lines.
6. Favoring proposals amenable to fairly rigorous estimates of prospective outlays and returns over those resting primarily on qualitative
   judgments of prospective results;
   > Although this tendency has been intensified by the popularity of
   > capital budgeting and cost-benefit analysis, the continuing im-
   > portance of other appeals seems to be evidenced by many recent
   > entries into international operations, integrated data processing
   > systems and research.

7. Favoring the extension of tight managerial controls over pressures in the opposite direction;

> This has led to progressively tighter controls over sales and office operations, but its limitations seem to be gaining recognition in respect to advertising, executive development and corporate planning.

Some of these illustrative "guidelines" overlap, of course, while others might have been added, but the point being emphasized here is that the bases for managerial decisions have already responded, albeit slowly, to the pressures generated by technological and other changes—though they continue to lag sufficiently to slow the adoption of innovations and to moderate, if not minimize, efforts to develop new advances. In order to understand more clearly how such generalized inclinations are brought to bear on the engendering of major technological innovations, it is necessary to examine the successive stages of such decision-making processes and this will be the primary task of the remainder of this paper.

Before turning to that undertaking, however, it seems useful to suggest a broadening of the concept of managerial decisions. Instead of regarding them as climatic actions which can be effectively isolated for analytical purposes, it may prove more useful to regard them as elements in a stream of successive temporary commitments, each of which is heavily conditioned by the network of prior decisions and is subject to repeated later alterations on the basis of additional information, adjusted goals and newly emerging pressures and alternatives. This shift in concept would serve both to decrease the significance of demonstrated deviations between *final* results and the expectations leading to the *initial* decisions and also to increase the importance of informational feedbacks and of organizational adaptability in determining the effectiveness of managerial responses to the changing determinants of successful performance.

## On the role of major innovations in promoting organizational objectives

Efforts to develop a more useful analytical framework may be initiated by first considering the role of technological innovations among the array of means for promoting the objectives of the firm and then examining the role of research and development in advancing defined innovational goals.

A. *Technological innovations and organizational objectives*
Basic hypotheses which may be hazarded in this area include:
1. That in most firms top management tends to have a reasonably

stable hierarchy of preferences among the means of promoting its primary objectives (such as improving or maintaining: profitability; growth; market position; security of assets; relative stability of operating levels; and a favorable public image);

2. That the highest ranking of these preferences generally involve policies providing for the continuation, or only moderate intensification, of familiar instrumentalities involving little risk to established organizational structures or patterns of resource allocations (e.g., modest improvements in products and distributive arrangements; relatively limited additions to productive capacity not involving major innovations in processes; and reductions in production costs via gradual improvements in techniques and facilities as well as progressive reductions in waste);

3. That the generation or pioneering adoption of major technological innovations is likely to rank low in the preceding hierarchy because it tends to involve heavy investments, substantial risks and readjustments in existing organizational arrangements and budgetary allocations affecting many functions and operating divisions;[21]

4. That there tends to be but limited resort to such lower ranking preferences except: (a) when more favored means prove inadequate; (b) when extra-market factors (e.g., governmental pressures or subsidies) alter the relative potentials or costs of hitherto low-ranked alternatives; (c) when technological advances by competitors threaten mounting disadvantages; or (d) when continuing internal technological development programs yield unexpectedly substantial potentials; and

5. That the belief is nevertheless widespread that technological progress is inevitable and important in the long run and hence cannot be entirely neglected without serious hazard.

One implication of these hypotheses is that in most organizations technological progress is not a primary or self-justifying objective at all, but merely one among an array of means of promoting more fundamental desiderata. This means that effective evaluation of given innovations requires determination of the particular purposes motivating their adoption—and might yield different results depending on the relative importance of various possible criteria (e.g., preventing increases in unit labor costs; improving product quality; matching a competitor's product modification, etc.). Recognition that technological innovations tend invariably to be part of a complex

21. Evidences of such tendencies are presented by Keezer *et al* [62, p. 59], Williams [144, p. 125], a study by Arthur D. Little, Inc. [77, p. 634], and Wiesner [143, p. 214]. Jewkes *et al* even point to industrial research laboratories as sources of resistance to change [58, pp. 184–185]. For indications of pressure to retain or restore established allocation shares among parts of the organization, see Gold [37, pp. 126–127] and Cyert and March [24, p. 30, Chapter 5, p. 120].

of policies and actions designed to be mutually reinforcing raises additional doubts about simplistic efforts to assess the outcome of technological innovations as though these could easily be isolated from the interacting system which gives rise to their introduction and through which they must work out their effects. In short, it seems analytically untenable to assume that the effects of technological innovations can be soundly assessed in terms of concomitant—or, for that matter, lagged—adjustments in profits. Instead, it would seem desirable to construct more intricate models indicating the complex of parallel and serial linkages through which technological innovations undertaken for any of a variety of purposes interact with other adjustments in input and output flows and in product and factor prices to shape cost, revenue and investment patterns.[22]

Another implication of the preceding hypotheses is that the extent of reliance on programs involving the promotion of technological progress would tend to differ among industries and firms at any given time,[23] and would also tend to differ within individual firms and industries, according to the adequacy of preferred alternatives for achieving organizational objectives both over the course of business cycles and over the course of longer term growth patterns.[24] This view opens the way to a variety of interesting speculations. For example, are there major "cultural differences" among industries in the continuity and seriousness of their reliance on technological progress? If so, are these traceable to the conditioning generated by the rate of past major technological advances (e.g., as reflected by the differences between chemicals and electronics on the one hand as compared with railroads and food canning)? Does concern with technological progress tend to be stimulated more by rising or by declining profits? by rising or by declining growth rates? Are technological potentials expected to contract as an industry grows older? It may be well to probe the range of experiences with technological leads and lags at considerably greater length than has been accomplished so far before assuming the universality of the stimuli and effects as well as of the processes involved. Surely, it is too early in the development of this field of inquiry to reject the possibility that greater understanding may be achieved

22. The need for more complex models is also indicated by Carter and Williams [19, pp. 5, 29, 151–152 and 160–164], and by Williams [144, pp. 117 et. seq.]. For a crude model, illustrative of some of these complexities, see Gold [37, p. 122]. For general philosophic support of such a position, see Kaplan [61, pp. 316–319].

23. Studies tending to support this view include Kendrick [64, pp. 248–275], Jewkes et al. [58, pp. 156–158, 184–185], Rubel [109, pp. 34, 39] and Carter and Williams [19, p. 18].

24. For cyclical and other intermediate term variations in pressures for technical changes, see Hicks [33, pp. 299–302], Sayers [115, pp. 275–291], Brozen [10, pp. 239–257], Holland [56, p. 15] and Cyert and March [24, pp. 278–279]. Longer term factors affecting interest in technological advances are discussed by Burns [14, pp. 120–158], Kuznets [72, Chapter 9], Schmookler [117, pp. 1–19] and Gold [38, pp. 62–63].

by permitting the emergence of various kinds of models to cover different sectors of industry and different sets of concomitant economic conditions.[25]

Still another implication of these hypotheses is that seeking to generate major technological innovations may rank low in management's hierarchy of resource allocation preferences because the essentially unfathomable uncertainties involved in estimating the timing and magnitude of prospective benefits (including the effects of attendant disruptions in other aspects of company operations) prevents their effective assessment within the analytical frameworks used to make decisions among more familiar allocation alternatives. For example, field studies have emphasized the need to consider—along with the extreme difficulties of estimating—the chances of achieving technical success on individual projects, of carrying such fortunate outcomes on to the development of commercially practicable products and of then finally reaping rewards from the entire process through efficient manufacturing, marketing and distribution. And, in addition, it is also necessary to estimate how long these sequential stages are likely to take, how much investment they will require, probable changes in price and demand over the five to fifteen year periods commonly involved and concomitant advances achieved by competitors.[26] Faithful adherence to formal capital budgeting procedures when so wide an array of required input data is unpersuasive provides little assurance to managements asked to stake huge sums on the undertaking, however much the introduction of assumed or subjective probabilities may facilitate the solution of classroom exercises.

Indeed, it is even conceivable that this area of inapplicability is less exceptional than appears to be the case—i.e., that the analytical techniques most widely used in the economic theory of the firm to provide rational solutions to decision-making problems may be directly applicable only to relatively routine issues of limited consequence, offering little more than vague conceptual guides and generalized computational procedures for coping with the really strategic decisions confronting top management. Thus, it may be necessary to experiment with new kinds of analytical frameworks to deal not only with allocations for developing major technological innovations, but also with other far-reaching decisions affecting additions to productive capacity, drastic shifts in the breadth of product lines, the invasion of new

25. For empirical findings suggesting such possibilities, see Gold [38, pp. 53–73] and [40, pp. 164–197].
26. A variety of studies provide helpful insights bearing on these problems, with the widest coverage offered by Jewkes *et al* [58, pp. 150 *et. seq.*, pp. 220–221, 237 and 266–267], Carter and Williams [19, pp. 89–92], Williams [144, pp. 121–122] and especially Enos [27, pp. 305], Mueller [96, pp. 342–344], Marshall and Meckling [92, pp. 461, 465, 471–475] and Klein [68, pp. 478, 480] and [69, p. 508]. More narrowly focusses findings and comments are offered by Carter and Williams [18, p. 19], Ulin [133, p. 27], Quinn and Cavanaugh [105, p. 115] and Hershey [50, p. 236].

markets, the reorganization of distributive channels, acquisitions or mergers with other firms, etc.[27] And the usefulness of such frameworks will probably rest less on the logic of computational procedures for aggregating, discounting and comparing assumed outlays and incomes than on the degree of penetration of their conceptions of the processes underlying the outcomes to be evaluated.

Finally, the combination of the preceding hypotheses implies a need for managements in many industries to develop a strategy for coping with two broadly opposing pressures. One, generated by extensive past experience indicating that the incidence of major technological advances is small and randomly distributed through time, suggests a low probability of such a development within any given operating period. The other, which may be rooted in that same experience, in addition to being reinforced by prevailing attitudes in industry at large, warns that when such major advances do emerge their effects on relative competitive positions may be drastic. Formulation of an approach towards balancing responses to these pressures would seem to require the clarification of objectives in this sector followed by elucidation of the conceptual bases for implementing specified intentions —both of which will be discussed in the following sections.

## B. *Managerial approaches to advancing technological levels*

The following hypotheses suggest some of the bases which may enter into the shaping of managerial objectives affecting the level and composition of allocations for advancing the technological base of its activities:

1. That, instead of seeking to achieve a significant technological lead over all competitors, most managements have sought only to keep pace on the average with their competitive peers, and some have even been willing to condone lags behind such peers, provided that such lags were either no greater than could be offset by the given firm's superiority in other respects (e.g., marketing) or no greater than could be overcome within, say, one year through feasible increases in allocations for this purpose.[28]

2. That, within the complex domain of technology, most managements have tended to exhibit well developed preferences among the possible foci of efforts to achieve advances:

(a) favoring improvements in products over adjustments in production

27. For other relevant observations, see Keynes [66, pp. 149–150], Carter and Williams [19, pp. 5, 29, 151–152, 160–164], Andrews and Brunner [2, pp. 355–356], Klein and Meckling [70, p. 362], Williams [144, pp. 121–122], Lamberton [74, pp. 122–146], and Gold [36, pp. 48–54].

28. For comments on the "defensive" aspects of research see Keezer [63, pp. 355–369], Quinn and Cavanaugh [105, p. 119], Shonfield [121, p. 370] and Carter and Williams [19, pp. 65–66].

operations, favoring modifications in the design and properties of established products over attempts to create entirely new kinds of products, favoring changes in operating methods over the redesign of facilities and equipment; and being still less favorable towards efforts to alter the foundations of basic processes;[29]

(b) preferring *tinkering* with minor improvements based on *ad hoc* suggestions over developing successive evolutionary gains along established lines of scientific and engineering progress, and preferring the *adoption* of major innovations developed and proved to be commercially practicable by others (via purchasing licenses or equipment or designs) over undertaking *basic research* in the hope of generating major advances;[30] and

3. That progressive experience with R & D tends to increase the resources devoted to such programs, to enhance their role in determining the rate and direction of technological progress in most firms and to reduce the ratio of "low risk–low payoff" projects.[31]

One implication of these hypotheses derives from the fact that similar tendencies towards limited commitments characterized early managerial approaches to other new corporate functions, including marketing, international operations, corporate planning and computerized information and control systems. But each developed gradually as increasingly knowledgeable specialists became available, as management became more familiar with the range and importance of its potential contributions, and as new criteria for evaluating such activities emerged. Accordingly, it may not be unrealistic to anticipate a similar exfoliation of R & D, or of a more broadly conceived innovational function reaching beyond products and processes alone. Effective appraisal of such possibilities, however, would seem to require supplementing the numerous studies of current resource allocations, organizational arrangements and work foci of R & D programs by analyses of historical changes in such patterns and of the factors associated with them. In particular, it seems important to learn to what extent the vague, global concept of R & D has been giving way in managerial thinking to an awareness of its more sharply defined components, e.g., separating quality control and the minor modification of products for special customer needs from more far-reaching explorations of new kinds of products and processes. And an associated need

29. Scattered evidences of such preference orders may be gleaned from: Bloom [6, pp. 603–617], Wiesner [143, p. 214], Comanor [22, pp. 374, 377–378], Markham [89, p. 595] and Carter and Williams [19, p. 56].

30. Similar general inclinations have been noted by Maclaurin [79, pp. 385–396], Keezer *et al.* [62, p. 62] and Villard [140, pp. 483–497].

31. For opposing viewpoints, see Keezer *et al.* [62, p. 62], Brozen [12, pp. 273–276], and Rubel [109, p. 40].

relates to the evolution of more clearly formulated conceptual bases for determining allocations for R & D projects and for the program as a whole.[32]

A second implication concerns the likelihood of wide differences among competitors in their reliance on, and in their expectations of, innovational programs. In part, this might merely reflect perceptions of relative strength in other major determinants of the firm's competitive position. But such differences may also derive from divergent views of the relative benefits of varying degrees of pioneering as over against "following the leader" or imitating. In a culture which regards it as an heroic virtue, executives are almost compelled to pay at least lip service to pioneering not only in publicity releases, where even fake lions can roar, but in the form of R & D budgets to be noted by security analysts and by stockholders. Is there evidence, however to support the mythology? Have the largest or the most profitable firms been the most prolific in generating major technological advances? Has the enormous growth and influence of the automobile industry and of its dominant firms, for example, been associated with a continuing torrent of major research advances? Relevant evidence would require long term studies of whether the rewards of consistent technological pioneering are frequent and large enough to offset the cumulative drains; of whether "catching up" with the actual discoveries made by others is a feasible strategy and also economically advantageous; and of whether the delays and difficulties involved in effective commercialization of proved technological advances seriously limits resulting benefits to the originating firm as compared with competitors tending to place a heavier emphasis on marketing strength than on technological pioneering. Moreover, the possibility must be considered that such questions may evoke disparate answers in different industries and that even objective analyses may yield results which differ with the length of the evaluative period used.[33]

Such considerations also suggest the possibility of fundamental contradictions between the actual roles assigned to R & D in many company programs and the criteria used by managers and external analysts to appraise resulting contributions. It is a commonplace, of course, that R & D covers a wide range of activities, but greater emphasis is needed on the fact that

---

32. For comments on the circularity, inconsistancy and variability of the rationales offered by some respondents, see Jewkes *et al.* [58, pp. 142–143] and Nelson [100, p. 122]. But the impression of groping confusion yielded by such cross-section studies may be quite different from the progressive (if still not complete) clarification of purposes emerging within companies over the years of experience in this area. One of the quite uncommon sources of support for the above view that R & D may be expected to move in the direction of more far-reaching projects is Kornhauser [71, Chapter 3].

33. Some consideration of these matters may be found in Marris [90, pp. 175 *et seq.*], Penrose [103, pp. 112–115], Sutherland [130, pp. 118–135], Gass [32, pp. 93–112] and Mansfield [84, pp. 1023–1051].

evaluative criteria may cover an equally broad spectrum and, hence, that relevance depends on carefully matching planned with actual performance. Even where R & D is dominated by essentially routinized efforts to effect successive small increments in the manufactured quality and in the service features of established products, efforts to appraise its success in terms of adjustments within one year or two in product sales, market shares and profitability may be considered appropriate only when one can persuasively neutralize the effects of concurrent changes in market conditions and all other company programs and policies—and when R & D was not devoted primarily to safeguarding established positions by keeping pace with competitive advances. But it might be quite misleading to apply these same criteria to R & D programs involving heavy commitments to more far-reaching advances which are likely to require longer periods, to absorb greater resources and to produce a higher ratio of failures. On the contrary, yields in such cases might have a greater bearing on long-term growth and even survival than on shorter term sales and profits; and might engender diversification into new fields instead of increasing shares in present markets.

It is frequently difficult even to define the specific outcomes of such projects, inasmuch as major innovations often produce ragged edges in the surrounding technological frontier, thereby establishing predisposing pressures and even partial commitments in given directions which may not only limit management's freedom in choosing next steps, but also represent a continuing fall-out of effects from earlier innovations. Thus, the use of the short term criteria by management might well serve to transform an R & D program with ostensible commitments to major advances into one with progressively dwarfed objectives. And the use of short term criteria by external analysts could accordingly vary widely in relevance according to the patterns of dominance of the programs being studied.

## On the processes of effecting major technological advances

In order to develop and compare alternative strategies for effecting major technological advances, it would appear necessary to begin with some conceptions, however vague, of the structure of variables and inter-relationships which constitute the *terraincognita* to be explored, of the means by which the existing boundaries of knowledge may be extended, and of bases for choosing the more promising targets among the innumerable possibilities which seem available.

A. *On the nature of current guiding models*
Relevant hypotheses which may be suggested in this connection include:

1. That, contrary to widespread managerial beliefs (or hopes), most scientists and engineers do not have access to widely accepted models of the terrain beyond current research frontiers (including the identification of promising targets and of the means as well as the risks of reaching them) and that such models as may have emerged tend to have but very limited claims to validity;[34]

2. That, as a result, research specialists faced by the necessity to make specific choices among the seemingly endless array of possibilities tend to recommend proposals which are likely to gain managerial acceptance and which are also likely to enhance their own records of performance as appraised and rewarded by management—thus being closely responsive to, rather than independent of, the structure of managerial preferences;[35] and

3. That the virtual absence of any effective analytical framework prevents the formulation of wholly rational or rigorously consistent decisions in most R & D programs, prevents cumulative improvement through the feedback of results, and tends to produce low levels of success in identifying high potential targets, in estimating the likelihood of effecting major advances, and in assessing resulting costs, time requirements and benefits.[36]

One implication of these hypotheses is that many managers have tended to overestimate the capacity of scientists and engineers to see beyond the frontiers of their respective fields, partly because of an understandable desire to shift some of the uncertainties of decision-making to others and partly because of a superficial conception of the nature of technological progress.[37] The remarkably tight-knit structure of science seems to support the view that advances represent the progressive extension of well-defined development paths, somewhat like adding courses of brick to build walls higher. Unfortunately, this hindsight perspective tends to overlook the frequency with which major advances have resulted from striking off in new directions, necessitating the tearing down of earlier accretions of brickwork

34. Among the numerous sources tending to support this more modest view of scientific capacities, the following are especially notable: Jewkes et al. [58, pp. 150–151, 225–227, 237], Klein [69, pp. 480, 508], von Braun [141, p. 1080], Carter and Williams [18, p. 19] and Marshall and Meckling [92, p. 463]. Although the temptation seems to be strong for laymen (and perhaps some managers) to outline seemingly infallible logical bases for attacking the unknown, and to assume that "good" scientists tend to have correct "hunches," the grounds for such views seem meager indeed: see Nelson [101, p. 300], [99, p. 571] and [100, pp. 114–115], and as a moving glimpse of the fallibility of distinguished scientists see Feynman's recent Nobel Prize address [29].
35. See Jewkes et al. [58, pp. 133–134], Carter and Williams [19, pp. 65–66], Siegel [122, pp. 161–177] and H. Gershinowitz [33, p. 417].
36. See footnote 16.
37. On the reasons for using "expert" opinion as a safeguard against the possible penalties of decisions which yield disappointing results, see the quotation from von Braun in Cherington et al. [20, p, 404], as well as Klein [68, p. 504]. For more general warnings about exaggerated views of R & D potentials, see Heald [49, p. 111] and Bush [15, p. 1102].

and replacing them to provide underpinning for the new findings which seem to be sounder and more promising. In view of top management's inescapable responsibility for all major corporate functions, it would seem urgent that more knowledgeable bases be developed at that level for choosing among alternative program recommendations.

Another implication is that management cannot retain the authority to hire, evaluate and reward research personnel without thereby curtailing their independence from managerial conceptions of performance desiderata. If the latter seem to favor short term undertakings, a high ratio of successful project completions and immediately discernible contributions to increased sales or reduced costs, these are obviously likely to become the dominant foci among research proposals, whatever scientists and engineers may consider to be the potentials of other kinds of undertakings. And such tendencies may be further reinforced by more subtle efforts to make R & D administrators, and even technical staff members, more "profit-conscious." Viewed more broadly, such pressures would tend to encourage continuing concentrations on taking small steps, and on remaining within the fields, and even along the specific paths, of investigation which have been fruitful in the past.

It would seem to follow, therefore, that the more effective development of R & D potentials may require both the redefinition of managerial objectives in this area and more vigorous leadership in formulating policies and organizational arrangements to reinforce such altered perspectives. A promising, and perhaps necessary, point of departure for such efforts is to dig beneath the superficialties imposed by viewing R & D as merely a special case either of the general problem of profit maximization under uncertainty or of the only slightly narrower problem of investment decisions. Innovational decisions can be fitted into these groupings, of course, but the distinctive problems confronting management in this area begin precisely at the points where they differ from the purchasing, production, marketing and other problems which the prevailing decision-making framework evolved to handle.

In respect to R & D objectives, for example, it may be necessary to reach beyond the hope of generalized contributions to profitability and growth by spelling out intermediate objectives relating to: gains in information,[38] the strengthening of personnel quality,[39] the prevention of erosion in

---

38. The emphasis on aggregate measures of the performance of the firm as a whole often encourages the neglect of more directly relevent measures of component sectors. Neither profitability nor growth provides an effective measure of the contributions of accounting or engineering or even of production or marketing for that matter. Surely such measures are at least equally inapplicable to the evaluation of R & D. Instead, there is obvious need for a structure of differentiated performance criteria. For some partial approaches to this, see Gold [39, pp. 299–301] and Gold and Kraus [41, pp. 109–127].

39. For emphasis on the extraordinary importance of the quality of personnel in determining

[*Continued on p.* 410

market shares through the lagging of "ordinary" improvements in products and processes behind the stream produced by competitors, the provision of safeguards against the severe consequences of "breakthroughs" by competitors by maintaining a strong ability to catch up with advances by others, the continuous exploration of diversification possibilities, etc. In defining such an array of targets, management may also see the need to redress imbalances involving neglect of the deeper scientific roots of potential major advances in products and processes. And in addition, it may be important to emphasize the integral relationship of an effective R & D program to all other company operations and to specify objectives for developing such mutual reinforcement.[40]

Managerial efforts to strengthen innovational programs may also consider several aspects of organizational arrangements. One concerns the possible need to separate the estimation of technical potentials and risks from the estimation of economic potentials and risks in the interests of increasing the independence of scientists and engineers and of enabling them to concentrate on their areas of specialized competence. A second relates to the possible need for more effective separations between longer term "high risk–high payoff" projects and shorter term "low risk–low payoff" projects to permit the differentiations in performance criteria and incentives without which an increasing proportion of the total effort is likely to gravitate towards the more cautious program. Another concerns the possibility of reprofiling the structure of management controls bearing on R & D activities so as to tighten controls at points where universities, too, have found discipline valuable (e.g., increasing the scientific rigor with which proposals are examined—including evidence of a careful survey of the literature, the outlining of proposed search procedures, the definition of initial targets, etc.—and also providing for comparably rigorous periodic reviews of achievements, difficulties and planned next steps) and loosening them at points representing unjustifiable carryovers of supervisory practices from other kinds of corporation activities. There may also be valuable returns from organizing regular means of inter-relating research programs and personnel with other operations and those staffing them, partly to facilitate the communication of questions, suggestions and puzzling experiences and

research output, see Jewkes *et al.* [58, pp. 145, 149], Williams [144, pp. 126–127], Rubel [109, p. 44] and Cherington *et al.* [20, p. 405]. Unfortunately for the prospects of deveoping R & D production functions and related analytical models for decision-making, the capacity of individuals to make important research advances is not yet detectable to any large degree; nor have many achieved a sizeable number of major advances.

40. Among the few who have emphasized such integration may be noted Carter and Williams [19, pp. 85–86] and Andrews and Brunner [2, pp. 355–356].

partly to develop greater receptivity towards innovations by those responsible for facilitating their commercialization.[41]

### B. *Some strategic conceptions underlying R & D programs*

The processes intervening between R & D inputs and eventual outputs seem commonly to be regarded as enclosed in a black box of technicalities which can be ignored in the formulation and evaluation of relevant managerial strategies. It seems apparent, however, that the programs proposed by research personnel must rest on implicit if not overt conceptions of "the game against nature" to be played, that the form of such conceptions may influence the selection of projects entering into the program and that subsequent results ought to help test the relevance of such guiding conceptions. Accordingly, however incomprehensible the highly sophisticated models underlying individual projects may be to those not specialized in the given disciplines, it may be increasingly necessary for management to become familiar with the more generalized models responsible for broader programs including the assumptions on which they rest as well as the larger implications of their expected outcomes. The following hypotheses are offered to illustrate the range of alternatives which may underlie current programs as well as to indicate their prospective bearing on resulting allocational decisions:

1. Programs designed to generate a succession of *small* improvements may rest upon hypotheses which view the opportunities for achieving individually modest technological gains:

   (a) as uniformly distributed around current outposts and hence likely to yield steady though modest rates of return to developmental efforts in any direction—like mining a surrounding bed of low grade minerals; or

   (b) as distributed continuously only along certain developmental paths and hence likely to yield reasonably steady but modest rates of return, though subject to occasional failures when new undertakings are found to diverge from optimal paths—like following a coal seam; or

   (c) as dotting the surrounding area with randomly distributed clottings—like a diamond field—and hence, while not all digging is fruitful, a broad sweep may be expected to yield a fluctuating but reasonably rewarding average level of returns.

2. Programs expected to yield a sufficient rate of *major* advances

41. For references to delays in the utilization of R & D findings because of inadequate understanding and organization biases, see Wiesner [142, p. 214] and Rubenstein [110, pp. 388–389].

despite primary commitments to generating a succession of *small* improvements may rest upon such hypotheses as the following:

(a) that major advances are merely the cumulative outcome of progressive small improvements; or

(b) that major advances represent the establishment of effective new equilibria after improvements in various components of a technical system make possible their reintegration; or

(c) that major improvements, or "high-payoff" nodes, are randomly distributed, cannot be effectively hunted out through direct search and, consequently, are just as likely to be discovered as the by-product of a continuing emphasis on small increments.

3. Programs specifically focused on generating *major* advances may rest upon such hypotheses as the following:

(a) that major advances represent giant steps along established lines of development and, hence, high potential targets may be identified by experts capable of extrapolating discernible "trends" in the relevant sectors of technology—perhaps like aiming at 200 miles per hour trains or super-large or Mach 3 aircraft; or

(b) that major advances require shifts to new directions of development and targets may, hence, be identified by bringing in specialists in other techniques or fields—e.g., computer experts or laser specialists; or

(c) that promising new nodes are most likely to be uncovered in the course of basic efforts to advance the frontiers of knowledge rather than through aiming directly at specific targets—like studying macromolecules instead of seeking a new synthetic fiber from the outset.

Even this oversimplified set of possibilities suggests a variety of implications. Thus, the number of possible combinations is large enough to make it hazardous for the outside analyst to guess the strategic conceptions underlying particular R & D programs. Similarly, it would be apparent in the course of managerial review that any particular conception might have reasonable alternatives and hence would justify discussion of the reasons for preferring one to the others as well as periodic reconsideration on the basis of subsequent experience. Even more important, it is apparent that these several strategies would be expected to differ substantially in the ratio of inputs to outputs, in the variability of such relationships, in the levels of attendant risks and in their prospective contributions to competitive advantage.[42]

42. Differences in program strategies may well account for some of the wide differences in empirical findings cited in footnotes above.

For example, in the case of evolutionary advances along recognizable paths—as covered above—technological progress may indeed be roughly proportional to increases in inputs because a greater overlapping of searches within a limited domain enhances the likelihood that most of the promising improvements will be uncovered. But resulting innovations are also likely to yield but short lived, as well as modest, competitive advantages because chance factors would tend to distribute individual successes among the competing groups and also because the intensive exploration of common ground tends both to sensitize each group to the potentials of new developments and also to strengthen its capacity to duplicate advances by others in reasonably short order.

In the case of major technological innovations, however, the relationship between the magnitudes of inputs and of outputs may be much more tenuous because: the range of possible approaches by competitors is so much greater that searches are unlikely to reach high levels of density, thereby allowing a greater role to chance; and the prospects of success may be determined in far greater measure by the qualitative characteristics of the personnel engaged (including their capacity to see holes in seemingly solid walls and including the representation of new kinds of expertise) than by their sheer numbers; and the correct path to the next high-payoff node may be so long and costly as to discourage many even among those who happen to find it—as has happened with the cessation of drilling in dry holes only to delay the discovery of rich oil fields at greater depths. Major advances would seem to offer larger and longer-lasting competitive benefits because striking off into new territory is likely to leave competitors farther behind in developing relevant kinds of specialized personnel, new knowledge, facilities and operating skills. Of course, catching up with a major advance may be less costly than effecting it originally, because pioneers often have to explore many blind alleys before finding a path which proves rewarding, while followers can concentrate more directly on the revealed target. But the time taken to catch up also enables the pioneers to achieve further advances especially on the basis of their greater momentum in exploring the new possibilities opened by the advance.

All of the foregoing assumes that outcomes accord with intentions, but conceptions such as that, which bridge between the other two extremes, would seem to urge caution in assuming that the boldness, or even the direction, of R & D program intentions can be correctly inferred from their eventual results—as is often implied by *ex post* analyses. On the contrary, past experience suggests that many major technological innovations may appropriately be characterized as representing "unintended revolutions," being the outcome of undertakings with far more limited objectives than came to be achieved.[43]

43. Relevant references were cited above.

While each of the preceding conceptions as well as others ought to be drawn into the development of generalized models for designing R & D programs, attention should also be given to the need for additional guides to cover the array of critical managerial decisions involved. For example, another common problem concerns when to terminate particular lines of exploration. If it is assumed that most major advances involve substantial periods of groping before promising new perspectives appear, and if it is also recognized that many looming treasures can keep receding just out of reach for maddening periods, it is apparent that deciding when to continue and when to stop may often be more difficult and more influential in determining R & D payoffs than choosing which projects to initiate. A related vexing problem concerns how to determine the prospective "relevance" of newly emerging findings to the guiding objectives of the firm. Inasmuch as effective R & D programs frequently reveal promising new paths of inquiry in various directions, the progressive dispersion of efforts can only be avoided by deliberately ignoring some (most?) of these—despite the tantalizing possibility that any one could prove highly rewarding. The still-vague conceptions underlying such decisions would seem to exert major influence on the extent to which R & D is used to promote diversification as over against strengthening concentration in established products and markets—thereby tending either to increase competition via cross-entry or to limit competition by enhancing the dominance of past leaders.

In short, a number of the decision foci confronting managers dealing with R & D pose the need not only for analytical models capable of being refined to yield increasing relevance in given sectors of industry, but also for empirical guides indicative of what may be considered "par" in the way of returns from various courses of action—e.g., does taking twice as long to go half as far as expected at double the outlay represent an exceptionally unfavorable experience or is it rather more favorable than the average in seeking to effect major advances? There is even urgent need to clarify the form in which R & D output may emerge—e.g., new information, new hypotheses, rising staff capabilities, new empirical findings, patent applications, product or process improvements, higher sales or lower costs—and the extent to which the later among such successive stages of yield may be attributable to factors largely separate from R & D activities.

And before leaving the question of how invasions of unknown territory come about, it may not be entirely amiss to express a bit of skepticism about the comprehensive rationales which are often offered by research executives to inquiries about why given programs were undertaken. Seldom is it admitted, lest it be considered unseemly or even evidence of incompetence, that able scientists and engineers were simply allowed to grope in the hope that "corners" might be turned which would reveal possibilities not discernible from the frontiers of the time. Yet technologies which have persisted for long periods would seem to attest to reasonably widespread acceptance of the existence of daunting obstacles on all sides. Under such conditions, waiting for a new theoretical vision may be less fruitful than sending out competent scouts to hunt, putter and dig for possible openings not detectable from afar. At any rate, there was obviously widespread resort to such quasi-scientific tactics in the past—and penetrating field inquiries might well reveal that similar expedients are still far from uncommon.

## On raising analytical perspectives in developing major technological innovations

Just as closer scrutiny tends to dispel the seeming uniformity seen from afar in any landscape or field of study, the intensive analysis of actual technological innovations soon compels the replacement of highly generalized (and often superficial) concepts by more distinctive means of dealing with their various, clearly differentiated aspects, the complex of pressures influencing their development and the numerous forms taken by their impacts on surrounding economic and other relationships.

A. *On the nature of technical change and technological innovations*
Some of the hypotheses which may be hazarded in this area include:
1. That the concepts which predominated in early economic studies of technical change can now be recognized as too narrow to encompass the multiple dimensions of technological development and to provide a realistic grasp of the intricate interweaving of technological innovations with economic and other adjustments;[44]
2. That, partly as a result of such conceptual shortcomings and partly as a result of statistical limitations which are often pointed out and then ignored during the course of subsequent analysis and interpretation, most of the measures which have been used to assess the extent and consequences of technological innovations are open to serious question; and
3. That effective exploration of the implications of increasing technological progress both for managerial decision-making and for broader economic problems has been impeded by the heavy concentration of efforts on seeking to determine the universal long term effects of highly abstract forms of technological innovations on traditional economic variables—to the

44. Among the most outstanding of such pioneering efforts may be cited: Abramowitz [1, pp. 5–23], Solow [126, pp. 89–104] and [127, pp. 76–86], Domar [26, pp. 709–729] and Massell [93, pp. 547–557]. For approaches to more complex conceptions, see Smith [124, pp. 281–301], Jorgensen [60, pp. 1–17] and Gold [36, p. 48].

comparative neglect of a wide range of questions which may prove more interesting from the standpoint of elucidating relevant economic processes and also more productive of useful guides to policy issues at the levels of the firm, the industry and the national economy.[45]

One of the implications of these hypotheses is the need for an analytical framework which reaches beyond the long prevailing central focus on changes in input-output ratios and unit costs at the point of application as the primary basis for measuring the dimensions and appraising the effects of technological innovations. The wide array of industrial operating characteristics which may be affected by technological innovations may be indicated by the following illustrations merely at the physical level:

(a) *Changes in physical inputs* involving not only the quantity of each per unit of output, but also: the kinds, quality grades and uniformity of the various purchased materials used; the specific skills and the composition skill of labor inputs as well as attendant restrictions on work loads; and such aspects of capital facilities and equipment as productive capacity, degree of specialization, normal working life, flexibility of use levels, alternative levels of scale and prospective obsolescence rates;

(b) *Changes in physical outputs* involving not only the aggregate quantity but also: the variety of products; the extent of design changes in each line; the range of quality grades and sizes in each; and alterations in their respective service features for buyers (including capacity, precision, service life, liability to breakdown, convenience, safety, etc.); and

(c) *Changes in physical aspects of production flows* including the degree of integration of successive operations; the controllability of output rates and the speed with which they can be altered; the variability of different inputs with changes in output levels and in product-mix; the average duration of the production cycle; incidence of downtime and attendant work-in-process inventory requirements; requirement of special working conditions; and accident and health hazards.

One reason for probing the complex machinery underlying the simple, abstract concept of technological advances is that only at this level can managerial choices be made among real alternatives. And it is apparent that management cannot either assess the effects of various past innovations, or

45. The long history of such disparate analytical foci is indicated by the strong contrast between Ricardo's brief chapter "On Machinery" [107, pp. 263–271] and Babbage's comprehensive discussion [5].

select which alternatives to promote in the future, except by penetrating beneath measures of aggregative effects to identify the distinctive outcomes (including disadvantages as well as benefits) likely to be associated with each. In addition, focusing on the working parts also provides the basis for studying the rich and still developing texture of technological progress, for innovations interact with adjacent arrangements often engendering a chain of adjustments before a workable equilibrium is reached—as in cases where improved product design necessitates alterations in processing methods, which lead to the introduction of new kinds of materials, whose effective utilization forces additional modifications in processing facilities. Thus, the analytical purview, already broadened to include arrays of component input-output ratios, might be extended further towards developing sequential flow measures designed to detect common interaction patterns [39].

Even more important, however, is the possibility of using the preceding structure of technical adjustment alternatives to explore the network of *economic* adjustments triggered by each of the preceding kinds of changes in the *physical* aspects of production. For example, shifts in the kinds (and sometimes merely in the grade) of materials required may alter supply availabilities, factor price responses to variations in demand, transportation and inventory requirements and even locational advantages. Changes in the composition of labor requirements may similarly affect the available supply, training requirements, the average wage level as well as the structure of wage differentials, the variability of employment levels with output fluctuations and the nature of issues to be negotiated with trade unions. In short, it is apparent that changes in physical inputs, production processes and physical outputs tend to engender direct economic adjustments through repercussions in factor and product markets as well as through alternations in the responsiveness of operations to managerial controls. These and other adjustments in physical quantities and prices of inputs and outputs may then be encompassed by an analytical framework elaborated to permit tracing the successive interactions involved in shaping production functions, factor and cost proportions, fixed and variable unit cost functions, and gross and net average revenue per unit of output—as has been suggested elsewhere [37].

Finally, it is apparent that efforts to appraise the effects of technological innovations effectively must reach beyond individual firms—to cover diffusion rates and competitive responses, etc.—and must also search out the pattern of progressively changing effects between the point of initial application of an innovation by one firm and its acceptance into general use by the industry, instead of concentrating solely at either end or at any single point. Indeed, there is good reason to believe that studies attempting to determine the lasting effects of technological innovations are bound to be insensitive to the network of reallocational responses by means of which the economy absorbs and gradually adapts to the succession of innovational impacts—as well as to the complex of intervening pressures which encourage, and influence selections among, new technological advances. Incidentally, past field studies also suggest the need to differentiate among innovational effects according to such special conditions as: (a) whether output levels are expanding or contracting; (b) whether the output potentials of the basic facilities involved are facilities-dominated (as in power plants) or resources-dominated (as in smelting plants) or labor-dominated (as in certain service activities); and (c) differences in the levels of industrialization of the economies (or economic sectors) studied, including the possible need to allow for the effects of progressive industrialization in long term studies [36].

Another basic implication of the above hypotheses is that many of the measurements now used to appraise the effects of technological innovations are of very limited value, and may even be misleading, for reasons other than concern the coverage and precision of the data employed. Illustrations of such vulnerable measures would include our widely used indexes of physical output, price changes, unit costs and productivity adjustments as well as most measures of capacity and of "physical capital." One reason for such shortcomings is that most of these measures are designed to be blind to technological innovations by assuming, in the interests of statistical comparability, no change in the nature of the inputs or outputs which they cover—despite the overwhelming evidence that they are in fact being altered progressively and substantially and that much of this is attributable to, and is an important outcome of, technological innovations. A second source of limitations, attributable to the same concern with statistical comparability, is the frequent assumption of no change in the composition of aggregates being measured—as when changes in the skill composition of labor inputs are ignored in measuring increases in average wage rates, although this is a common point of impact by technological innovations. Inasmuch as the validity of using such measures to assess the effects of technical change depends on fully separating out concommitant changes in costs and prices, it is apparent that errors on one side are mirrored on the other—as when technological improvements in products are discounted by attributing all of attendant price increases to pricing power.

The fundamental difficulties of separating changes in price from changes in the nature of the commodity may be illustrated by the case of capital facilities and equipment. The very concept of capital aggregates consisting of homogeneous units is as unrealistic as the concept of capital units remaining essentially unchanged through time (or as the concept of a meaningful index of capital goods prices over extended periods), because technological development has demonstrated both the economic superiority of designing production facilities so as to integrate the specialized contributions of individually differentiated kinds of equipment and also the tendency in increasingly industrialized economies to apply technological advances to production in substantial measure through altering capital equipment and facilities.[46]

Finally, it may be worth noting that efforts to apply economic analysis to the management of R & D have already gone through two disappointing stages. The first, in response to the prevailing enthusiasm for input-output studies in all directions, produced a shower of aggressively quantitative determinations of research "productivity" and of "research production functions" at company, industry and national levels. To this there has developed an increasingly powerful counter-pressure proclaiming that there are no effective measures either of research inputs or of research outputs. While the critical input is recognized to be the utilization of scientists and engineers, there is also general agreement that the numbers employed have far less bearing on the outcome than their levels of creativity, imagination and other admired but inadequately defined and still unmeasurable qualities.[47] Even the cost of inputs, which is considered to be a less significant determinant of results, is often difficult to determine because of the deliberate or unavoidable intermixing of costs for an array of activities ranging from conventional testing and customer servicing through fundamental research, development programs, pilot plant operations and even later stages of commercialization.[48] On the output side, serious deficiencies are reported in the usefulness of patents and in attempts to measure the amount of new information or the number of inventions and discoveries. This has led to suggestions that the best measure of R & D outputs may be the magnitude of its inputs (although this assumption of a fixed relationship between them is based neither on logic nor on evidence), thus completing a fruitless circle for, as was just noted, the inputs cannot be measured either.[49] Nor can the practical manager by-pass these difficulties by concentrating on the control of unit costs, because these cannot be measured until units of output are defined.

46. Efforts to deal with such problems include Shaw [120, pp. 287 *et. seq.*], Denison [25, pp. 215–284], Ruggles [112, 387 *et. seq.*], Gordon [42, pp. 937–957], Kendrick [64, pp. 34–36, 51–54], Gold [36, pp. 18–30] and Marquard [91]. Quite another area of statistical problems underlying the testing of economic hypotheses is suggested by Godfrey [34, p. 315 *et. seq.*].
47. For such judgments, see Kuznets [73, p. 42], Machlup [78, p. 147] and Sanders [114, pp. 53–63].
48. In this connection, see Jewkes [58, pp. 147–149], Sanders [114, pp. 58–60] and Quinn and Cavanaugh [105, p. 111].
49. Sanders [114, pp. 63–75] and Worley [147, p. 234].

Perhaps the most astonishing feature of this situation has been the general failure to recognize that these difficulties are inevitable, widespread and inconsequential. There are no authoritative measures of the "productivity" or "efficiency" of any corporation as a whole, nor of any subsector of corporate activities providing nonrepetitive services (which covers virtually all staff functions as well as supervisory, technical and policy-making personnel). Nor can such measurements be made of professional services anywhere else, whether in universities or government, and even their usefulness in major sectors of national production are open to serious question. Yet all of these have managed to function because input-output measurements are essentially a means of summarizing the results of complex activity systems rather than providing the basis for understanding or managing the intricate and usually highly specialized processes involved. Indeed, such measurements are likely to become useful only as a result of progressive understanding of the functioning of whatever system is of concern—for only in that way can we learn which variables and which relationships are important for particular control or evaluative purposes. In short, when we don't understand the system—as is patently true of R & D—we cannot devise strategically significant measures of its "productivity" or "efficiency" or determinations of its production functions [39].

## B. *Governmental and private roles in promoting technological advances*

The following hypotheses bear upon some of the issues in this area which have attracted increasing attention during recent years:

1. That the national interest in advancing technological progress and in speeding its diffusion and utilization is stronger, and also broader in scope, than that of individual firms or governmental agencies, to say nothing of universities;

2. That governmental agencies are no more committed to R & D, or to its basic research components than private corporations, each tending to regard such activities as merely one means of promoting its more fundamental objectives;

3. That, although the R & D interests of governmental and private organizations overlap to some extent—mostly in respect to joint or cooperative undertakings—their largely disparate roles in the functioning of the US economy tend to ensure substantial differentiation of their operational interests, with consequent limitations of the extent of spillovers from advances in one sector to the other; and

4. That the continued expansion and diversification of private needs

and public responsibilities combined with the continued unfolding of R & D potentials suggests that a variety of new policies and organizational forms will have to be explored by private, public and nonprofit agencies to provide the larger array of differentiated innovative services likely to be required.

One implication of these hypotheses is to contest the common assumption in relevant economic analyses that "the government" is inherently more deeply committed to technological progress and basic research than private industry, because the social benefits of such efforts may be expected to exceed what is privately appropriable.[50] The relevance of such an ultimate proposition for the shaping of policies over the next fifty years or more depends, however, on: (a) how close we are to the point where privately appropriable benefits from technological innovations are recognizedly less than attendant private costs over major portions of what is considered to comprise the private sector of the economy; and (b) the extent to which the behavior of actual governmental agencies is likely to coincide with theoretical conceptions of the bases for promoting the general welfare over the long run.

With respect to the first of these questions, frequent insinuations that we are close to, or already at such a point, are unsupported by any evidence whatever. Indeed, in view of the infant stage of our grasp of R & D processes and potentials—perhaps akin to the development of manufacturing seventy-five years ago—such gloomy forebodings about their imminent limitations would seem to border on the ludicrous. As for the second question, it takes little exploration of the literature of political theory and the history of governmental performance to indicate the enormous gulf between idealistic visions of unflagging devotion to the general welfare and the actual achievements of individual government agencies, and of entire "administrations" for that matter, under the inescapable pressures of conflicting interest groups, limited funds, short term performance criteria, the career interests of government officials and the frequent absence of policy guides which are scientifically authoritative and also politically appealing.[51] Hard evidence shows that the government lagged far behind industry in pioneering and supporting technological progress and basic research over marty decades preceding 1940; that its commitments since then have been far more narrowly concentrated than those of private industry; that resulting programs have been overwhelmingly dominated by strongly mission-oriented objectives centering primarily around defense-related needs; that attendant allocations for basic research have been restricted to quite minor proportions

50. For illustrations of such views, see Brozen [10], Villard [140, pp. 483–497], Nelson [101, pp. 297–304] and Arrow [4, pp. 616–619].
51. For a detailed illustration of the enormous power of such pressures even under mobilization conditions, see "Conflicting Pressures and Practical Economic Planning" in Gold [35, pp. 487–543].

of the total; and that much even of these meager contributions seems to be more convincingly attributable to the government's concern with producing more scientists and engineers and to its statutory responsibilities for supporting higher education than to any generalized dedication to advancing all frontiers of knowledge in the hope of eventual social benefits of some kind.[52]

The foregoing obviously does not imply that government agencies are incapable of making major contributions to basic research and technological progress. On the contrary, growing awareness of these needs in our culture has helped to stimulate (and to enable) such agencies to follow the earlier lead of industry in seeking to harness R & D potentials on an increasing scale; and there is every reason to expect comparably rewarding results. But sound policies to promote the general welfare through enhancing technological progress and basic research must encompass both the vast unmet needs still to be found within the public sector and the seemingly limitless possibilities in the private sector—indicating the necessity of making the most of all sources of contributions.

Another implication of these hypotheses is that effective utilization of the limited resources available to further basic research and technological progress will require more tough-minded appraisals of the strengths and limitations of each of the major sources of contributions. For example, while private firms are likely to have their innovational horizons limited by the pattern of expected or hoped-for profit potentials, government agencies may have their horizons limited by the relative popularity of, or political support of, alternatives; and even universities seem to have horizons which are responsive to the grant-generating or fame-promising potentials of different lines of exploration. Although the uncertainty of innovational outcomes tends to be discouraging to all who undertake them, its effects on the optimality of allocations may be distorted by the divergent impacts of expenditures on projects which turn out unsuccessfully: in private industry, they represent outright losses which may be justifiable but only within specified limits; in universities, they involve little or no financial burden because such projects are usually supported by outside funds or by the unpaid extra efforts of faculty members; and in government agencies with operational responsibilities, it is not uncommon to find both the prospective beneficiaries of solutions and the representatives of the regions in which the funds were

52. Recent Congressional hearings concerning the role of research and technology in the economy have elicited a wide array of data and judgments bearing on these matters. For example, see Rubel [109, pp. 30–45], Bush [15, p. 1,091], Seaborg [119, p. 1,100], Kistiakowsky [67, p. 1,102], and Wiesner [142, p. 1,106] and also the summary report of the House of Representatives Select Committee on Government Research [46, pp. 11, 26 and 34]. It is also interesting to note the report in *Business Week* (May 21, 1966, p. 109) that the pressure for fast practical results is so great in some government programs as to concern even directors of industrial research programs.

spent reacting by supporting renewed or even expanded allocations for such projects. Indeed, the point has been made that in many government projects (especially in defense and space) results are all that count and, therefore, that projects are adjudged successful on the basis of performance criteria, even when several-fold increases in cost would have characterized them as catastrophes within the private framework. Turning in still another direction, it would appear that private industry may be better staffed and organized than government agencies to convert new laboratory findings through to practical application, whereas universities usually have little or no capacity to do so. In short, these and other possible illustrations—including the relative degrees of stimulus from competition—would seem to suggest that comprehensive analyses along these lines might serve both to sidetrack further disputes about which single channel for innovational developments is best and to provide additional constructive bases for guiding such division of labor in the future.[53]

One remaining implication of the hypotheses which introduced this section is that R & D activities seem to be far more highly differentiated than had been expected—or even realized until recently—either by analysts seeking to generalize about the economic, organizational or psychological aspects of such activities, or by administrators seeking to integrate such groups into existing corporate structures. As a result, the spillover of technological advances has been surprisingly limited both among industries and as between the defense programs and civilian manufacturing and questions have also been asked about the effectiveness with which findings in university laboratories have been digested and utilized by industry.[54] Another result has been the increasing need by all but the largest laboratories for help in coming effectively to grips with problems bearing upon, but technically outside, the firm's relatively narrow areas of specialized expertise. Such developments may be regarded as reflecting the need for new forms of organizations to serve as intermediate nodes (containing specialized knowledge and offering specialized services) in networks which interconnect private corporations, government agencies and universities.[55] Responses may include not only the proliferation of nonprofit organizations like the Mellon Institute and the Battelle Institute as well as research-oriented consulting

53. Comments relating to some of these or closely associated points may be found in Rubel [109, p. 35], Quinn and Cavanaugh [105, p. 113], Arrow's reference to Hitch [4, p. 624] and Hitch [55, p. 626].
54. See Wiesner [143, p. 214], Rubel [109, pp. 30, 34–35, 43] and Holloman [57, p. 1,227].
55. Such possibilities have been discussed by Carter and Williams [18, pp. 38–41], Jewkes [58, pp. 242–243], Hitch [55, p. 626] and also in his [59], Calkins [17, pp. 1,085, 1,088], A. D. Little, Inc. [77, pp. 642–643, 651], Schonfield [121, p. 372] and Graham [44, pp. 128–138].

firms like Arthur D. Little and the Stanford Research Institute, but the pioneering of new kinds of co-operative (or jointly sponsored) organizations supported by industry and the government, by industry and universities, and by the universities and the government. In addition, industry-wide research may be reinvigorated; interuniversity groups may grow in numbers; and new undertakings at the municipal and state government levels may also take root. The point to be emphasized is that efforts to choose among the forms which have emerged during the past twenty years of groping, or to design "optimal" arrangements on the basis of the relatively limited and highly differentiated experiences encompassed to date, may prove far less useful than seeking to determine current pressures for change, to identify needs not being met, and to assess the nature of difficulties emerging in R & D organizations which are growing in size and which are gradually expanding their spheres of service. Similarly, efforts to increase spillover may well benefit less from recent emphases on multiplying communication channels through publications and conferences than from bridging the gap between the mutually alien problems, skills, facilities and expertise of different industries through new organizations committed to becoming expert enough in the characteristics of several to actively assist in making such transfers. For example, such intermediaries may facilitate the transformation of steel and aluminum companies into a more broadly oriented materials engineering industry.

### C. On extra-quantitative guides to managerial allocation decisions

Widespread empirical evidence that rigorous quantitative models play only a minor role in managerial decisions relating to major innovations and other investments suggests that redoubled efforts to convert "the heathen" may be less rewarding than trying to learn how executives supplement (or surmount) inadequate analytical guides and data in making decisions involving large sums and possibly severe penalties. Instead of urging the bumble bee to reshape itself and stop flouting prevailing notions of aerodynamics, more attention might be given to studying executive bumble bees in the process of coping with problems reaching beyond the restricted boundaries of available normative models. Pioneering along these lines has already been initiated by Simon and his associates, yielding valuable ideosyncratic models of the criteria and evaluative processes used by executives in making certain actual operating decisions.[56] In order to comprehend broader policy decisions, however, such as are involved in adopting major innovational programs or in major extensions of the scope and scale of R & D, it may prove necessary to explore the determinants of changes in the

56. See March and Simon [88], and also Cyert and March [24].

structure of top management's values and supporting behavior patterns, which underlies all major decisions.

Accordingly, one set of inquiries might seek to examine how changes are induced in top management's conceptions: of acceptable trade-offs between current profit rates, longer term growth prospects and other desiderata; of acceptable levels of risk; and of minimum acceptable responses to innovational pressures. And in respect to R & D in particular, another set of inquiries might probe into how changes are induced in top management's conceptions: of the kinds of contributions to be expected realistically of such programs; of the length of time needed to evaluate resulting performance soundly; and of the desired degree of boldness in research targets, perhaps as represented by changes in acceptable rates of project failures.

Such foci obviously illustrate the valuational roots of whole classes of major decisions by top management. Hence, field studies which penetrate these decision-making foundations are likely to prove necessary to increase our understanding of responses not only to available and potential technological innovations, but also to a wide range of other major allocational issues.

## Concluding observations

1. Although a number of valuable contributions have already been made, studies of the sources, effects and means of guiding technological innovations are still in a very rudimentary state of development.

2. It is not surprising that the concepts and tools borrowed from other areas of study in order to fill the initial void have proved quite inadequate; nor that the harvest of our first fragmentary studies still resembles a bramble bush of conflicting observations and insights.

3. Although, to paraphrase Carl Sandburg, we academicians have always tended to be nervously loquacious in the face of the unknown, there seems to be no reason to doubt that increasing research, especially with an enriched mixture of field studies, will soon yield more useful analytical models for dealing with at least some of the variety of already discernible problem foci.

4. It may also be worth emphasizing, however, that R & D is itself in such an early stage of development that analysis must be focused on its changing patterns of growth as well as on the relative efficiency of different policies and organizational arrangements at any given time—thus urging increased study of the problems and adjustment experiences of laggard companies and industries as well as of the leaders.

This essay is a substantially expanded version of a paper presented to the Conference sponsored by the Inter-University Committee on the Micro-Economics of Technological Change and Economic Growth at the University of Pennsylvania on March 25–26, 1966. Grateful acknowledgement is made to the Committee and to Resources for the Future, Inc. for research grants in partial support of the underlying studies.

# REFERENCES

1. M. Abramovitz, "Resource and Output Trends in the U.S. Since 1870," *American Economic Review*, May 1956.
2. P. W. S. Andrews and Elizabeth Brunner, *Capital Development in Steel* (Oxford: Blackwell, 1952).
3. Robert N. Anthony and John S. Day, *Management Controls in Industrial Research Organizations* (Cambridge: Harvard Uuiversity Press, 1952).
4. K. J. Arrow, "Economic Welfare and the Allocation of Resources for Invention," [106].
5. C. Babbage, *On the Economy of Machinery and Manufactures* (London: Charles Knight, 3rd edition, Enlarged, 1933).
6. Gordon F. Bloom, "Union Wage pressure and Technological Discovery," *American Economic Review*, September 1951.
7. P. W. Bridgman, *Reflections of a Physicist* (New York: Philosophical Library, 1950).
8. Irwin D. J. Bross, "Algebra and Illusion," *Science*, June 3, 1966.
9. William Henry Brown, "Innovation in the Machine Tool Industry," *American Economic Review*, May 1951.
10. Yale Brozen, "Invention, Innovation, and Imitation," *American Economic Review*, May 1951.
11. ——, "Determinants of the Direction of Technical Change," *American Economic Review*, May 1953.
12. ——, "Trends in Industrial Research and Development," *Journal of Business*, July 1960.
13. ——, "The Future of Industrial Research and Development," [106].
14. A. F. Burns, *Production Trends in the United States Since 1870* (New York: National Bureau of Economic Research, 1934).
15. Vannevar Bush, [138].
16. *Business Week*, May 21, 1966.
17. Robert D. Calkins, [138].
18. C. F. Carter and B. R. Williams, *Industry and Technical Progress* (London: Oxford University Press, 1957).
19. ——, *Investment in Innovation* (London: Oxford University Press, 1958).
20. P. W. Cherington, M. J. Peck and F. M. Scherer, "Organization and Research and Development Decision Making within a Government Department," [106].
21. J. F. Coales, "Financial Provision for Research and Development in Industry," *Journal Industrial Economics*, July 1957.
22. W. S. Comanor, "Research and Competitive Product Differentiation in the Pharmaceutical Industry in the United States," *Economica*, November 1964.
23. ——, "Research & Technical Change in the Pharmaceutical Industry," *Review of Economic Statistics*, May 1965.
24. R. M. Cyert and J. G. March, *A Behavioral Theory of the Firm* (New Jersey: Prentice-Hall, Inc., 1963).
25. Edward F. Denison, "Theoretical Aspects of Quality Change, Capital Consumption, and Net Capital Formation," in *Problems of Capital Formation* (Studies in Income and Wealth, XIX), (Princeton: Princeton University Press, 1957).
26. E. Domar, "On the Measurement of Technological Change," *Economic Journal*, December 1961.
27. J. L. Enos, "Invention and Innovation in Petroleum Refining Industry," [106].
28. W. Fellner, "Does the Market Direct the Relative Factor-Saving Effects of Technological Change?" [106].
29. R. P. Feynman, "The Development of the Space-Time View of Quantum Electrodynamics," *Science*, August 12, 1966.
30. C. Freeman, "Research and Development: A Comparison Between British and American Industry," *National Institute Economic Review*, May 1962.
31. J. K. Galbraith, *American Capitalism* (Cambridge, Mass.: Houghton Mifflin, 1952).
32. J. R. Gass, "The Human Element in the Application of Science," *Impact of Science on Society*, June 1954.

33. H. Gershinowitz, quoted in Merrill [106].
34. M. D. Godfrey, "Certain Problems in the Application of Mathematical Economics," [121A].
35. Bela Gold, *Wartime Economic Planning in Agriculture* (New York: Columbia University Press, 1949), Part V.
36. ——, *Foundations of Productivity Aanalysis* (Pittsburgh: University of Pittsburgh Press, 1955).
37. ——, "Economic Effects of Technological Innovations," *Management Science*, September 1964.
38. ——, "Industry Growth Patters: Theory and Empirical Results," *Journal of Industrial Economics*, November 1964.
39. —— "Productivity Analysis and System Coherence," *Operations' Research Quarterly*, September 1965.
40. ——, "New Perspectives on Cost Theory and Empirical Findings," *Journal of Industrial Economics*, April 1966.
41. —— and R. M. Kraus, "Integrating Physical with Financial Measures for Managerial Controls," *Journal of Academy of Management*, June 1964.
42. R. A. Gordon, "Differential Changes in the Prices of Consumer's and Capital Goods," *American Economic Review*, December 1961.
43. ——, statement: Senate Hearings on *Technology in the Nation's Economy* [138].
44. B. Graham, "The Nonprofit Research Institute: A Nonuniversity Approach" in B. R. Keenan (ed.), *Science and the University* (New York: Columbia University Press, 1966).
45. Zvi Griliches, "Comment," [106].
46. See [135].
47. See [134].
48. C. G. Harrel, "Selecting Projects for Research," in C. C. Furnas (ed.), *Research in Industry* (New York: D. Van Nostrand Co., Inc., 1948), Chapter 8.
49. Henry T. Heald [134].
50. R. L. Hershey, "Finance and Productivity in Industrial Research and Development," *Research Management*, July 1966.
51. D. B. Hertz, *The Theory and Practice of Industrial Research* (New York: McGraw-Hill, 1950).
52. J. R. Hicks, *The Theory of Wages* (London: Macmillan & Co. Ltd., 1932), Chapter 6.
53. ——, *Value and Capital* (Oxford: Clarendon Press, 1939).
54. C. J. Hitch, "Character of Research and Development in a Competitive Economy," *Proceedings of a Conference on Research and Development and Its Impact on the Economy*, N.S.F., 1958.
55. ——, "Comment" [106].
56. Maurice Holland, *Management's Stake in Research* (New York: Harper & Bros., 1958), Chapter 2.
57. J. Herbert Hollomon [138].
58. J. Jewkes, D. Sawers and R. Stillerman, *The Sources of Invention* (New York: St. Martin's Press, 1959).
59. Charles Jones, "Criteria used by Industrial Research in Evaluating a Specific Research Project," [138].
60. D. W. Jorgenson, "The Embodiment Hypothesis," *Journal of Political Economy*, February 1966.
61. Abraham Kaplan, *The Conduct of Inquiry* (San Francisco: Chandler Publications, 1964).
62. Keezer, *et al.*, *New Forces in American Business* (New York: McGraw-Hill, 1959)
63. ——, "The Outlook for Expenditures on Research and Development during the Next Decade," *American Economic Review*, Papers and Proceedings, May 1960.
64. J. Kendrick, "Productivity Trends: Capital and Labor," *Review of Economic Statistics*, August 1956.
65. C. Kennedy, "Induced Bias in Innovation and the Theory of Distribution," *Economic Journal*, September 1964.
66. J. M. Keynes, *The General Theory of Employment, Interest and Money* (London: Macmillan, 1936).
67. George B. Kistiakowsky [106].

68. B. H. Klein, "Reply and Rejoinder," [106].
69. ———, "The Decision Making Problem in Development," [106].
70. ——— and W. Meckling, "Application of Operations Research to Development Decision," *Operations Research*, May–June 1958.
71. A. W. Kornhauser, *Scientists in Industry* (Los Angeles: University of California Press, 1962), Chapter 3.
72. S. Kuznets, *Economic Change* (New York: W. W. Norton and Company, Inc., 1953), Chapter 9.
73. ———, "Inventive Activity: Problems of Definition and Measurement," [106].
74. D. M. Lamberton, *The Theory of Profit* (Oxford: Blackwell, 1965), Chapter 5.
75. W. M. Larrabie, *et al.*, *Profit, Performance and Progress* (New York: American Telephone and Telegraph Co., 1959), [123].
76. S. B. Littauer, "Conceptualization and Formalization—The Impossible and The Obvious," *Management Science*, October 1965.
77. A. D. Little, Inc. [139].
78. Fritz Machlup, "The Supply of Inventors and Inventions," [106].
79. W. R. Maclaurin, "Federal Support for Scientific Research," *Harvard Business Review*, March–April 1947.
80. ———, "The Process of Technological Innovation: The Launching of a New Scientific Industry," *American Economic Review*, March 1950.
81. ———, "The Sequence from Invention to Innovation and Its Relation to Economic Growth," *Quarterly Journal of Economics*, February 1953.
82. ———, "Technological Progress in Some American Industries," *American Economic Review*, 1954.
83. E. Manfield, "Technical Change and Rate of Imitation," *Econometrica*, October 1961.
84. ———, "Entry, Gibrat's Law, Innovation, and the Growth of Firms," *American Economic Review*, December 1962.
85. ———, "Speed of Response of Firms to New Techniques," *Quarterly Journal of Economics*, May 1963.
86. ———, "Industrial Research and Development Expenditures: Determinants, Prospects, and Relation to Size of Firm and Inventive Output," *Journal of Political Economy*, August 1964.
87. ———, "Rates of Return from Industrial Research and Development," *American Economic Review*, May 1965.
88. J. G. March and H. A. Simon, *Organizations* (New York: John Wiley & Sons, Inc., 1958), Chapter 7.
89. J. W. Markham, "Inventive Activity: Government Controls and the Legal Environment," [106].
90. R. Marris, *The Economic Theory of Managerial Capitalism* (New York: Free Press of Glencoe, 1964).
91. C. Marquard, *Costs in the Electrical Machinery Industry* (Unpublished M.A. Thesis, University of Pittsburgh, 1960).
92. A. W. Marshall and H. W. Meckling, "Predictability of the Costs, Time, and Success of Development" [106].
93. B. F. Massell, "A Disaggregated View of Technical Change," *Journal of Political Economics*, December 1961.
94. J. R. Minasian, "The Economics of Research and Development," [106].
95. Motley and Newton, "The Selection of Projects for Industrial Research," *Operations Research Quarterly*, November–December 1959.
96. W. F. Mueller, "The Origins of the Basic Inventions Underlying DuPont's Major Product and Process Innovations, 1920 to 1950," [106].
97. ———, "Case Study of Product Discovery and Innovation Cost," *Southern Economic Journal*, July 1957.
98. R. R. Nelson, "The Background for the Conference," [106].
99. ———, "The Link Between Science and Invention: The Case of the Transistor," [106].
100. ———, "Economics of Invention—A Survey of the Literature," *Journal of Business*, April 1959.
101. ———, "The Simple Economics of Basic Scientific Research", *Journal of Political Economy*, June 1959.

102. M. J. Peck, "Inventions in the Postwar American Aluminum Industry," [106].
103. E. T. Penrose, *The Theory of the Growth of the Firm* (New York: John Wiley, 1959).
104. E. Piore, "Is System Science a Discipline?", [131].
105. J. B. Quinn and R. M. Cavanaugh, "Fundamental Research Can Be Planned," *Harvard Business Review*, January–February, 1964.
106. *The Rate and Direction of Inventive Activity: Economic and Social Factors*, National Bureau of Economic Research Special Conference, Series No. 13 (New Jersey: Princeton University, 1962).
107. D. Ricardo, *The Principles of Political Economy and Taxation* (New York: E. P. Dutton—Everyman's Library, 1933).
108. N. Rosenburg, "Capital Goods, Technology and Economic Growth," *Oxford Economic Papers*, 1963.
109. J. H. Rubel, Statement: [136].
110. A. H. Rubenstein: "Organization and Research and Development Decision Making within the Decentralized Firm," [106].
111. ——, "Setting Criteria for Research and Development," *Harvard Business Review*, January 1957.
112. R. and N. Ruggles, "Concepts of Real Capital Stocks and Services," in *Output, Input and Productivity Measurement*, Conference on Income and Wealth, No. 25 (New Jersey: Princeton University Press, 1961).
113. W. E. G. Salter, *Productivity and Technical Change* (Cambridge: Cambridge University Press, 1960).
114. B. S. Sanders, "Some Difficulties in Measuring Inventive Activity" [106].
115. R. S. Sayers, "Springs of Technical Progress in Britain, 1919–1939," *Economic Journal*, June 1950.
116. J. Schmookler, "The Level of Inventive Activity," *Review of Economic Studies*, May 1956.
117. ——, "The Economic Sources of Inventive Activity," *Journal of Economic History*, March 1962.
118. J. Schumpeter, *Capitalism, Socialism and Democracy* (New York: Harper, 1950).
119. G. T. Seaborg [136].
120. W. H. Shaw, *The Value of Commodity Output Since 1869* (New York: National Bureau of Economic Research, 1947).
121. A. Shonfield, *Modern Capitalism* (London: Oxford University Press, 1965).
122. I. H. Siegel, "Conditions of American Technological Progress," *American Economic Review*, May 1954.
123. L. Silk, *The Research Revolution* (New York: McGraw-Hill, 1960).
124. V. L. Smith, "Engineering Data and Statistical Techniques in the Analysis of Production and Technological Change: Fuel Requirements of the Trucking Industry," *Econometrica*, April 1957.
125. R. M. Solow, "Technical Change and the Aggregate Production Function," *Rev. Econ. Stat.*, August 1957.
126. ——, "Investment and Technical Progress," K. J. Arrow *et al.* (eds.), *Mathematical Methods in the Social Sciences* (California: Stanford University Press, 1960).
127. ——, "Technical Progress, Capital Formation and Economic Growth," *American Economic Review Proceedings*, May 1962.
128. J. J. Spengler, "Comment," [106].
129. W. P. Strassmann, "Interrelated Industries and the Rate of Technological Change," *Review of Economic Studies*, October 1959.
130. A. Sutherland, "Diffusion of an Innovation in Cotton Spinning," *Journal of Industrial Economics*, March 1959.
131. *System Theory*, Microwave Research Institute Symposia Series, Vol. XV (New York: Polytechnic Press, 1965).
132. N. E. Terleckyj, "Research and Development Funds: Sources and Applications," Peter M. Gutmann (ed.), *Economic Growth* (New Jersey: Prentice-Hall, 1964).
133. R. P. Ulin, "Thinking Ahead: What Will Research Bring About?," *Harvard Business Review*, January–February 1958.
134. U.S. Congress House. Select Committee on Government Research, *Summary of Hearings, Federal Research and Development Programs*, 88th Congress, First and Second Sessions, 1964.

135. U.S. Congress House. Select Committee on Government Research, *Report, National Goals and Policies*, Study No. 10, 88th Congress, 2nd Session, 1964.
136. U.S. Congress Senate. Subcommittee of the Select Committee on Small Business, *Hearings: The Role and Effect of Technology in the Nation's Economy*, 88th Congress, First Session, 1963 (Part 1).
137. U.S. Congress Senate. Subcommittee of the Select Committee on Small Business, *Hearings: The Role and Effect of Technology in the Nation's Economy*, 88th Congress, First Session, 1963 (Part 2).
138. U.S. Congress Senate. Subcommittee of the Select Committee on Small Business, *Hearings: The Role and Effect of Technology in the Nation's Economy*, 88th Congress, First Session, 1963 (Part 3).
139. U.S. Congress Senate. Subcommittee of the Select Committee on Small Business, *Hearings: The Role and Effect of Technology in the Nation's Economy*, 88th Congress, First Session, 1963 (Part 5).
140. H. H. Villard, "Competition, Oligopoly and Research," *Journal of Political Economy*, December 1958.
141. W. von Braun, "Evaluation of End Results of Research," [138].
142. J. B. Wiesner [138].
143. ——, [137].
144. B. R. Williams, "Information and Criteria in Capital Expenditure Decisions," *Journal of Management Studies*, September 1964.
145. W. W. Wirtz [135].
146. W. Woodruff, "Origins of Invention and Inter-Continental Diffusion of Techniques of Production in the Rubber Industry," *Economic Review*, December 1962.
147. J. S. Worley, "The Changing Direction of Research and Development Employment Among Firms," [106].

# VALUES AND SCIENTISTS

# Motivation underlying the brain drain

## *James A. Wilson*

*"Children of Britain, matriculate: You have nothing to sell but your brains."*

So says Professor P. M. S. Blackett (1963) and the "talented children" of Britain have been taking his advice in ever-increasing numbers. British scientists and other professionals have been developing their talents and selling them on the world-talent market in numbers which have, rather belatedly, concerned (amongst others) the British Government, many educators, the Royal Society and the heads of the D.S.I.R. scientific establishments in Britain.

Britain—having lost an Empire rich in raw materials, labor and markets, she herself lacking in basic raw materials, unable to raise more than half of her own food—increasingly must *live on her wits*: Britain's largest and most valuable national resource is the *talent*—the *skill* of her people. It has been clear since the middle 1950's that one of the major potential threats to the British talent pool has been the loss through emigration of well-educated and well-trained scientists, physicians, academics, students, engineers, technologists, and other professionals.

The research at hand was an exploratory effort to ascertain the extent of the loss in relation to present statistics available—to verify that which was available; to seek out, identify, and question a large sample of British migrants in North America. Then, to compile their responses and to interpret the findings, to seek any existent patterns or trends therein, and to find the meaning behind the migratory behavior.

## Introduction

The investigation was an exploratory study within the general field of the Social Psychology of Emigration. Specifically, it concerns British migrant scientists and other British professionals migrating to North America during the last decade or so. The inspiration for the present research was provided by the Royal Society, which in 1963 published a quantitative analysis of the contemporary flow of British scientific and engineering talent—all with Ph.D.s—from the United Kingdom. The purpose of the present research was to extend, insofar as possible, the quantitative and qualitative aspects of this Royal Society Report, which was entitled *Emigration of Scientists from the United Kingdom.*

Scientists have always been migrants and Britain has for many centuries been an emigrant nation. However, during the early and middle 1950's articles and letters began to appear in the popular press and in professional journals that discussed the possibility that this flow of professional, scientific, academic, and technical talent was more than Britain could now bear, that it was increasing, and that it included some of the more gifted persons now being produced in Britain.

It was hypothesized that British scientists and other professionals were being attracted or "pulled" into North America by the greater professional and economic opportunities available there. It was also alleged that these scientists and professionals were being "pushed" out from Britain by the *lack*, relatively speaking, of funds, equipment, facilities, scientific enthusiasm, and a lower standard of living. It had been suggested that, in fact, North America, and especially, the USA had become a "magnet" attracting scholars, scientists, and professionals from all over the world, that this was a generalized pattern of talent loss that was now involving Britain. In addition, it was felt that while perhaps as many as one-half of the migrants eventually returned to Britain, many remained overseas for the whole of their professional careers. This loss of excellently trained scientists and professionals was difficult to bear in the first instance because the cost of educating them had been borne—in the main—by the whole society. That many of those lost to British science, universities, and industry were destined for a competing socioeconomic complex was highly disconcerting. That the flow of outward bound scientists and others was on the increase and was unbalanced by any significant return flow of North American talent, and that it included some recognized national names, added fuel to the controversy.

The present investigation set out to find, in a word, *who* the British migrant scientists were, in the sense of social, economic and professional background, *why* they had left Britain, *when* they had emigrated, *where* they settled in North America, *what sort* of work they were now doing, *how satisfied* they were with their original decision to emigrate, and *what* their intentions were concerning the future. We were interested in why many— perhaps one-half—of the departing British scientists had chosen North

America, and we were interested to ascertain if the quantitative materials in the well-known Royal Society Report (1963) could be substantiated from sources other than the British Universities which had been the Royal Society's source for their report.

The purpose of the research was not to make an exhaustive study of the "causes" of emigration among contemporary British professionals; this would have demanded more extensive sociological, demographic and penetrative psychological methods—for which funds and time did not suffice. Aside from the now famous Royal Society Report and a few informal and popular surveys, literally nothing had been accomplished in the area as such; the critical need now was for a body of facts and information upon which others could build. The technique was to explore what literature existed on this issue, to validate the statistics which did exist by checking that which was available on the alternate side of the Atlantic, but mainly, to *go to the migrants and allow them to speak for themselves*. The first effort was to locate a sufficient number of migrants in order to construct a valid sample, to identify them and then to question them via an empirical instrument to ascertain any general and specific trends or patterns concerning basis for self-selection, social grouping, motivations, and intentions for the future. Naturally, we were interested in the question of causation but were modest in our expectations about being able to offer definitive answers in this regard. However, the causes of and reasons for emigration, as found in the press and professional journals and in Parliamentary speeches could be tested, if only to minimal extent. Thus, the central idea of the present investigation was to allow these migrants to speak for themselves; to allow them to "explain" their migratory behavior and to allow any micro or macro explanations *to emerge from their own explanations of their own behavior*.

Central to the question of loss of talent by emigration is the definition of British "talent" itself. "Talent" cannot be equated with I.Q. level, any particular personality trait or any specific academic or educational experience other than the possession of a British "primary" degree of "good" quality. There is a possible difficulty involved in distinguishing between the concepts of "manpower" and "talent" since, in terms of their potentialities, the migration of some British professionals would appear to be a "manpower" loss rather than a loss of "talent." What is suggested is that among the British pool of trained-graduate manpower, there is a core, whose number is unknown, of gifted, often creative, and unusually well-educated scientists; these are frequently the innovators of the society in which they work. Education is an important factor here, and many if not most of this group would have been educated beyond the baccalaureate level and sometimes beyond the doctoral level. It is not suggested that every holder of a "higher" degree in science possesses all these marks of the creative and talented innovator; it is not suggested that all Ph.D.s in science are "talented," as defined above, but the expectation that we should find our most creative and productive scientists, technologists, and academics among the holders of higher degrees and "good" first degrees will be fairly well accepted.

National resources of scientific talent then are indeed those knowledgeable and highly educated and trained professional workers—frequently possessing a higher degree—upon which modern industrial societies depend for scientific, industrial, technical, and academic services and for the innovations necessary to keep the society in balance with, and, happily, ahead of other competing industrial societies. They are "national" resources of human talent because it is the nation, Britain, which has subsidized their becoming professionals and it is the nation itself which ultimately looks to these persons for its professional needs. Consequently, *any* depletion of these national resources of scientific talent must be regarded with some concern as a potential threat to the socioeconomic health of a nation. *Post hoc*, time will reveal clearly enough individual differences in level of performance and originality between such scientific workers whose initial graduate status is similar; it seems to be most satisfactory simply to accept the holder of a good quality first degree or a higher degree in science as potentially a member of this talent group.

The approach here is to attempt to find a pattern, especially in the area of values, in the present migratory flow of professionals from Britain to North America during the period of 1952 to 1964. This period was specifically chosen because it coincides generally with that of the Royal Society Report on the same subject. We were primarily interested in the physical sciences, particularly physicists and chemists as well as engineers, but academics and physicians also figured since these are the particular professionals about whom most anxiety is expressed in Britain because of their relevance to modern industrial life.

A few words about the relative size of the flow of scientific talent from Britain. In 1962, an *ad hoc* Committee of the Royal Society, with Sir Gordon Sutherland as Chairman, began an effort among more than 500 science departments of British universities to ascertain the amount of loss due to emigration, of Ph.D. holders in those departments. Only Ph.D. holders were included—and only the university records were used—both conditions being open to serious criticism. The Royal Society concluded that the annual rate of *permanent* emigration of recent Ph.D.s is about 12 percent of the total output in the fields included in the survey; that about 140 p.a. depart each year with sixty entering the USA, twenty entering Canada, thirty-five to other Commonwealth countries, and twenty-five to all other countries.

Further, they conclude that the flow of recent Ph.D.s has increased by a factor of about 3 in the decades of 1952–1962. The Report concludes that if *temporary* emigrants are included, the annual rate of migration to all countries of recent Ph.D.s is "now" (1962) 260, or over 22 percent of the total annual output in the subjects investigated—1,000 to 1,400 such graduates being at risk in any single year. The Report makes no allowance for entering British or American scientists and others; all statistics are gross losses and the "net" position remains in considerable doubt. The Report concludes that the emigration to the USA has doubled in the last ten years and is "still increasing." Cumulatively, the record reflects that of 8,537 known recipients of Ph.D. degrees in science, 1,136 emigrated permanently during the decade. A further 1,053 Ph.D. holders emigrated on a "mostly temporary" basis, of whom 545 have returned, 143 have not returned and the location of 365 was not known. The Royal Society concludes that the overall average loss during the decade was 16 percent of the annual British Ph.D. production in the various fields of science and that approximately half emigrated to the USA. But the actual annual *rate* of emigration has fluctuated between the 8 percent in 1952 to 19 percent in 1957. The rate for non-Ph.D. holders in science is about 2 percent per year to the USA of all degree holders in science.

Specifically, what are the dangers to Britain of the so-called "drain of brains" from its shores to the science establishments of other countries, especially North America?

1. Loss of the national financial resources which the education of such high-level scientific talent represents and the saving entailed by the USA and Canada in *not* having to underwrite such educational costs.
2. The loss to a competing socio-economy of productive scientists in actual fact, a subsidy of a competing industrial power (all too clear, for example, in the US air-frame industry).
3. Teachers as well as their students emigrate; the loss of the producers of science Ph.D.s tends to decelerate Ph.D. production in British science.
4. There is the loss of the actual products of the research of the lost scientists; and with these, the profits that could have been gained to the British economy. The worst has already happened—not once but many times: British institutions have had to pay licensing fees and such upon patented techniques produced by British scientists abroad.
5. The migration of scientists tends to continue the shift of the center of scientific excellence out of Britain; talent attracts talent, and to make North America more attractive only accentuates the problem.

6. Aside from the more routine findings, functions, and contributions of immigrant British scientists, there is always the possibility of the major breakthrough, i.e., how much is the equivalent of an Einstein "worth"? a Fermi? Should such an emigrant scientist make such a breakthrough, the benefit will be America's and not Britain's, in any economic sense.

What causes such a migratory trend—if indeed it is a trend? The following points have been put by responsible persons in explanation of such migration.

1. Inadequate salaries for scientific researchers in British universities, government, and industry establishments.
2. Inadequate equipment, laboratories, and general facilities in these science establishments.
3. Inadequate postgraduate facilities in British universities; primarily posts, stipends, and opportunities for research. Many buildings allegedly are old and cramped.
4. That inadequate time for research is provided to university research personnel.
5. That Britain currently "overproduces" or "underabsorbs" talent; that fewer posts—especially at middle or senior levels—exist than talent available to fill such posts.
6. That scientific research *as such* is not respected; that scientists are not welcomed into general industrial management; that the rewards in Britain go to the liberal-arts trained Oxbridge and Eton types.
7. Even if adequate funds can be gained for basic research in the sciences, there are inadequate funds to maintain equipment, make modifications to buildings, provide funds for payment of ancillary personnel, etc.
8. That the balance of power in science has now shifted, the two polarities now being Russia and the USA; that the latter is to Britain what Germany used to be to Britain and the USA during the twenties and thirties—the scientific center of the world.
9. The low state of morale in Britain and British science has been cited as well as the major change in Britain from a major Empire to a "small offshore island" on the European coast. The feeling is that British science and perhaps Britain herself are becoming increasingly "irrelevant" to the world situation in matters scientific, political and economic.

It has been alleged that the current level of migration is a "wastage"; but it appears that migration cannot be equated to *scientific* wastage as such.

The talent of these emigrating scientists and other professionals is not being wasted in North America although it may be *lost to Britain*. But scientific talent *can* be wasted if it remains in Britain in a condition of being unsupported, unstimulated, and frustrated in what it intends.

The problem of "cause" remains; but merely noting the "push" and "pull" factors seems inadequate to explain the migration of specific British scientists; any explanation would appear to have to be subtle enough to explain the migration of some and the nonmigration of others similarly qualified. Britain is "full" of scientists and other professionals who have turned down lucrative and exciting offers from North America and elsewhere that seem to attract others. In a word, why is migration the response of some and not of others? The answer would not appear to lie in the environment, because the environmental factors seem to evoke migration *and* nonmigration; the deciding factor appears to be in the "motivational" and value patterns of the individuals themselves. What is the *meaning* of the migration of such scientists and professionals? To what are they, in truth, responding? What is it they seek? What values do they hold which render emigration an understandable response? Some answers to this problem emerge from the research at hand.

## The investigation—THE SAMPLE

Made up of two "one-hundred percent groups"; all North American members of the British Institute of Physics and the Physical Society and the Royal Institute of Chemistry; 556 and 306 members, respectively; 345 others drawn from a variety of sources; TOTAL, 1,207.

## The questionnaire

The question concerning "personalities factors" is wholly a suggestive question; we are suggesting the possibility now (rather than probing obviously for an answer later) in order to prepare the respondents for answering the open-ended portions of the questionnaire which follows. Many of the items on the last two pages, such as those concerning American television and advertising, are mere "fillers" proving opportunities for the migrants to be negative concerning the American culture; this technique was used to reduce any potential dissonance between their feelings and their answers in the check list as they emerged. We also wanted to avoid the production of any chauvinist-oriented guilt feelings which might bias later responses, i.e., we did not want the respondent to have to "look for opportunities" to be negative. (We knew that migrants were highly critical of American television, journalism, advertising, etc., based upon our correspondence.) We were primarily interested in the work situation, opportunities for research, advancement, and other professional factors. Nine items from the "check list" had to be deleted because they were ambiguously received by the respondents.

## Selected findings of the recent investigation

Almost 90 percent of the *estimated* maximum percentage of questionnaire return for the gross sample was achieved. In effect, almost 800 questionnaires of the estimated maximum of 925 were returned. Over 50 percent of the questionnaires returned were from physicists and chemists and it was this group of 517 "hard" scientists, including some engineers and other miscellaneous scientists such as astronomers and mathematicians, which received the most detailed analysis. Unless otherwise stated, materials reported and discussed here concern this group of 517 "hard scientists."

Before the values and motivation patterns of the migrating British scientists can be discussed, it is necessary to focus on "which" scientists, in actual fact, selected themselves for migration.

If it is true that "we are what we value"—that we value that which we are—-and that which we value moves us to action, it can be said that the scientific values of this migrant group (coupled with other personality factors such as activism which renders them increasingly vulnerable) tend to predispose these migrant scientists toward contributing their considerable talent resources to the North American scientific establishment. Acting upon, and acting out, their value systems which place science and scientific professionalism ahead of congenial living in a culture which they, as a group, prefer theoretically explains the nonidiosyncratic migration as such and the self-selection of many of the specific scientists who migrate. Their migratory behavior, similar yet highly personal and individual—activist but not ideological—expresses what these twentieth century migrants feel. And these feelings have profound consequences, once they are articulated and acted upon. The migration feeds on itself as the migrants tend to attract others of similar mood and values to North America.

One of the first factors which emerged from the study is the fact that London, Oxford and Cambridge Universities contributed over 50 percent of the total sample of migrating scientists. Although this factor, in part, reflects the larger productivity of science Ph.D.s in these institutions in relation to the other institutions of higher learning in Britain, these institutions appear to be over-represented in relation to their contribution of science Ph.D.s to the science establishment of Britain. London University, in particular, with over 35 percent of the migrating scientists receiving terminal degrees from that institution is markedly over-represented. In addition, it is interesting to note that 32.8 of the migrant scientists report the London area as a last address before migration and another 18.8 percent report either Oxford or Cambridge. London and "Oxbridge" are obviously major staging areas for migrating scientists and all three have major science establishments known for the sustained excellence of their scientific work.

It is in the area of academic quality that one of the most obvious and striking relationships occurs: although, generally speaking, only 10 percent (approximately) of the British graduates achieve a First Class Honours degree, 174 of our hard science sample of 517 had done so. Two hundred and twenty seven of the remaining scientists were awarded a Second Class Honours Degree and only twelve obtained a Third Class Honours Degree. It is important to note that one need not have a degree of any sort to gain membership in either of the scientific societies from which the majority of the sample was drawn. But, interestingly enough, only 135 persons in our sample of 517 had *not* gained a *higher* degree of some sort; in fact, 30 obtained a M.Sc. in the United Kingdom before emigrating, 325 had obtained a Ph.D. or D.Phil. degree (twelve more *since* emigrating) and eleven migrants held D.Sc.'s. There were nine Fellows of the Royal Society in the sample.

This is a "young" group of *productive* scientists (only twenty-three of the several hundred physicists and chemists report themselves as *not* being engaged in active research) in the prime of their productive careers: the range as to age is from twenty-four to seventy-three years of age, but 33.3 percent are thirty years of age or younger, 29.1 are between thirty-one and forty-five years of age and 17.7 are between thirty-six and forty.

Thirteen percent of the scientists are in government work, 39.3 percent are in industry and 39.8 percent are in university work, while 7.9 percent of the remainder are in "other" types of institutions such as nonprofit research foundations.

Although this is a comparatively youthful group of scientists well-seeded with students and postdoctoral Fellows earning mere subsistence amounts, the median salary of the British scientists in North America was, in mid-Summer, 1964, more than $10,000 and less than $12,500. The median salary for those employed in university work is over $8,000 and under $10,000, while the median salary for those employed in industry is over $12,500 and under $15,000 per year. There are seventy-two men in the entire hard science sample earning more than $18,500 per year, including several academics (of the twenty in university work above this salary level) earning approximately $40,000 per year. The majority of these high-salary researchers and administrators emigrated after 1955 and eighteen arrived between 1961 and January 1964, which appears to indicate that a number of British migrant scientists take up posts of higher responsibility immediately upon or soon after their arrival in North America. Only one of this group of high-salary people intends to return to the U.K. and thirty-two have already become Canadian or American citizens.

There are several other significant and related factors reflected in the findings: in the "hard science" sample, 77.1 percent had themselves initiated negotiations with their first North American employer, 22.9 had been contacted by the first North American employer; 95.7 "do not regret" their decision to emigrate, 1.0 percent "regret" their decision, and 3.3 are "uncertain"; 72.1 percent are "definitely permanent" or "will probably remain" in North America while 27.9 percent will "definitely" or "probably" return to the United Kingdom. Over 89 percent of the migrants "have fulfilled their professional expectations in North America" and another 5 percent or so are "in process of doing so"; over 55 percent "would tend to encourage" a colleague to emigrate to North America (40.1 "would take no position") and 39.1 percent of the respondents felt that the flow of British scientific talent to North America would "increase", and 50.6 indicate that, in their opinion, it "will remain the same." Only 10.3 percent indicate that they think the flow will "diminish."

Central to the issue at hand are the results of the questionnaire "check list" concerning work and conditions for scientific work, the results of which are reported opposite.

Averaging the percentages on these work items for the total sample, the percentage "gain" is 62.7 percent; percentage "loss" is 4.3 percent; "little difference" 29.7 and "does not apply to me" 3.3 percent. One of the interesting factors to emerge is that in spite of improved quality of research equipment, generally higher financial rewards, and increased amounts of available equipment, 59.2 percent of the "temporary" emigrants and 48.6 percent of the "permanent" emigrants indicate that there is little difference in the *quality* of their work. Approximately 40 percent report a "gain," but for many emigrants, the "gain" in North America is apparently personal rather than professional.

It is obvious that the open-ended questions numbered one to six (excluding five) had to do with values, attitudes, and motivation; further, that they overlap. This overlapping was intentional in order to ascertain if similar themes and percentages as to themes would emerge in each; the pattern which emerged *was* strikingly similar as to subject and theme with the only real, although not significant, variation being between questions two and three (Wilson, 1964, pp. 395–397).

(G = gain  L = loss  LD = little  difference  NAM = not  apply  to  me)

| Items | "TEMPORARY" MIGRANTS | | | | "PERMANENT" MIGRANTS | | | |
|---|---|---|---|---|---|---|---|---|
| | G | L | LD | NAM | G | L | LD | NAM |
| FACTORS OF THE WORK-SETTING | | | | | | | | |
| Working conditions | 76.7 | 6.0 | 14.7 | 2.6 | 75.6 | 4.9 | 17.1 | 2.4 |
| "Room at the top" for advancement | 65.4 | 0.0 | 15.4 | 19.2 | 82.5 | 2.5 | 12.5 | 2.5 |
| Administrative freedom on job | 40.8 | 11.1 | 25.9 | 22.2 | 47.2 | 5.0 | 42.5 | 5.3 |
| Flexibility in work organization | 50.0 | 6.3 | 43.7 | 0.0 | 63.9 | 2.8 | 30.5 | 2.8 |
| Amount of communication with superiors | 53.8 | 7.7 | 38.5 | 0.0 | 80.1 | 5.0 | 12.4 | 2.5 |
| FACTORS CONCERNING RESEARCH, PER SE | | | | | | | | |
| Freedom to research | 46.4 | 3.6 | 46.4 | 3.6 | 48.8 | 4.9 | 39.0 | 7.3 |
| Quality of research equipment | 66.7 | 3.7 | 22.2 | 7.4 | 67.6 | 2.5 | 22.5 | 7.4 |
| Time for research | 32.1 | 10.7 | 53.5 | 3.7 | 35.9 | 10.2 | 38.4 | 15.5 |
| Amount of available research equipment | 67.9 | 7.1 | 14.3 | 10.7 | 76.2 | 7.1 | 9.6 | 7.1 |
| Ancillary services for research | 64.3 | 10.7 | 21.4 | 3.6 | 62.7 | 12.2 | 17.6 | 7.5 |
| Scientific exploitation of my work | 45.5 | 9.1 | 31.8 | 13.6 | 47.2 | 2.8 | 33.3 | 16.7 |
| FACTORS CONCERNING CAREER AND PROFESSION | | | | | | | | |
| Intellectual stimulation | 42.3 | 22.9 | 34.8 | 0.0 | 52.4 | 17.3 | 30.3 | 0.0 |
| Opportunity to advance professionally | 71.4 | 7.4 | 16.5 | 3.7 | 85.1 | 2.4 | 10.0 | 2.5 |
| Opportunity to specialize | 40.0 | 3.8 | 40.0 | 16.2 | 35.1 | 2.6 | 44.1 | 18.2 |
| Spirit of urgency in my work | 35.7 | 10.7 | 50.0 | 3.6 | 50.2 | 5.0 | 44.8 | 0.0 |
| Rapidity of promotion in my work | 42.3 | 0.0 | 34.6 | 23.1 | 64.8 | 0.0 | 27.1 | 8.1 |
| Quality of my work | 40.8 | 0.0 | 59.2 | 0.0 | 43.6 | 5.2 | 48.6 | 2.6 |
| STANDARD-OF-LIVING FACTORS | | | | | | | | |
| Annual income | 89.3 | 0.0 | 10.7 | 0.0 | 97.5 | 0.0 | 2.5 | 0.0 |
| Standard of living | 75.0 | 0.0 | 25.0 | 0.0 | 95.1 | 0.0 | 4.9 | 0.0 |
| Financial reward for skill increase | 53.8 | 3.8 | 19.0 | 23.4 | 80.1 | 2.2 | 15.0 | 2.7 |

## Question 2

## "When asked, I explain my emigration to North America by saying":

(The following types of reply are not mutually exclusive.)

The type of reply "Low status for scientists" and "Science in United Kingdom is demoralized" was mentioned by 14.1 percent. "Britain frustrating and depressing" 12.5 percent, and *if* this remark was extended, the source of frustration mentioned tended to be the British social class system.

"Lack of facilities in the United Kingdom": 10.4 percent.

"Low United Kingdom salaries": 6.2 percent.

"Britain is overcrowded": 5.3 percent.

"To get out of taxes, conscription and/or defence research": 2.3 percent.

"Depressing British climate": 2.1 percent.

(The *above* types of reply can be classified as "Push" factors.)

The reply, "Greater professional opportunities in North America"
(opportunity to use their talents?)

"Higher salary in North America": 18.0 percent.

"Higher standard of living": 10.6 percent.

"Higher social standing": 6.5 percent.

"For the benefit of my children": 3.9 percent.

"Retire here at a later age": 1.2 percent.

(The *above* six types of reply can be classified as "Pull" factors.)

A reply indicative of "wanderlust" was mentioned by 12.7 percent of
the 517 "hard scientists."

"To widen my scientific experience" by 12.7 percent.

"I was invited" or "the offer came from there" by 7.9 percent.

"Specific interest to visit North America" by 6 percent.

"Come for — years experience" by 4.6 percent, and 2.8 percent went
either because wife was American or wanted to "visit" America.

(These last six types of reply were regarded as "neutral" factors: i.e.,
the person was neither strongly pushed out of the United Kingdom nor
strongly pulled into North America.)

Dividing the responses into "Push," "Pull," "Neutral" or any
combination of these, it was found that 17.5 percent mentioned *only*
being pushed out of the United Kingdom, and only eleven of these
seventy-six (actual number) intend returning to the United Kingdom.
27.8 percent mentioned only being attracted (pulled) to North America,
and only twenty-two of these 121 (actual number) intend to return to
the United Kingdom, but, what is more surprising is that seventy-eight
of these (who went out of "curiosity" etc.) intend to remain in North
America. 10.1 percent mentioned both "push and pull" reasons; 5.5
percent mentioned "push and neutral" reasons; 9.9 percent mentioned
"pull and neutral" reasons, and the remaining 1.2 percent gave *all*
three types of reply.

## Question 3
## "I do not normally speak of the following reasons
## for emigration":

351 of the 517 "hard scientists" had no "hidden" (*their* interpretation of this question) or inarticulate reasons for emigrating. Of those
that had, their replies tended to fall into the following nonmutually
exclusive categories:

"Irritation with British—" mentioned by 36.7 percent; in the majority of cases, the causes of irritation were conditions in the British Universities, Scientific Civil Service, or in British industrial and commercial employment.

"Irritation with the British class system": 20.3 percent.

"Snob values among British intellectuals": 19.0 percent.

"High Taxation": 8.9 percent.

"Financially better off in North America" or just "MONEY": 20.9 percent.

"Better recreational and social facilities in North America": 8.9 percent.

"Better climate in North America": 6.3 percent.

"Wanderlust": 7.0 percent.

"Boundless possibilities in North America": 5.7 percent.

5.7 percent have " 'hidden' personal reasons", and 3.2 percent "Wish to make a complete change".

Of the 166 who have some "hidden" reason for emigrating, 125 intend to remain in North America, and only forty-one intend to return to the United Kingdom. It would seem, therefore, that a "hidden" or inarticulated reason for emigrating increases the likelihood of the emigration being permanent. It appeared that the *inarticulated* reasons were closer to the motivational materials imbedded in the comments volunteered by the migrants.

Dividing all the responses into those dealing with work, professional and socioeconomic aspects, "neutral" reasons such as "wanderlust", or any combination of these three it was found that 32.3 percent of the respondents made comments concerning work or working conditions. Only 11.9 gave only replies of the professional or socioeconomic type, while 32.1 percent gave only neutral reasons and, surprisingly enough, only 25 of the 140 (actual number) in this neutral category intend to return to the United Kingdom. In addition, 15.4 percent on the comments pertained to both socioeconomic and work conditions; 41.6 percent mentioned both work and neutral reasons, and the remaining 0.9 percent mentioned all three types of response themes.

It is obvious that some of the migrants are *pulled* into North America by higher salaries, a higher standard of living, more funds for research, and more and better equipment for research. They come for more freedom to follow their own research aspirations and for more time for the pursuit thereof. But, just as obviously, it is a minority of migrants who invoke such factors in explanation of their own case. And, when they do suggest such motivation, they frequently indicate that these factors are themselves not ends but mere means to other more important ends, such as increasing the quality of their work, more opportunities to exploit—in the scientific sense—their findings, or to add to their experience and skills or often simply to find greater meaning and challenge in their scientific work. Just as surely, some of the migrants come because they have been thwarted and frustrated in their work or because they are irritated with things British—often the class-system, or the autocratic one-professor university-departments; these are the kind of factors they cite as *pushing* them from Britain. However, this factor alone would effectively explain little more than a third of the sample (if that, because such individuals cite other factors as well) in respect of social situation or individual motivation. When serious thwarting does appear, it appears very definitely and usually with great strength. A few of the migrants seem to be natural nomads and they indicate the next one or two countries in which they hope to live and work following their stay in North America. Some few others indicate that long service in the armed forces or in colonial service "dislodged" and alienated them from life in Britain—broke their sometimes already tenuous ties with the British culture—and prepared them for residence elsewhere. A very few, similar to Martin Green (1960) appear to be saying that they never did feel at home in Britain, never really penetrated and became one with the culture. Some few migrant scientists cite specifically personal reasons for emigration, having little to do with their profession, for example, the following two cases:

My father being a knight and a rather well-known person in English academic life, I wanted to make my career without his help.

I wished to undertake research on the history and theology of Mormonism and this was possible only in Utah. (From a scientist.)


## Values and motivation: British migrant scientists

But, it is the factor of "personality" at work among the migrant group, that which Richardson (1959, p. 329) calls "his general behavioral tendencies" which clearly emerge as the most dynamic of the factors or influences operating toward emigration in this migrant sample. It is the dynamism of "personality factors", a mix of *values*, inclinations, attitudes and traits, that emerges so forcefully as one of the two major demonstrations of this investigation. The other demonstration being: that environmental factors, including salary factors, acting alone, are inadequate to explain either the contemporary migration of British scientists or the nonmigration of similarly trained (and we assume, similarly competent) professional colleagues. However, personality, motivational and value pattern factors *are* sufficiently catholic to be compatible with the remaining in Britain of many scientists and the departure of others. It is emphatically suggested by the recent investigation that any future empirical enquiries into migration of scientists from Britain should concentrate their efforts in this direction. An obvious second-level attack upon this problem appears to be the necessity for a comparative study with migrant scientists and matched nonmigrant controls, similar to the studies of Richardson (1956, 1959) among British manual workers destined for Australia.

What *does* emerge from the recent investigation is a very generalized migrant typology that appears to be unmistakeable. Central to the issue at hand is the question of *quality*; it is clearly not the academic failures in science who tend to emigrate. The high percentage of First Class Honors degrees, and those holding doctorates (coupled with a low percentage of Third Class, "General," "Pass" or no degree) appears to be indicative of a high-quality scientific group. Secondly, the large number of migrants who received their degrees from the older and most prestigious universities of Britain is another factor in support of the quality argument. Further, the comparatively large number of "high" salaries, in excess of $18,500, the number of migrants holding posts (often in their "thirties") of responsibility, including department headships in North American universities and being paid up to $40,000 for their contribution, is another indication of quality. Financially speaking, the British scientists are certainly doing at least as well as similarly educated North American colleagues and it would appear that they may be doing better as a group. It is obvious that this is a comparatively young group of fairly recent arrivals in the prime of their productive careers; the median age group is 31 to 35 and 54.7 percent of the "hard science" sample emigrated between 1961 and January 1964. *Within* this group, 146 or 52.5 percent emigrated in 1963, which would suggest some sort of possible acceleration in emigration of scientists from Britain. In addition, it is fairly well known that responsible seekers and interviewers of British talent in America such as I.C.I. can hire up to 70 percent of the British scientists they interview in North America and only 50 percent of those interviewed in Britain meet their standards (Hughes, 1964). (Doubtless some of this higher rate of hiring is specifically due to the additive American experience as such.) However, the fact that the British government in the person of the Scientific Civil Service Joint Board and several of the large British industrial corporations find it advisable to carry on extensive recruiting activities among resident British scientists in America speaks well of the quality of these emigrants.

These are not only young, very well educated, successful scientists, they also seem to have some of the personality factors such as high-energy, ambition, and "drive" which have come to be associated (if only in the

cultural sense) with creative excellence and scientific productivity. There is
a discernible migrant "type" in the sample, which stands revealed in the
comments, the descriptions of self and situation, and the explanation of their
emigration which the migrant scientists provided via the questionnaire. The
findings of the recent investigation agree closely with the findings of
Richardson (1959, p. 332) who, in testing "intending" British migrants of
skilled manual occupation (and nonmigrant controls) found that the " . . .
*emigrants* appear to be more ambitious, more motivated, *more* interested in
action and hard work, than the nonmigrants" (italics ours). It would not be
an invalid extension to indicate that such apparent motivational factors can
be translated to a situation of *valuing*, in the Baier (1965, p. 2) sense;
opportunities to express or proceed toward that which is valued, i.e., *more*
opportunity for *more* hard work, more challenge, more advancement, more
dynamic science. The migrant sample appears to have more than its share of
people with "high-boiling points." The migrant group can be characterized
by invoking such adjectives as "active," "energetic," and especially "ambitious," but even "ambitious" is not strong enough or specific enough to
characterize the aura cast by the group. Certainly the British migrants are
not "ambitious" in the more materialistic sense of merely wanting bigger
salaries and a higher standard of living; these things emerge as desirable by-
products of achieving *other* more meaningful goals and not as the major
goals themselves. It apparently is *Achieving*, as such, that greatly interests
this group. The migrant sample appears to be "ambitious" in the sense of
demonstrating a high level of aspiration, a high need-for-achievement; they
are ambitious (hungry) for *experience* of all kinds—and, at the core of things,
*they seem most to want an opportunity to use their rather extensive talents.*
This last item is a central theme in the commentaries of these professional
workers; like most professionals they seem to express themselves as persons
most vitally in their work, and it appears that in the deepest sense, they are
vested in their work and want to be allowed to get on with it. This is not
unlike the findings of other researchers such as Eiduson (1962, pp. 202–205).
Migration is seen as a means toward this end—towards the best use of their
professional talents, and not as a means to an easier life, more money, more
leisure, or the like.

Not much guilt or chauvinism is apparent in our sample. Emigration
tends not to be seen as a moral issue; emigration is not perceived as a *political*
act and patriotism figures only to the extent that a number of scientists
allude to the fact that their professional education was provided by the State.
There is very little "rejection of Britain" in the responses of the migrant-
scientists. The migrant sample seems thoroughly "British" in the cultural
sense and there is much love of "home" and much nostalgia concerning

things British in their replies, which, oddly enough, were sometimes couched in very American-sounding terminology. The migrants keep in touch with "home," they make frequent visits back, they read British nonprofessional publications regularly, they miss their "Blue Bass," the "good theatre," and the "B.B.C."

Every country and every period in a country's history produces its own expatriates, but what appears to emerge from the recent study is that economic, social, political, and certainly *scientific* conditions in Britain seem to be setting into migratory motion an unusually large number of scientists, technologists, physicians, and other professionals. The more vulnerable personality types in these groups can only be discerned at this point in rather broad dimensions. This potentially migratory group at risk appears to be made up of people for whom Britain, as such, seems to have little "holding power"; at the very least, it can be said that, for this group, there are *more* important goals than living in Britain as such, and the migratory group evidently feels that the specific goals, and above all the interests of *their scientific work*, can best be realized *outside* Britain.

This seems to be a group of men who "work hard and play hard" and they are not put off by what they indicate as the "faster pace" of North America; if anything, they appear to *prefer* this pace to others. One emigrant commented that he found the social system of North America "less congenial but more stimulating." Another migrant scientist indicates that he came to the USA because here he can voluntarily come into his lab to work at seven o'clock in the morning, while in Britain he would be criticized for doing so. As a group, the emigrants appear to prefer stimulation to congeniality, change to stability, and challenge to relative tranquility. The image of North American culture appearing in their comments is one of lusty competition at professional and economic levels; the rewards go to those who work hard, produce, are not shy about broadcasting their successes and who meet any situation "agressively" *as an individual*. The group appears to be admirably equipped to do just that. The desire to maintain and express their individuality is a theme which runs through much of the emigrant comment. Yet, they seem to prefer the more egalitarian class structure of North America to the class structure which obtained in Britain.

As a whole, the migrant sample seems to be one which might have more than its share of creative innovators apart from the bias in respect of professional quality which seems to exist; this is suggested not only by the verve and affective intensity which appears in many of the questionnaire responses but more obviously and more universally by the lively humor present. Although many of the emigrants are wry, satirical, often sarcastic, playful, and facetious in reply, humor is almost always used in order to communicate more effectively. It is humor with a "bite" and it is visited indiscriminately upon things British, American, self and others, friend and foe, alike. The relationship between creativity and such good and insightful use of humor remains poorly defined but there are some hints that these two factors are closely related (Getzels and Jackson, 1962, pp. 89, 102–105).

Scientists have always been nomadic and the best of them tend to be the most nomadic of all because the better they are, the more they are known and sought after; thus, the greater their mobility. The British migrant scientists—these intellectual free men of the world—want to go where their needs and aspirations, their desire to give of their best—can best be met. The era of noncritical acceptance of an economic system, a society, a scientific establishment has ended for many. Now, allegiance must be *earned* and especially is this true in the case of those gifted and well-educated persons of scientific talent who are now potentially the most mobile of men, and paradoxically, those also who can make the largest contribution to their country and society of origin. The contemporary British migrant scientist appears to be leaving Britain because his needs and aspirations—in the largest possible sense—are not being met, and this goes far beyond mere salary levels. Britain seems to be "right" about many of the small items to which the emigrants are attached, but North America is "right" about many of the "big" items that move them, such as offering greater opportunities for professional development and self-expression in their work. Even the extending-of-the-self professionally is not enough for some in the sample: several give the impression of wanting to test themselves against the experience of emigration and of working and living in another culture. Some say they wanted to see "how they stood in relation to North American science and scientists"; emigration appears to be a kind of crucible for the testing of their own mettle in what they felt to be the strongest running stream. Others seem to be responding to the opportunity to exercise personal power in the *benign* sense; to reach the top of a research laboratory or to head a university department—to form something new and uniquely theirs with their own hands and minds and to see it take form before their eyes. Opportunities to do so are more crucial than living in Britain for this group.

## Conclusion

Because of its size, direction, excellence, and vitality, the science establishment of the USA is now being compared with pre-1939 era of German science; responsible British senior scientists such as Professor J. W. Mitchell, (1965) ex-head of the National Chemical Laboratory in Britain and now of the Department of Physics, University of Virginia, have made strong public statements concerning the leadership of American science.

> There can be no doubt as to the present strength of science and technology in the United States of America. . . . Research has been one of the important growth industries of the United States during the past twenty years and there is no question of the fact that the strength of American science and technology is founded directly upon the strength of the American scientific community, which is formed by a relatively large number of research groups of super-critical size (Mitchell, 1965, p. 923).

Science, technology and research are not only critical values of themselves *within* the American culture but are having increased operational impact *on* many facets of life as we know them today; this is exemplified by the necessity of sponsoring and carrying forward conferences and research projects such as the very one in which we are presently engaged. Further, it is all *too* clear that the role that most of us play, personally and institutionally,— staggering as we are under the impact of this revolution in and of science— is a *passive* one. It is all too clear that we play the dependent variable to the independence of science.

It is the strength and excellence of this American science establishment to which the British migrant scientists are responding. They are responding in numbers heretofore unknown. That their expectations are fulfilled—that their scientific and professional needs are met—would seem to indicate that the value patterns they bring with them are shared and reinforced by the American science institutions to which they go. Here, science as means and science as end (these have never been adequately distinguished in the USA) have altered the direction, rate, and quantity of scientific emigration from Britain. That which such scientists value is more easily achieved here; there can be no greater compliment to American science and to the values of American scientists, coming as it does from men and women who love their homeland and look back more in sorrow than in anger.

> "I am an individual . . . I give my allegiance as a free man to those agencies most likely to meet my criteria for a meaningful existence."

## REFERENCES

Kurt Baier, "The Concept of Value" in this volume.

P. M. S. Blackett, "Universities and the Nation's Crisis," in Blackett, P. M. S., Ayer, A. J. and Zacharias, J., *British Association/Granada Guildhall Lectures 1963*, Manchester: Granada T.V. (distributed by MacGibbon and Kee).

Bernice T. Eiduson, *Scientists: Their Psychological World* (New York: Basic Books, 1962).

Jacob W. Getzels and P. W. Jackson, *Creativity and Intelligence* (New York: Wiley, 1962).

Martin Green, *A Mirror for Anglo-Saxons* (London: Longmans, 1960).

D. B. Hughes, Personal communication (interview), 24 February 1964.

J. W. Mitchell, The organization of basic research for the British chemical industry. Chemistry and Industry (London), 29 May 1965.

A. Richardson, *British emigrants to Australia: A Study of Some Psycho-Social Differences Between Emigrant and Non-Emigrant Skilled Manual Workers.* (Unpublished Ph.D. thesis, University of London, 1956).

A. Richardson, "Some Psycho-Social Aspects of British Emigration to Australia." *British Journal of Sociology*, 1959, 10, 327–337.

Royal Society, *Emigration of Scientists from the United Kingdom.* Report of a committee appointed by the Council of the Royal Society (London: Royal Society, 1963).

James A. Wilson, *The Depletion of National Resources of Human Talent in the United Kingdom: A Special Aspect of Migration to North America 1952–1964* (unpublished Ph.D. thesis; The Queen's University of Belfast, 1964.)

## A QUESTIONNAIRE FOR BRITISH PROFESSIONALS RESIDENT IN NORTH AMERICA

My profession, or occupation, is................................................... Date...............................

My research field (if relevant), is.........................................................................................

Age............ I am male............ female............ My father's occupation is/was..................

I am: married............ single............ divorced............ separated............ widowed............

My wife (husband) is British............ Canadian............ American............ Other (specify)............

I have (No.)....................... children. Their ages are.................................................

My place of birth was.........................................................................................

I now live in (City and State/Province)....................................................................

My last address in the UK was (town/county).............................................................

The approximate date of my last entry to North America was.............................................

This is my (No.) ........................... visit or period of residence in North America.

I hold the following type of Visa or Entry Permit: Exchange..............................................

Immigrant.................... Visitor.................... Refugee.................... (Other).......................

I am a national of the UK................ USA................ Canada.................... (Other)............

I attended a "Public"............... Grammar (State or private) ............ Technical ..................

Secondary Modern............... Other (specify).......................................................

I did.................. did not .................. attend a boarding school.

I was awarded the ........................ degree(s) from.............................................. University(s)

in (date)........................ The degree "class" of my first degree was.....................................

I was awarded the following professional qualifications.....................................................

I am a member of the following *British* Learned or Professional Societies :...................................
.........................................................................................................................

My last professional position and title in the UK was......................................................
.........................................................................................................................

I have changed jobs ............................... times since emigrating to North America.

My present position and title is......................................................................, in a

governmental.................. industrial.................. university.................. (other) ..................entity.

My present position is a temporary..................... permanent........................ appointment.

Negotiations for my first position in North America were initiated by me.....................................my

employer..................... Negotiations were carried on via telephone.............................................

written correspondence.................... interviews.................... (other)....................................

I received approximately £....................................... gross per annum from my last UK job.

My *present* gross salary per annum is :

............subsistence only during full-time           ............ over 12,500 and under 15,000 dollars

                study or research            ............ over 15,000 and under 18,500 dollars

............ over 5,000 and under 8,000 dollars     ............ over 18,500 and under 25,000 dollars

............ over 8,000 and under 10,000 dollars    ............ over 25,000 and under 40,000 dollars

............ over 10,000 and under 12,500 dollars   ............ over 40,000 dollars

My children are in American............ Canadian............ UK............ (other)............ schools.

I first really got the idea of emigrating from ................................................................. when I

was about ............................... years of age.

I considered migrating for a period of .................................................. before finally deciding.

I have.................... have not.................... been contacted by British government,

industrial, or research entities with a view to accepting a position in the UK.

Specify :  ...............................................................................................................

I subscribe to or regularly see the following British nonprofessional publications :...........................
.........................................................................................................................

I have.................... have not.................... purchased a house or flat in North America.

I intend........................ do not intend........................ to alter my present national status.

Hypothetically speaking, my income per annum would probably be £...............................had I remained in the UK.

I consider myself to be better trained............... less well trained............... equivalently trained..................... in comparison with North American colleagues.

I am satisfied........................ unsatisfied......................... uncertain........................ concerning the quality of North American schooling for my children.

I would..................... would not..................... prefer a British education for my children.

I would............... would not............... (uncertain)............... welcome job offers from the UK.

Should a UK colleague broach the subject of emigrating to North America, I would................... would not............... tend to encourage him. (Or, would take no position...............).

Holding economic and professional motivations constant I do................. do not................. think that "personality factors" figured in my decision to emigrate.

I continue to stay abroad for reasons different from those that brought me here: Agree................... disagree................... uncertain...................

I have............... have not............... fulfilled my professional expectations in North America.

My social and emotional ties are now strongest in the UK............... North America...............

I see myself as: definitely permanent..................... probably permanent............... probably temporary.................. definitely temporary.................. in North America.

I have................. have not................. experienced what might be termed a "degree of guilt" about leaving the UK. (Answer only if you are a "permanent" emigrant).

I regret.................. do not regret.................. (uncertain).................. my decision to emigrate.

In my area, the dollar equivalent to the £ in "real" goods and services is approximately................. ................... (for example, 3.50 to the £).

I feel the flow of talent from Britain to North America will diminish................................ increase ..................... remain about the same..................... during the next few years.

If I voted in the next British General Election, I would vote Labour....................... Conservative ......................... Liberal....................... other.......................

I would give the following advice to a British colleague about to embark for North America:
.....................................................................................................................................
.....................................................................................................................................
.....................................................................................................................................

When asked, I explain my emigration to North America by saying, ".............................................
.....................................................................................................................................
..............................................................................................................................."

I do not normally speak of the following reasons for emigrating: ...............................................
.....................................................................................................................................
.....................................................................................................................................

What influenced me most heavily toward migrating was ...........................................................
.....................................................................................................................................
.....................................................................................................................................

What my parents thought about my emigrating amounted to this:................................................
.....................................................................................................................................
.....................................................................................................................................

I chose North America primarily because...............................................................................
.....................................................................................................................................
.....................................................................................................................................
.....................................................................................................................................

Indicate whether, on balance, *you* have gained or lost, etc., as a result of emigrating:

|  | Gain | Loss | Little difference | Not apply to me |
|---|---|---|---|---|
| working conditions | ............... | ............... | ............... | ............... |
| quality of food | ............... | ............... | ............... | ............... |
| cultural opportunities | ............... | ............... | ............... | ............... |
| awareness of political corruption | ............... | ............... | ............... | ............... |
| conditions of climate | ............... | ............... | ............... | ............... |
| amount of leisure time | ............... | ............... | ............... | ............... |
| freedom to research | ............... | ............... | ............... | ............... |
| sense of political involvement | ............... | ............... | ............... | ............... |
| education for my children | ............... | ............... | ............... | ............... |
| awareness of being "British" | ............... | ............... | ............... | ............... |
| quality of research equipment | ............... | ............... | ............... | ............... |

| | Gain | Loss | Little Difference | Not apply to me |
|---|---|---|---|---|
| number of good friends | .............. | .............. | .............. | .............. |
| ease of domestic chores | .............. | .............. | .............. | .............. |
| opportunity to be creative | .............. | .............. | .............. | .............. |
| quality of domestic journalism | .............. | .............. | .............. | .............. |
| feelings of self-respect | .............. | .............. | .............. | .............. |
| awareness of crime and violence | .............. | .............. | .............. | .............. |
| time for research | .............. | .............. | .............. | .............. |
| satisfaction with my marriage | .............. | .............. | .............. | .............. |
| technical "know-how" in society | .............. | .............. | .............. | .............. |
| feelings of "rootlessness" | .............. | .............. | .............. | .............. |
| respect for North American education | .............. | .............. | .............. | .............. |
| awareness of advertising | .............. | .............. | .............. | .............. |
| annual income | .............. | .............. | .............. | .............. |
| intellectual stimulation | .............. | .............. | .............. | .............. |
| religious freedom | .............. | .............. | .............. | .............. |
| amount of available research equipment | .............. | .............. | .............. | .............. |
| quality of social services | .............. | .............. | .............. | .............. |
| "room at the top" for advancement | .............. | .............. | .............. | .............. |
| clean urban conditions | .............. | .............. | .............. | .............. |
| access to medical services | .............. | .............. | .............. | .............. |
| feelings of being part of an "elite" | .............. | .............. | .............. | .............. |
| ancillary services for research | .............. | .............. | .............. | .............. |
| standard of living | .............. | .............. | .............. | .............. |
| quality of television | .............. | .............. | .............. | .............. |
| probability of achieving personal goals | .............. | .............. | .............. | .............. |
| respect of society for research | .............. | .............. | .............. | .............. |
| tension on job | .............. | .............. | .............. | .............. |
| respect for British education | .............. | .............. | .............. | .............. |
| satisfaction with Great Britain | .............. | .............. | .............. | .............. |
| depth in friendship | .............. | .............. | .............. | .............. |
| amount of personal prestige or status | .............. | .............. | .............. | .............. |
| administrative freedom on job | .............. | .............. | .............. | .............. |
| feelings of "anti-Americanism" | .............. | .............. | .............. | .............. |
| sense of frustration | .............. | .............. | .............. | .............. |
| respect of society for science | .............. | .............. | .............. | .............. |
| opportunity to advance professionally | .............. | .............. | .............. | .............. |
| intellectual freedom | .............. | .............. | .............. | .............. |
| congenial social system | .............. | .............. | .............. | .............. |
| flexibility in work organization | .............. | .............. | .............. | .............. |
| hopeful as to future | .............. | .............. | .............. | .............. |
| opportunity for my children | .............. | .............. | .............. | .............. |
| freedom of speech | .............. | .............. | .............. | .............. |
| financial reward for skill increase | .............. | .............. | .............. | .............. |
| economic security for retirement years | .............. | .............. | .............. | .............. |
| amount of "red-tape" at work | .............. | .............. | .............. | .............. |
| ability to save money in any form | .............. | .............. | .............. | .............. |
| opportunity to specialize | .............. | .............. | .............. | .............. |
| friendly relations between "classes" | .............. | .............. | .............. | .............. |
| anxiety about job | .............. | .............. | .............. | .............. |
| amount of communication with superiors | .............. | .............. | .............. | .............. |
| spirit or urgency in my work | .............. | .............. | .............. | .............. |
| my wife's happiness (or, husband's) | .............. | .............. | .............. | .............. |
| scientific exploitation of my work | .............. | .............. | .............. | .............. |
| rapidity of promotion in my work | .............. | .............. | .............. | .............. |
| quality of my work | .............. | .............. | .............. | .............. |

# VALUES AND PLANNING

# Economic consequences of technological change

## Martin Bronfenbrenner

## Introduction

One must consider technological change in the "software" as well as the "hardware" sense of the term. To illustrate with the electronic computer, we should include under the head of technological change not only the development of the infernal machine itself, but also the adaptation of algorithms for its use and the education of specialists to utilize and extend its capabilities. I include both my colleague Herbert Simon, or rather his computer simulations of human thought and his improvements in computer languages, as technological improvements, along with whatever new-model computers he is currently baby sitting.

Given this broad definition of technological change, we can organize the principal present and prospective effects of technology upon our economic value systems under three heads, as follows: (1) The expanded "Revolution of rising expectations," which is already a hackneyed phrase; (2) The greater feasibility of direct-control and central-planning alternatives to the market economy; and (3) The upgrading (still largely pending) of "leisure time," both as against "work" and as against "economic goods and services." I shall also say something about impacts on specifically *international* economic values—the case for trade in general and "free trade" in particular.

## The revolution of rising expectations

By accelerating the potential rate of economic progress, especially for "the wretched of the earth" and in the underprivileged regions of the globe, technology is forcing a painful rethinking of personal and collective evaluations of economic growth and future income as against present consumption, and also, indirectly, of economic equality as against personal freedoms of the "Bill of Rights" variety.

453

Please permit at this point a lengthy digression, I have found it convenient to list six criteria for comparing economic systems with each other by their works, or for comparing the performance of a given system at different dates. The six criteria are:

a. The present standard of living, indicated, however imperfectly, by per capita income.[1]

b. The prospective future standard of living, indicated yet more imperfectly by the same imperfect index (per capita income) as forecast imprecisely over time for an indefinite period.

c. The immunity of the living standard from such short-term downward shocks as arise from business depression and price-level changes, as well as such long-term ones as may arise from technological change and international disturbances.

d. The equity—not necessarily the equality—of the distribution of living standards, as affected by both relative income and wealth. Notions of equity relate not only to distributions by size groups and social classes, but to distribution by region, by occupation, and (in a context of unstable price levels to distribution between fixed and variable income receivers and wealth holders.

e. The compatibility of the economic system with civil liberties in the conventional liberal sense. This is more meaningful in the converse sense of its *lack* of dependence on forced labor, monopoly of propaganda, or "cruel and unusual punishments" for "economic crimes."

f. Finally, the compatibility of the economic system with physical and mental health. Again conversely, we mean its *lack* of dependence on working people to death or driving them crazy in competitive or administrative rat races, whether these involve keeping up with the Joneses or keeping up with the assembly line.

The first two members of this sextet entrap between them the rate of the economic growth, which indeed might logically be substituted for either of the two. Also, the last two members of the sextet are only quasi-economic. (The last one in particular includes a good deal of what my esteemed teacher Henry Simons called "social-work twaddle.")

My primary thesis in this section is that, as of two or three generations ago, criterion (b)—future living standard—was almost irrelevant because it was so largely indistinguishable from (a)—present living standard—in most countries, but that technological change has brought it into its own. Hence

1. There is no need to dwell on the ambiguities and deficiencies of this measure. One may say in its defense that it correlates well with such other measures as life expectancy at birth, literacy rates, the percentage of consumption left open for items other than food, etc.

the "revolution of rising expectations." My secondary thesis is that, as the growth criterion (b) has gained relative importance, the criteria which have lost relative importance, for most people in most places, or at least for most "madmen in authority, who hear voices in the air," are (a), (e), and (f). We, meaning our madmen in authority, care less than their predecessors did about the present living standards, the personal liberties, the health, and even the lives of the fixed income groups, the petty bourgeoisie, the intellectuals, and the middle-classes generally, insofar as they stand in the way of economic growth. (I am generalizing globally here. The US, Canada, and a few other swanky suburbs of the world, are still 50 percent exceptions to the generalization.)

A century ago, the economic orthodoxy exemplified by Ricardo, the Mills, and Long-Run Malthus,[2] was a dismal science, more dismal than scientific. It saw (almost) no hope for major long-term improvement of the living standard of anyone except landlords in any important part of the world. Classical economies would grow, but only in size, meaning by "population explosion." The long-term trend of wage rates was to a subsistence minimum. The subsistence minimum, being psychological as well as physiological, was capable of improvement, but only slowly. The long-term trend of gross profits, which included interest, was to so low a level, as capital accumulated, that gross saving would fall to replacement of capital instruments as they wore out. Gains accrued to the landlord class. Land was the scarce, or strategic, factor of production, and its price and rent would rise over time. Such was the stationary state under free competition, than which no rival system was either better or more consonant with human nature. And that was essentially that, with the *caveat* that we cannot be sure how conventionally accepted this "conventional wisdom" ever was, even in Great Britain its *fons et origo*.

Subsequently, for almost the first time in relevant history, rapid technological change has come to the world, including the "unchanging East" and the yet-more-unchanging tropics. Economic growth has advanced from fantasy to reality. As we "consume" more of the commodity called economic progress, its marginal utility has contradicted the laws and stability conditions of neo-classical economics, and risen where it "should" have fallen. Far from sating itself, the demand for growth has risen, especially in that wide range of countries, formerly called "backward," which we now label "underdeveloped" or "l.d.c's." If the cost of growth includes lowering the living standards of the upper quarter or half of the income and wealth

2. We do not include Adam Smith, who was an optimist, or Short-Run Malthus, who worried about overproduction. To balance these, we also exclude the Marxian "principle of increasing misery," in all its several meanings, which out-dismalled the dismal scientists.

pyramids, not to mention the holders of monetary assets, if the cost includes the civil liberties of "the learned handmaidens of Wall Street," if it includes forced labor on multiple jobs at unconscionable industrial-accident and industrial-illness rates—growth seems, within surprisingly wide limits, worth its cost.[3]

The advanced-country manifestations of this revolution of values are only slightly less striking. There is of course an important element of what Richard Nixon christened "growthmanship"—concern with the growth-rate statistics *qua* statistics as a weapon of international competition—but it may not survive any cooling of the Cold War. More important and pervasive are other reactions. Now that technology has ushered in J. Kenneth Galbraith's *Affluent Society* (more effluent than affluent, along our riverbanks and lake shores), we can afford Wars on Poverty, tolerate feather-bedding, restriction of output, and padding of cost. We can also squander resources to cultivate latent demands, to maintain somebody's purchasing power, or to keep someone else off the labor market. We have come to consider and practice, in all but name, "retirement at birth" for those segments of our population for whom neither "socially-necessary" nor "interest-absorbing" jobs are available at ever-rising minimum-wage rates. Examples are concentrated in agriculture, construction, marketing—yes, and also in education.

But what of it? Far be it from me to play Mrs. Grundy, Praisegod Barebone, or the "conventional economist." If this is what we really want, why not have it? We can afford it, can we not? I am not trying to be humorous here, but simply to suggest that our economic values already may have changed, under the impact of technology, Professor Galbraith, and the Triple Revolution, to a greater extent than most of us are willing to admit.

The twin flies in this ointment, or lotos-land, have been nuclear war and population explosion. The first—an exceptionally obvious consequence of technological advance—I leave to the contemplation of those with stronger stomachs than mine. On the second fly in the ointment, population, let me join the minority suggesting that we have already swatted said fly in our sleep, although the results are not yet apparent. Furthermore, the fly has been swatted by technological innovations, just as population growth originally leaped because medical technology spread. In the Western World, we have and are cheapening pills, loops, rubber goods, and allied hardware. In the East, the most promising fly swatters seem to be software ones—legitimized abortion, sterilization (and, to a lesser extent, homosexuality),

3. Ask students from underdeveloped countries the simple True-False question, "The optimum growth rate is the fastest possible growth rate." Since the end of World War II, the affirmative answers have won in a walk, even among prospective economists. The affirmative margin, furthermore, shows few signs of abating. (Japan is a possible exception here, but by what standards can we call Japan under-developed?)

official propaganda against early marriage, work patterns separating the sexes, pervasive housing shortages, and the "obvious and simple system" of working people long and hard enough to delibidinize them. Let me venture to wonder whether new editions of Professor Joseph Spengler's *France Faces Depopulation* may not be called for during my lifetime, and about other countries than France. (The American-birth rate has been falling for over a decade, and the Eastern European rate is heading downward simultaneously.) It is of course hard to include in this optimistic time table the numerous countries of Latin America, Asia, and Africa, which have become the real population trouble spots, but even there, now that cheap techniques are known, we may require no more than an extra generation or two to bring the Malthusian bogey under control.

## The feasibility of central direction

As of 1900, it is no exaggeration to say that there existed no concrete alternative to the market economy outside the jungles of Bongo-Bongo and "duodecimo editions of the New Jerusalem." The issue with regard to Socialism and Anarchism in each of their 57 varieties, and likewise the various other "isms," was not how they might compare to supply-and-demand, but whether they would work at all, on a large scale in an advanced society. Could they determine in any rational way the *what*, the *how*, and the *for whom* of economic production and distribution? The Italian economist Enrico Barone put the matter technically, in terms of the impossibly large number of simultaneous mathematical equations a collectivist Ministry of Production would have to solve in every planning period to make the entire economy mesh with the desires of its economic subjects. The man in the street put the matter platitudinously: no bureaucrat could repeal the Law of Supply and Demand.

Among the reformers themselves, the *fin-de-siecle* crop of Utopians[4] usually relied on some form of "maximalism"—meaning, in this context, an economy of "abundance" rather than "scarcity," where demands were limited to the "natural" ones, where work was no longer arduous and was volunteered freely in whatever small amounts might be necessary to produce the essential goods in the required quantities. Naturally they assumed both domestic and international peace. They also relied frequently on fantastic and futuristic technological changes as well—many of which have since come about! Karl Marx himself, for all his abhorrence of blue-prints for Socialist Utopias, may have taken a similar position, with less technological

4. The best known writers (at least in English) were Edward Bellamy in America and H. G. Wells in England.

gadgetry—but only after the Revolution had internationalized itself over the civilized world and bred a generation or two of Socialist men.

The unfavorable critics, including nearly all professional economists,[5] saw Socialism and the other "isms" in terms of chaos, of arbitrary fiat, of technical limitation to Utopian colonies, or to pallid imitation of solutions already reached in market economies past and present. Perhaps the most outspoken of the critics has been an Austrian, Ludwig von Mises. As late as 1956 he held to an "imitation" theory in explaining Soviet Russian survival,[6] with the corollary that Socialism would be completely unworkable on any worldwide basis, with no capitalist economies to imitate. Clearly the constructive or "practical" case for collectivism was weaker than the destructive, or "anti-capitalist" one.

Against this background, let us consider the technological innovations of the first two-thirds of this century. In the first place, there have been revolutionary advances in statistical information, both in quantity and in quality. (In the US for example, usable quarterly national income estimates start from 1929, on the basis of work done in the "thirties.") There have been qualitative improvements in coverage, accuracy, fineness of breakdowns, the continuity and comparability of statistical series. We are still far from perfection, however, as witness Oskar Morgenstern's *Accuracy of Economic Observations*. In addition to the national income data, quantitative improvements have been made in production, consumption, inventories, the labor force, employment, international balances, interindustry relations (often called input-output), and indeed, over the entire spectrum. We might note that the improvements are more striking at the national than at the regional or local level, although there are exceptions to this generalization. Incidentally, more than one *laissez-faire* economist has suggested, and sometimes with success, that we stop developing or publishing one or more types of these statistics, not because they cost money or are useless, but precisely because they are liable to be used by the wrong people (planners) for the wrong purposes (planning). I have myself referred to Professor Wassily Leontief's input-output analysis as "The Economics of 1984."

Along with improved statistical raw materials have come improved methods of processing them quickly. On the hardware side, let me repeat the sacred word "computer" and pass on. On the software side, equally sacred words are "sampling theory" and "survey research." Other participants in this colloquium know more than I about both of these, but the main point is an optimum combination of economy with accuracy in learning about a

5. The best example of this literature is Ludwig von Mises, *Socialism* (New York, 1951).
6. Professor Mises repeated his imitation theory at a conference at the University of North Carolina in 1956, at which I was present. (I do not imply any subsequent change of heart.)

statistical "universe" from the attributes of a carefully selected sample, and in framing requests for information so that they can be answered intelligently and realistically by the average respondent.

Improved theories and techniques, employing these increased volumes of improved statistical data, have accompanied the accumulation of data on both sides of the Iron Curtain. One example is input-output analysis, which I have mentioned already and which seems to have been originally of Russian origin. One of its principal uses has been to identify potential bottlenecks in advance when a certain process changes, or when the bill of goods demanded changes, in some given way. Input-output analysis tries to answer questions like: How many "guns" (military goods) can we produce without cutting our consumption of "butter" (civilian goods) below some preassigned level? Or, on the other hand, in what regions and industries can we expect unemployment or labor-shortage problems in the event disarmament permits replacement of military spending by equal amounts of public expenditures of the welfare-state variety?

Another new technique is linear programming, also developed originally in the Soviet Union. An example of a "linear programming" question is: What is the maximum growth rate of per capita income consistent with a certain input-output table, certain population growth rates, certain requirements for "necessary" consumption, public service, and national defense, and certain receipts of foreign assistance? (It is the expression of the growth rate and its restrictions or "constraints" as constants, or as linear combinations, which makes the programming "linear." (More general, non-linear, methods are also coming into use.)

A third example of a novel technique is the computer simulation of economic processes over time. An economic question this technique may soon answer is: On the basis of our present knowledge of relations between income, consumption, investment, etc., and of the statistics for 1929, to what extent would our present tools of monetary and fiscal policy have damped down or reversed the depression of the 1930's by, let us say, the beginning of 1933?

A fourth technical innovation, less well developed thus far and less frequently applied to actual data, is economic-stability analysis. It has been adapted from electrical engineering to answer such questions as: Given the economy's delayed pattern of reactions to changes in the quantity of money, the price level, and the rate of interest, what patterns of money and interest-rate movements will be most effective in reducing the number and the amplitude of economic oscillations of the business-cycle type, and likewise in damping them (if they occur) and returning quickly to a neighborhood of moving equilibrium?

Combinations of these and other techniques, under the heads of "operations research" and "management science," have already been and are being applied and improved, both in private planning by individual business firms and in public planning for cities like Pittsburgh, regions like the Upper Midwest, and countries like Egypt, Holland, and Poland. Sometimes the initial results of such techniques are wide of the mark; a minor programming error caused the Japanese National Railways to print and sell ten tickets for each seat on one of its crack trains when this operation was first computerized. Techniques is only imperfect "stupidity insurance." Furthermore, none of the specimen questions I have just given you has yet, to my knowledge, been answered completely, satisfactorily, or in full detail. However, you can see the direction in which things are moving.

Fear has also been expressed by Socialist critics of American society (Michael Harrington, for example) that these technical developments have proceeded so much more rapidly in the large corporations and the Armed Services than in the civilian public economy as to threaten some kind of big-business feudalism or military Fascism which few of us consciously want. Time will tell how realistic these forebodings will have been.

We should also include, as new planning techniques, improvements in enforcing whatever controls planning may involve on the behavior of individuals, corporations, and other groups. For example, broad-based income taxes and mass social-insurance schemes have become feasible only recently, and are now in process of widespread automation. The existence of income-tax returns and social-security members, including the variety of information included on the tax returns, can now facilitate such "direct controls" as rationing of consumer goods and allocation of producer goods over prolonged periods, if a plan so requires. Auditory, visual, and radio controls have also been advised to supervise production, provide continuous reporting of operations, and put the right man in the right place at the right time. Some of the results, like the radio-directed taxi driver, have become familiar in the private economy. Others resemble the "telescreen" ("Big Brother Is Watching You") which Orwell forecast only for 1984. (Trade unions are increasingly protesting against the use of closed-circuit TV to watch workers at their machines or during their "breaks.")

I feel bound to warn you again that the preceding paragraphs stray close, here and there, to "amazing science fiction" in fields where I lack any claim to competence.[7] The fact is, unfortunately, that economic wind-tunnels, guinea pigs, and testing laboratories are fewer than we would wish,

7. My information about management science and operations research, in particular, is "journalistic" in the pejorative sense of the term. My chief informant is my enthusiastic colleague, William W. Cooper, who is not to blame for any distortions of his statements.

and a number of plans and projections have been acted upon, when their engineering equivalents would have been sent "back to the drawing board." The results have sometimes been most horrid. Let me limit myself to four instances from as many different countries: (a) The American post-war forecasts of six to eight million unemployed in 1946–47; (b) The British attempt to develop Nigeria, and incidentally ease the sterling-area balance-of-payments problem, by raising "ground-nuts" (peanuts) and extracting vegetable oil on a large scale; (c) The neglect of agriculture in several Soviet and Indian Five-Year Plans; and (d) The back-yard steel-mills of the Chinese "Great Leap Backward" of 1958–60.

Perhaps also, as an additional *caveat*, I should remind you that the controversy which followed Friedrich von Hayek's *Road to Serfdom* (in the mid-forties) has not been resolved. Hayek, a leading follower of Mises, propounded the thesis that economic planning, by the best-intentioned neo-Liberals and Democratic Socialists, led eventually to dictatorship by the worst elements in the community, namely Fascists or Stalinists, and illustrated his proposition by German experience over the sixty year period from Bismarck to Hitler.[8] There were rebuttals aplenty, but the debate petered out inconclusively, and Hayek's problem has been swept under the table rather than solved. (The same thing may have happened with the theological issues of the Religious Wars of the 16th and 17th centuries!) Also, a logical fallacy has invaded the controversy, twisting it in a direction undeservedly favorable to the planners. The fallacy is this: The late Senator McCarthy, the Birch Society, the Ku Klux Klan and similar manifestations suggest that the market economy does not generate or guarantee civil liberties under all circumstances. This has been (fallaciously) taken to mean that Hayek was wrong, or that more Socialist planning would necessarily further personal freedom, since Birch Societies are no problem in Scandinavia.

The case for the market economy has simultaneously been weakened by other theoretical developments associated less directly, if at all, with any of the techniques I have been mentioning. In economics, there has been a burgeoning of imperfect competition theories, downgrading Adam Smith's invisible hand to a special "purely competitive" case. There has been Keynesian economics, restating in academic terms the Marxian proposition that economic equilibrium generally involves less than full employment. Again, Sir Roy Harrod in Britain and Evsey Domar in America have shown, under restrictive assumptions, that the path of economic growth may follow an unstable "knife-edge" equilibrium, ever threatening to lapse into runaway inflation or deep depression. More recently, a number of writers, among whom Professor Galbraith has had the greatest public impact, have elabor-

8. George Orwell's *Nineteen Eighty-Four* (New York, 1949), makes a similar point by analogy.

ated the proposition that the market economy systematically starves its public relative to its private sector. These four examples will illustrate my point on the economic side.

One can make a similar point in social psychology, which is far from my field of specialization, with important economic implications. The case for permitting "consumers' sovereignty" over the economy has been weakened by our increasing knowledge of how supposedly-sovereign demanders of goods, suppliers of labor, and voters on policy can be and have been manipulated by their ostensible subjects, the business community.[9]

## Work versus leisure

More far-fetched is the possibility that technological change will shortly require us to rethink our "Puritan" or "Calvinist" ethical system, which makes work a good thing in itself and leisure a bad one, or at least a dangerous luxury like alcohol. Some writers, however, most notably at the moment a group calling itself the Ad Hoc Committee for the Triple Revolution,[10] maintain that "shortly" really means "the day before yesterday," and that our problems of crime, unemployment, and more besides result from our inability to rethink our values in time.

The problem is, of course, the possible prospective shortage—some call it a real and present shortage—of interesting or meaningful work in many skill categories at reasonable wages. At first, the groups hit hardest seem to have been unskilled—teenagers from minority groups, with high-school education or less. In the longer term, it is now forecast, competition between men and machines will intensify for people with more education and training, just as the musician already competes with records and television, or the teacher competes with teaching machines and closed-circuit broadcasting. The eventual comparative advantage may come to rest at the extremes of the skill distribution. These are, at one end, the highest reaches of intellectual and artistic ability, including major decision making, and also, at the other end, some of our lowest grade and most disagreeable, but at the same time, least routinized, tasks. The collection of rubbish is an example Simon has used, garbage collection having been automated by the Disposall (at some cost in water pollution).

9. Insofar as planning agencies can use the same devices and techniques as Madison Avenue, social psychology has played its part, by developing them, in increasing the feasibility of central direction in the economy.

10. The chief spokesman for the Ad Hoc Committee on economic matters has been Robert Theobald. The Committee's "Manifesto" was published in *Liberation* (April, 1964). See Norbert Wiener, *The Human Use of Human Beings* (Boston, 1954). Two Theobald books are *Free Men and Free Markets* (New York, 1963) and *The Guaranteed Income* (New York, 1966).

It is quite conceivable, if human productivity rises faster than spontaneous human demand, to attain an "economy of abundance" in the limited sense that society can provide all members income sufficient for some psychologically adequate standard of living, even those members who spend their lives playing games, making love, and staging political demonstrations.[11] The Ad Hoc Committee believes we are there already, but do not know it. The Technocrats thought the same thing in the early 1930's, and earlier instances are available to the intellectual historian.

Rather than devalue work, as befits an economy of abundance, we are allegedly searching out feather-bedding, busy-work, and made-work substitutes for the genuine and meaningful tasks which are petering out. We are supposedly wasting the time, in some cases even the lives, of the people engaged in such work.

As a matter of fact, our value system has not yet adjusted completely to justifying income without *manual*, or equivalently *irksome*, forms of work. Most of the participants at this conference are students, teachers and civil servants. Have any of us *not* been told we don't "really" work or deserve our incomes, because so much of what we do is not only clean and light, but positively enjoyable? Is it fair to the manual worker that *our* hobbies—teaching, studying, researching—should be remunerative, while *his* hobbies—bowling, hunting, and fishing—all cost him real money?

Socialist propaganda makes much of the basic unity of interest between "workers with hand and brain," but it is common knowledge that mutual distrust and discrimination persist in all Socialist societies, where it is hard to blame them on John Calvin. Mutual suspicion is supposedly ameliorated in some Socialist countries by requiring mental workers to spend so many weeks or months per year at manual tasks—less often the reverse, which is probably significant. Possibly the Ad Hoc Committee and other economy-of-abundance thinkers assume that all jobs which survive automation will be easy and pleasant. If true, this will ease the value transition by eliminating the need for heavy manual labor. But they are probably wrong in assimilating all future work to their own "reumunerative hobbies," and may not have faced sufficiently the problems of getting dirty, smelly, dangerous, unmechanized jobs done under their system. Will recipients of Theobald's "due income," for example, be required to spend a certain number of days or weeks a year collecting rubbish, doing structural iron work on skyscrapers, or even directing traffic in extremes of weather? It not, would he be willing

---

11. This is what the literary critic Paul Goodman calls "Growing Up Absurd." *Liberation*, *op. cit.*, p. 10 f. This version of the economy of abundance is "limited" by comparison with the "maximalist" one in which all goods are free to all, with no work requirement.

to pay volunteers the rates it might take to get such jobs done in a world where all could live well by making love?

From the nagging friction between manual and mental workers it is safe to predict that, under anything like our present value system, any further attenuation of the link between disagreeable work and receipt of income will give rise to more serious conflicts, both between people and within individual psyches. Already, second-generation and third-generation recipients of relief hand outs are said to form a pariah group, inhabiting *The Other America*. It is certainly plausible to blame a great part of our current alienation, mental illness, and crimes of violence to these particular pariahs, who can neither find work above relief scales or reconcile themselves to life without working.

It is not easy to avoid some measure of pessimism at this point. We dare not foresee our work-leisure evaluation either changing rapidly enough to extract us from our present troubles, or being enforced stringently enough to drive people off relief into whatever substandard jobs and wages they would then perforce accept (probably after a bigger-and-better crime wave than any we have yet seen).

An attractive alternative, at least for the short term, would be to batter down the multitudinous economic walls, from apprenticeship rules to occupational licensing and professional standards, which keep so many pleasant and rewarding jobs closed to so many "other Americans." (When, one wonders, will house-painting be restricted to Art School alumni, and television repairing to certified graduate electrical engineers?) Most conventional economists would opt for some such effort before resigning to the Triple Revolution or accepting the status quo. But what politician or administrator will simultaneously brave the building tradesmen, printers, and barbers, let nurses or civilian "medical corpsmen" handle minor ailments, restore routine legal matters to notaries, refurbish two-year normal schools to cure teacher shortages, or even cut the fraying cord between the Ph.D. degree and undergraduate instruction in our own institutions?

It is, of course, also and always possible that nothing need be done at all. The status quo may right itself, without changes in either values or institutions. Technological advance may expand productivity sufficiently, and in appropriate patterns, to maintain jobs for all at merrily rising rates of compensation. "The other America" will then merge with "the American dream," and nobody need do much of anything. Indeed, since World War II, wages have kept pace with (rising) productivity, consumption has kept pace with (rising) personal income, the labor share in national income has, if anything, risen, and the capital stock per unit of output has shown no "overheating" tendency to spawn excess capacity by rising. The problem has (from Korea to Vietnam) been an upward drift of unemployment. Once this is solved, with or without a corresponding acceleration of price inflation, all may be well. What makes this writer, on balance, a pessimist, is not denial that all this *can* happen, but only denial that it *must* happen, and consequent concern about the chance of its *not* happening.

## International repercussions

This subject, even on the purely domestic front, is too broad for this paper. Let me nevertheless call attention to three changes in specifically international-economic value in addition, brought about by technical progress.

Economists, particularly the international-economic sub-species, have demonstrated again and again, to each other's satisfaction, the benefits of international division of labor, international trade, and international capital movements. Economic internationalism seemed for a time a value in itself, supporting an auxiliary *prima facie* case for free trade or against tariffs, quotas, and similar devices. With the international spread of the newer technologies, however, especially cheap power, cheap transport, and cheap synthetics, much of this doctrine has become old hat. The celebrated "gains from trade" have probably lessened, although not vanished, for the technologically advanced countries taken singly (the American case) or in small groupings (the Western European Six). Conversely, a higher degree of autarchy has become attainable at smaller real cost for technologically-advanced countries than Adam Smith, David Ricardo, or John Stuart Mill could have expected.

Let me illustrate with reference to steel, Pittsburgh's basic industry: I learned in several classrooms that countries without coking coal, without limestone, and without iron ore necessarily depended on international trade for their supplies of basic steel. Now, it would seem, this classroom lesson is obsolete. Navigable water will do as well as coal, limestone, and iron ore. Italy and Japan, with seacoasts and harbors, have turned to importing the ingredients for steel rather than the steel itself, reducing the total volume of their imports by the "value added" of the steel mills. The free-trader's whole value system is threatened by such changes, which came about by technological changes increasing the economy and speed of marine carriage of the ingredients of steel, and other technological changes automating the loading and unloading of ships.

Another value of international trade and international capital movements is embodied in the so-called Heckscher-Ohlin Theorem. This theorem says that international trade tends to equalize input prices, including wage and interest rates, as between the trading partners. Therefore it usually also tends to equalize real incomes per head; we say "usually" only because changes in material and human capital per head may occasionally offset the consequences of input price equalization.

International equality is, at any rate, the value concerned. However, insofar as advanced technology remains concentrated in the wealthier countries, or insofar as they extend their technological lead over the rest of the world, there may result instead a set of circumstances—call it a "techno-logical gap"—which makes the Heckscher-Ohlin Theorem quite irrelevant. Input qualities seem, in fact, to be diverging at least temporarily as between advanced and developing countries, so that input prices are diverging with them. Just as the Heckscher-Ohlin Theorem pointed in the general direction of increased income equality between trading partners, the technological gap points in the opposite direction. Trade and capital movements have become associated with increased international inequality, and there has arisen increased concern with methods for avoiding it. Professor Gunnar Myrdal's *International Economy* has become a theoretical manifesto for this "newer" set of values; the United Nations Conference on Trade and Development at Geneva in 1964 attempted to develop a set of rules to reverse the trend of the income gap between rich and poor countries. In any event, the volume of international trade is likely to be reduced as a proportion of world income, and the pattern is also likely to be transformed, to the detriment of exchanges of raw materials for finished consumer goods.

My final "international" point is pessimistic in its overtones. Countries may be unable or unwilling to adapt their economic values, and hence their economic policies, to contemporary technological changes. Instead, they may rely more heavily on "exporting" such unemployment as may develop, either in the form of goods or (less frequently) in the form of unskilled emigrants. (No country wants its brains drained!) Also, except under such special circumstances as famine or inflation, countries hate to import their neighbors' unemployment, and the export of unemployment increases international friction, as the United States discovered after the Smoot-Hawley Tariff of 1930. With increasing international friction, the economic promise of higher living standards from improved technology may be dissipated by concentration on military components, if not by international war. Defense spending seems, especially in times of strain, the path of least resistance to maintaining, full employment without questioning existing economic values. But its effect on civilian standards and progress is not clearcut. Complaints are already appearing, most audibly from Seymour Melman, of another widening technological gap—this time between the technological level of the military and civilian economies, as the former bids away the cream of our engineering and scientific talent. Treating the economics of war and defense as a branch of international economic relations, the old chestnut about "whither are we drifting?" becomes applicable.

## Concluding remarks

Lest this paper degenerate into a Theme and Variations on Gloom and Doom in some minor key, let us mention a few outworn economic ideas which we seem at long last to be casting off, sometimes after major catastrophes but hopefully in time to avoid fatal ones. Here are half a dozen instances, passing in rapid review.

We have abandoned our faith in Say's Law (or, more accurately, in Say's Identity[12]) not indeed as a dogma, which it never was, but as insurance against overproduction and underconsumption. This change has permitted the value of guaranteed full employment, requiring active monetary and fiscal policy, to replace the values of self-reliance and austerity, requiring belt-tightening, liquidation, and what was sometimes called "healthy bankruptcy" as a remedy for depression and recession.

We are in the process of abandoning the exaggerated valuation, ethical as well as economic, placed on "the gold standard" to guarantee the purchasing power of our money. (It is not always clear whether the gold standard was a value in itself or a means to price-level stability and other dimly defined economic values.) It is interesting that President Johnson was able, in 1965, to reduce the silver content of American subsidiary coinage, and eliminate the gold backing of Federal Reserve Bank deposits, with only the faintest complaints of "debasement"—emanating mainly from mining interests in mining States.

We have displaced two Siamese-twin idols—the annually-balanced budget and the minimal national debt—which we formerly worshipped together, like Castor and Pollux, under the joint title of Sound Finance. The economic value of "soundness"—for value it indeed became, compounded of "honesty" and "prudence"—seems always to have been based on a logical fallacy of composition, to the effect that the economy was a private person writ large, so that the country should react to changing circumstances in the same way as an individual.

Nor do we today intone "the law of supply and demand" to excuse inactivity in economic policy, any more than we intone "the law of gravity"

---

12. A simple statement of Say's Law is that, in the aggregate, supply creates its own demand. Say's Law would add, "at *some* positive price level," whereas Say's Identity might read or "at *any* positive price level."

to excuse inactivity in aviation or outer space. Perhaps it is a value of economic automaticity or impersonality which is being displaced by or diluted with such values as rationality in the sense of planning. In the same way, we now reject the notion of inevitability of economic fluctuations, including the related notion that "whatever goes up must come down," because the economy is, or ought to be, an automatic mechanism. There are some signs of shifts to the other extreme, namely, the worship of planning for planning's sake, or activism for activism's sake, or providing guarantees to an extent incompatible with progress and change.

Finally (for our present argument, that is to say) we have diluted the great old value of self-reliance yet further by an expanding modicum of public relief, insurance, and allied protection against a widening range of possible economic calamities. A recent American example is the "Medicare" progam of insurance against certain costs of illness, including chronic illness, in old age. In America, as in most of Western Europe, the welfare state is becoming a genuine value, replacing not only self-reliance but, at the same time, solidarity within families and other small social groups. There is talk of extending this particular value from the national to the global level, although the "global welfarists" remain a small relatively ineffectual minority.

These examples, and more could have been found, suggest that a number of economic values—"sound finance," "impersonality," "self-reliance," and so on—have been chipped away in the small, and for reasons at least partially technological. Chipped away, one might add, not necessarily for the better; some of the successor shibboleths, such as the more coercive varieties of "planning," may be worse than their Victorian predecessors. What is possible in the small, furthermore, is also possible in the large, sometimes more quickly than is conceivable before it happens. Russia in 1917, China in 1949, and Cuba in 1959 are all examples of revolutions in economic values as well as economic institutions.

We may even end by demoting, and not necessarily for the better, what has long been the greatest economic value of all. This is economic efficiency itself, in the conventional sense of allocating our scarce resources optimally among their alternative uses. Efficiency may, in other words, continue to give ground to equity, variously conceived, guaranteed employments and income, a higher statistical growth rate, planning for planning's sake, or what have you. Secretary McNamara has currently (1965–66) been having his troubles selling economics and economic efficiency to the American military, sheltered from the facts of life by an expansible defense budget. If some similar measure of abundance spreads, thanks to technology, to the civilian sector, McNamara's civilian counterparts can expect equal trouble with voters, taxpayers, and other pressure groups—always including the Ad Hoc Committee for the Triple Revolution.[13]

## TECHNICAL APPENDIX

After reading a draft of this paper, one critic (Professor Lewis Dexter) observed that he could find in it no formal model of the process by which I supposed technological progress might affect economic values. Since the point is well taken (although such points can easily be overdone), I devote this Appendix to remedying the deficiency in part, using some elementary theoretical-economic apparatus for the purpose.

At the back of my (subconscious) mind there has been at work not one model but some combination of two models, illustrated by Figures 1 and 2 respectively.

Suppose there are two economic goods, which may also be economic values, which we call $x$ and $y$, and which we assume measurable. We can indicate the maximum amounts available by "production frontiers" in these two figures. The slope of such a frontier at any point represents the marginal rate of substitution or "trade-off" in production between the two goods or values $x$ and $y$. The frontier is drawn downward sloping and concave downward to illustrate an allegedly pervasive tendency to diminishing returns in production of both $x$ and $y$.

A second relation between $x$ and $y$ is a social "indifference curve." Actually, we conceive of a family of such curves, but consider only the highest one consistent with the production frontier. (Mathematically, we consider only the particular indifference curve *tangent* to the production frontier.) The society is presumed indifferent as between all combinations of $x$ and $y$ on this indifference curve. The slope of an indifference curve at any point represents the marginal rate of substitution or trade-off in demand for the two goods or values $x$ and $y$. The indifference curve is drawn downward sloping and concave upward to illustrate the allegedly pervasive tendency to diminishing utility.

In addition to production frontiers or indifference curves, the diagrams include straight lines. These are loci of the amounts of $x$ and $y$ which can be "bought" at some given pair of prices $p_x$ and $p_y$, and the slope of the price line represents the relative price ($p_x/p_y$). The steeper the downward slope, the "cheaper" is $y$ relative to $x$, since, if the economic subject used all his

13. These remain conditional and qualified semi-forecasts. If private wants continue to expand with total output, so that the private saving ratio does not rise, these semi-forecasts will probably be wrong. And similarly, as Hansen and Galbraith have stressed, if public wants, expenditures, and employment expand to fill any gap or vacuum developing in the private sector.

resources on $y$, the greater the amount he could obtain for the same "price" as would be required to buy any given amount of $x$. (*Mutatis mutandis*, we can argue, the steeper the downward slope of the price line, the "dearer" is $x$ relative to $y$, and so on.)

Let us come to the point, namely, the influence of technological change upon values, or rather, upon society's choice among values. Two cases are examined, in Figures 1 and 2.

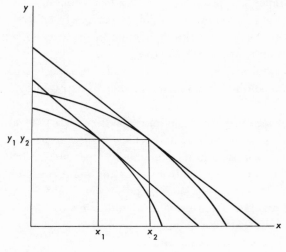

Figure 1

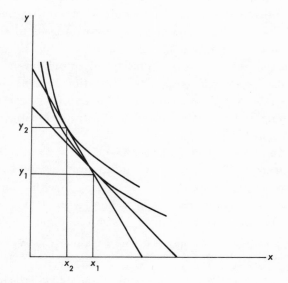

Figure 2

1. Figure 1 applies to the first illustration in the text, the upgrading of economic growth. Let the rate of growth be $x$, and the present standard of living $y$. Suppose a technological change which affects the production frontier in an asymmetrical manner, making much more growth $x$ available at any present standard $y$, but little more present goods $y$ available at any growth rate $x$. Let us also suppose no change in the relative "prices" of $x$ and $y$, so that the price line in the "new situation" (subscript 2) has the same slope as the one in the "old situation" (subscript 1). The moral of Figure 1 is that the desired growth rate rises $(x_2 > x_1)$ to a greater extent than the desired standard of living; in fact, in the special case of our diagram, the latter does not rise at all $(y_2 = y_1)$ and it may even fall $(y_2 < y_1)$.

2. Figure 2 applies to the second illustration of the text, the case of centralized and comprehensive economic planning—"planning," for short. We suppose such planning to involve some diminution of personal liberty, as per *The Road to Serfdom*.

This time, we set up our original solution with an indifference curve and a price line. The variable $x$ now represents "freedom," while the variable $y$ represents the measured growth rate. The optimal solution is $(x_1, y_1)$. Now we suppose, but do not show directly, some such technical change as electronic data processing, whose main effect is to lower the difficulty of planning, and therefore to lower its relative price. This accordingly raises the relative price of freedom—relative, that is to the growth rate $y$.

Let us also assume that the original solution $(x_1, y_1)$ remains efficient, in the technical sense that technology still prevents the achievement of any combination of $x$ and $y$ such that both $(x > x_1)$ and $(y > y_1)$. The new price relation, however, with relatively cheaper growth and dearer freedom, then permits the society to move to a higher indifference curve (a more highly esteemed position) like $(x_2, y_2)$ with $(y_2 > y_1)$ but $(x_2 < x_1)$, or, in words, with a higher measured growth rate and a lower level of economic freedom. (If the old combination $(x_1, y_1)$ had been rendered inefficient by the technical change, we might have had simultaneous increases in both $x$ and $y$.)

The other cases in the text can, I believe, be represented diagrammatically along the lines of these two figures, singly or in combination.

# Bibliography on technological progress and future-oriented studies

This list of references is far from comprehensive. It seeks to give merely an overview of the more important and the more accessible publications. In compiling the list, most helpful recourse was had to Annette Harrison, *Bibliography on Automation and Technological Change and Studies of the Future*, RAND Corporation Research Paper P-3365-2 (March, 1967). Erich Jantsch's 1966 volume contains a 413 item bibliography that is largely nonredundant with this one.

No attempt at topical organization has been made here: entries are registered alphabetically by author, apart from anonyma, which are listed alphabetically by title.

## A

*Abstracts of Articles on the Social Aspects of Automation*, Automation Programme, International Labour Office, Geneva, Switzerland, Aut/Doc/4, 1964.

Almon, Clopper, Jr., *The American Economy to 1975: An Interindustry Forecast*, Harper & Row, New York, 1966.

Anderson, Allan H., Donald T. Cannell, Terrance A. Gibbons, G. Peter Grote, John Henn, J. Bradley Kennedy, Michael B. Muir, Norman D. Potter, and Robert H. Whitby, *An Electronic Cash and Credit System*, American Management Association, New York, 1966.

*Annual Report of the Secretary-General on the Work of the Organization* (16 June 1963–15 June 1964), General Assembly, Official Records: Nineteenth Session, Supplement No. 1 (A/5801); United Nations, New York, 1964.

Anshen, Melvin, and George Leland Bach, *Management and Corporations 1985*, McGraw-Hill Book Company, Inc., New York, 1960.

Armer, Paul (ed.), *Computers and Changing Employment Patterns* (AFIPS Symposium, November 1963, Las Vegas, Nevada), American Federation of Information Processing Societies, New York, 1964.

Army Research Office, *Long-Range Technological Forecast*, 1963.

Arnold, Thurman W., Adolphe A. Berle, Jr., Morris L. Ernst, Lloyd K. Garrison, and Sir Alfred Zimmerman, *The Future of Democratic Capitalism*, A. S. Barnes and Company, Inc., New York, 1961.

Asbell, Bernard, *The New Improved American*, McGraw-Hill Book Company, Inc., New York, 1965.

Ashford, Douglas Elliott, *Morocco-Tunisia: Politics and Planning* (National Planning Series), Syracuse University Press, Syracuse, New York, 1965.

*Automation (What Automation Means to America* issue), Vol. 11, No. 4, April 1964.

*Automation: A Discussion of Research Methods* (Labour and Automation Bulletin No. 1), International Labour Office, Geneva, 1964.

*Automation and the Library of Congress*, The Council on Library Resources, Inc., Library of Congress; U.S. Government Printing Office, Washington, D.C., 1964.

*Automation and the Middle Manager: What Has Happened and What the Future Holds*, American Foundation on Automation and Employment, Inc., New York, 1966.

*Automation and the Small Bank*, Department of Automation and Marketing Research, The American Bankers Association, New York, 1964.

*Automation: Impact and Implications* (Focus on Developments in the Communications Industry), Communications Workers of America, AFL-CIO, Washington, D.C., 1965.

**B**

Baade, Fritz, *The Race to the Year 2000*, trans. by Ernst Pawel, Doubleday and Company, Inc., Garden City, New York, 1962.

Bagdikian, Ben H., *In the Midst of Plenty: A New Report on the Poor in America*, The New American Library, New York, 1964.

Bagrit, Sir Leon, *The Age of Automation* (The BBC Reith Lectures 1964), The New American Library, New York, 1965.

Barach, Arnold B., *1975 and the Changes to Come*, Harper and Row, Evanston, Illinois, 1962.

Barnes, Harry Elmer, and Oreen M. Ruedi, *The American Way of Life*, Prentice-Hall, Inc., New York, 1951.

Bates, Marston, *Expanding Population in a Shrinking World* (Public Affairs Pamphlets), The American Library Association, New York, 1963.

Bauer, Raymond A. (ed.), *Social Indicators*, The M.I.T. Press, Cambridge, Massachusetts, 1966.

Bazelon, David T., *The Paper Economy*, Random House, New York, 1963.

Beaumont, R. A., and R. B. Helfgott, *Management, Automation and People* (Industrial Relations Monograph No. 24), Industrial Relations Counselors, New York, 1964.

Becker, Joseph, and Robert M. Hayes, *Information Storage and Retrieval: Tools, Elements, Theories*, John Wiley & Sons, Inc., New York, 1963.

Bell, Frederick W., *The Economics of the New England Fishing Industry: The Role of Technological Change and Government Aid*, Research Report 31 to the Federal Reserve Bank of Boston, Boston, Massachusetts, February 1966.

Bennett, Edward, James Degan, and Joseph Spiegel (eds.), *Military Information Systems: The Design of Computer-Aided Systems for Command*, Frederick A. Praeger, New York, 1964.

Berkeley, Edmund C., *The Computer Revolution*, Doubleday and Company, Inc., Garden City, New York, 1962.

Blau, Peter, *Exchange and Power in Social Life*, John Wiley and Sons, Inc., New York, 1964.

Boguslaw, R., *The New Utopians: A Study of System Design and Social Change*, Prentice-Hall, Inc., Englewood Cliffs, New Jersey, 1965.

Borko, Harold (ed.), *Computer Applications in the Behavioral Sciences*, Prentice-Hall, Inc., Englewood Cliffs, New Jersey, 1962.

Boulding, Kenneth E., *The Meaning of the Twentieth Century: The Great Transition*, Harper and Row, Evanston, Illinois, 1964.

Bourne, Charles P., *Methods of Information Handling*, John Wiley & Sons, Inc., New York, 1963.

Bowen, Howard R., and Garth L. Mangum (eds.), *Automation and Economic Progress*, Prentice-Hall, Inc., Englewood Cliffs, New Jersey, 1966.

Boyko, Hugo, *Science and the Future of Mankind*, W. Junk, The Hague, 1961.

Brickman, William W., and Stanley Lehrer (eds.), *Automation, Education, and Human Values*, School and Society Books, New York, 1966.

Bright, James R., *Automation and Management*, Division of Research, Graduate School of Business Administration, Harvard University, Boston, 1958.

Brittain, Robert, *Let There Be Bread*, Simon and Schuster, New York, 1952.

Brown, Harrison, *The Challenge of Man's Future*, Viking Press, New York, 1954.

Brown, Harrison, James Bonner, and John Weir, *The Next Hundred Years*, The Viking Press, New York, 1958.

Bryson, Lyman, *The Next America*, Harper, New York, 1952.

——, *Facing the Future's Risks*, Harper, New York, 1953.

Buckingham, Walter, *Automation: Its Impact on Business and People*, The New American Library, New York, 1963.

Burck, Gilbert, and the Editors of *Fortune; The Computer Age and Its Potential for Management*, Harper and Row, Evanston, Illinois, 1965.

Burke, Fred G., *Tanganyika: Preplanning* (National Planning Series), Syracuse University Press, Syracuse, New York, 1965.

Burke, John G. (ed.), *The New Technology and Human Values*, Wadsworth Publishing Company, Inc., Belmont, California, 1966.

## C

Calder, Nigel (ed.), *The World in 1984*, Vols. 1 and 2, Penguin Books, Baltimore, Maryland, 1965.

*Case Studies of Displaced Workers: Experiences of Workers After Layoff*, Bureau of Labor Statistics, U.S. Department of Labor, Bulletin No. 1408; U.S. Government Printing Office, Washington, D.C., 0-739-351, 1964.

*Catalogue of FAO Publications 1945–1962*, Food and Agriculture Organization of the United Nations, Rome, 1963.

*1970 Census Questions*, Hearings before the Committee on Post Office and Civil Service, House of Representatives, 89th Congress, 2nd Session, August 23, 24, 25, 1966; U.S. Government Printing Office, Washington, D.C., 68-478, 1966.

Chase, Edward T., "The Shape of Things to Come," *The New Republic*, vol. 153 (1965), pp. 28–29.

*Chemistry: Opportunities and Needs*, National Academy of Sciences, National Research Council, Printing and Publications Office, Washington, D.C., Publication No. 1292, 1965.

Clark, Grenville, and Louis B. Sohn, *World Peace Through World Law*, 2d rev. ed., Harvard University Press, Cambridge, Massachusetts, 1964.

Clarke, Arthur C., *Profiles of the Future*, Harper and Row, New York, 1962.

*The Computer and Invasion of Privacy*, Hearings before a Subcommittee of the Committee on Government Operations, House of Representatives, 89th Congress, 2nd Session, July 26, 27, 28, 1966; U.S. Government Printing Office, Washington, D.C., 67–715, 1966.

*A Constitution for the World* (Papers on Peace), Center for the Study of Democratic Institutions, Santa Barbara, California, 1965.


**D**


*Daedalus* (*Conditions of World Order* issue), Vol. 95, No. 2, Spring 1966.

*Daedalus* (*Toward the Year 2000* issue), Vol. 96, No. 3, Summer 1967.

Darwin, C. G., *The Next Million Years*, Doubleday and Co., New York, 1952.

Deighton, Len, *The Billion Dollar Brain*, G. P. Putnam's Sons, New York, 1966.

de Jouvenel, Bertrand, *Futuribles*, The RAND Corporation, P-3045, January, 1965.

de Jouvenel, Bertrand, *The Art of Conjecture*, trans. by Nikita Lary, Basic Books, Inc., New York, 1967.

——, *L'Art de la Conjecture*, Editions de Rocher, Monaco, 1964.

——, (ed.), *Futuribles: Studies in Conjecture*, Droz Library, Geneva, 1963.

*Determinants and Consequences of Population Trends* (Population Studies, No. 17), Population Division, Statistical Office, Department of Social Affairs, United Nations, New York, 1953.

Deutsch, Gertrude (ed.), *The Economic Almanac 1964*, National Industrial Conference Board, New York, 1964.

Diamond, Sigmund (ed.), *The Nation Transformed: The Creation of an Industrial Society*, George Braziller, New York, 1963.

Diebold, John, *Beyond Automation*, McGraw-Hill Book Company, Inc., San Francisco, 1964.

*Digital Computer Needs in Universities and Colleges*, National Academy of Sciences, National Research Council, Washington, D.C., Publication 1233, 1966.

Ducoff, Louis J., *Human Resources of Central America, Panama, and Mexico, 1950–1980, in Relation to Some Aspects of Economic Development*, Technical Assistance Programme of the United Nations, Economic Commission for Latin America, United Nations, New York, 1960.

Dunlop, John T. (ed.), *Automation and Technological Change*, Prentice-Hall, Inc., Englewood Cliffs, New Jersey, 1962.


**E**


Ellul, Jacques, *The Technological Society*, trans. by John Wilkinson, Alfred A. Knopf, New York, 1964.

*Employment and Earnings Statistics for the United States 1909–64*, Bureau of Labor Statistics, U.S. Department of Labor, Bulletin No. 1312-2; U.S. Government Printing Office, Washington, D.C., 0-757-888, 1964.

*Employment Forecasting*, International Seminar on Employment Forecasting Techniques, Organisation for Economic Co-operation and Development, Paris, 1963.

*Experience of Other Countries in Dealing with Technological Unemployment*, Bureau of Employment Security, Manpower Administration, U.S. Department of Labor; U.S. Government Printing Office, Washington, D.C., 0-705-690, 1963.

*L'Exploration de la Future*, *Réalités*, No. 245, June 1966, pp. 50–58.

*Exploring the Dimensions of the Manpower Revolution* (Selected Readings in Employment and Manpower, Vol. 1), Subcommittee on Employment and Manpower of the Committee on Labor and Public Welfare, U.S. Senate; U.S. Government Printing Office, Washington, D.C., 36-510, 1964.

## F

Fabricant, Solomon, *Measurement of Technological Change*, (Seminar on Manpower Policy and Program, July 1965), Manpower Administration, Office of Manpower, Automation and Training; U.S. Government Printing Office, Washington, D.C., 0-772-275, 1965.

Feigenbaum, Edward A., and Julian Feldman (eds.), *Computers and Thought*, McGraw-Hill Book Company, Inc., San Francisco, 1963.

Feinstein, Otto (ed.), *Two Worlds of Change: Readings in Economic Development*, Doubleday and Company, Inc., Garden City, New York, 1964.

Felix, F., "Growth of Energy Consumption and National Income Throughout the World," *IEEE Spectrum*, Vol. 1 (1964), pp. 81–102.

Fink, Donald G., *Computers and the Human Mind*, Doubleday & Company, Inc., Garden City, New York, 1966.

Fischman, Leonard L., Joseph L. Fisher, and Hans H. Landsberg, *et al. Resources in America's Future*, Oxford University Press, New Jersey, 1963.

Forsythe, George, "Educational Implications of the Computer Revolution," *Applications of Digital Computers*, W. F. Freiberger (ed.), Ginn and Co., Boston, 1963.

Foster, David, *Modern Automation*, Sir Isaac Pitman and Sons, Ltd. and Rowse Muir Publications, Ltd., London, 1963.

Fourastié, Jean, *The Causes of Wealth*, trans. and ed. Theodore Caplow, The Free Press, Glencoe, Illinois, 1960.

Francois, William, *Automation: Industrialization Comes of Age*, Collier Books, New York, 1964.

Friedman, Milton, *Capitalism and Freedom*, The University of Chicago Press, Chicago, 1964.

Fuller, R. Buckminster, *Education Automation—Freeing the Scholar to Return to His Studies*, Southern Illinois University Press, Carbondale, Illinois, 1964.

——, *World Design Science Decade 1965–1975: Phase I (1964), Document 2: The Design Initiative*, World Resources Inventory, Southern Illinois University Press, Carbondale, Illinois, 1963.

Fuller, R. Buckminster, and John McHale, *World Design Science Decade 1965–1975: Phase I (1963), Document 1: Inventory of World Resources, Human Trends, and Needs*, World Resources Inventory, Southern Illinois University Press, Carbondale, Illinois, 1963.

*The Future of Man: Triumph or Chaos*, The Travelers Insurance Companies, New York, April 19, 1965.

## G

Gabor, Dennis, *Inventing the Future*, Alfred A. Knopf, New York, 1964.

Galbraith, John Kenneth, *The Affluent Society*, The New American Library, New York, 1958.

Galton, Lawrence, "Science Stands at Awesome Thresholds," *New York Times Magazine*, December 2, 1962.

Gibson, E. Dana, *International Data Processing*, The Business Press, Elmhurst, Illinois, 1965.

Ginzberg, Eli (ed.), *Technology and Social Change*, Columbia University Press, New York, 1964.

Gordon, T. J., *The Future*, St. Martin's Press, New York, 1965.

——, *Ideas in Conflict*, St. Martin's Press, New York, 1966.

Gordon, T. J., and Olaf Helmer, *Report on a Long-Range Forecasting Study*, The RAND Corporation, P-2982, September 1964.

*Governing Council of the Special Fund: Report on Its Thirteenth Session* (11–18 January 1965), Economic and Social Council, Official Records: Thirty-Ninth Session, Supplement No. 11; United Nations, New York, 1965.

Grabbe, Eugene M. (ed.), *Automation in Business and Industry*, John Wiley and Sons, Inc., New York, 1957.

Graham, Benjamin, *The Flexible Work-Year: An Answer to Unemployment*, Center for the Study of Democratic Institutions, Santa Barbara, California, 1964.

Green, Bert F., Jr., *Digital Computers in Research*, McGraw-Hill Book Company, Inc., San Francisco, 1963.

Greenberger, Martin (ed.), *Management and the Computer of the Future*, Massachusetts Institute of Technology Press, Cambridge, and John Wiley and Sons, Inc., New York, 1962.

## H

Hacker, Andrew (ed.), *The Corporation Takeover*, Harper and Row, Evanston, Illinois, 1964.

Harrington, Michael, *The Other America*, The Macmillan Company, New York, 1964.

Harris, Norman C., *Technical Education in the Junior College: New Programs for New Jobs*, American Association of Junior Colleges, Washington, D.C., 1964.

*Health and Safety Aspects of Automation and Technological Change: A Collection of Abstracts 1956–1962*, International Labor Office, Geneva, Switzerland; Office of Manpower, Automation and Training, Manpower Administration, U.S. Department of Labor; U.S. Government Printing Office, Washington, D.C., 0-716-653, 1964.

Hearle, Edward F. R., and Raymond J. Mason, *A Data Processing System for State and Local Governments*, Prentice-Hall, Inc., Englewood Cliffs, New Jersey, 1963.

Heilbroner, Robert L., *The Future as History*, Harper and Brothers, New York, 1960.

Heilbroner, Robert L., and Peter L. Bernstein, *A Primer on Government Spending*, Random House, Inc., New York, 1963.

Heller, Walter W., *New Dimensions of Political Economy*, Harvard University Press, Cambridge, Massachusetts, 1966.

Helmer, Olaf, *Social Technology*, Basic Books, New York, 1966.

Hilton, Alice Mary (ed.), *The Evolving Society*, Institute for Cybercultural Research (ICR) Press, New York, 1966.

Hoos, Ida R., *Automation in the Office*, Public Affairs Press, Washington, D.C., 1961.

Horowitz, David, *World Economic Disparities: The Haves and the Have-Nots*, Center for the Study of Democratic Institutions, Santa Barbara, California, 1962.

Hugh-Jones, E.M., *Automation in Theory and Practice*, Basil Blackwell, Oxford, England, 1956.

Huxley, Aldous, *Brave New World*, Harper and Brothers, New York, 1962.

——, *The Politics of Ecology: The Question of Survival*, Center for the Study of Democratic Institutions, Santa Barbara, California, 1963.


**I**


*Impact of Office Automation in the Insurance Industry*, Bureau of Labor Statistics, U.S. Department of Labor, Bulletin No. 1468; U.S. Government Printing Office, Washington, D.C., 0-797-566, 1966.

*Impact of Office Automation in the Internal Revenue Service: Study of the Manpower Implications During First Stages of Changeover*, Bureau of Labor Statistics, U.S. Department of Labor, Bulletin No. 1364, July 1963; U.S. Government Printing Office, Washington, D.C., 0-694-485, 1963.

*Implications of Automation and Other Technological Developments: A Selected Annotated Bibliography*, Bureau of Labor Statistics, U.S. Department of Labor, Bulletin No. 1319, February 1962; U.S. Government Printing Office, Washington, D.C., 0-629-668, 1962.

*Implications of Automation and Other Technological Developments: A Selected Annotated Bibliography*, Bureau of Labor Statistics, U.S. Department of Labor, Bulletin No. 1319-1, December 1963; U.S. Government Printing Office, Washington, D.C., 0-717-051, 1964.

*Industrial Retraining Programs for Technological Change: A Study of the Performance of Older Workers*, Bureau of Labor Statistics, U.S. Department of Labor, Bulletin No. 1368, June 1963; U.S. Government Printing Office, Washington, D.C., 0-690198, 1963.

*Information*, A Scientific American Book, W. H. Freeman and Company, San Francisco, 1966.

Institute of Radio Engineers, *Symposium on Communications and Electronics— 2012 A.D.*, with contributions by Lloyd V. Berkner, Henri Busignies, J. H. Delliner, Peter Goldmark, W. D. Lewis, G. A. Morton, Ernst Weber, Harold Wheeler, and Harold A. Zahl; I.R.W., May, 1962.

*International Social Sciences Bulletin*, Vol. 4, 1952.


**J**


Jacoby, Neil H., *Can Prosperity be Sustained?*, Henry Holt and Company, New York, 1956.

Jantsch, Erich, *Technological Forecasting in Perspective*, Organization for Economic Co-operation and Development, Paris, 1966. [Annex B, pp. 347–437 gives an extensive bibliography.]

Johnston, Denis F., and Sophia Cooper, "Special Labor Force Report: Labor Force Projections 1970–1980," *Monthly Labor Review*, Vol. 88, No. 2, February 1965, pp. 129–140; Bureau of Labor Statistics, U.S. Department of Labor; U.S. Government Printing Office, Washington, D.C., o-760-922, 1965.

Juenger, Friedrich Georg, *The Failure of Technology*, Henry Regnery Company, Chicago, 1956.

## K

Kelso, Louis O., and Mortimer J. Adler, *The Capitalist Manifesto*, Random House, Inc., New York, 1958.

——, *The New Capitalists*, Random House, Inc., New York, 1961.

Kennedy, Thomas, *Automation Funds and Displaced Workers*, Division of Research, Graduate School of Business Administration, Harvard University, Boston, 1962.

Kershaw, Joseph A., and Roland N. McKean, *Teacher Shortages and Salary Schedules*, McGraw-Hill Book Company, Inc., San Francisco, 1962.

Keynes, John Maynard, *The General Theory of Employment, Interest, and Money*, Harcourt, Brace and World, Inc., New York, 1964.

Keyserling, Leon H., *Progress or Poverty: The U.S. at the Crossroads*, Conference on Economic Progress, Washington, D.C., 1964.

## L

*Labour Market Policy in Sweden* (O.E.C.D. Reviews of Manpower and Social Policies), Organisation for Economic Co-operation and Development, Paris, 1963. (Also available from McGraw-Hill Book Company, OECD-Unit, New York.)

Laird, Donald A., and Eleanor C. Laird, *How to Get Along with Automation*, McGraw-Hill Book Company, Inc., San Francisco, 1964.

Landsberg, Hans H., Leonard L. Fischman, and Joseph L. Fisher, *Resources in America's Future*, The Johns Hopkins Press, Baltimore, Maryland, 1963.

Leavitt, Harold J. and Thomas L. Whisler, "Management in the 1980's," *Harvard Business Review*, Vol. 36, No. 6, November-December 1958, pp. 41–48.

Lebergott, Stanley (ed.), *Men Without Work: The Economics of Unemployment*, Prentice-Hall, Inc., Englewood Cliffs, New Jersey, 1964.

Lecht, Leonard A., *The Dollar Cost of Our National Goals*, Center for Priority Analysis, National Planning Association, Washington, D.C., May 1965.

——, *Goals, Priorities, and Dollars: The Next Decade*, The Free Press, New York, 1966.

Lerner, Abba P., *Economics of Employment*, McGraw-Hill Book Company, Inc., New York, 1951.

Levitan, Sar A., *Federal Aid to Depressed Areas*, The Johns Hopkins Press, Baltimore, Maryland, 1964.

Lindberg, Ferdinand, *The Coming World Transformation*, Doubleday & Co., New York, 1963.

Lindblom, Charles E., *The Intelligence of Democracy: Decision Making Through Mutual Adjustment*, The Free Press, New York, 1965.

Lipstreu, Otis, and Kenneth A. Reed, *Transition to Automation*, University of Colorado Press, Boulder, Colorado, 1964.

## M

MacGowan, Roger A., and Frederick I. Ordway III, *Intelligence in the Universe*, Prentice-Hall, Inc., Englewood Cliffs, New Jersey, 1966.

Maddison, Angus, *Economic Growth in the West: Comparative Experience in Europe and North America*, The Twentieth Century Fund, New York, 1964.

Malik, Rex (ed.), *Penguin Survey of Business and Industry 1966*, Penguin Books, Baltimore, Maryland, 1966.

*Management Decisions to Automate*, Stanford Research Institute, Menlo Park, California, AD 603194; U.S. Department of Commerce, Office of Technical Services, Washington, D.C., 1964.

*Management Decisions to Automate* (Manpower/Automation Research Monograph No. 3), Office of Manpower, Automation and Training, Manpower Administration, U.S. Department of Labor; U.S. Government Printing Office, Washington, D.C., 0-755-876, 1965.

*Manpower and Automation Research*, Office of Manpower, Automation and Training, Manpower Administration, U.S. Department of Labor, July 1, 1963– June 30, 1964; U.S. Government Printing Office, Washington, D.C., 0-749-281, 1964.

*Manpower Challenge of the 1960s*, U.S. Department of Labor; U.S. Government Printing Office, Washington, D.C., 0-597-636, 1961.

*Manpower Policies for Youth: Priorities in Meeting the Youth Employment Crisis* (symposium, September 23–25, 1964, Washington, D.C.), National Committee on Employment of Youth, National Child Labor Committee, New York, 1964.

*Manpower Policy and Programs in the United States* (O.E.C.D. Reviews of Manpower and Social Policies), Organisation for Economic Co-operation and Development, Paris, 1964. (Also available from McGraw-Hill Book Company, OECD-Unit, New York.)

*Manpower Report of the President: A Report on Manpower Requirements, Resources, Utilization and Training*, U.S. Department of Labor, March 1964; U.S. Government Printing Office, Washington, D.C., 0-716-276, 1964.

*Manpower Report of the President: A Report on Manpower Requirements, Resources, Utilization, and Training*, U.S. Department of Labor, March 1965; U.S. Government Printing Office, Washington, D.C., 0-759-918, 1965.

*Manpower Report of the President: A Report on Manpower Requirements, Resources, Utilization, and Training*, U.S. Department of Labor, March 1966; U.S. Government Printing Office, Washington, D.C., 0-797-615, 1966.

*Manpower Research and Training Under the Manpower Development and Training Act*, Secretary of Labor, U.S. Department of Labor, March 1964; U.S. Government Printing Office, Washington, D.C., 0-724-917, 1964.

Markham, Charles (ed.), *Jobs, Men and Machines: Problems of Automation*, Frederick A. Praeger, New York, 1964.

Martini, Carl H., *Impacts of Scientific and Technological Innovations on the Role of Politics and Government*, 2d ed., Education and World Affairs, New York, July 1964.

McLuhan, Marshall, *The Gutenberg Galaxy: The Making of Typographic Man*, University of Toronto Press, Toronto, Canada, 1965.

———, *Understanding Media*, McGraw-Hill Book Company, Inc., San Francisco, 1964.

*The Measurement and Interpretation of Job Vacancies*, National Bureau of Economic Research, New York, 1966. (Distributed by Columbia University Press, New York.)

Meier, Richard L., *Science and Economic Development: New Patterns of Living*, published jointly by the Technology Press of M.I.T. and John Wiley & Sons, Inc., New York, 1956.

Mendlovitz, Saul H. (ed.), *Legal and Political Problems of World Order*, Preliminary Edition, The Fund for Education Concerning World Peace through World Law, New York, 1962.

*Methods and Principles for Projecting Future Energy Requirements*, Economic Commission for Europe, United Nations, New York, ST/ECE/ENERGY/2, 1964.

Meyerson, Martin, and Edward C. Banfield, *Boston: The Job Ahead*, Harvard University Press, Cambridge Massachusetts, 1966.

Michael, Donald N., *Cybernation: The Silent Conquest*, Center for the Study of Democratic Institutions, Santa Barbara, California, 1962.

———, *The Next Generation: The Prospects Ahead for the Youth of Today and Tomorrow*, Vintage Books, New York, 1965.

*Money and Credit: Their Influence on Jobs, Prices, and Growth* (Report of the Commission on Money and Credit), Prentice-Hall, Inc., Englewood Cliffs, New Jersey, 1961.

*Monthly Labor Review* (*50th Anniversary* issue), Vol. 88, No. 7, July 1965; Bureau of Labor Statistics, U.S. Department of Labor; U.S. Government Printing Office, Washington, D.C., 0-775-992, 1965.

Moore, Wilbert E., *Social Change*, Prentice-Hall, Inc., Englewood Cliffs, New Jersey, 1963.

Morison, Elting E., *Men, Machines, and Modern Times*, The M.I.T. Press, Massachusetts Institute of Technology, Cambridge, Massachusetts, 1966.

Morse, Dean, and Aaron W. Warner (eds.), *Technological Innovation and Society*, Columbia University Press, New York, 1966.

Mudd, Stuart (ed.), *The Population Crisis and the Use of World Resources*, Indiana University Press, Bloomington, Indiana, 1964.

Mumford, Lewis, *The Highway and the City*, The New American Library, New York, 1964.

Myrdal, Gunnar, *Rich Lands and Poor: The Road to World Prosperity*, Harper and Row, New York, 1957.

**N**

National Manpower Council, *Government and Manpower*, Columbia University Press, New York, 1964.

*Nation's Manpower Revolution*, Parts 1–5, 8–9, Hearings before the Subcommittee on Employment and Manpower of the Committee on Labor and Public Welfare, U.S. Senate; U.S. Government Printing Office, Washington, D.C., 98–961, 1963 and 1964.

Nelson, Richard R., Merton J. Peck, and Edward D. Kalachek, *Technology, Economic Growth and Public Policy*, A RAND Corporation and Brookings Institution Study, The Brookings Institution, Washington, D.C., 1967.

von Neumann, John, "Can We Survive Technology?" *Fortune*, vol. 51 (1955), pp. 106–108 and 151–152.

*New York Times Magazine*, Symposium on *The Future*, with contributions by H. S. Commager, H. L. Dryden, J. B. S. Haldane, Margaret Mead, Clarence Randall, and Arnold Toynbee, April 19, 1964.

## O

*Occupations in Electronic Computing Systems*, U.S. Department of Labor, Manpower Administration, Bureau of Employment Security, U.S. Government Printing Office, Washington, D.C., 0-772-219, 1965.

*On Coexistence*, Center for the Study of Democratic Institutions, Santa Barbara, California, 1965.

*On the Developed and the Developing*, Center for the Study of Democratic Institutions, Santa Barbara, California, 1965.

*On the World Community*, Center for the Study of Democratic Institutions, Santa Barbara, California, 1965.

*One-Third of a Nation: A Report on Young Men Found Unqualified for Military Service*, President's Task Force on Manpower Conservation; U.S. Government Printing Office, Washington, D.C., 0-719-418, 1964.

## P

Packard, Vance O., *The Naked Society*, David McKay Company, Inc., New York, 1964.

Paloczi-Horvath, George, *The Facts Rebel: The Future of Russia and the West*, Secker and Warburg, London, 1964.

Parkhill, D. F., *The Challenge of the Computer Utility*, Addison-Wesley Publishing Company, Palo Alto, California, 1966.

Patterson, Barbara, *et al.*, *The Price We Pay for Discrimination*, Southern Regional Council, Atlanta, Georgia; and Anti-Defamation League of B'nai B'rith, New York, June 1964.

Philipson, Morris (ed.), *Automation: Implications for the Future*, Random House, Inc., New York, 1962.

Piel, Gerard, *Consumers of Abundance*, Center for the Study of Democratic Institutions, Santa Barbara, California 1961.

Pierson, John H. G., *Insuring Full Employment*, The Viking Press, New York, 1964.

Platt, John R., *The Step to Man*, John Wiley & Sons, Inc., New York, 1966.

Polak, Fred L., *The Image of the Future*, Vols. I and II, Oceana Publications, New York, 1961.

*Political and Economic Planning: World Population and Resources*, Allen and Unwin, London, 1955.

Pollock, Frederick, *Automation: A Study of Its Economic and Social Consequences*, trans. by W. O. Henderson and W. H. Chaloner, Frederick A. Praeger, New York, 1957.

Pool, Ithiel de Sola, Robert P. Abelson, and Samuel L. Popkin, *Candidates, Issues, and Strategies: A Computer Simulation of the 1960 and 1964 Presidential Elections*, Massachusetts Institute of Technology Press, Cambridge, Massachusetts, 1965.

*La Population de l'Asie et de l'Extrême-Orient, 1950–1980: Estimation de la population future par sexe et par âge* (Quatrième Rapport), Organisation des Nations Unies, Départment des affaires économiques et sociales, New York, ST/SOA Series A/31, 1960.

Potter, David M., *People of Plenty*, The University of Chicago Press, Chicago, 1965.

Price, Don K., *The Scientific Estate*, The Belknap Press of Harvard University Press, Cambridge, Massachusetts, 1965.

*Private Trade Barriers and the Atlantic Community* (Economic Policies and Practices, Paper No. 4), Joint Economic Committee, Congress of the United States; U.S. Government Printing Office, Washington, D.C., 31-525 0, 1964.

*Proceedings of the National Automation Conference 1964*, Department of Automation and Marketing Research, The American Bankers Association, New York, 1964.

*Prospective Changes in Society by 1980: Including Some Implications for Education*, Reports prepared for the First Area Conference "Designing Education for the Future," An Eight-State Project, Project Office, 1362 Lincoln Street, Denver, Colorado, July 1966.

*Provisional Report on World Population Prospects, As Assessed in 1963*, Department of Economic and Social Affairs, United Nations, New York, ST/SOA/SER.R/7, 1964.


**Q**


Quinn, Francis X., S.J. (ed.), *The Ethical Aftermath of Automation*, The Newman Press, Westminster, Maryland, 1962.


**R**


Ramo, Simon, "The Coming Technological Society," *Engineering and Science*, Vol. 28 (1964), pp. 9–13.

*Register of Projects Approved Under the Manpower Development and Training Act through June 1965*, Office of Manpower, Automation and Training, Manpower Administration, U.S. Department of Labor; U.S. Government Printing Office, Washington, D.C., 0-784-558, 1965.

*Restoring the Quality of Our Environment*, Environmental Pollution Panel, President's Science Advisory Committee; U.S. Government Printing Office, Washington, D.C., 0-792-122, 1965.

*A Review of Recent Soviet Literature on the Social Aspects of Automation and Technological Change in the U.S.S.R.*, Automation Program, International Labor Office, Geneva, Aut/Doc/3, 1964.

*Revised List of Descriptors, 1 August 1964*, Preparatory Documentation Unit, International Labor Office, Geneva, Aut/Doc/5, 1964.

Rogers, Everett M., *Diffusion of Innovations*, The Free Press of Glencoe, New York, 1962.

Roslansky, John D. (ed.), *The Control of Environment*, (A Discussion at the Nobel Conference, organized by Gustavus Adolphus College, St. Peter, Minnesota, 1966), North-Holland Publishing Company, Amsterdam, 1967.

—— (ed.), *Genetics and the Future of Man*, (1965 Nobel Symposium, Gustavus Adolphus College, St. Peter, Minnesota, January 7–8, 1965), North-Holland Publishing Company, Amsterdam, 1966.

Ross, Arthur M. (ed.), *Employment Policy and the Labor Market*, University of California Press, Los Angeles, 1965.

Rostand, Jean, *Can Man Be Modified?*, trans. by Jonathan Griffin, Basic Books, Inc., New York, 1959.

Russell, Sir E. John, *World Population and World Food Supplies*, George Allen and Unwin, Ltd., London, 1954.

## S

Sarnoff, David, "By the End of the 20th Century," *Fortune*, Vol. 60 (May, 1964), pp. 116–119.

——, "The Social Impact of Computers" address to the National Automation Conference sponsored by the American Bankers Association. New York World's Fair, July 16, 1964. (Cf. *New York Times*, July 17, 1964; col. 6.)

Schoeffler, Sidney, *The Failures of Economics: A Diagnostic Study*, Harvard University Press, Cambridge, Massachusetts, 1955.

Schultz, Theodore W., *Economic Crises in World Agriculture*, The University of Michigan Press, Ann Arbor, Michigan, 1965.

*Scientific American* (*Cities* issue), Vol. 213, No. 3, September 1965.

*Scientific American* (*Information* issue), Vol. 215, No. 3, September 1966.

*Scientific American* (*Technology and Economic Development* issue), Vol. 209, No. 3, September 1963.

Scott, W. H. (ed.), *Office Automation: Administrative and Human Problems*, Social Affairs Division, Manpower and Social Affairs Directorate, Organisation for Economic Co-operation and Development, Paris, 1965.

Seligman, Ben B., *Most Notorious Victory: Man in an Age of Automation*, The Free Press, New York, 1966.

Semenov, N. N., "The World of the Future," *Bulletin of the Atomic Scientists*, vol. 20 (1964), pp. 10–15.

Shapley, H., *Of Stars and Men: The Human Response to an Expanding Universe*, Beacon Press, Boston, 1964.

Shils, Edward B., *Automation and Industrial Relations*, Holt, Rinehart and Winston, San Francisco, 1963.

Silk, Leonard S., *The Research Revolution*, McGraw-Hill Book Company, Inc., San Francisco, 1963.

Simon, Herbert A., *The Shape of Automation*, Harper and Row, New York, 1965.

*Six Billions to Feed* (World Food Problems No. 4), Food and Agriculture Organization, United Nations, Rome, 1962.

Smith, Adam, *The Wealth of Nations: Representative Selections*, The Bobbs Merrill Company, Inc., Indianapolis, Indiana, 1961.

———, *The Wealth of Nations*, Vol. 1, Richard D. Irwin, Inc., Homewood, Illinois, 1963.

Smith, F. G. Walton, and Henry Chapin, *The Sun, the Sea, and Tomorrow*, Charles Scribner's Sons, New York, 1954.

Smith, Richard Austin, *Corporations in Crisis*, Doubleday and Company, Inc., Garden City, New York, 1963.

Södersten, Bo, *A Study of Economic Growth and International Trade*, Almqvist and Wiksell, Stockholm, 1964.

Solow, Robert M., *The Nature and Sources of Unemployment in the United States*, Almqvist and Wiksell, Stockholm, 1964.

*Space, Science and Urban Life* (Proceedings of Conference, Dunsmuir House, Oakland, California, March 28–30, 1963), Office of Scientific and Technical Information, National Aeronautics and Space Administration; U.S. Government Printing Office, Washington, D.C., 0-708-399, 1963.

Stanley, David T., *The Higher Civil Service*, The Brookings Institution, Washington, D.C., 1964.

*1965 Statistical Yearbook*, United Nations Educational, Scientific and Cultural Organization, Paris, 1966. (Also available from UNESCO Publications Center, New York.)

Steele, George, and Paul Kircher, *The Crisis We Face*, McGraw-Hill Book Company, Inc., San Francisco, 1960.

Sterling, Theodor D., and Seymour V. Pollack, *Computers and the Life Sciences*, Columbia University Press, New York, 1965.

Stone, Richard (ed.), *A Computable Model of Economic Growth*, The M.I.T. Press, Massachusetts Institute of Technology, Cambridge, Massachusetts, 1964.

*Studies in Long-Term Economic Projections for the World Economy*, Department of Economic and Social Affairs, United Nations, New York, E/3842, ST/ECA/80, 1964.

*A Study of the Impact of Automation on Federal Employees*, U.S. Civil Service Commission, and Subcommittee on Census and Government Statistics of Committee on Post Office and Civil Service, House of Representatives; U.S. Government Printing Office, Washington, D.C., 1964.

*A Survey of Current Literature on Automation and Other Technological Changes: A Selected Annotated Bibliography*, Committee on Education and Labor, House of Representatives; U.S. Government Printing Office, Washington, D.C., 34-781, 1964.

T

Teague, Walter Dorwin, *Land of Plenty*, Harcourt, Brace and Company, New York, 1947.

*Technological Trends and National Policy*, Report of the Subcommittee on

Technology to the National Resources Committee, 75th Congress, 1st Session, House Document No. 360, June 1937; U.S. Government Printing Office, Washington, D.C., 8778-37-2, 1937.

*Technological Trends in 36 Major American Industries: A Study Prepared for the President's Committee on Labor-Management Policy*, Office of Productivity and Technological Developments, Bureau of Labor Statistics, U.S. Department of Labor, Washington, D.C., 1964.

*Technology and the American Economy*, Vol. 1, National Commission on Technology, Automation, and Economic Progress; U.S. Government Printing Office, Washington, D.C., 0-788-561, February 1966.

*The Outlook for Technological Change and Employment*, Appendix Volume I, U.S. Government Printing Office, Washington, D.C., 206-754-66-Vol. I, February 1966.

*The Employment Impact of Technological Change*, Appendix Volume II, U.S. Government Printing Office, Washington, D.C., 206-754-66-Vol. II, February 1966.

*Adjusting to Change*, Appendix Volume III, U.S. Government Printing Office, Washington, D.C., 206-754-66-Vol. III, February 1966.

*Educational Implications of Technological Change*, Appendix Volume IV, U.S. Government Printing Office, Washington, D.C., 206-754-66-Vol. IV, February 1966.

*Applying Technology to Unmet Needs*, Appendix Volume V, U.S. Government Printing Office, Washington, D.C., 206-754-66-Vol. V, February 1966.

*Statements Relating to the Impact of Technological Change*, Appendix Volume VI, U.S. Government Printing Office, Washington, D.C., 0-211-724, February 1966.

Terborgh, George, *The Automation Hysteria*, Machinery and Allied Products Institute, and Council for Technological Advancement, Washington, D.C., 1965.

Theobald, Robert, *The Challenge of Abundance*, The New American Library, New York, 1962.

——, *Free Men and Free Markets*, Clarkson N. Potter, Inc., New York, 1963.

——, *The Rich and the Poor*, The New American Library, New York, 1961.

—— (ed.), *The Guaranteed Income: Next Step in Economic Evolution?*, Doubleday and Company, Inc., Garden City, New York, 1966.

Thirring, Hans, *Energy for Man*, Harper and Row, New York, 1962.

Thomas, Shirley, *Computers: Their History, Present Applications and Future*, Holt, Rinehart and Winston, Inc., New York, 1965.

Thomson, Sir George, *The Foreseeable Future*, rev. ed., Cambridge University Press, Cambridge, England, 1960.

*Toward Full Employment: Proposals for a Comprehensive Employment and Manpower Policy in the United States*, Subcommittee on Employment and Manpower, Committee on Labor and Public Welfare, U.S. Senate; U.S. Government Printing Office, Washington, D.C., 30-418, 1964.

*The Triple Revolution*, Ad Hoc Committee on The Triple Revolution, Santa Barbara, California, 1964.

## U

*Unemployment Programs in Sweden* (Economic Policies and Practices, Paper No. 5), Joint Economic Committee, Congress of the United States; U.S. Government Printing Office, Washington, D.C., 31-775, 1964.

United States Department of Labor, *Technological Trends in Major American Industries*, Bulletin No. 1474, Washington, 1966.

*Use of Electronic Data Processing Equipment*, Part 4, American Federation of Government Employees, National Federation of Federal Employees, Department of Defense; Hearing before the Subcommittee on Census and Government Statistics of the Committee on Post Office and Civil Service, House of Representatives, July 9, 1963; U.S. Government Printing Office, Washington, D.C., 20-156, 1963.

*Use of Electronic Data Processing Equipment in the Federal Government*, Committee on Post Office and Civil Service, House of Representatives, October 16, 1963; U.S. Government Printing Office, Washington, D.C., 24-433, 1963.

## V

Vassiliev, Mikhail, and Sergi Gouschev (eds.), *Life in the Twenty-First Century*, trans. by H. E. Crowcroft and R. F. Wason, Penguin Books, Middlesex, England, 1960.

Venn, Grant, *Man, Education and Work*, American Council on Education, Washington, D.C., 1964.

Vickers, Sir Geoffrey, *The Art of Judgment: A Study of Policy Making*, Basic Books, Inc., Publishers, New York, 1965.

## W

Ware, Willis H., *Future Computer Technology and Its Impact*, The RAND Paper Corporation, P-3279, Santa Monica, March 1966.

Warner, Aaron W., Dean Morse, and Alfred S. Eichner (eds.), *The Impact of Science and Technology*, Columbia University Press, New York, 1965.

*Water Desalination in Developing Countries*, United Nations, New York, 1964.

*Water Desalination: Proposals for a Costing Procedure and Related Technical and Economic Considerations*, Department of Economic and Social Affairs, United Nations, New York, ST/ECA/86, 1965.

Watson, Goodwin (ed.), *No Room at the Bottom: Automation and the Reluctant Learner*, National Education Association, Washington, D.C., 1963.

Weissbourd, Bernard, *Segregation, Subsidies, and Megalopolis*, Center for the Study of Democratic Institutions, Santa Barbara, California, 1964.

Wiener, Norbert, *The Human Use of Human Beings*, Doubleday and Company, Inc., Garden City, New York, 1954.

——, *God and Golem, Inc.*, The Massachusetts Institute of Technology Press, Cambridge, Massachusetts, 1964.

Wilkinson, John, *The Quantitative Society or, What Are You to Do With Noodle?*, Center for the Study of Democratic Institutions, Santa Barbara, California, 1964.

Wolstenholme, Gordon (ed.), *Man and His Future*, Little, Brown and Company, Boston, 1963.

## Y

*Yearbook of National Accounts Statistics 1963*, Statistical Office of the United Nations, Department of Economic and Social Affairs, United Nations, New York, 1964.

## Z

Zvorikine, A., *Les Conséquences Sociales de la Mécanisation et de l'Automatisation en URSS*, United Nations Educational, Scientific, and Cultural Organization, Paris-7ᵉ, 1963.

# Bibliography
# on the theory of value

The aim of this list of references is not to give a comprehensive bibliography of the subject but rather to provide a *bibliographic introduction* to the study of values on both the philosophical and the scientific sectors of the domain. The listing is organized topically, and most topics have been treated in a highly selective way, including items sometimes because of their own importance as contributions to this domain, sometimes because they furnish a good introduction to its problems and above all to its *literature*. The reader who wishes to probe more deeply into value-problems within the area at issue will find helpful guidance by consulting these works, and will also find help in the reference-works listed in the section on *Bibliographies*. A general introduction to the field, together with a more complete bibliography than that given here, is given in Nicholas Rescher's *Introduction to Value Theory* (Englewood Cliffs, 1968), from which the present bibliography is extracted. A newly-founded quarterly, *The Journal of Value Inquiry*, whose first issue appeared in the spring of 1967, should prove of substantial value to students and workers in this field.

## I. *Methodological issues*

A.   METHODS OF VALUE INQUIRY

Albert, Ethel M., "Value Sentences and Empirical Research." *Philosophy and Phenomenological Research*, Vol. 17 (1957), pp. 331–338.

Baier, Kurt, "The Concept of Value," in K. Baier and N. Rescher (eds.), *Values and the Future* (New York, 1968).

Baylis, Charles A., "The Confirmation of Value Judgments." *The Philosophical Review*, Vol. 61 (1952), pp. 50–58.

Berelson, Bernard, *Content Analysis* (New York, 1952).

von Ehrenfels, Christian, *System der Werttheorie* 2 vols. 's (Leipzig, 1897; 1898). [An extensive study of valuation based on the concept of value as degree of "desirability." See also the other references given in sect. III A 1 b.]

Hartman, Robert S., *The Structure of Value* (Carbondale, 1967).

Hull, Clark L., "Value, Valuation, and Natural Science Methodology." *Philosophy of Science*, Vol. 4 (1944), pp. 125–141.

Kluckhohn, Clyde, "The Scientific Study of Values," in *idem*, *Three Lectures* (Toronto, 1959), pp. 25–54.

——, "The Study of Values," in D. N. Barett (ed.), *Values in America* (Notre Dame, 1961).

Kluckhohn, Clyde, "Values and Value Orientations in the Theory of Action," in T. Parsons and E. Shils (eds.), *Towards a General Theory of Action* (Cambridge, Mass.; 1951), pp. 388–433.

Kluckhohn, Florence R. and F. L. Strodbeck, *Variations in Value Orientations* (Evanston, 1961).

Koffka, Kurt, "The Ontological Status of Value," in H. M. Kallen and S. Hook (eds.), *American Philosophy Today and Tomorrow* (New York, 1935).

Köhler, Wolfgang, *The Place of Value in a World of Fact* (New York, 1938).

Ledden, J. E., "On the Logical Status of Value." *The Philosophical Review*, Vol. 59 (1950), pp. 354–369.

Lee, Harald Newton, *Essays on the Theory of Value and Valuation*, ed. by Lee (Minneapolis, 1935).

——, "Methodology of Value Theory," in R. Lepley (ed.), *Value; A Cooperative Inquiry* (New York, 1949).

Lepley, Roy, *Verifiability of Value* (New York, 1944).

——, *Value: A Cooperative Inquiry*, ed. by Roy Lepley (New York, 1949).

——, *The Language of Value*, ed. by Roy Lepley (New York, 1957).

Lewis, Clarence Irving, *An Analysis of Knowledge and Valuation* (La Salle, 1946).

Meinong, Alexius, *Psychologisch-ethische Untersuchungen Zur Werttheorie*, (Graz, 1894). [See also the other references given in sect. III A 1 b.]

Morris, Charles, *Varieties of Human Value* (Chicago, 1956).

Perry, O. L., "The Logic of Moral Valuation." *Mind*, Vol. 66 (1957), pp. 42–62.

Pickard-Cambridge, Sir Arthur Wallace, "On Our Knowledge of Value." *Proceedings of the Aristotelian Society*, Vol. 17 (1917), pp. 216–255.

Rescher, Nicholas, *Introduction to Value Theory* (Englewood Cliffs, 1968).

Taylor, Paul W., *Normative Discourse* (New York, 1961).

Urban, Wilbur Marshall, "Value Propositions and Verifiability." *The Journal of Philosophy*, Vol. 34 (1937), pp. 589–602.

White, Ralph K., *Value Analysis: The Nature and the Use of its Methods* (Glen Gardner, N.J.; 1951).

## B.   MODELS FOR VALUE DESCRIPTION

### 1. Empirical Models

See also Pts. I and III of this Bibliography.

Allport, Gordon W. and Philip E. Vernon, and Gardner Lindsey, *A Study of Values* (Boston, 1951, revised edition).

——, *Manual for the Study of Values* (Boston, 1960).

Barton, Allen, "Measuring the Values of Individuals." *Review of Recent Research Bearing on Religious and Character Formation* (Research Supplement to *Religious Education*, July/August, 1962).

——, *Organizational Measurement* (New York, 1961).

Carter, Roy E., "An Experiment in Value Measurement." *American Sociological Review*, Vol. 21 (1956), pp. 156–163.

Fallding, Harold, "A Proposal for the Empirical Study of Values." *American Sociological Review*, Vol. 30 (1965), pp. 223–233.

Graham, James L., "Some Attitudes Towards Values." *Journal of Social Psychology*, Vol. 12 (1940), pp. 405–414.

Lepley, Roy, *The Verifiability of Value* (New York, 1944).

Podell, Lawrence, "An Interviewing Problem in Values Research." *Social Science Research*, Vol. 41 (1956), pp. 121–126.

Scott, William A., "Empirical Assessment of Values and Ideologies." *American Sociological Review*, Vol. 24 (1959), pp. 299–310.

Streffre, Buford, "Concurrent Validity of the Vocational Values Inventory." *Journal of Educational Research*, Vol. 52 (1959), pp. 339–341.

Van Dusen, A. C.; S. Wimberly, and C. I. Moisier, "Standardization of a Values Inventory." *Journal of Educational Psychology*, Vol. 30 (1939), pp. 53–62.

Wilkening, E. A., "Techniques of Assessing Form Family Values." *Rural Sociology*, Vol. 19, (1959), pp. 39–49.

## 2. Formal Models

Ackoff, Russell L., "On a Science of Ethics." *Philosophy and Phenomenological Research*, Vol. 9 (1949), pp. 663–672.

Anderson, Alan Ross, "The Logic of Norms." *Logique et Analyse*, Vol. 1 (1958), pp. 84–91.

——, "Logic, Norms and Roles." *Ratio*, Vol. 4 (1962), pp. 36–49.

——, "The Formal Analysis of Normative Systems," in N. Rescher (ed.), *The Logic of Decision and Action* (Pittsburgh, 1967), pp. 147–213.

Ayres, Clarence E., "The Value Economy" in R. Lepley (ed.), *Value: A Cooperative Inquiry* (New York, 1949), pp. 43–63.

Boulding, Kenneth E., "Some Contributions of Economics to the General Theory of Value." *Philosophy of Science*, Vol. 23 (1956), pp. 1–14.

Churchman, C. West, *Prediction and Optimal Decision: Philosophical Issues of a Science of Values* (Englewood Cliffs, 1961).

Churchman, Charles West and Russell L. Ackoff, "An Approximate Measure of Value." *Operations Research*, Vol. 2 (1954), pp. 172–187.

Davidson, Donald, J. C. C. McKinsey and Patrick Suppes, "Outline of a Formal Theory of Value." *Philosophy of Science*, Vol. 22 (1955), pp. 140–160.

Hare, Richard M., *The Language of Morals* (Oxford, 1952).

Morris, Charles W., "Axiology as the Science of Preferential Behavior," in Roy Lepley (ed.), *Value: A Cooperative Inquiry*, (New York, 1949), pp. 211–222.

——, *Varieties of Human Value* (Chicago, 1956).

Perry, David L., "What Things Can Be Evaluated?" *The Journal of Philosophy*, Vol. 61 (1964), pp. 186–192.

Smith, Nicholas M., Jr., "The Theory of Value and the Science of Decision—A Summary," ed. by Nicholas M. Smith, Jr., *Journal of the Operations Research Society of America*, Vol. 1 (1953), pp. 103–113.

——, "A Calculus for Ethics; A Theory of the Structure of Value." *Behavioral Sciences*, Vol. 1 (1956); Pt. I, pp. 111–142; and Pt. II, pp. 186–211.

## C.   VALUES AND SCIENCE

Bain, Read, "The Scientist and his Values." *Social Forces*, Vol. 31 (1952), pp. 106–109.

Benne, Kenneth and G. E. Swanson, "Values and the Social Scientist," ed. by Kenneth Benne and G. E. Swanson, *The Journal of Social Issues*, Vol. 6 (1950), no. 4, pp. 2–7.

Benoit-Smullyan, E., "Value Judgments and the Social Sciences." *The Journal of Philosophy*, Vol. 42 (1945), pp. 197–210.

Bowman, Claude C., "Evaluations and Values Consistent with the Scientific Study of Society." *American Sociological Review*, Vol. 10 (1945), pp. 709–715.

——, "Is Sociology Too Detached?" *American Sociological Review*, Vol. 21 (1956), pp. 563–568.

Bronowski, Jacob, *Science and Human Values* (New York, 1958).

Caws, Peter, *Science and the Theory of Value* (New York, 1967).

Cohen, Morris R., "Values, Norms, and Science," in *A Preface to Logic* (New York, 1964), pp. 155–178.

Edel, Abraham, *Ethical Judgment: The Uses of Science in Ethics* (Glencoe, 1955).

Hall, Everett W., *Modern Science and Human Values* (Princeton, 1957).

Holls, William L., "The Impugnment of Moral Values on Sociology." *Sociological Problems*, Vol. 2 (1954), pp. 66–70.

Irving, John A., *Science and Values* (Toronto, 1952).

Jeffrey, Richard C., "Valuation and Acceptance of Scientific Hypotheses." *Philosophy of Science*, Vol. 23 (1956), pp. 237–246.

Knight, Frank H., "Fact and Value in Social Science" in R. Aushen (ed.), *Science and Man* (New York, 1942).

Köhler, Wolfgang, *The Place of Value in a World of Facts* (New York, 1938; paperback ed.).

——, "Value and Fact." *The Journal of Philosophy*, Vol. 41 (1944), pp. 197–212.

Lippitt, Ronald, "Action Research and the Values of the Social Scientist." *Journal of Social Issues*, Vol. 6 (1950), pp. 50–55.

Lundberg, George A., "Science, Scientists, and Values." *Social Forces*, Vol. 30 (1952), pp. 373–379.

Mitchell, Wesley C., "Facts and Values in Economics." *The Journal of Philosophy*, Vol. 41 (1949), pp. 212–219.

Myrdal, Gunnar, *Value and Social Theory* (New York, 1958).

Nagel, Ernest, "Methodological Problems in the Social Sciences," in *idem*, *The Structure of Science* (New York, 1961).

Northrop, Filmer S. C., *Logic of the Sciences and the Humanities* (New York, 1947).

——, "The Physical Sciences, Philosophy, and Human Values" in E. M. Wigner (ed.), *Physical Science and Human Values* (Princeton, 1947),

Polanyi, Michael, *Science, Faith and Society* (London, 1946).

Rescher, Nicholas, "The Ethical Dimension of Scientific Research," in R. Colodny (ed.), *Beyond the Edge of Certainty* (Pittsburgh, 1965).

Riemer, Svend, "Values and Standards in Research." *American Journal of Sociology*, Vol. 55 (1949), pp. 131–136.

Rudner, Richard, "The Scientist *Qua* Scientist Makes Value Judgments." *Philosophy of Science*, Vol. 20 (1953), pp. 1–6.

Schumpeter, Joseph A., "Science and Ideology." *American Economic Review*, Vol. 39 (1949), pp. 345–369.

Sherrington, Sir Charles, "An Essay in the Relation of Science to Human Values," in D. P. Geddes (ed.), *An Analysis of the Kinsey Reports on Sexual Behavior in the Human Male and Female* (New York, 1954).

Snow, C. P., *Two Cultures and the Scientific Revolution* (New York, 1959).

Thorndike, Edward C., "Science and Values." *Science*, Vol. 83 (1936), pp. 1–8.

Urban, Wilbur M., "Science and Value." *Ethics*, Vol. 51 (1941), pp. 291–306. ·
Waldo, Dwight, " 'Values' in Political Science," in R. Young (ed.), *Approaches to the Study of Politics* (Evanston, 1958), pp. 96–111.
Weber, Max, *The Methodology of the Social Sciences*, tr. E. A. Shils and H. A. Finch (Glencoe, 1949).
Wigner, Eugene, *Physical Science and Human Values* ed. by E. Wigner (Princeton, 1947).
Znaniecki, Florian, "Should Sociologists Be Also Philosophers of Values?" *Sociology and Social Research*, Vol. 37 (1952), pp. 79–84.

## D.   DIMENSIONS OF VALUE AND VALUE CLASSIFICATION

Albert, Ethel M., "The Classification of Values: A Method and Illustration." *American Anthropologist*, Vol. 58 (1956), pp. 221–248.
Dodd, Stuart A., "On Classifying Human Values." *American Sociological Review*, Vol. 16 (1951), pp. 645–653.
Hilliard, Albert Leroy, *The Forms of Value—The Extension of a Hedonistic Axiology* (New York, 1950).
von Mering, Otto, *A Grammar of Human Values* (Pittsburgh, 1961).
Morris, Charles W., *Varieties of Human Value* (Chicago, 1956).
Pepper, Stephen C., *A Digest of Purposive Values* (Berkeley, 1947).
——, *The Sources of Value* (Berkeley, 1958).
Perry, Ralph Barton, *Realms of Value: A Critique of Human Civilization* (Cambridge, Mass.; 1959).
Polin, Raymond, *Du Laid, du mal, du faux* (Paris, 1948).
Rescher, Nicholas, *Introduction to Value Theory* (Englewood Cliffs, 1968).
Rhode, Sven Edward, *Ueber die Möglichkeit einer Werteinteilung* (Lund, 1937).
Rickert, Heinrich, *Lebenswerte und Kulturwerte: Vom System der Werte* in *Logos*, Vol. 3 (1912) and Vol. 4 (1913).
Sparshott, J. E., *An Inquiry into Goodness* (Toronto, 1958).
Taylor, Paul W., *Normative Discourse* (Englewood Cliffs, 1961).
von Wright, Georg Henrik, *The Varieties of Goodness* (London, 1963).

## E.   RULES OF VALUATION AND THE MEASUREMENT OF VALUE

(See also category III B.)

Baylis, Charles A., "Grading, Values, and Choice." *Mind*, Vol. 67 (1958), pp. 485–501.
Carter, Roy E., Jr., "An Experiment in Value Measurement." *American Sociological Review*, Vol. 21 (1956), pp. 156–163.
Clarke, Mary E., *A Study in the Logic of Value* (London, 1929).
Dodd, Stuart C., "How to Measure Values." *University of Washington Research Studies*, Vol. 18 (1950), pp. 163–168.
Friedman, Bertha B., *Foundations of the Measurement of Values* (New York, 1946).
Raths, Louis, "Approaches to the Measurement of Values" *Educational Research Bulletin*, Vol. 19 (1940), pp. 175–282, 304.
Rescher, Nicholas, *Distributive Justice* (New York, 1966).
——, *Introduction to Value Theory* (Englewood Cliffs, 1968).
Thurstone, Lewis Leon, *The Measurement of Values* (Chicago, 1959).

Urmson, John O., "On Grading." *Mind*, Vol. 59 (1950), pp. 145–169.

Weinberg, Alfred, "Value Interpretation: The Methodological Formulation of a Psychological Discipline." *Ethics*, Vol. 38 (1922–1928), pp. 44–57.


## II. *Anglo-American writers on general value theory*

Aiken, Henry D., "Definitions of Value and the Moral Ideal." *The Journal of Philosophy*, Vol. 42 (1945), pp. 337–352.

Alexander, Samuel, "The Idea of Value." *Mind*, Vol. 1 (1892), pp. 32–55.

——, *Beauty and Other Forms of Value* (London, 1933).

Ayer, Alfred Julius, *Language, Truth and Logic* (London, 1953).

Blanshard, Brand, *Reason and Goodness* (London, 1961).

Bosanquet, Bernard, *The Principle of Individuality and Value* (London, 1912).

Brandt, Richard B., "Some Puzzles for Attitude Theories of Value," in R. Lepley (ed.), *The Language of Value* (New York, 1957), pp. 153–171.

Brightman, E. S., *Nature and Values* (New York, 1945).

Brogan, Albert P., "The Fundamental Value Universal." *The Journal of Philosophy*, Vol. 16 (1919), pp. 96–104.

——, "Urban's Axiological System." *The Journal of Philosophy*, Vol. 18 (1921), pp. 197–209.

——, "Philosophy and the Problems of Value." *The Philosophical Review*, Vol. 42 (1933), pp. 105–129.

Campbell, C. A., "Moral and Non-Moral Values: A Study in the First Principles of Axiology." *Mind*, Vol. 44 (1935), pp. 273–299.

Cerf, Walter, "Value Decisions." *Philosophy of Science*, Vol. 18 (1951), pp. 26–34.

Clarke, Mary E., *A Study of the Logic of Value* (London, 1929).

Dashiell, J. Frederic, *The Philosophic Status of Values* (New York, 1913).

Dewey, John, "The Problem of Value." *The Journal of Philosophy*, Vol. 10 (1913), pp. 268–269.

——, "Values, Liking, and Thought." *The Journal of Philosophy*, Vol. 20 (1923), pp. 617–622.

——, "The Meaning of Value," *The Journal of Philosophy*, Vol. 23 (1924), pp. 126–133.

——, "Some Questions About Value." *The Journal of Philosophy*, Vol. 41 (1944), pp. 449–455.

——, "Theory of Valuation," in *International Encyclopedia of Unified Science* (Chicago, 1939), reprinted 1952.

Evans, Daniel Luther, *The Status of Value in New Realism: A Study of New Realism from the Standpoint of Axiology* (Columbus, Ohio; 1923).

Feiblemann, James K., "Towards an Analysis of the Basic Value System." *American Anthropologist*, Vol. 56 (1954), pp. 421–432.

Feigl, Herbert, "The Difference Between Knowledge and Valuation," in K. Benne and G. E. Swanson (eds.), "Values and the Social Scientist." *Journal of Social Issues*, Vol. 6 (1950).

——, "Valuation and Vindication: An Analysis of the Nature and the Limits of Ethical Arguments" in W. Sellars and J. Hospers (eds.), *Readings in Ethical Theory* (Appleton, 1952).

Findlay, J. N., *Values and Intentions* (London, 1961).

Fisher, D. Warren, "Professor Urban's Value-Theory." *The Journal of Philosophy*, Vol. 17 (1920), pp. 570–582.

Garnett, Arthur Campbell, *Reality and Value: An Introduction to Metaphysics and an Essay on the Theory of Value* (London, 1937).

——, *Reality and Value* (New Haven, 1937).

Golightly, Cornetius L., "Value as a Scientific Concept." *The Journal of Philosophy*, Vol. 53 (1956), pp. 233–245.

Gotshalk, Dilman W., "Value Science." *Philosophy of Science*, Vol. 19 (1952), pp. 183–192.

Graham, Angus Charles, *The Problem of Value* (London, 1961).

Gruber, Frederick C., *Aspects of Value* ed. by F. C. Gruber (Philadelphia, 1959).

Hahn, Lewis E., "A Contextualist Looks at Values," in R. Lepley (ed.), *Value: A Cooperative Inquiry* (New York, 1949), pp. 112–124.

Hall, Everett W., "A Categorical Analysis of Value." *Philosophy of Science*, Vol. 14 (1947), pp. 333–344.

——, *What is Value?—An Essay in Philosophical Analysis* (New York, 1952).

Handy, Rollo, "Philosophy's Neglect of the Social Sciences." *Philosophy of Science*, Vol. 25 (1958), pp. 117–124.

Hart, Samuel L., *A Treatise on Value* (New York, 1949).

Hartmann, Robert S., *The Structure of Value* (Carbondale, 1967).

Hilliard, Albert Leroy, *The Forms of Value: The Extension of a Hedonistic Axiology* (New York, 1950).

Hook, Sydney, *Nature and Values* (New York, 1945).

Jessup, Bertram E., *Relational Value Meanings* (Eugene, 1943).

Jury, G. S., *Value and Ethical Objectivity* (London, 1937).

Kecskemeti, Paul, *Meaning, Communication, and Value* (Chicago, 1952).

Kruse, Cornelius, "Cognition and Value Reexamined." *The Journal of Philosophy*, Vol. 34 (1937), pp. 225–234.

Kuhn, Helmut, "Fact and Value in Ethics." *Philosophy and Phenomenological Research*, Vol. 2 (1942), pp. 501–510.

Kurtz, Paul W., "Human Nature, Homeostasis, and Value." *Philosophy and Phenomenological Research*, Vol. 17 (1956), pp. 36–55.

Ladd, John, "Value Judgments, Emotive Meaning, and Attitudes." *The Journal of Philosophy*, Vol. 46 (1949), pp. 119–128.

Laird, John, *The Idea of Value* (Cambridge, 1929).

Lamont, William Dawson, *The Value Judgment* (Edinburgh, 1955).

Lepley, Roy, "The Dawn of Value Theory." *The Journal of Philosophy*, Vol. 34 (1937), pp. 365–372.

——, "The Verifiability of Different Kinds of Facts and Values." *Philosophy of Science*, Vol. 7 (1940), pp. 464–475.

Lewis, Clarence Irving, *An Analysis of Knowledge and Valuation* (La Salle, 1946).

Leys, Wayne A. R., "Human Values in the Atomic Age." *Annals of the American Academy of Political and Social Science*, Vol. 290 (1953), pp. 127–133.

Losski, N. O., *Value and Existence* (London, 1935).

McCracken, D. J., *Thinking and Valuing* (New York, 1950).

McGreal, Ian, "A Naturalistic Analysis of Value Terms." *Philosophy and Phenomenological Research*, Vol. 10 (1949) pp. 73–84.

McIntyre, James Lewis, "Value Feelings and Judgments of Value." *Proceedings of the Aristotelian Society*, 1904–1905 (1905), pp. 53–73.

McKeon, Richard, "Conflicts of Values in a Community of Cultures." *The Journal of Philosophy*, Vol. 47 (1950), pp. 197–210.

Mackenzie, John Stuart, *Ultimate Values* (London, 1924).

——, "Spiritual Values." *International Journal of Ethics*, Vol. 33 (1923), pp. 248f.

——, "Notes on the Theory of Value." *Mind*, N. S., Vol. 4 (1895), pp. 425–449.

Margenau, Henry, "The Scientific Basis of Value Theory," in A. H. Maslow (ed.), *New Knowledge in Human Values* (New York, 1958).

Montague, William Pepperhill, "The True, the Good, and the Beautiful from a Pragmatic Standpoint." *The Journal of Philosophy*, Vol. 6 (1909), pp. 233–238.

Moore, George Edward, *Principia Ethica* (Cambridge, 1903).

——, "The Conception of Intrinsic Value," in *Philosophical Studies*, (London, 1922), pp. 253–275.

Morris, Charles W., "Axiology as the Science of Preferential Behavior," in R. Lepley (ed.), *Value: A Cooperative Inquiry* (New York, 1949), pp. 211–222.

——, *Varieties of Human Value* (Chicago, 1956).

Morris, Charles W. and Lyle V. Jones, "Value Scales and Dimensions." *Journal of Abnormal Social Psychology*, Vol. 51 (1955), pp. 523–535.

Northrop, Filmer S. C., "Conflicts of Values in a Community of Cultures." *The Journal of Philosophy*, Vol. 47 (1950), pp. 197–210.

——, "Cultural Values," in A. L. Kroeber (ed.), *Anthropology Today* (Chicago, 1952), pp. 668–681.

——, "The Physical Sciences, Philosophy, and Human Values," in E. M. Wigner (ed.), *Physical Science and Human Values* (Princeton, 1947), pp. 78–113.

Osborne, Harold, *Foundations of the Philosophy of Value: An Examination of Value and Value Theories* (Cambridge, 1933).

Pap, Arthur, "The Verifiability of Value Judgments." *Ethics*, Vol. 56 (1946), pp. 178–185.

Parker, DeWitt H., "The Notion of Value." *The Philosophical Review*, Vol. 38 (1929), pp. 303–325.

——, "Value as Any Object of Any Interest." *Ethics*, Vol. 40 (1930), pp. 465–495.

——, *Human Values* (New York, 1931).

——, "Reflections of the Crisis in Theory of Value. Part I: Mostly Critical." *Ethics*, Vol. 56 (1946), pp. 193–207.

——, *The Philosophy of Value* (Ann Arbor, 1957).

Parsons, Talcott and Edward A. Shils, *Toward a General Theory of Action*, ed. by T. Parsons and E. A. Shils (Cambridge, Mass.; 1951).

Peirce, Charles S., *Values in a Universe of Chance* (Stanford, 1958).

Pepper, Stephen C., *The Equivocation of Value* (Berkeley, 1923; University of California Publications in Philosophy, Vol. 4).

——, *A Digest of Purposive Values* (Berkeley, 1947).

——, *The Sources of Value* (Berkeley, 1958).

Perry, Charner M., "Some Difficulties in Current Value Theory." *The Journal of Philosophy*, Vol. 25 (1928), pp. 281–287.

——, "Principles of Value and the Problem of Ethics." *Revue Internationale de Philosophie*, Vol. 1 (1939), pp. 666–683.

Perry, Ralph Barton, "The Definition of Value." *The Journal of Philosophy*, Vol. 11 (1914), pp. 141–162.

——, "Religious Values." *The American Journal of Theology*, Vol. 19 (1915), pp. 1–16.

——, *General Theory of Values* (New York, 1926).

——, "Value as an Objective Predicate." *The Journal of Philosophy*, Vol. 28 (1931), pp. 477–484.

——, *Realms of Value: A Critique of Human Civilization* (Cambridge, 1954).

Prall, David Wright, *A Study in the Theory of Value* (California, 1921; University of California Publications in Philosophy, Vol. 3, no. 2).

——, "The Present Status of the Theory of Value," in G. Adams and J. Lowenberg (eds.), *Issues and Tendencies in Contemporary Philosophy* (Berkeley, 1923), pp. 77–103.

Rashdall, Hastings, *The Theory of Good and Evil*, 2 vols. (Oxford, 1924).

Reid, John R., *A Theory of Value* (New York, 1938).

Rescher, Nicholas, *Introduction to Value Theory* (Englewood Cliffs, 1968).

Rice, Philip Blair, "Toward a Syntax of Evaluation." *The Journal of Philosophy*, Vol. 71 (1944), pp. 309–320.

Rose, M. C., "Value Experience and the Means-Ends Continuum." *Ethics*, Vol. 65 (1954), pp. 44–54.

Ross, William David, *The Right and the Good* (Oxford, 1930).

Schiller, F. S. C., "Truth, Value, and Biology." *The Journal of Philosophy*, Vol. 17 (1920), pp. 36–44.

Schneider, Herbert W., "The Theory of Value." *The Journal of Philosophy*, Vol. 14 (1917), pp. 141–157.

Schuster, Cynthia A., "Rapprochement in Value Theory." *The Journal of Philosophy*, Vol. 50 (1953), pp. 653–662.

Sheldon, William Henry, "An Empirical Definition of Value." *The Journal of Philosophy*, Vol. 11 (1914), pp. 113–124.

Smith, James Ward, "Should the General Theory of Value be Abandoned?" *Ethics*, Vol. 57 (1947), pp. 274–288

Sorley, William Ritchie, "Value and Reality," in J. H. Muirhead (ed.), *Contemporary British Philosophy* (London, 1925).

Stace, Walter Terence, *What Are Our Values?* (Lincoln, 1950).

Stevenson, Charles L., "The Emotive Meaning of Ethical Terms." *Mind*, Vol. 66 (1937), pp. 14–31.

——, *Ethics and Language* (New Haven, 1944).

——, *Facts and Values* (Hew Haven, 1963).

Storer, Thomas, "The Logic of Value Imperatives." *Philosophy of Science*, Vol. 13 (1946), pp. 25–40.

Taylor, Henry Osborn, *Human Values and Virtues* (New York, 1928).

Taylor, Paul W., *Normative Discourse* (Englewood Cliffs, 1961).

Urban, Wilbur M., "Definition and Analysis of the Conscienceness of Value." *Psychological Review*, Vol. 14 (1907), pp. 1–36, 92–121.

——, "The Individual and the Social Value Series." *The Philosophical Review*, Vol. 11 (1902), pp. 125–128.

——, "What Is the Function of a General Theory of Value?" *The Philosophical Review*, Vol. 17 (1908), pp. 42–62.

Urban, Wilbur, M., *Valuation: Its Nature and Laws* (New York, 1909).

——, "Knowledge of Value and the Value Judgment." *The Journal of Philosophy*, Vol. 13 (1916), pp. 673–687.

——, "Appreciation and Description and the Psychology of Values." *The Philosophical Review*, Vol. 14 (1905), pp. 645–668.

——, "Value and Existence." *The Journal of Philosophy*, Vol. 13 (1916), pp. 449–465.

——, "The Pragmatic Theory of Value." *The Journal of Philosophy*, Vol. 14 (1917), pp. 701–706.

——, "Ontological Problems of Value." *The Journal of Philosophy*, Vol. 14 (1917), pp. 309–327.

——, "Value Theory and Esthetics." *Philosophy Today* (Chicago, and London, 1928), pp. 54–75.

——, "The Present Situation in Axiology." *Revue internationale de philosophie*, Vol. 1 (1939), pp. 609–621.

Ward, Leo Richard, *Philosophy of Value: An Essay in Constructive Criticism* (New York, 1930).

Wells, Donald A., "Phenomenology and Value Theory." *The Journal of Philosophy*, Vol. 52 (1955), pp. 64–70.

Werkmeister, William Henry, "Problems of Value Theory." *Philosophy and Phenomenological Research*, Vol. 12 (1952), pp. 495–512.

——, "Prolegomena to Value Theory." *Philosophy and Phenomenological Research*, Vol. 14 (1954), pp. 239–308.

White, Morton G., "Value and Obligation in Dewey and Lewis." *The Philosophical Review*, Vol. 58 (1949), pp. 321–329.

Wood, Ledger, "Cognition and Moral Value." *The Journal of Philosophy*, Vol. 34 (1937), pp. 234–239.

## III. *Scientific approaches to value*

A.   THE PSYCHO-BIOLOGY OF VALUATION

For a comprehensive bibliography of this domain see:

Dukes, William, "Psychological Studies of Values." *The Psychological Bulletin*, Vol. 52 (1955), pp. 24–50.

*      *      *

For the Allport-Vernon Test, which has dominated work in this area see in particular:

Allport, Gordon W., Philip E. Vernon, and Gardner Lindsey, *Study of Values* (New York, 1931; revised ed. Boston 1951).

——, *Study of Values: Manual of Directions for the Study of Values* (Cambridge, Mass.; 1951).

Brogden, Hubert E., "The Primary Personal Values Measured by the Allport-Vernon Test, 'A Study of Values'." *Psychological Monographs*, Vol. 66 (1952), no. 16.

Cantril, Hadley and Gordon Allport, "Recent Applications of the Study of Values." *Journal of Abnormal and Social Psychology*, Vol. 28 (1933), pp. 259–273.

Duffy, Elizabeth, "A Critical Review of Investigations Employing the Allport-Vernon Study of Values and Other Tests of Evaluative Attitude." *The Psychological Bulletin*, Vol. 37 (1940), pp. 597–612.

Gage, N. L., "Review of Allport-Vernon Literature." *Fifth Mental Measurements Yearbook* (New Jersey, 1959), pp. 199–202.

Harris, Daniel, "Group Differences in Values Within a University." *Journal of Abnormal Social Psychology*, Vol. 29 (1934), pp. 95–102.

Hartmann, George W., "Six Differences in Valuational Attitudes." *Journal of Social Psychology*, Vol. 5 (1934), pp. 106–112.

——, "Value as the Unifying Concept of the Social Sciences." *Journal of Social Psychology*, Vol. 10 (1939), pp. 563–575.

McGinnies, Elliott M., "Personal Values as Determinants of Word Association." *Journal of Abnormal Social Psychology*, Vol. 45 (1950), pp. 28–36.

Meehl, Paul, "Review of AVL Literature." *Third Mental Measurements Yearbook*, (New Brunswick, 1949).

Schafer, Benjamin R., "The Validity and Utility of the Allport-Vernon Study of Values Test." *Journal of Abnormal and Social Psychology*, Vol. 30 (1936).

Shorr, J. E., "The Development of a Test to Measure the Intensity of Values." *Journal of Educational Psychology*, Vol. 44 (1953), pp. 266–274.

Spoerl, Dorothy Tilden, "The Values of the Post-War College Student." *Journal of Social Psychology*, Vol. 35 (1952), pp. 217–225.

Vernon, Philip E. and Gordon W. Allport, "A Test for Personal Values." *Journal of Abnormal and Social Psychology*, Vol. 26 (1931), pp. 231–248.

Whitely, Paul L., "A Study of the Allport-Vernon Test for Personal Values." *Journal of Abnormal and Social Psychology*, Vol. 28 (1933), pp. 6–13.

——, "The Constancy of Personal Values." *Journal of Abnormal and Social Psychology*, Vol. 33 (1938), pp. 405–408.

*   *   *

Some other works in this area are:

Auerbach, J. G., "Value Changes in Therapy." *Personality*, Vol. 1 (1950), pp. 63–67.

Beebe-Center, J. G., *The Psychology of Pleasantness and Unpleasantness* (New York, 1932).

Brickner, Richard M., "Man and His Values Considered Neurologically." *The Journal of Philosophy*, Vol. 41 (1944), pp. 225–243.

Creegan, Robert F., "Recent Trends in the Psychology of Values," in A. A. Roback (ed.), *Present-Day Psychology* (New York, 1955), pp. 949–960.

Dembo, Tamara, *Investigation of Concrete Psychological Value Systems* (Washington, 1953; Report of the U.S. Public Health Service, Institute for Mental Health.)

Ehrle, Gertrud, *Aus Dem Werterleben des Kleinkindes* (Münster in Westfalen, 1930).

Graham, James L., "Some Attitudes Towards Values." *Journal of Social Psychology*, Vol. 12 (1940), pp. 405–414.

Haering, Theodor, "Untersuchungen zur Psychologie der Wertung." *Archiv für die gesamte Psychologie*, Vol. 26/27 (1913), pp. 269-360.

Harding, D. W., *Social Psychology and Individual Values* (London, 1953).

Harding, Lawry W., "A Value-Type Generalizations Test; A Value-Type Problemmaire." *Journal of Social Psychology*, Vol. 19 (1944), pp. 53-79, 115-144.

——, "Experimental Comparisons Between Generalizations and Problems as Indices of Values." *Journal of General Psychology*, Vol. 38 (1948), pp. 31-50.

Kelly, E. Lowell, "Interest-Values Inventory," in O. K. Buros (ed.), *The Third Mental Measurements Yearbook* (New Brunswick, 1949), pp. 53-54.

Lalande, André, *La Psychologie des jugements de valeur* (Cairo?, 1939).

Lurie, Walter A., "A Study of Spranger's Value-Types by the Method of Factor Analysis." *Journal of Social Psychology*, Vol. 8 (1937), pp. 17-37.

Miller, Daniel R. and Max C. Hutt, "Value Interiorizations and Personality Development." *Journal of Social Issues*, Vol. 5 (1949), pp. 2-30.

Mullahy, Patrick, "Values, Scientific Method, and Psychoanalysis." *Psydiatry*, Vol. 6 (1943), pp. 139-146.

Muller, H. J., "Human Values in Relation to Evolution." *Science*, Vol. 127 (1958), pp. 625-629.

Piaget, Jean, *Le jugement morale chez l'enfant* (Paris, 1932). Tr. as *The Moral Judgment of the Child* (New York, 1929).

Renda, Antonio, *Teoria psicologica del valori* (Rome, 1920).

Rosenthal, David, "The Selection of Stimulus Words for Value." *Journal of Abnormal Social Psychology*, Vol. 50 (1955), pp. 403-404.

Snygg, Donald, "The Psychological Basis of Human Values," in A. D. Ward (ed.), *Goals of Economic Life* (New York, 1953), pp. 335-364.

Störring, Gustav E., "Experimentelle Untersuchungen uber das Werterlebnis." *Archiv für die gesamte Psychologie*, Vol. 73 (1929).

Thorndike, Edward L., "The Value of Reported Likes and Dislikes for Various Experiences and Attitudes or Indications of Personal Traits." *Journal of Applied Psychology*, Vol. 20 (1936), pp. 285-313.

——, "Individual Differences in Valuation." *Journal of Abnormal Social Psychology*, Vol. 33 (1938), pp. 71-85.

Thurstone, L. L., "The Measurement of Values." *Psychological Review*, Vol. 61 (1954), pp. 47-58.

Trow, William C., "The Value Concept in Educational Psychology." *Journal of Educational Psychology*, Vol. 44 (1953), pp. 449-462.

Urban, Wilbur Marshall, "Recent Tendencies in the Psychological Theory of Values." *Psychological Bulletin*, Vol. 4 (1905).

Van Dusen, Albert C.; Stan Wimberly, and Charles L. Mosier, "Standardization of a Values Inventory." *Journal of Educational Psychology*, Vol. 30 (1939), pp. 52-62.

White, Ralph K., "Value Analysis: A Quantitative Method for Describing Qualitative Data." *Journal of Social Psychology*, Vol. 19 (1944), pp. 351-358.

——, "Value Analysis: A Qualitative Method for Describing Qualitative Data." *Journal of Social Psychology*, Vol. 19 (1944), pp. 351-358.

——, *Value Analysis: The Nature and Use of its Methods* (Glen Gardner, 1951).

Wolff, Werner, *Values and Personality: An Existential Psychology of Crisis* (New York, 1950).

Woodruff, Asahel D., "Reasoned Values and the Direction of Behavior." *The School Review*, Vol. 50 (1942), pp. 32–42.


B.   ANTHROPOLOGICAL AND SOCIOLOGICAL STUDIES

**1. Comparative and General Studies**

NOTE: For a considerably more extensive bibliography of this area see:

Albert, Ethel M. and Clyde Kluckhohn, *A Selected Bibliography on Values Ethics and Esthetics* (Glencoe, 1959).

*          *          *

Adler, Franz, "The Value Concept in Sociology." *American Journal of Sociology*, Vol. 62 (1956), pp. 272–279.

Anderson, Alan Ross and Omar K. Moore, "The Formal Analysis of Normative Concepts." *American Sociological Review*, Vol. 22 (1957), pp. 9–17.

Barton, Allen, "Measuring the Values of Individuals: Review of Recent Research Bearing on Religious and Character Formation." Research Supplement to *Religious Education*, July–August, 1962.

Becker, Howard, "Supreme Values and the Sociologist." *American Sociological Review*, Vol. 6 (1941), pp. 155–172.

———, *Through Values to Social Interpretation* (Durham, 1950).

Belshaw, Cyril S., "The Identification of Values in Anthropology." *American Journal of Sociology*, Vol. 64 (1959), pp. 555–562.

Benedict, Ruth, "Configurations of Culture in North America." *American Anthropologist*, Vol. 34 (1932), pp. 1–27.

———, *Patterns of Culture* (New York, 1934).

Bidney, David, "The Concept of Value in Modern Anthropology," in *idem* (ed.), *Anthropology Today* (Chicago, 1953), pp. 682–699.

Bouglé, C., *L'Evolution des valeurs* (Paris, 1922). Tr. by H. S. Sellars as *The Evolution of Values* (New York, 1926).

Burgess, Ernest W., "Values and Sociological Research." *Social Problems*, Vol. 2 (1954), pp. 16–20.

Carter, Roy E., "An Experiment in Value Measurement." *American Sociological Review*, Vol. 21 (1956), pp. 156–163.

Case, Clarence Marsh, "The Value Concept in Sociology and Related Fields." *Sociology and Social Research* Vol. 23 (1939), pp. 403–430.

———, *Essays in Social Values* (Los Angeles, 1944).

Catton, William R., Jr., "Exploring Techniques for Measuring Human Values." *American Sociological Review*, Vol. 19 (1954), pp. 49–55.

———, "A Retest of the Measurability of Certain Human Values." *American Sociological Review*, Vol. 21 (1956), pp. 357–359.

———, "A Theory of Value." *American Sociological Review*, Vol. 24 (1959), pp. 310–317.

Collier, John, "Values and the Introduction of Change." *Merrill-Palmer Quarterly*, Vol. 1 (1955), pp. 148–157.

Dahlke, Otto, *Values in Culture and Classroom: A Study of the Sociology of the School* (New York, 1958).

Easton, David, "Shifting Images of Social Science and Values." *Antioch Review*, Vol. 15 (1955), pp. 3–18.

Firth, Raymond, "The Study of Values by Social Anthropologists." *Man*, Vol. 53 (1953), pp. 146–153.

Geiger, George R., "Values and the Social Sciences." *Journal of Social Issues*, Vol. 6 (1950), pp. 8–16.

Geiger, Theodore, "Evaluational Nihilism." *Acta Sociologica*, Vol. 1 (1955), pp. 18–25.

Goldschmidt, Walter, "Values and the Field of Comparative Sociology." *American Sociological Review*, Vol. 18 (1953), pp. 287–293.

Gurth, William B. and Renato Tagiuri, "Personal Values and Corporate Strategy," *Harvard Business Review*, Vol. 43 (1965), pp. 123–132.

Harding, D. W., *Social Psychology and Individual Values* (London, 1953).

Hart, Harwell, "A Reliable Scale of Value Judgments." *American Sociological Review*, Vol. 10 (1945), pp. 473–481.

Herskovits, Melville J., "On the Values in Culture." *Scientific Monthly*, Vol. 54 (1942), pp. 557–560.

——, "Tender and Tough Minded Anthropology and the Study of Values in Culture." *South-Western Journal of Anthropology*, Vol. 7 (1951), pp. 22–31.

Himes, Joseph S., "Value Analysis in the Theory of Social Problems." *Social Forces*, Vol. 33 (1955), pp. 259–262.

Hyman, Herbert H., "The Value Systems of Different Classes, in R. Bendix and S. M. Lipset (eds.), *Class, Status, and Power* (Glencoe, 1953).

Inkeles, Alex, "Industrial Man: The Relation of Status to Experience, Perception, and Value." *The American Journal of Sociology*, Vol. 66 (1960), pp. 1–31.

Kluckhohn, Clyde M., "Values and Value Orientations in the Theory of Action," in T. Parsons and E. A. Shils (eds.), *Toward a General Theory of Action* (Cambridge, Mass.; 1951).

——, "A Comparative Study of Values in Five Cultures," in E. Z. Vogt (ed.), *Navaho Veterans: A Study of Changing Values* (Cambridge, Mass.; 1951; Publications of the Peabody Museum of Harvard University, vol. 41, no. 1).

——, "Universal Values and Anthropological Relativism," in *idem, Modern Education and Human Values* (Pittsburgh, 1952), pp. 87–112.

——, "Ethical Relativity." *The Journal of Philosophy*, Vol. 52 (1955), pp. 663–677.

——, "Toward a Comparison of Value-Emphases in Different Cultures," in L. D. White (ed.), *The State of the Social Sciences* (Chicago, 1956), pp. 116–132.

——, "The Scientific Study of Values and Contemporary Civilization." *Proceedings of the American Philosophical Society*, Vol. 102 (1958), pp. 469–476.

Kluckhohn, Florence R., "Dominant and Variant Value-Orientations," in C. Kluckhohn, H. Murray, and D. Schneider (eds.), *Personality in Nature, Culture, and Society* (New York, 1953), pp. 342–357.

——, "Value Orientations," in R. R. Grinker (ed.), *Toward a Unified Theory of Human Behavior* (New York, 1956).

——, *Variations in Value Orientations* (Evanston, 1961).

Kolb, Wilson L., "The Changing Prominence of Values in Modern Sociological Theory," in H. Becker and A. Boskoff (eds.), *Modern Sociological Theory* (New York, 1957).

Kroeber, Alfred L., "Values as a Subject of Natural Science Inquiry." *Proceedings of the National Academy of Sciences*, Vol. 35 (1949), pp. 261–264.

Lewin, Kurt and Paul Grable, "Conduct, Knowledge, and Acceptance of New Values." *Journal of Social Issues*, Vol. 1 (1945), pp. 53–64.

Linton, Ralph, "The Problem of Universal Values," in *Method and Perspective in Anthropology*, ed. R. F. Spencer (Minneapolis, 1954).

Lipset, Seymour, "The Value Patterns of Democracy: A Case Study in Comparative Analysis." *American Sociological Review*, Vol. 28 (1963), pp. 515–531.

Maslow, Abraham, *New Knowledge in Human Values*, ed. by A. Maslow (New York, 1959).

von Mering, Otto, *A Grammar of Human Values* (Pittsburgh, 1961).

Miller, David L., "Norms, Values, and the Social Sciences." *Southwestern Social Science Quarterly*, Vol. 32 (1951), pp. 132–149.

Mitchell, E. T., "Values, Valuing, and Evaluation," in R. Lepley (ed.), *Value: A Comparative Inquiry* (New York, 1949), pp. 190–210.

Mogar, Robert E., "Value Orientations of College Students: Preliminary Data and Review of the Literature." *Psychological Reports*, Vol. 15 (1964), pp. 739–770.

Mukerjee, Radhakamal, *The Social Structure of Values* (London, 1953).

——, "The Sociology of Values," *Sociology and Social Research.*, Vol. 31 (1946), pp. 101–109.

Parsons, Talcott, "The Place of Ultimate Values in Sociological Theory." *Ethics*, Vol. 45 (1935), pp. 285.

——, "Evolutionary Universals in Society." *American Sociological Review*, Vol. 29 (1964), pp. 339–357.

Parsons, Talcott and Edward A. Shils, "Values, Motives, and Systems of Action," in T. Parsons and E. A. Shils (eds.), *Toward a General Theory of Action* (Cambridge, Mass.; 1951).

Partridge, P. H., "Value, Judgments and the Social Sciences." *Australian Journal of Politics and History*, Vol. 1 (1956), pp. 210–222.

Rescher, Nicholas, "The Dynamics of Value Change," in K. Baier and N. Rescher (eds.), *Values and the Future* (New York, 1968).

Rettig, Salomon, "Changes in Moral Values as a Function of Adult Socialization." *Social Problems*, Vol. 7 (1959), pp. 117–125.

——, "Moral Value Structure and Social Class." *Sociometry*, Vol. 24 (1961), pp. 117–125.

Riesman, David, "Values in Context." *American Scholar*, Vol. 22 (1952), pp. 29–39.

Rose, Arnold M., "Values in Social Research," in *idem*, *Theory and Method in the Social Sciences* (Minneapolis, 1954).

——, "Sociology and the Study of Values." *British Journal of Sociology*, Vol. 7 (1956), pp. 1–17.

Roshwald, M., "Value-Judgments in the Social Sciences." *British Journal for the Philosophy of Science*, Vol. 6 (1955), pp. 186–208.

Schellenberg, James, "Social Choice and Similarity of Personal Values." *Sociology, and Social Research*, Vol. 41 (1957), pp. 270–273.

Schwarzweller, Harry, "Value Orientations in Educational and Occupational Choices." *Rural Sociology*, Vol. 24 (1959), pp. 246–256.

——, "Values and Occupational Choice." *Social Forces*, Vol. 39 (1960), pp. 126–235.

Scott, William A., "Factors Affecting the Learning of Personal Values Through Social Reinforcement." *American Psychologist*, Vol. 11 (1956), pp. 407–408.

——, "Empirical Assessment of Values and Ideologies." *American Sociological Review*, Vol. 24 (1957), pp. 299–310.

Seeley, John; Alexander Sim and Elizabeth Loosley, "Differentiation of Values in a Modern Community." *The Family*, (New York, 1960).

Siegel, Bernard J., "Currents of Anthropological Theory and Value Concepts." *South-Western Journal of Anthropology*, Vol. 4 (1948), pp. 199–210.

Tagiuri, Renato, "Value Orientations and Relationships of Managers and Scientists." *Administrative Science Quarterly*, Vol. 10 (1965), pp. 39–51.

Tiryakian, Edward, *Sociological Theory, Values and Sociological Change*, ed. by E. Tiryakian (New York, 1963).

Tolmain, Edward C., "Value Standards, Pattern Variables, Social Roles, Personality," in T. Parsons and E. A. Shils (eds.), *Toward A General Theory of Action* (Cambridge, Mass.; 1951), pp. 343–354.

Turner, Ralph H., "The Quest for Universals in Sociological Research." *American Sociological Review*, Vol. 18 (1953), pp. 604–611.

——, "Value Conflict in Social Disorganization." *Sociology and Social Research*, Vol. 38 (1954), pp. 301–308.

Veroff, Joseph and M. R. B. Klinger, "Cross-Cultural Dimensions." *Personal and Guidance Journal*, Vol. 42 (1964), pp. 899–903.

Vogt, Evon Z. and John M. Roberts, "A Study of Values." *The Scientific American*, Vol. 195 (1956), pp. 25–31.

Vogt, Evon Z. and Thomas F. O'Dea, "A Comparative Study of the Role of Values in Social Action in Two Southwestern Communities." *American Sociological Review*, Vol. 18 (1953), pp. 645–654.

Warren, Roland L., "Philosophy and Social Science in the Field of Values." *The Journal of Philosophy*, Vol. 38 (1941), pp. 404–409.

Weigel, Wenzel, *Vom Wertreich des Jugendlichen*, 2 vols. (Leipzig, 1926).

Westermarck, Edward, *Origin and Development of the Moral Ideas*, 2 vols. (New York, 1906).

White, Ralph K., *Value Analysis* (Glen Gardner, N.J.; 1951).

Wieman, Henry N., "Science in Service of Values." *Journal of Social Issues*, Vol. 6 (1950), pp. 33–38.

Wilkening, Eugene A., "Techniques of Assessing Form Family Values." *Rural Sociology*, Vol. 19 (1955), pp. 39–49.

## 2. Special Studies of American Values

NOTE: For a considerably more extensive bibliography of this area see:

Albert, Ethel M. and Clyde Kluckhohn, *A Selected Bibliography on Values, Ethics and Esthetics* (Glencoe, 1959).

\*     \*     \*

Albert, Ethel M., "Conflict and Change in American Values: A Culture-Historical Approach." *Ethics*, Vol. 74 (1963), pp. 272–279.

Albrecht, Milton C., "Does Literature Reflect Common Values?" *American Sociological Review*, Vol. 21 (1956), pp. 722–729.

Barrett, Donald N., *Values in America*, ed. by D. N. Barrett (Notre Dame, 1961).

Cuber, John F. and Robert A. Harper, *Problems of American Society: Values in Conflict* (New York, 1948; new ed. with William F. Kendal, 1956).

DuBois, Cora, "The Dominant Value Profile of American Culture." *American Anthropologist*, Vol. 57 (1955), pp. 1232–1239.

Gillin, John P., "National and Regional Cultural Values in the U.S." *Social Forces*, Vol. 34 (1955), pp. 107–113.

Greenstein, Fred I., "New Light on Changing American Values." *Social Forces*, Vol. 42 (1964), pp. 441–450.

Herman, Abbot P., "Values of Individualism." *Sociology and Social Research*, Vol. 33 (1949), pp. 196–203.

Jacob, P. E., *Changing Values in College* (New York, 1957).

Johns-Heine, Patrick and Hans H. Gerth, "Values in Mass Periodical Fiction: 1921–1940." *Public Opinion Quarterly*, Vol. 13 (1949), pp. 103–113.

Kluckhohn, Clyde M., "The Evolution of Contemporary American Values." *Daedalus*, Vol. 87 (1958), pp. 78–109.

——, "Shifts in American Values," in E. Morison (ed.), *The American Style* (New York, 1958).

——, "Have There Been Discernible Shifts in American Values During the Past Generation?" in E. Morison (ed.), *The American Style* (New York, 1958), pp. 145–217.

——, "Shifts in American Values." *World Politics*, Vol. 11 (1959), pp. 251–261.

Kluckhohn, Florence R., "American Women and American Values," in L. Bryson (ed.), *Facing the Future's Risks* (New York, 1953), pp. 175–199.

Mead, Margaret, *And Keep Your Power Dry* (New York, 1942).

Parsons, Talcott, "American Values," in *idem, On American Society* (Glencoe, 1956?).

Parsons, Talcott and Winston White, "Continuity and Change in American Values," in S. M. Lipset and L. Lowenthal (eds.), *Culture and Social Character; The Work of David Riesman Reviewed* (Glencoe, 1961).

Rosenberg, Morris, Edward A. Suchman, and Rose K. Goldsen, *Occupations and Values* (Glencoe, 1952).

Roths, Louis, "Appraising Changes in Values of College Students." *Journal of Educational Research*, Vol. 35 (1942), pp. 557–564.

Williams, Robin, *American Society* (New York, 1951; 2nd ed., 1960).

C. ECONOMIC VALUATION AND RELATED TOPICS

## 1. Theory of Economic Value

Arrow, Kenneth J., *Social Choice and Individual Values* (New York, 1951; 2nd ed., New Haven, 1963).

Balz, Albert G., *The Value Doctrine of Marx* (New York, 1943).

Baumol, William M., *Welfare Economics and the Theory of the State* (Cambridge, 1952).

Boulding, Kenneth, *Principles of Economic Policy* (Englewood Cliffs, 1958).

Bower, Howard B., *Toward Social Economy* (New York, 1948).

Carver, Thomas N., *Essays in Social Justice* (Cambridge, Mass.; 1925).

Cowles Commission for Research in Economics, *Rational Decision-Making and Economic Behavior*. 19th Annual Report, 1950–1951. (Chicago, 1951).

Danhof, Clarence H., "Economic Values in Cultural Perspective," in A. O. Ward (ed.), *Goals of Economic Life* (New York, 1953), pp. 84–117.

Edgeworth, F. Y., *Mathematical Psychics* (London, 1881; New York, 1961).

Fetter, Frank A., "Value and the Larger Economics." *Journal of Political Economy*, Vol. 31 (1925), pp. 790–803.

Flubacher, Joseph Francis, *The Concept of Ethics in the History of Economics* (New York, 1950).

Graaff, Johannes de Villiers, *Theoretical Welfare Economics* (Cambridge, 1957).

Haney, Lewis H., *Value and Distribution* (New York, 1939).

Heimann, Eduard, *History of Economic Doctrines* (New York, 1945).

Hicks, J. R., "The Foundations of Welfare Economics." *Economic Journal*, Vol. 69 (1939), pp. 696–712.

——, *The Social Framework: An Introduction to Economics* (London, 1942).

——, *Value and Capital* (Oxford, 1946) 2nd ed.

——, *The Theory of Wages* (London, 1951).

Hobson, John A., *Economics and Ethics: A Study in Social Values* (Boston, 1929).

Hutchinson, T. W. A., *A Review of Economic Doctrines* (Oxford, 1953).

Jevons, W. Stanley, *The Theory of Political Economy* (London, 1885; 4th edn., 1911).

Kaldor, Nicholas, "Welfare Propositions in Economics." *Economic Journal*, Vol. 69 (1939), pp. 549–552.

——, "Alternative Theories of Distribution." *Review of Economic Studies*, Vol. 23 (1955–1956), pp. 83–100.

——, *Essays on Value and Distribution* (London, 1960).

Keynes, John Maynard, *The General Theory of Employment, Interest and Money* (London, 1936).

——, *Essays in Biography* (New York, 1933).

Keynes, John Neville, *The Scope and Method of Political Economy* (London and New York, 1891).

Lange, Oskar, "The Foundations of Welfare Economics." *Econometrica*, Vol. 10 (1942), pp. 215–228.

Levin, Harvey J., "Standards of Welfare in Economic Thought." *Quarterly Journal of Economics*, Vol. 70 (1956), pp. 117–138.

Little, Ian M. D., *A Critique of Welfare Economics* (Oxford, 1950) 2nd edn. 1957).

Marshall, Alfred, *Principles of Economics* (London, 1890; 8th edn., 1920). See especially ch. 6 on "Value and Utility."

Myint, Hla, *Theories of Welfare Economics* (London, 1948).

Myrdal, Gunnar, *An International Economy: Problems and Prospects* (New York, 1956).

——, *Beyond the Welfare State* (London, 1960).

Oliver, Henry M., Jr., *A Critique of Socio-Economic Goals* (Bloomington, 1954).

——, "Economic Value Theory as a Policy Guide." *Ethics*, Vol. 68 (1958), pp. 186–193.

Pareto, Vilfredo, *Manuel d'économie politique*. Tr. from Italian by Alfred Bonnet (Paris, 1909).

Pigou, A. C., *Wealth and Welfare* (London, 1912).

——, *The Economics of Welfare* (London, 1920; 4th ed., 1932).

Pigou, A. C., "Some Aspects of Welfare Economics." *American Economic Review*, Vol. 41 (1951), pp. 287–302.

Rescher, Nicholas, *Distributive Justice* (New York, 1966).

Robbins, Lionel, *An Essay on the Nature and Significance of Economic Science* (London, 1932).

Rothenberg, Jerome, *The Measurement of Social Welfare* (Englewood Cliffs, 1961).

Samuelson, Paul Anthony, *Foundations of Economic Analysis* (Cambridge, 1947).

Schumpeter, Joseph A., *Capitalism, Socialism and Democracy* (London, 1943).

——. "On the Concept of Social Value," in R. V. Clemence (ed.), *Essays* (Cambridge, 1951), pp. 1–20.

Scitovsky, Tibor, *Welfare and Competition* (London, 1952).

——, *Papers on Welfare and Growth* (London, 1964).

Senior, Nassau, *Four Introductory Lectures on Political Economy* (London, 1852).

Smart, William, *An Introduction to the Theory of Value on the Lines of Menger, Wieser, and Böhm-Bawerk* (London, 1931).

Spranger, Edward, *Ueber die Stellung der Werturtheile in der Nationalokonomie* (Munich, 1914).

Stigler, George J., "The New Welfare Economics." *American Economic Review*, Vol. 33 (1943), pp. 355–359.

——, "The Economists and Equality," in *idem*, *Five Lectures on Economic Problems* (London, 1949).

——, *The Goals of Economic Policy* (Chicago, 1958).

Sweezy, Alan R., "The Interpretation of Subjective Value Theory in the Writings of the Austrian Economists." *Review of Economic Studies*, Vol. 1 (1934), pp. 176–185.

Thompson, William, *Inquiry into the Principles of the Distribution of Wealth* (London, 1824; 2nd edn., 1850).

Walras, Léon, *Eléments d'économie politique pure*, 2 vols., (Lausanne, 1874–1877).

Weisskopf, Walter A., "Hidden Value Conflicts in Economic Thought." *Ethics*, Vol. 61 (1951), pp. 195–204.

Wicksteed, Philip Henry, *An Essay on the Co-ordination of the Laws of Distribution* (London, 1894).

——, *Common Sense of Political Economy* (London, 1910; Revised edition, London, 1933).

Wieser, Friedrich von, *Natural Value*, tr. C. A. Mallock (New York, 1930).

## 2. Utility Theory

NOTE: This listing is highly selective, and addresses itself more to the content of the utility concept than to the formal machinery of its implementation. The following three works may be consulted for fuller bibliographic data:

Edwards, Ward, "The Theory of Decision Making." *Psychological Bulletin*, Vol. 5 (1954), pp. 380–417.

Luce, R. Duncan and Howard Raiffa, *Games and Decisions* (New York, 1957).

Savage, Leonard J., *The Foundations of Statistics* (New York, 1954).

\* \* \*

Adams, E. W., "A Survey of Bernouillian Utilities and Applications." *Technical Report No. 9 of the Behavioral Models Project*, (Columbia University, 1954).

Armstrong, W. E., "Uncertainty and the Utility Function." *Economic Journal*, Vol. 58 (1948), pp. 1–10.

——, "The Determinateness of the Utility Function." *Economic Journal*, Vol. 49 (1939), pp. 453–467.

——, "Utility and the Theory of Welfare." *Oxford Economic Papers*, N.S. No. 3 (Oxford, 1951), pp. 259–271.

Baumol, W. J., "The Neuman-Morgenstern Utility Index: An Ordinalist View." *Journal of Political Economy*, Vol. 59 (1951), pp. 61–66.

Bohnert, Herbert G., "The Logical Structure of the Utility Concept." In *Decision Processes*, Robert M. Thrall, *et al.*, eds. (New York, 1954).

Boulding, Kenneth E., "Some Contributions of Economics to the General Theory of Value." *Philosophy of Science*, Vol. 23 (1956), pp. 1–14.

Coombs, Clyde H., "Psychological Scaling Without a Unit of Measurement." *Psychological Review*, Vol. 57 (1950), pp. 145–158.

——, "Social Choice and Strength of Preference." In *Decision Processes*, R. M. Thrall, *et al.*, eds. (New York, 1954).

Davidson, Donald; J. C. C. McKinsey, and Patrick Suppes, "Outlines of a Formal Theory of Value." *Philosophy of Science*, Vol. 22 (1955), pp. 140–160.

Edgeworth, F. Y., *Mathematical Psychics* (London, 1881; reprinted New York, 1961).

Friedman, Milton J., and L. J. Savage, "The Utility Analysis of Choices Involving Risk." *Journal of Political Economy*, Vol. 56 (1948), pp. 279–304. Reprinted with a correction in G. S. Stigler and K. E. Boulding (eds.), *Readings in Price Theory* (Chicago, 1952).

——, "The Experted-Utility Hypothesis and the Measurability of Utility." *Journal of Political Economy*, Vol. 60 (1952), pp. 463–474.

Georgescu-Roegen, Nicholas, "Choice, Expectations and Measurability." *Quarterly Journal of Economics*, Vol. 68 (1954), pp. 503–534.

Harsanyi, John C., "Cardinal Welfare, Individualistic Ethics, and Interpersonal Comparisons of Utility." *Journal of Political Economy*, Vol. 63 (1955), pp. 309–321.

Herstein, I. N. and John W. Milnor, "An Axiomatic Approach to Measurable Utility." *Econometrica*, Vol. 21 (1953), pp. 291–297.

Housner, Melvin, "Multimentional Utilities," in R. M. Thrall, C. H. Combs and R. L. Davis (eds.), *Decision Processes* (New York, 1954).

Houthakker, H. S., "Revealed Preference and the Utility Function." *Economica*, Vol. 17 (1950), pp. 159–174.

Lange, Oscar, "The Determinateness of the Utility Function." *Review of Economic Studies*, Vol. 1 (1934), pp. 218–225.

Little, I. M. D., *A Critique of Welfare Economics* (Oxford, 1950).

Lyons, David, *Forms and Limits of Utilitarianism* (Oxford, 1965).

McNaughton, Robert, "A Metrical Conception of Happiness." *Philosophy and Phenomenological Research*, Vol. 14 (1954), pp. 172–183.

Markowitz, Harry, "The Utility of Wealth." *Journal of Political Economy*, Vol. 60 (1952), pp. 151–158.

Marshak, Jacob, "Rational Behavior, Uncertain Prospects, and Measurable Utility." *Econometrica*, Vol. 18 (1950), pp. 111–141.

Marshall, Alfred, *Principles of Economics* (London, 1890).

Mosteller, Frederich and Philip Nogee, "An Experimental Measurement of Utility." *Journal of Political Economy*, Vol. 59 (1951), pp. 371–404.

von Neumann, John and Oskar Morgenstern, *Theory of Games and Economic Behavior* (Princeton, 1953).

Pareto, Vilfredo, *Manuel d'économie politique*. Tr. from Italian by Alfred Bonnet, (Paris, 1909).

Pigou, A. C. and N. Georgescu-Roegen, "Marginal Utility of Money and Elasticities of Demand." *Quarterly Journal of Economics*, Vol. 50 (1936), pp. 532–539.

Rader, Trout, "The Existence of a Utility Function to Represent Preferences." *Review of Economic Studies*, Vol. 30 (1963), pp. 229–232.

Rescher, Nicholas, *Distributive Justice* (New York, 1966).

Robbins, Lionel, "Interpersonal Comparisons of Utility: A Comment." *Economic Journal*, Vol. 68 (1938), pp. 635–641.

——, *An Essay on the Nature and Significance of Economic Science* (London, 1935). 2nd edn. 1935.

Robertson, D. H., *Utility and All That* (London, 1952).

Rubin, Herman, *The Existence of Measurable Utility and Psychological Probability* (Chicago, 1949; Cowles Commission Discussion Paper, Statistics, N. 331.)

Samuelson, Paul Anthony, *Foundations of Economic Analysis* (Cambridge, Mass., 1947).

Sonnenschein, Hugo, "The Relationship Between Transitive Preference and the Structure of the Choice Space." *Econometrica*, Vol. 33 (1965), pp. 624–634.

Stigler, George J., "The Development of Utility Theory." *Journal of Political Economy*, Vol. 58 (1950), pp. 307–327.

Suppes, Patrick and Muriel Wiment, "An Axiomatization of Utility Based on the Notion of Utility Differences." *Management Science*, Vol. 1 (1955), pp. 259–270.

Suppes, Patrick, "Behavioristic Foundations of Utility." *Econometrica*, Vol. 29 (1961), pp. 186–202.

Thrall, Robert M., "Multidimensional Utility Theory." In *Decision Processes*, R. M. Thrall, *et al.*, eds. (New York, 1954).

Uzawa, Hirofumi, "Preference and Rational Choice in the Theory of Consumption." *Proceedings on a Symposium on Mathematical Methods in the Social Sciences* (Stanford, 1960).

Wold, Herman, "Ordinal Preferences or Cardinal Utility?" *Econometrica*, Vol. 20 (1952), pp. 661–664.

### 3. Decision Theory and Cost-Benefit Analysis

A useful bibliography of decision theory is given in the work by R. D. Luce and H. Raiffa cited in Sect. 3 above. As regards cost-benefit analysis, see:

DonVito, P. A., *Annotated Bibliography of Systems Cost Analysis* (Santa Monica, 1967; RAND Corporation Research Memorandum RM-4848-1-PR).

### a. Formal Models (General Theory, Statistical Approaches, Operations Research)

Ackoff, Russell L., "The Development of Operations Research as a Science." *Operations Research*, Vol. 4 (1956), pp. 265–295.

——, *Progress in Operations Research* (New York, 1961).

Arrow, Kenneth J., "Alternative Approaches to the Theory of Choice in Risk-Taking Situations." *Econometrica*, Vol. 19 (1951), pp. 404–437.

——, *Social Choice and Individual Values* (New York, 1951).

Bates, James, "A Model for the Science of Decision." *Philosophy of Science*, Vol. 21 (1954), pp. 326–339.

Blackwell, David and M. A. Girshik, *Theory of Games and Statistical Decisions* (New York, 1954).

Bross, Irwin, *Design for Decision* (New York, 1953).

Churchman, C. West, *Prediction and Optimal Decision* (Englewood Cliffs, 1961).

Churchman, C. West, Russell L. Ackoff, and E. Leonard Arnoff, *Introduction to Operations Research* (New York, 1957).

Cowles Commission for Research in Economics, *Rational Decision-Making and Economic Behavior*. 19th Annual Report, 1950–1951. (Chicago, 1951).

Davidson, Donald; Patrick Suppes and Sidney Siegel, *Decision-Making: An Experimental Approach* (Stanford, 1957).

Enke, Stephen, *Defense Management* (Englewood Cliffs, 1967).

Girshick, Meyer A., "An Elementary Survey of Statistical Decision Theory." *Review of Educational Research*, Vol. 24 (1954), pp. 448–466.

Handy, Rollo and Paul Kurtz, *A Current Appraisal of the Behavioral Sciences*. Sect. 7 Supplement to *American Behavioral Scientist*, Vol. 7, no. 7 (1964). Ch. 14 "Decision-Making Theory" (pp. 126–130).

Jacobs, Philip E., "Functions of Values in Policy Processes. *American Behavioral Scientist*, Vol. 5 (1962), pp. 28–34.

Jeffrey, R. C., *The Logic of Decision* (New York, 1965).

Oppenheim, Felix E., "Rational Choice." *The Journal of Philosophy*, Vol. 50 (1953), pp. 341–350.

——, "Preferential Behavior: Decision-Making Theory." *American Behavioral Scientist*, Vol. 7, no. 7 (1964).

Sasieni, Maurice; Arthur Jaspur and Lawrence Friedman, *Operations Research: Methods and Problems* (New York, 1959).

Simon, Herbert A., *Models of Man, Social and Rational* (New York, 1957). See especially chs. 14–16.

Smith, Nicholas M., Jr.; Stanley S. Walters, Franklin C. Brooks, and David H. Blackwell, "The Theory of Value and the Science of Decision; A Summary." *Journal of the Operations Research Society of America*, Vol. 1 (1953), pp. 103–113.

Snyder, Richard C., H. W. Bruck and Burton Sapin, *Decision-Making as an Approach to the Study of International Politics* (Princeton, 1954).

——, "A Decision-Making Approach to the Study of Political Phenomena," in *Approaches to the Study of Politics* (Evanston, 1958), pp. 3–38.

Suppes, Patrick, "The Philosophical Relevance of Decision Theory." *Journal of Philosophy*, Vol. 58 (1961), pp. 605–614.

Thrall, Robert M.; Clyde H. Coombs and Robert L. Davis, *Decision Processes* (New York, 1954).

Washburne, N. F., *Decisions, Values and Groups*, Vol. 2 (New York, 1962).

Wasserman, Paul, *Bibliography on Decision-Making* (Ithaca, 1957). Dittoed.

Willner, Dorothy, *Decisions, Values and Groups*, Vol. 1 (New York, 1960).

**b. Empirical Studies**

Coombs, Clyde H., "Social Choice and Strength of Preference," in *Decision Processes*, R. M. Thrall, *et al.*, eds. (New York, 1954).

Coombs, Clyde H. and David C. Beardsley, "On Decision-Making Under Uncertainty," in *Decision Processes*, R. M. Thrall, *et al.*, eds. (New York, 1954).

Dahl, Robert A., "Hierarchy, Democracy, and Bargaining in Politics and Economics," in *Research Frontiers in Politics and Government*, Brookings Lectures (Washington, D.C., 1955), pp. 45–69.

Edwards, Ward, "The Theory of Decision Making." *Psychological Bulletin*, Vol. 51 (1954), pp. 380–417.

Raup, R. Bruce, "Choice and Decision in Social Intelligence." *Journal of Social Issues*, Vol. 6 (1950), pp. 45–49.

Siegel, Sidney, "Level of Aspiration and Decision-Making." *Psychological Review*, Vol. 64 (1957), pp. 253–262.

Simon, Herbert A., *Administrative Behavior: A Study of Decision-Making Processes in Administrative Organization*, 2nd edn. (New York, 1957).

**4. Preference Aggregation and Social Welfare Functions**

Arrow, Kenneth J., *Social Choice and Individual Values* (New York, 1951; Cowles Commission Monograph No. 12.)

——, "The Meaning of Social Welfare: A Comment on Some Recent Proposals." *Technical Report No. 2 of the Department of Economics and Statistics, Stanford University* (Stanford, 1951).

Black, Duncan, "On the Rationale of Group Decision Making." *Journal of Political Economy*, Vol. 56 (1948), pp. 23–24.

——, *The Theory of Committees and Elections* (Cambridge, 1958).

Blau, J. H., "The Existence of Social Welfare Functions." *Econometrica*, Vol. 25 (1957), pp. 302–313.

Buchanan, James M., "Individual Choice in Voting and the Market." *Journal of Political Economy*, Vol. 62 (1954), pp. 334–343.

——, "Social Choice, Democracy, and Free Markets." *Journal of Political Economy*, Vol. 62 (1954), pp. 114–123.

Coombs, C. H., "Social Choice and Strength of Preference" in R. M. Thrall, C. H. Coombs and R. L. Davis (eds.), *Decision Processes* (New York, 1954), pp. 69–86.

Goodman, L. A., "On Methods of Amalgamation" in R. M. Thrall, C. H. Coombs and R. L. Davis (eds.), *Decision Processes* (New York, 1954), pp. 39–48.

Goodman, L. A. and Harry Markovitz, *Social Welfare Functions Based on Rankings*. Cowles Commission Discussion Paper, Economics, N. 2017 (New York, 1951).

——, "Social Welfare Functions Based on Individual Rankings." *American Journal of Sociology*, Vol. 58 (1952), pp. 257–262.

Hildreth, Clifford, "Alternative Conditions for Social Orderings." *Econometrica*, Vol. 21 (1953), pp. 81–94.

Kemeny, John G. and J. Laurie Snell, "Preference Rankings: An Axiomatic Approach" in J. G. Kemeny and J. L. Snell (eds.), *Mathematical Models in the Social Sciences* (New York, 1962), pp. 9–23.

May, K. O., "Intransitivity, Utility, and the Aggregation of Preference Patterns." *Econometrica*, Vol. 22 (1954), pp. 1–13.

Rescher, Nicholas, *Distributive Justice* (New York, 1966).

——, *Introduction to Value Theory* (Englewood Cliffs, 1968).

Rothenberg, Jerome, *Measurement of Social Welfare* (Englewood Cliffs, 1961).

Weldon, J. C., "On the Problem of Social Welfare Functions." *Canadian Journal of Economics and Political Science*, Vol. 18 (1952), pp. 452–463.

## IV. *Bibliographies*

Albert, Ethel M. and Clyde Kluckhohn, *A Selected Bibliography on Values, Ethics, and Esthetics in the Behavioral Sciences and Philosophy: 1920–1958* (Bloomington, 1959).

Dashiell, J. Frederick, "An Introductory Bibliography on Value." *The Journal of Philosophy*, Vol. 10 (1913), pp. 472–476.

Eaton, Howard O., *The Austrian Philosophy of Values* (Norway, 1930). [Pp. 373–375 give a bibliography of writings on value theory by Brentano, Ehrenfels, and Meinong.]

Ferrater Mora, José, "Valor" in *idem, Diccionario de Filosofía*, Vol. II (5th ed.; Buenos Aires, 1965), pp. 867–872.

Hartmann, Robert S., "General Theory of Value" in R. Klibansky (ed.), *Philosophy in Mid-Century*, Vol. 3 (Firenz, 1956), pp. 3–41.

Heyde, J. E., "Gesamtbibliographie des Wertbegriffes." *Literarische Berichte aus dem Gebiet der Philosophie*, publ. by A. Hoffmann, fasc's 15–20 (1928–1929); A *Nachtragsheft* was issued in 1930.

von Mering, Otto, *A Grammar of Human Values* (Pittsburgh, 1961). [See the Bibliography on pp. 265–282.]

Reid, T. E. H., *Values in Conflict*, ed. by T. E. H. Reid (Toronto, 1963). [See the Selected Bibliography on pp. 125–130.]

Rescher, Nicholas, *Introduction to Value Theory* (Englewood Cliffs, 1968).

Varet, Gilbert, *Manuel de Bibliographie Philosophique*, Vol. II (Paris, 1956). [See pp. 864–910 devoted to "Philosophies de l'Etre et de la Valeur."]

Ward, Leo Richard, *Philosophy of Value: An Essay in Constructive Criticism* (New York, 1930). [See the Bibliography on pp. 233–259.]

# INDEXES

# INDEX OF NAMES*

*Index is exclusive of the bibliography.

# SUBJECT INDEX